FUNCTIONS OF A COMPLEX VARIABLE

BY

JAMES PIERPONT, LL.D.

PROFESSOR OF MATHEMATICS IN YALE UNIVERSITY

GINN AND COMPANY

BOSTON · NEW YORK · CHICAGO · LONDON
ATLANTA · DALLAS · COLUMBUS · SAN FRANCISCO

PRINTED IN THE UNITED STATES OF AMERICA

933.1

The Athenæum Press
GINN AND COMPANY · PRO-
PRIETORS · BOSTON · U.S.A.

SEINEM HOCHVEREHRTEN FREUNDE
HERRN PROFESSOR DR. G. VON ESCHERICH
IN HERZLICHER DANKBARKEIT
ZUGEEIGNET
VOM VERFASSER

PREFACE

The present volume has arisen from lectures on the Theory of Functions of a Complex Variable which the author has been accustomed to give to juniors, seniors, and graduate students of Yale University during the last twenty years.

As these students often do not intend to specialize in mathematics, many topics which might properly find a place in a first course in the function theory have not been treated; for example, Riemann's surfaces. On the other hand the author, having in mind the needs of students of applied mathematics, has dwelt at some length on the theory of linear differential equations, especially as regards the functions of Legendre, Laplace, Bessel, and Lamé. As a splendid application of the principles of the function theory and also on account of their intrinsic value, three chapters have been devoted to the elliptic functions.

The author wishes to acknowledge in a general way his indebtedness to the works of C. Jordan, H. Weber, C. de la Vallée-Poussin, W. Jacobsthal, and others, but to L. Schlesinger his debt is especially great for the treatment of linear differential equations here given.

The author wishes also to express his deep appreciation of the assistance so cheerfully given by his colleagues, Professor W. A. Wilson of Yale University and Professor E. L. Dodd of the University of Texas, and by his pupils P. R. Rider and G. H. Light.

Last but not least the author fulfills a very pleasant duty in tendering his thanks to the house of Ginn and Company for the great care they have given to the make-up of the book and for the generous manner in which they have met his every wish.

JAMES PIERPONT

NEW HAVEN

CONTENTS

CHAPTER I

ARITHMETICAL OPERATIONS

CHAPTER II

REAL TERM SERIES

CHAPTER III

SERIES WITH COMPLEX TERMS

CHAPTER IV

THE ELEMENTARY FUNCTIONS

CHAPTER VIII

INFINITE PRODUCTS

CHAPTER IX

B *AND* Γ *FUNCTIONS, ASYMPTOTIC EXPANSIONS*

Asymptotic Expansions

CHAPTER X

FUNCTIONS OF WEIERSTRASS

CHAPTER XI

FUNCTIONS OF LEGENDRE AND JACOBI

CHAPTER XII

THETA FUNCTIONS

CHAPTER XIII

LINEAR DIFFERENTIAL EQUATIONS

CHAPTER XIV

FUNCTIONS OF LEGENDRE AND LAPLACE

Laplace's Functions

CHAPTER XV

BESSEL AND LAMÉ FUNCTIONS

Lamé Functions

NOTE

As a book of this kind is meant to appeal to a variety of readers, any one who wishes to study only the more elementary parts of the Theory of Functions may *omit with advantage* the following sections: 8, 23, 34, 37, 42, 43, 71, 77, 78, 79, 108, 125, 151–159, 189, 190; all of Chapters XIII, XIV, XV, if not interested in Differential Equations, otherwise sections 212–220, 249–253, 260–265 inclusive.

FUNCTIONS OF A COMPLEX VARIABLE

CHAPTER I

ARITHMETICAL OPERATIONS

1. Historical Sketch. In elementary mathematics we use for the most part only real numbers. There is however a branch of elementary mathematics, viz. algebra, where a wider class of numbers, the complex numbers, are employed almost from the start. The quadratic equation

$$x^2 - 2ax + b = 0 \tag{1}$$

has the two roots

$$a \pm \sqrt{a^2 - b}, \tag{2}$$

provided $a^2 > b$. If $a^2 < b$, there is no real number which satisfies 1). As long as we restrict ourselves to the system of real numbers, the expression 2) is devoid of meaning. In fact the square root of a number c, in symbols $\sqrt{c}$, is a number d such that $d^2 = c$. But there is no real number d whose square is negative. Thus $\sqrt{a^2 - b}$ does not exist in the real number system when $a^2 < b$. The older algebraists found it extremely convenient to enlarge their number system, in order that the equation 1) should have two roots even when $a^2 < b$. The new numbers are denoted by $a + b\sqrt{-1}$, or setting $i = \sqrt{-1}$, by $a + bi$. When $b = 0$, they reduce to the real numbers a. Thus the new class contains the class of real numbers as a subclass. With these new numbers it was found that not only the roots of the quadratic, but also of the cubic, the biquadratic, in short the roots of all algebraic equations could be expressed. By their introduction, the theory of algebraic equations attained a simplicity and comprehensiveness quite impossible without them. Complex numbers are to-day indispensable in algebra.

In other branches of mathematics, the importance of complex numbers was perceived much later. By means of a formula discovered by Euler

$$e^{i\phi} = \cos\phi + i\sin\phi, \tag{3}$$

an intimate relation was established between exponentials and analytic trigonometry. Indeed, a good part of this subject may be developed from this formula.

In the system of real numbers, the logarithm of a negative number $-a$ does not exist. In the system of complex numbers it does. We have, in fact,

$$\log(-a) = \log a + (2n+1)\pi i, \tag{4}$$

where n is any integer, including zero. It is thus infinite valued like the inverse circular functions.

A great discovery made nearly a century ago by Abel rendered the complex numbers as necessary to analysis as they long had been in algebra. He found that the elliptic functions, whose properties had been carefully studied by Legendre, admit a second period, when one passes from the real to the complex number system. Possessed of this fact, Abel and his contemporary Jacobi were able to develop the theory of elliptic functions in a manner undreamed of before.

About the same time the illustrious French mathematician Cauchy began to show what great advances could be made in the theory of differential equations when the variables are allowed to take on complex values instead of being restricted to real values alone. By the year 1850 complex numbers had proved to be of incalculable value in many and widely separated branches of mathematics, and before long the theory of functions of a complex variable sprang into existence.

To-day this theory has grown to gigantic size. It forms the foundation on which much of modern mathematics is built. Without a knowledge of its elements, a student of mathematics finds himself somewhat in the position of a traveler in a strange land; every one is using a language which he does not comprehend. Even the physicist and astronomer find that the masters in these subjects are using freely the function theory. It is thus becoming daily more important for them to gain some familiarity with this theory.

The present work is intended to give the general reader an account of some of the elementary parts of the theory of functions of a complex variable. For further study we add the following list. The easier books are placed first. The last two are intended for the specialist.

E. B. Wilson, Advanced Calculus.
Ginn and Company. Boston, 1912.

G. Humbert, Cours d'Analyse.
2 vols., Paris, 1904.

E. Goursat, Cours d'Analyse Mathématique.
3 vols., 2d edition, Paris, 1910.

H. Burkhardt, Einführung in die Theorie der Analytischen Funktionen.
Leipzig, 1903.

R. Fricke, Analytisch-Funktionen-theoretische Vorlesungen.
Leipzig, 1900.

Durège-Maurer, Theorie der Funktionen einer komplexen veränderlichen Grösse.
Leipzig, 1906.

E. Picard, Traité d'Analyse.
3 vols., 2d edition, Paris, 1905.

E. Whittaker, A Course of Modern Analysis.
Cambridge, 1902.

A. Forsyth, Theory of Functions of a Complex Variable.
2d edition, Cambridge, 1900.

W. Osgood. Lehrbuch der Funktionentheorie.
2d edition, Leipzig, 1912.

2. Arithmetical Operations. 1. As the reader has already studied the arithmetical operations on complex numbers, we treat this topic but briefly. The complex numbers are represented by the symbol $a + a'i$, where a, a' are real numbers and i is a symbol to be defined later. The plus sign between its two parts has, of course, no meaning as yet. It is convenient to denote $a + a'i$ by a symbol as α. We have then

$$\alpha = a + a'i. \tag{1}$$

With 1) we will associate a point A whose abscissa and ordinate are respectively a and a' as in Fig. 1. Conversely to a point whose abscissa is x and whose ordinate is y we will associate a complex number $x + yi$.

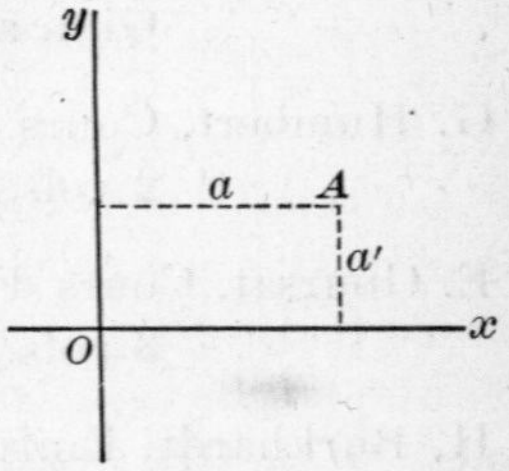

FIG. 1.

From this correspondence we are led to call a the *abscissa* of the complex α, and a' its *ordinate*. We write

$$a = \text{Abs}\,\alpha \quad , \quad a' = \text{Ord}\,\alpha.$$

When $a' = 0$ in 1) we assign to α the value a, and denote $a + 0i$ more shortly by a. The associated points lie on the x-axis which we call the *real axis*. When $a = 0$, we say α is *purely imaginary;* we denote $0 + a'i$ more shortly by $a'i$. The associated points lie on the y-axis, which we call the *imaginary axis*.

2. Two complex numbers

$$\alpha = a + a'i \quad , \quad \beta = b + b'i$$

are *equal*, when

$$a = b \quad , \quad a' = b', \tag{2}$$

or in symbols

$$\text{Abs}\,\alpha = \text{Abs}\,\beta \quad , \quad \text{Ord}\,\alpha = \text{Ord}\,\beta\,; \tag{3}$$

that is, when the associated points are coincident. In particular

$$\alpha = a + a'i = 0$$

only when

$$a = 0 \quad , \quad a' = 0.$$

The *sum* of α and β is

$$\alpha + \beta = (a + b) + (a' + b')\,i\,; \tag{4}$$

their difference is

$$\alpha - \beta = (a - b) + (a' - b')\,i. \tag{5}$$

Let us show how the points corresponding to 4) and 5) may be found.

Let A, B in Fig. 2 be the points associated with α, β. Let us construct the parallelogram whose two sides are OA, OB. Then

$$OA' = a \quad AA' = a',$$
$$OB' = b \quad BB' = b'.$$

Obviously

$$OC' = OA' + A'C' = a + b,$$
$$CC' = C'C'' + C''C = a' + b'.$$

Thus C has the coördinates $a + b$, $a' + b'$ and hence is the point associated with $\alpha + \beta$ in 4).

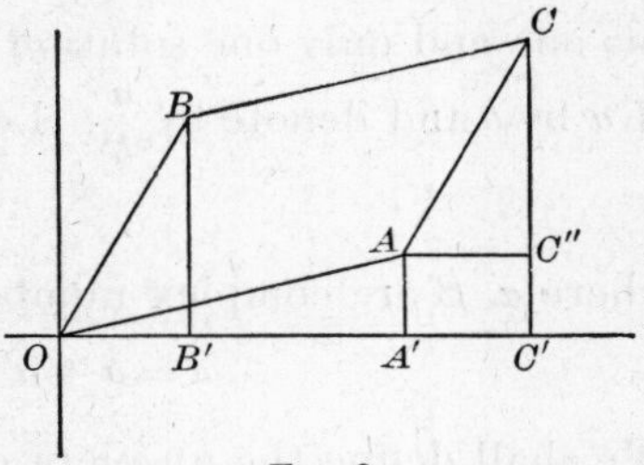

FIG. 2.

To find the point associated with $\alpha - \beta$ in 5), let A, B in Fig. 3 be the points associated with α, β. We produce OB backward so that $OC = OB$. Obviously C has the coördinates $-b$, $-b'$. Thus if we set

$$\gamma = -b - b'i,$$

we see that

$$\alpha - \beta = \alpha + \gamma,$$

since both are

$$(a - b) + (a' - b')i.$$

But we have seen how to plot the point corresponding to $\alpha + \gamma$. It is in fact the vertex D in the parallelogram two of whose sides are OA, OC.

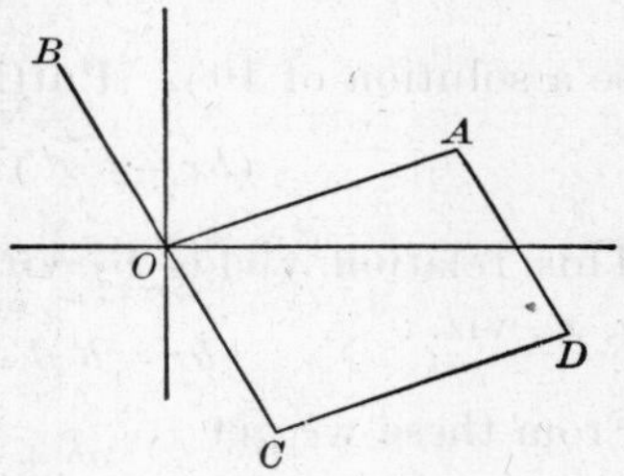

FIG. 3.

3. We note that in adding and subtracting α, β in 4), 5) we have treated i as if it were a real number. We do the same in defining *multiplication*, except that we agree that

$$i^2 = -1 \qquad (6$$

Thus

$$\alpha\beta = ab + ab'i + a'bi + a'b'i^2,$$

or using 6)

$$\alpha\beta = (ab - a'b') + (ab' + a'b)i. \qquad (7$$

We take 7) as the definition of multiplication.

From 6), 7) we have

$$i^3 = -i \quad , \quad i^4 = 1\,; \qquad (8$$

and hence

$$i^{4n+m} = i^m, \qquad (9$$

where m, n are positive integers or zero.

4. To define the *quotient* of two complex numbers we recall that in real numbers

$$bx = a$$

has one and only one solution when $b \neq 0$, this we call the quotient of a by b and denote by $\frac{a}{b}$. Let us consider the analogous equation

$$\beta\xi = \alpha \tag{10}$$

where α, β are complex numbers

$$\alpha = a + a'i \quad , \quad \beta = b + b'i.$$

We shall define the quotient of α by β to be the number or numbers ξ which satisfy this relation.

Let us first suppose $\beta \neq 0$. Then b, b' are not both $= 0$. Let

$$\xi = x + x'i$$

be a solution of 10). Putting this in 10) gives

$$(bx - b'x') + i(bx' + b'x) = a + a'i \tag{11}$$

This relation yields by virtue of 3) two equations to determine x, x', viz.:

$$bx - b'x' = a \quad , \quad bx' + b'x = a'. \tag{12}$$

From these we get

$$x = \frac{ab + a'b'}{b^2 + b'^2} \quad , \quad x' = \frac{a'b - ab'}{b^2 + b'^2}$$

Thus the solution of 10) is

$$\xi = \frac{\alpha}{\beta} = \frac{ab + a'b'}{b^2 + b'^2} + \frac{a'b - ab'}{b^2 + b'^2} \cdot i \tag{13}$$

when $\beta \neq 0$.

Suppose $\beta = 0$. Then $b = b' = 0$, and 12) requires that $a = a' = 0$, or $\alpha = 0$. Putting these values in 12) we see that the equations are satisfied however x, x' are chosen, that is, for every value of ξ. We have thus the following result:

When $\beta \neq 0$, *the equation* 10) *admits one and only one solution* ξ *which is given by* 13). *When* $\beta = 0$, *the equation admits no solution unless* $\alpha = 0$. *In this case it is satisfied for every value of* ξ.

For this reason division by 0 is excluded in modern mathematics. As some students have not been trained in accordance with this law, we wish to emphasize its inviolate character.

5. We prove now the important theorem :

If a product $\alpha\beta = 0$, *then either* α *or* β *must* $= 0$.

This theorem we know is true for real numbers. On effecting the multiplication of α by β we get the relation

$$(ab - a'b') + (ab' + a'b)i = 0.$$

Hence by 3),

$$ab - a'b' = 0 \quad , \quad ab' + a'b = 0. \tag{14}$$

We show that these equations cannot hold if both α and $\beta \neq 0$. For since $\alpha \neq 0$ either a or $a' \neq 0$; suppose $a \neq 0$. Also since $\beta \neq 0$, either b or $b' \neq 0$; suppose $b \neq 0$. From the first relation of 14) we get

$$a' = \frac{ab}{b'}.$$

This put in the second equation of 14) gives

$$ab'^2 + ab^2 = 0,$$

or

$$a(b^2 + b'^2) = 0.$$

As $a \neq 0$, we must have

$$b^2 + b'^2 = 0.$$

This requires that both b and $b' = 0$, and this is contrary to hypothesis. In a precisely similar manner we may treat the other cases. In each case we are led to a contradiction. Thus the assumption that $\alpha \cdot \beta$ may $= 0$ without either α or β being $= 0$ is untenable.

In an elementary work like the present, it would be out of place to demonstrate that the *formal laws* governing the arithmetical operations on real numbers go over without change to complex numbers. Thus the reader knows that

$$\alpha\beta = \beta\alpha,$$

that

$$\alpha(\beta + \gamma) = \alpha\beta + \alpha\gamma,$$

etc., just as if α, β, γ were real numbers.

6. Two complex numbers

$$\alpha = a + ib \quad , \quad \beta = a - ib$$

as in the figure are called *conjugate* numbers. We note that

$$\alpha + \beta = 2a$$

is *real*, and that

$$\alpha - \beta = 2\,ib$$

is *purely imaginary*.

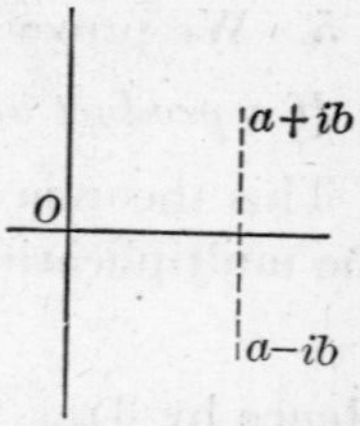

Also the product

$$\alpha\beta = a^2 + b^2$$

is *real and positive*.

3. Critical Remarks. 1. We have now defined the *four rational operations* on complex numbers, viz. the operations of addition, subtraction, multiplication, and division. At this point we may return to the symbol

$$a + a'i \tag{1}$$

which we have employed to represent a complex number. We can show what its component parts mean. We begin by considering the two numbers

$$\beta = a' \quad , \quad \gamma = i.$$

The rule for multiplication, 2, 7) gives

$$\beta \cdot \gamma = a'i.$$

Thus the term $a'i$ in 1) may be regarded as a' times the number i. The number i may be called the *imaginary unit* in contradistinction to the *real unit* 1.

Again let

$$\beta = a \quad , \quad \gamma = a'i.$$

The rule for addition, 2, 4) gives

$$\beta + \gamma = a + a'i.$$

Thus the complex number 1) may be regarded as the sum of a real units and a' imaginary units. We may call a the *real part* and $a'i$ the *imaginary part* of 1). When we introduced the symbol 1) in 2, we did not say that it was the *sum* of these two parts for the reason that we had not defined addition and multiplication of these new numbers. Indeed we expressly stated that the symbols + and i had at that stage no meaning. They acquired meaning only after the arithmetical operations on the symbols 1) had been defined.

2. Instead of denoting the new numbers by the symbol 1), let us denote them by some other symbol, say by

$$(a, a'). \tag{2}$$

We may proceed then as follows: Two numbers

$$\alpha = (a, a') \quad , \quad \beta = (b, b')$$

are equal when and only when

$$a = b, a' = b'.$$

The sum of α and β is defined to be the number

$$(a + b, a' + b'); \tag{3}$$

their difference is defined as the number

$$(a - b, a' - b').$$

Their product shall be

$$(ab - a'b', ab' + a'b). \tag{4}$$

When $\beta \neq 0$ the quotient of α by β shall be the number

$$\left(\frac{ab + a'b'}{b^2 + b'^2}, \frac{a'b - ab'}{b^2 + b'^2}\right).$$

The number $(a, 0)$ shall be the real number a, and for brevity we will write

$$(a, 0) = a.$$

The number $(0, 1)$ we will denote more briefly by i. Then 4) gives

$$(a', 0) \cdot (0, 1) = (0, a') = a'i. \tag{5}$$

Also 1) and 5) give

$$(a, a') = (a, 0) + (0, a') = a + a'i.$$

Thus another representation of the complex number (a, a') is $a + a'i$, and we have reached the standpoint taken in 2.

In both cases we start with a symbol; in one case with $a + a'i$, in the other with (a, a'). These at the start are mere marks to indicate that the new numbers are a complex of two real numbers a, a'. These marks take on a meaning when we give them the above arithmetical properties. The complex then becomes a definite concept which we call a number.

3. We wish now to make another remark of a critical nature. The complex numbers are often called *imaginary numbers*, and we have in the present work followed usage as far as to call the numbers $a'i$ purely imaginary, the number i the imaginary unit, and the axis of ordinates the imaginary axis. For the beginner the term imaginary is most unfortunate; and if it had not become so ingrained in elementary algebra, much would be gained if it could be dropped and forgotten.

The use of the term imaginary in connection with the number concept is very old. At first only positive integers were regarded as true numbers. To the early Greek mathematician the ratio of two integers as $\frac{4}{5}$ was not a number. After rational numbers had been accepted, what are now called negative numbers forced themselves on the attention of mathematicians. As their usefulness grew apparent they were called fictitious or imaginary numbers. To many an algebraist of the early Renaissance it was a great mystery how the product of two such numbers as $-a$, $-b$ could be the real number ab.

Hardly had the negative numbers become a necessary element to the analyst when the complex numbers pressed for admittance into the number concept. These in turn were called imaginary, and history repeated itself. How many a boy to-day has been bothered to understand how the product of two imaginary numbers ai and bi can be the real number $-ab$. As well ask why in chess the knight can spring over a piece and why the queen cannot. The pawns, the knights, the bishops, etc. are mere pieces of wood till the laws governing their moves are laid down. They then become chessmen.

The symbols (a, a') or $a + a'i$ are mere marks until their laws of combination are defined, they then become as much a number as $\frac{2}{3}$ or -5. The student must realize that all integers, fractions, and negative numbers are imaginary. They exist only in our imagination. Five horses, three quarters of a dollar, may have an objective existence, but the numbers 5 and $\frac{3}{4}$ are imaginary. Thus all numbers are equally real and equally imaginary. Historically we can see how the term imaginary still clings to the complex numbers; pedagogically we must deplore using a term which can only create confusion in the mind of the beginner.

4. The Polar Form. 1. Let A be the point associated with

$$\alpha = a + a'i \tag{1}$$

Let $OA = \rho$ and angle $AOB = \theta$. We call ρ the ***modulus*** or *absolute value* of α. We have

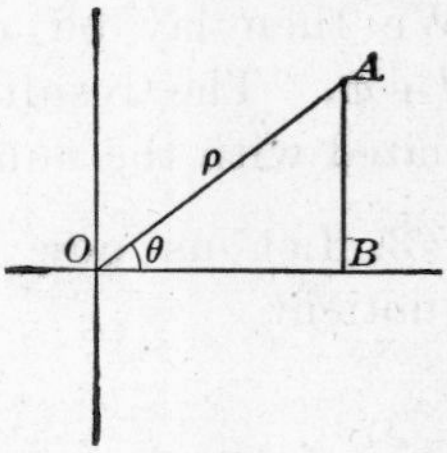

$$\rho = \sqrt{a^2 + a'^2}$$

the radical having the positive sign. The modulus of α is also denoted by

$$|\alpha|$$

It is the distance of A from the origin.

The angle θ is called the *argument* of α; we have

$$\tan\theta = \frac{a'}{a}, \quad a \neq 0.$$

We often write

$$\theta = \text{Arg}\ \alpha.$$

Making use of ρ and θ we have

$$a = \rho\cos\theta, \quad a' = \rho\sin\theta$$

and

$$\alpha = \rho(\cos\theta + i\sin\theta). \tag{2}$$

This is called the *polar form* of α. The form 1) may be called in contradistinction the *rectangular form.*

2. The rule for multiplication and division of complex numbers is particularly elegant when the polar form is used. In fact let

$$\beta = b + b'i = \sigma(\cos\phi + i\sin\phi). \tag{3}$$

Then

$$\alpha\beta = \rho\sigma\{\cos\theta\cos\phi - \sin\theta\sin\phi + i(\cos\theta\sin\phi + \sin\theta\cos\phi)\},$$

or

$$\alpha\beta = \rho\sigma\{\cos(\theta + \phi) + i\sin(\theta + \phi)\}. \tag{4}$$

From this we have

$$|\alpha\beta| = \rho\sigma = |\alpha| \cdot |\beta|. \tag{5}$$

$$\text{Arg}(\alpha\beta) = \theta + \phi = \text{Arg}\ \alpha + \text{Arg}\ \beta. \tag{6}$$

This may be expressed as follows : —

The modulus of the product is the product of the moduli, and the argument of the product is the sum of the arguments.

The above enables us to plot the product $\alpha\beta$ very easily. Having plotted α and β, we compute the product $\rho\sigma$ and describe a circle about the origin O with the radius. We then lay off on this circle the angle $\theta + \phi$. The resulting point is that associated with the number $\alpha\beta$, as in the figure.

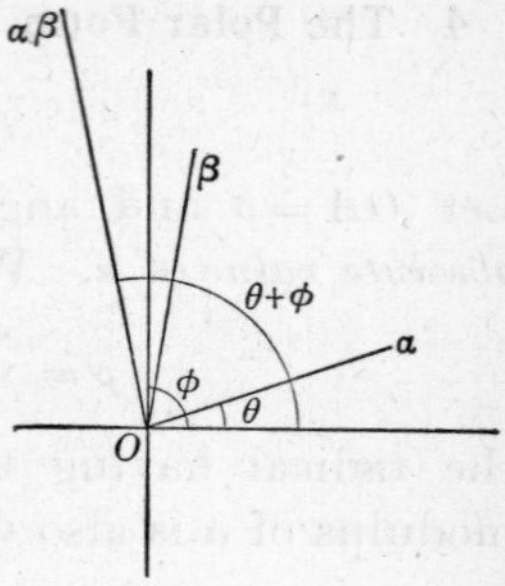

3. Let us now turn to *division*. The quotient

$$\xi = \frac{\alpha}{\beta} \quad , \quad \beta \neq 0$$

is defined by 2, 13). This expression is complicated and not easy to remember. If, however, we use the polar forms 2), 3) of α, β, we can readily prove that

$$\frac{\alpha}{\beta} = \frac{\rho}{\sigma}\{\cos(\theta - \phi) + i\sin(\theta - \phi)\} ; \tag{7}$$

or that

$$\left|\frac{\alpha}{\beta}\right| = \frac{\rho}{\sigma} = \frac{|\alpha|}{|\beta|} \tag{8}$$

and

$$\text{Arg}\frac{\alpha}{\beta} = \text{Arg}\,\alpha - \text{Arg}\,\beta. \tag{9}$$

This may be expressed as follows :

The modulus of the quotient is the quotient of the moduli, and the argument of the quotient is the difference of the arguments.

The proof of 7) may be effected by replacing a, a', b, b' in 2, 13) by their values

$$a = \rho\cos\theta,\ a' = \rho\sin\theta,\ b = \sigma\cos\phi,\ b' = \sigma\sin\phi,$$

and performing the necessary reduction. A more instructive way is the following : Since $\beta \neq 0$ by hypothesis, the equation

$$\beta\xi = \alpha \tag{10}$$

admits one and only one solution. The relation 7 states that this solution is

$$\xi = \frac{\rho}{\sigma}\{\cos(\theta - \phi) + i\sin(\theta - \phi)\} \tag{11}$$

This is indeed so, for by the foregoing rule of multiplication

$$|\beta\xi| = \sigma \cdot \frac{\rho}{\sigma} = \rho = |\alpha|$$

$$\text{Arg}\,(\beta\xi) = \phi + (\theta - \phi) = \theta = \text{Arg}\,\alpha.$$

Thus $\beta \cdot \xi$ having the same modulus and argument as α is in fact α. Thus 11) satisfies 10).

The above enables us to plot the quotient α/β very easily. Having plotted α and β, we compute the quotient ρ/σ and describe a circle about the origin with this radius. We then lay off on this circle the angle $\theta - \phi$. The resulting point is that associated with α/β.

4. We have seen that two complex numbers α, β are equal when and only when their associated points coincide. Let us suppose α, β are expressed in their polar forms 2), 3). Then from the relation

$$\alpha = \beta$$

we may conclude at once that

$$\rho = \sigma. \tag{12}$$

We cannot conclude, however, that

$$\theta = \phi.$$

We can only conclude that θ can differ from ϕ by a multiple of 2π, or that

$$\theta = \phi + 2n\pi \tag{13}$$

where n is an integer or 0.

In particular we have:

For α to $= 0$, it is necessary and sufficient that its modulus $= 0$.

5. Some Inequalities. Geometrical Correspondence. 1. Let us plot the points A, B, C corresponding to

$$\alpha,\ \beta,\ \alpha + \beta$$

as in Fig. 1. Then

$$|\alpha + \beta| = OC,$$

a very useful relation. Since from geometry we have

$$OC \leq OA + AC$$

we conclude a relation of utmost importance

$$|\alpha+\beta| \leq |\alpha|+|\beta|. \qquad (1$$

The $<$ sign holds unless O, A, B are collinear, and A, B are on the same side of O.

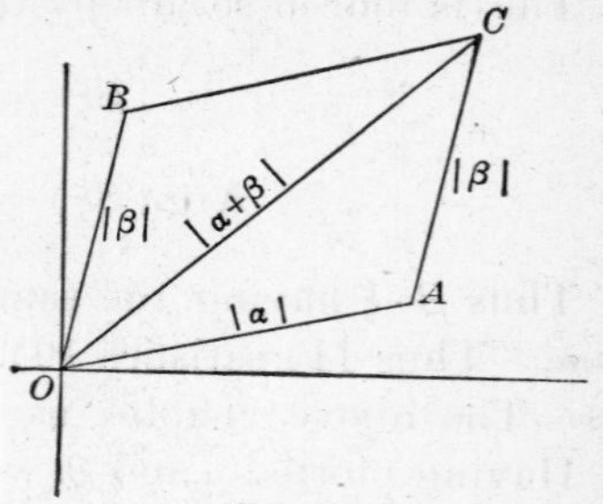

Fig. 1.

From 1) we have

$$|\alpha+\beta+\gamma| \leq |\alpha|+|\beta|+|\gamma|, \qquad (2$$

and so on for any finite number of terms.

To prove 2) we note that

$$\alpha+\beta+\gamma=\alpha+(\beta+\gamma).$$

Hence

$$|\alpha+\beta+\gamma|=|\alpha+(\beta+\gamma)| \leq |\alpha|+|\beta+\gamma|, \text{ by 1)}$$
$$\leq |\alpha|+|\beta|+|\gamma|, \text{ also by 1)}.$$

2. Let us now consider $|\alpha-\beta|$.

Let A, B in Fig. 2 be the points associated with α, β. Then, following the construction given in 2, the point D is associated with $\alpha-\beta$.

Thus

$$OD=|\alpha-\beta|.$$

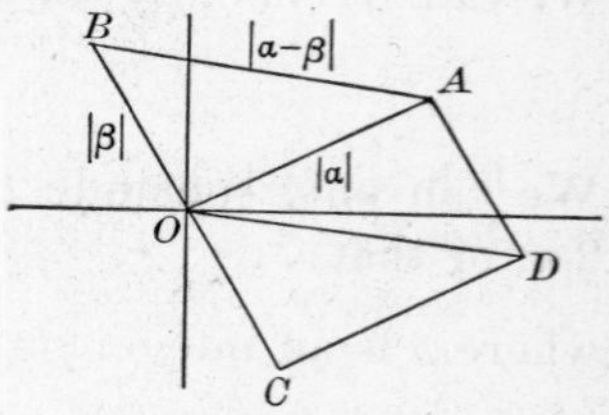

Fig. 2.

But obviously $AB=OD$, hence

$$|\alpha-\beta|=AB.$$

This gives us a result we shall often use:

If A, B are the points associated with α, β, then the length of AB is $|\alpha-\beta|$.

3. Let us also note the relation

$$|\alpha-\beta| \leq |\alpha|+|\beta|. \qquad (3$$

For

$$\alpha-\beta=\alpha+(-\beta).$$

But

$$|-\beta|=|\beta|.$$

Thus

$$|\alpha-\beta|=|\alpha+(-\beta)| < |\alpha|+|-\beta|=|\alpha|+|\beta|.$$

4. Let a be a real positive number and β any complex number. We wish to find the points Z associated with the complex numbers ζ which are subjected to the relation

$$|\zeta-\beta| < a. \tag{4}$$

If B in Fig. 3 is associated with β, the condition 4) says that ZB must be $< a$. Thus Z is restricted to the interior of a circle whose center is B and whose radius is a.

The condition

$$|\zeta-\beta| = a$$

states that Z must lie on the circumference of this circle. The condition

$$|\zeta-\beta| \leq a$$

requires that Z lie within or on the circumference of the circle.

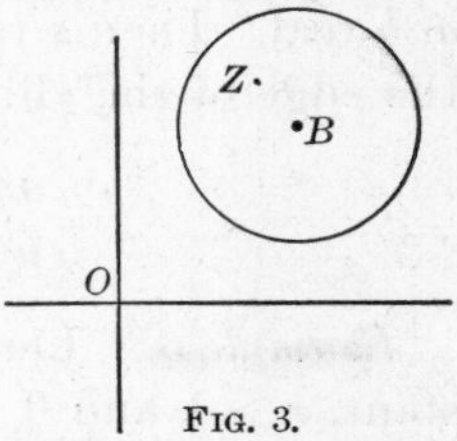

FIG. 3.

In the following pages we shall make great use of the geometrical interpretation of complex numbers by points in a plane. The point associated with a complex number α may be called its *image*. Moreover, instead of using another letter as A to denote this point, we shall usually denote it by the same letter α. This will not produce any ambiguity and is shorter.

We shall introduce another change. Up to the present we have usually denoted real numbers, angles excepted, by Roman letters as $a, b, c \cdots$ and complex numbers by Greek letters $\alpha, \beta, \gamma \cdots$ in contradistinction. There is no further need of this; any letter may denote a complex number. It may be well to recall that real numbers are merely a special case of complex numbers, just as integers are a special case of rational numbers. Thus when we say let a be a complex number we do not at all mean that it may not be real.

As in algebra and the calculus, so in the theory of functions we deal with *constants* and *variables*. The former are usually denoted by the first letters of the alphabet, the latter by the last.

Let us consider a few examples of a variable:

Example 1. Let $z = a + yi$, where a is a real constant and y is real and ranges from $-\infty$ to $+\infty$. Then the point associated with

z in Fig. 4 ranges over the right line AA'; or more shortly we say z ranges over AA'.

Example 2. Let $z = x + yi$, where x, y are real numbers satisfying the inequality

$$\frac{x^2}{a^2} + \frac{y^2}{b^2} \leq 1,$$

a, b real. Then z ranges over the interior and the edge of the ellipse

$$\frac{x^2}{a^2} + \frac{y^2}{b^2} = 1.$$

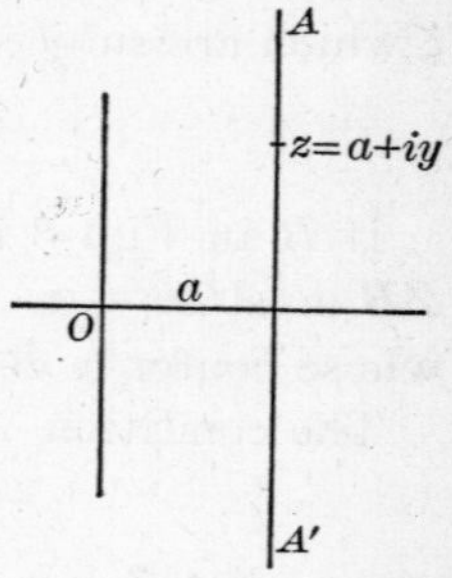

FIG. 4.

Example 3. Let $z - a = r(\cos\theta + i\sin\theta)$ where a is any constant, $r > 0$, and $0 \leq \theta < 2\pi$.
Then z ranges over a circle whose center is a and whose radius is r.

Example 4. Let $z = x + yi$,
where x, y are real and satisfy the relation

$$y = f(x). \tag{5}$$

Then z ranges over the curve whose equation is 5).

5. Let us note the following relations:

$$|a - b| = |b - a| \tag{6}$$

Also if $|a - b| < \epsilon$ and $|b - c| < \eta$

then

$$|a - c| < \epsilon + \eta \tag{7}$$

To prove 7) we observe that

$$a - c = (a - b) + (b - c)$$

Hence by 3)

$$|a - c| \leq |a - b| + |b - c|$$
$$< \epsilon + \eta$$

6. Let us recall from algebra the notation

$$\sum_{m=1}^{n} a_m = a_1 + a_2 + \cdots + a_n, \tag{8}$$

$$\prod_{m=1}^{n} a_m = a_1 \cdot a_2 \cdot a_3 \cdots a_n. \tag{9}$$

Thus the left side of 8) is read: the sum from $m=1$ to n of a_m is, etc. The left side of 9) is read: the product from $m=1$ to n of a_m is, etc.

6. Moivre's Formula. In 4 we saw that any complex number α can be written

$$\alpha = \rho(\cos\theta + i\sin\theta). \tag{1}$$

Then by 4, 4)

$$\alpha^2 = \rho^2(\cos 2\theta + i\sin 2\theta),$$

and in general

$$\alpha^n = \rho^n(\cos n\theta + i\sin n\theta). \tag{2}$$

Let us take $|\alpha| = \rho = 1$. Then 1), 2) give

$$(\cos\theta + i\sin\theta)^n = \cos n\theta + i\sin n\theta \tag{3}$$

which is *Moivre's Formula.*

Now, the Binomial Theorem for a positive integral exponent n is

$$(a+b)^n = a^n + \binom{n}{1}a^{n-1}b + \binom{n}{2}a^{n-2}b^2 + \cdots + \binom{n}{1}ab^{n-1} + b^n. \tag{4}$$

Here

$$\binom{n}{1} = \frac{n}{1}\ ,\quad \binom{n}{2} = \frac{n(n-1)}{1\cdot 2}\ ,\quad \binom{n}{3} = \frac{n(n-1)(n-2)}{1\cdot 2\cdot 3}\cdots$$

are the *binomial coefficients.* Let us make use of the relation 4) to develop the left side of 3). It becomes

$$\cos^n\theta + i\binom{n}{1}\cos^{n-1}\theta\sin\theta - \binom{n}{2}\cos^{n-2}\theta\sin^2\theta$$
$$- i\binom{n}{3}\cos^{n-3}\theta\sin^3\theta + \cdots \tag{5}$$

Thus 3) may be written

$$\cos n\theta + i\sin n\theta = \cos^n\theta - \binom{n}{2}\cos^{n-2}\theta\sin^2\theta + \cdots$$
$$+ i\left\{\binom{n}{1}\cos^{n-1}\theta\sin\theta - \binom{n}{3}\cos^{n-3}\theta\sin^3\theta + \cdots\right\}$$

Equating the real and imaginary parts of this relation by 2, 2) we get

$$\cos n\theta = \cos^n\theta - \binom{n}{2}\cos^{n-2}\theta\sin^2\theta + \binom{n}{4}\cos^{n-4}\theta\sin^4\theta - \cdots \tag{6}$$

$$\sin n\theta = \binom{n}{1}\cos^{n-1}\theta\sin\theta - \binom{n}{3}\cos^{n-3}\theta\sin^3\theta$$
$$+ \binom{n}{5}\cos^{n-5}\theta\sin^5\theta - \cdots \tag{7}$$

Giving n the values 2, 3, 4 ... in these equations, we find

$$\begin{aligned} \cos 2\theta &= \cos^2\theta - \sin^2\theta \\ \cos 3\theta &= \cos^3\theta - 3\cos\theta\sin^2\theta \\ \cos 4\theta &= \cos^4\theta - 6\cos^2\theta\sin^2\theta + \sin^4\theta \\ &\cdots\cdots \end{aligned} \tag{8}$$

$$\begin{aligned} \sin 2\theta &= 2\cos\theta\sin\theta \\ \sin 3\theta &= 3\cos^2\theta\sin\theta - \sin^3\theta \\ \sin 4\theta &= 4\cos^3\theta\sin\theta - 4\cos\theta\sin^3\theta \\ &\cdots\cdots \end{aligned} \tag{9}$$

In the relation 8) we notice that $\sin\theta$ occurs only in even powers. Since $\sin^2\theta = 1 - \cos^2\theta$, we see that:

$\cos n\theta$ can be expressed as a rational integral function of $\cos\theta$ of degree n.

Making this substitution, we get

$$\begin{aligned} \cos 2\theta &= 2\cos^2\theta - 1 \\ \cos 3\theta &= 4\cos^3\theta - 3\cos\theta \\ \cos 4\theta &= 8\cos^4\theta - 8\cos^2\theta + 1 \\ &\cdots\cdots \end{aligned} \tag{10}$$

In equations 9) we notice that $\cos\theta$ enters in even powers when n is odd, and in odd powers when n is even. Thus we see that:

$\sin n\theta$ is an integral rational function of $\sin\theta$ of degree n when n is odd. When n is even, it is the product of $\cos\theta$ and a rational integral function of $\sin\theta$ of degree $n-1$.

Making the substitution $\cos^2\theta = 1 - \sin^2\theta$ in 9) we get

$$\begin{aligned} \sin 2\theta &= 2\cos\theta\sin\theta \\ \sin 3\theta &= 3\sin\theta - 4\sin^3\theta \\ \sin 4\theta &= \cos\theta(4\sin\theta - 8\sin^3\theta) \\ &\cdots\cdots \end{aligned} \tag{11}$$

7. Extraction of Roots. 1. In the domain of real numbers

$$x^n = a \quad , \quad a > 0$$

has one root if n is an odd positive integer, and two roots if n is even. The equation

$$x^n = -a \quad , \quad a > 0$$

has one root if n is odd, and no root if n is even. Let us now pass to the domain of complex numbers. We ask how many roots has

$$z^n = a \tag{1}$$

where a is any complex number, and n is a positive integer. Let us write a and z in polar form

$$a = \alpha(\cos\theta + i\sin\theta) \tag{2}$$

$$z = \zeta(\cos\phi + i\sin\phi). \tag{3}$$

Then if 3) satisfies 1) we must have

$$\zeta^n(\cos n\phi + i\sin n\phi) = \alpha(\cos\theta + i\sin\theta). \tag{4}$$

Then from 4), 12), 13) we have

$$\zeta^n = \alpha \tag{5}$$

and

$$n\phi = \theta + 2k\pi \quad , \quad k \text{ an integer or } 0. \tag{6}$$

From 5) we have

$$\zeta = \sqrt[n]{\alpha}, \tag{7}$$

and from 6) we have

$$\phi = \frac{\theta}{n} + k \cdot \frac{2\pi}{n} \cdot \tag{8}$$

Thus the modulus ζ and the argument ϕ of any number z which satisfies 1) must have the form 7), 8). On the other hand by actual multiplication we see at once that

$$z_k = \sqrt[n]{\alpha}\left\{\cos\left(\frac{\theta}{n} + k\frac{2\pi}{n}\right) + i\sin\left(\frac{\theta}{n} + k\frac{2\pi}{n}\right)\right\} \tag{9}$$

is a solution of 1). In fact z_k^n is a number whose modulus is the nth power of $\sqrt[n]{\alpha}$ and whose argument is n times $\frac{\theta}{n} + k\frac{2\pi}{n}\cdot$ But this number has therefore the modulus α and the argument $\theta + 2k\pi$, or neglecting multiples of 2π, the argument θ. It is thus a. Hence the nth power of 9) is a.

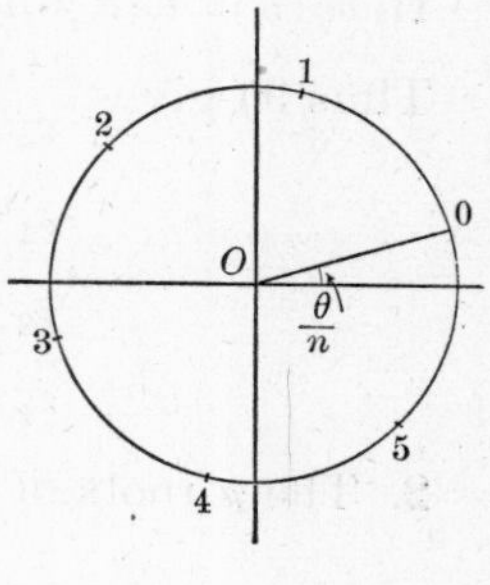

To plot the numbers 9) we describe about the origin as in the figure a circle whose radius is $\sqrt[n]{\alpha}$. On this circle we lay off the angle $\frac{\theta}{n}\cdot$ Let us call this point z_0. Starting from z_0 we now divide the circle into n equal parts which give the points $z_1, z_2, \cdots z_{n-1}$ in the figure, corresponding to $k=1, 2, \cdots n-1$ in 9).

If now we give to k any other integral value, we will get one of the values $z_0, z_1, \cdots z_{n-1}$ already obtained. Thus 1) has just n roots whose values are obtained by giving k in 9) the values $0, 1, 2, \cdots n-1$.

Example 1.

$$z^3 = 1.$$

Here $n=3,\ a=1,\ \alpha=1,\ \theta=0,\ \dfrac{2\pi}{n}=120°.$

Thus 9) gives

$$z_0 = 1,$$

$$z_1 = \cos 120° + i \sin 120° = \frac{-1+i\sqrt{3}}{2},$$

$$z_2 = \cos 240° + i \sin 240 = \frac{-1-i\sqrt{3}}{2}.$$

Example 2.

$$z^3 = -8.$$

Here $n=3,\ a=-8,\ \alpha=8,\ \theta=\pi,\ \dfrac{\theta}{n}=60°.$

Thus 9) gives

$$z_0 = 2\{\cos 60° + i \sin 60°\} = 1 + i\sqrt{3},$$

$$z_1 = 2\{\cos(60°+120°) + i\sin(60°+120°)\} = -2,$$

$$z_2 = 2\{\cos(60°+240°) + i\sin(60°+240°)\} = 1 - i\sqrt{3}.$$

Example 3.

$$z^4 = 1.$$

Here $n=4,\ \alpha=1,\ \theta=0,\ \dfrac{2\pi}{n}=90°.$

Thus 9) gives

$$z_0 = 1,$$

$$z_1 = \cos 90° + i \sin 90° = i,$$

$$z_2 = \cos 180° + i \sin 180° = -1,$$

$$z_3 = \cos 270° + i \sin 270° = -i.$$

2. The n roots of

$$\omega^n = 1 \qquad (10$$

are called *unit roots.* They are of great importance in algebra, and occur in other branches of mathematics. Their values are given by 9) on setting $a = 1$, $\theta = 0$. We get

$$\omega_0 = 1,$$
$$\omega_1 = \cos\frac{2\pi}{n} + i\sin\frac{2\pi}{n},$$
$$\omega_2 = \cos 2\cdot\frac{2\pi}{n} + i\sin 2\cdot\frac{2\pi}{n}, \tag{11}$$
$$\cdots\cdots\cdots$$
$$\omega_{n-1} = \cos(n-1)\frac{2\pi}{n} + i\sin(n-1)\frac{2\pi}{n}.$$

We notice that ω_1 has the property that

$$\omega_2 = \omega_1^2 \quad , \quad \omega_3 = \omega_1^3 \quad , \quad \cdots \omega_{n-1} = \omega_1^{n-1} \quad , \quad \omega_0 = \omega_1^n;$$

that is all the roots of 10) are merely powers of ω_1. Such a root is called a *primitive* unit root. It is easy to show that:

If m is relatively prime to n, then $\omega = \omega_m$ is a primitive root; that is, that

$$\omega,\ \omega^2,\ \omega^3,\ \omega^4 \cdots \omega^n \tag{12}$$

are all roots of 10) *and are all different.*

For
$$\omega^s = \omega_m^s = \left(\cos m\cdot\frac{2\pi}{n} + i\sin m\frac{2\pi}{n}\right)^s$$
$$= \cos ms\cdot\frac{2\pi}{n} + i\sin ms\cdot\frac{2\pi}{n}.$$

Let now
$$ms = ln + p.\quad \text{Then}$$
$$\omega^s = \cos p\cdot\frac{2\pi}{n} + i\sin p\frac{2\pi}{n} = \omega_p$$

Thus ω^s is a root of 10). To show that the roots 12) are all different let us suppose that
$$\omega^r = \omega^s.$$

Then their arguments $rm\frac{2\pi}{n}$, $sm\frac{2\pi}{n}$ can differ only by a multiple of 2π. Hence, e denoting an integer,

$$rm\cdot\frac{2\pi}{n} - sm\frac{2\pi}{n} = e\,2\pi$$

or
$$m(r-s) = en. \tag{13}$$

As m and n are relatively prime, they have no factor in common; e must be divisible by m as 13) shows. Thus if we set $e = gm$ 13) gives

$$r - s = gn$$

or $r-s$ is a multiple of n. This is impossible, as r, s are both $\leq n$. Hence no two of the roots 12) are equal.

3. Let us now return to 9). We set

$$\omega = \cos\frac{2\pi}{n} + i\sin\frac{2\pi}{n},$$

and notice that

$$z_1 = \omega z_0 \quad , \quad z_2 = \omega^2 z_0 \quad , \quad \cdots z_{n-1} = \omega^{n-1} z_0, \tag{14}$$

where

$$z_0 = \sqrt[n]{\alpha}\left(\cos\frac{\theta}{n} + i\sin\frac{\theta}{n}\right). \tag{15}$$

This may be easily generalized as follows :

All the roots of 1) *may be obtained from any root by multiplying this root by the n roots of unity.*

Hence in particular the two roots of $z^2 = a = \alpha(\cos\theta + i\sin\theta)$ are

$$z_0 = \sqrt{\alpha}\left(\cos\frac{\theta}{2} + i\sin\frac{\theta}{2}\right), \tag{16}$$

$$z_1 = -z_0. \tag{17}$$

The three roots of $z^3 = a$ are

$$z_0 = \sqrt[3]{\alpha}\left(\cos\frac{\theta}{3} + i\sin\frac{\theta}{3}\right), \tag{18}$$

$$z_1 = \omega z_0 \quad , \quad z_2 = \omega^2 z_0 \tag{19}$$

where ω is the first imaginary cube root of unity, viz. :

$$\omega = \frac{-1 + i\sqrt{3}}{2}. \tag{20}$$

8. The Casus Irreducibilis. As an application of the foregoing let us consider the irreducible case of Cardan's solution of the cubic

$$x^3 - px + q = 0, \; p, q \text{ real}. \tag{1}$$

The roots of 1) have the well-known form

$$x = \sqrt[3]{-\tfrac{1}{2}q + \sqrt{R}} + \sqrt[3]{-\tfrac{1}{2}q - \sqrt{R}} \tag{2}$$

where

$$R = \tfrac{1}{4}q^2 - \tfrac{1}{27}p^3 = -\Delta. \tag{3}$$

Now when the roots of 1) are all real, it is shown in algebra that Δ is positive, hence R is negative, and $\sqrt{R}$ is purely imaginary. Thus 2) expresses the real roots x as the sum of imaginaries. To Cardan and his contemporaries, who had no idea how such cube roots could be found, this case was highly paradoxical. Since that time mathematicians have attempted to present these real roots as sums of real radicals. As their efforts were unsuccessful, this case, that is, the case when $\Delta > 0$, was called the *casus irreducibilis.* It is only recently that a proof has been given that this case is indeed irreducible.* Let us see how the roots 2) may be computed, using our new complex numbers.

We set

$$-\tfrac{1}{2}q + i\sqrt{\Delta} = r(\cos\phi + i\sin\phi).$$

Then

$$\sqrt[3]{-\tfrac{1}{2}q + i\sqrt{\Delta}} = \sqrt[3]{r}\left\{\cos\left(\frac{\phi}{3} + k\frac{2\pi}{3}\right) + i\sin\left(\frac{\phi}{3} + k\frac{2\pi}{3}\right)\right\},$$

$$\sqrt[3]{-\tfrac{1}{2}q - i\sqrt{\Delta}} = \sqrt[3]{r}\left\{\cos\left(\frac{\phi}{3} + k\frac{2\pi}{3}\right) - i\sin\left(\frac{\phi}{3} + k\frac{2\pi}{3}\right)\right\}.$$

Thus the three roots of 1) are

$$x_k = 2\sqrt[3]{r}\cos\left(\frac{\phi}{3} + k \cdot 120^\circ\right),\quad k = 0, 1, 2. \tag{4}$$

Example. Let us take the equation

$$x^3 - 2x^2 - x + 2 = (x-1)(x+1)(x-2) = 0, \tag{5}$$

whose roots are

$$x = 1,\ 2,\ -1.$$

To reduce this to the form 1) we set

$$x = \tfrac{2}{3} + y. \tag{6}$$

Then 5) goes over into

$$y^3 - \tfrac{7}{3}y + \tfrac{20}{27} = 0, \tag{7}$$

whose roots by 6) are

$$y = \tfrac{1}{3},\ \tfrac{4}{3},\ -\tfrac{5}{3}.$$

* Hölder, *Math. Annalen*, vol. 38 (1891), p. 307.

Here

$$p = \tfrac{7}{3} \quad , \quad q = \tfrac{20}{27} \quad , \quad \Delta = \frac{243}{27^2},$$

$$-\frac{1}{2}q + i\sqrt{\Delta} = -\frac{10}{27} + i\frac{\sqrt{243}}{27}, \tag{8}$$

$$r^2 = \frac{1}{4}q^2 + \Delta = \frac{1}{27}p^3 = \frac{343}{27^2}.$$

Hence

$$r = \frac{\sqrt{343}}{27}.$$

Also

$$\tan\phi = -\frac{2\sqrt{\Delta}}{q} = -\frac{\sqrt{243}}{10}.$$

$$\log 243 = 2.3856,$$

$$\log\sqrt{243} = 1.1928,$$

$$\log(-\tan\phi) = 0.1928 \quad , \quad \phi = 122^\circ\, 41',$$

as ϕ lies in the second quadrant by 8).

Hence

$$\tfrac{1}{3}\phi = 40^\circ\, 54',$$

$$\log 343 = 2.5353,$$

$$\log\sqrt{343} = 1.2676,$$

$$\log 27 = 1.4314,$$

$$\log r = 9.8362,$$

$$\log\sqrt[3]{r} = 9.9454,$$

$$\log 2 = 0.3010,$$

$$\log\cos\tfrac{1}{3}\phi = 9.8784,$$

$$\log y_0 = 0.1248 \quad , \quad y_0 = 1.333 = \tfrac{4}{3}.$$

$$\tfrac{1}{3}\phi + 120^\circ = 160^\circ\, 54' \quad , \quad \cos 160^\circ\, 54' = -\cos 19^\circ\, 6',$$

$$\log\cos 19^\circ\, 6' = 9.9754,$$

$$\log 2\sqrt[3]{r} = 0.2464,$$

$$\log(-y_1) = 0.2218 \quad , \quad y_1 = -1.666 = -\tfrac{5}{3}.$$

$$\tfrac{1}{3}\phi + 240^\circ = 280^\circ\, 54' \quad , \quad \cos 280^\circ\, 54' = \sin 10^\circ\, 54',$$

$$\log\sin 10^\circ\, 54' = 9.2767,$$

$$\log 2\sqrt[3]{r} = 0.2464,$$

$$\log y_2 = 9.5231 \quad , \quad y_2 = .333 = \tfrac{1}{3}.$$

CHAPTER II

REAL TERM SERIES

9. The reader is already familiar with infinite series. An important chapter in the calculus treats of Taylor's development

$$f(a+x)=f(a)+\frac{x}{1\,!}f'(a)+\frac{x^2}{2\,!}f''(a)+\cdots$$

By its means we find for example that

$$\cos x = 1-\frac{x^2}{2\,!}+\frac{x^4}{4\,!}-\frac{x^6}{6\,!}+\cdots \qquad (1$$

$$\sin x = \frac{x}{1\,!}-\frac{x^3}{3\,!}+\frac{x^5}{5\,!}-\frac{x^7}{7\,!}+\cdots \qquad (2$$

$$e^x = 1+\frac{x}{1\,!}+\frac{x^2}{2\,!}+\frac{x^3}{3\,!}+\cdots \qquad (3$$

Infinite series were first used to compute the values of a function. Later it was found that they could be used to great advantage to study the analytical nature of a function in the vicinity of a given point. They are still used for the purpose of computation especially in constructing tables ; but their chief value to-day in the theory of functions is the aid they afford us in establishing existence theorems, and in studying the properties of functions.

We propose in this chapter to develop only as much of the theory of infinite series as is necessary for our immediate purpose. Later we will give further details.

10. Definitions. 1. Let $a_1, a_2, a_3 \cdots$ be an infinite sequence of real numbers. The symbol

$$a_1+a_2+a_3+\cdots \qquad (1$$

is called an *infinite series*. We may also denote it by

$$\sum_{m=1}^{\infty} a_m$$

or by

$$\Sigma a_m, \qquad m = 1, 2, 3 \cdots$$

We call

$$A_n = a_1 + a_2 + \cdots a_n$$
$$= \sum_{m=1}^{n} a_m,$$

the *sum of the first n terms* of 1). Suppose that as n increases indefinitely, A_n converges to a definite value. Then we say 1) is *convergent* and assign this value to the series; we call it the *sum* of 1).

If A_n does not converge to some definite value as n increases indefinitely, we say the series 1) is *divergent*. Whether 1) converges or diverges, it is often convenient to denote it by a single letter, as A; we may write

$$A = a_1 + a_2 + a_3 + \cdots \tag{2}$$

When this series converges, it is customary to denote its sum by the same letter A. This notation may be slightly confusing at first, but the reader will soon recognize in which sense A is used in any given case.

Associated with the series 2) is the series

$$\bar{A}_n = a_{n+1} + a_{n+2} + \cdots \tag{3}$$

It is called the *deleted series*, or the *remainder after n terms*. It will be convenient to denote the sum of the first s terms of the series 3) by $\bar{A}_{n,s}$; thus

$$\bar{A}_{n,s} = a_{n+1} + a_{n+2} + \cdots + a_{n+s}. \tag{4}$$

Let us now recall a notation with which the reader is already familiar.

When A_n converges to A as n increases indefinitely, we write

$$\lim_{n=\infty} A_n = A$$

and read it: "the limit of A_n for $n = \infty$ is A." The same fact may be expressed by the notation

$$A_n \doteq A \text{ as } n \doteq \infty.$$

The symbol $\doteq$ is read "converges to."

2. Let us establish here the obvious theorem :

Let $A = a_1 + a_2 + \cdots$. *The series* $B = ka_1 + ka_2 + \cdots$ *where* $k \neq 0$, *converges or diverges simultaneously with* A. *When convergent,* $B = kA$.

For

$$B_n = kA_n.$$

If now A or B is convergent, we have

$$\lim B_n = k \lim A_n,$$

or

$$B = kA.$$

11. The Geometric Series. This is

$$G = 1 + g + g^2 + g^3 + \cdots \qquad (1$$

Let $g \neq 1$. Then by elementary algebra

$$\frac{1}{1-g} = 1 + g + g^2 + \cdots + g^{n-1} + \frac{g^n}{1-g}. \qquad (2$$

This identity is often useful and the reader should memorize it. Then using the notation of 10

$$G_n = 1 + g + g^2 + \cdots + g^{n-1}$$

$$= \frac{1}{1-g} - \frac{g^n}{1-g} \qquad (3$$

by 2). Now when $|g| < 1$, $\lim_{n=\infty} g^n = 0$.

Hence in this case

$$\lim_{n=\infty} \frac{g^n}{1-g} = 0.$$

Thus 3) gives

$$\lim G_n = \frac{1}{1-g} \quad , \quad |g| < 1$$

The series 1) is therefore convergent when $|g| < 1$ and in this case

$$G = 1 + g + g^2 + \cdots = \frac{1}{1-g}.$$

If $g = 1$, $\quad G = 1 + 1 + 1 + \cdots$

Hence $\quad G_n = n$

and $\quad \lim_{n=\infty} G_n = +\infty.$

Thus G is divergent when $g = 1$.

When
$$G = -1,\ G = 1 - 1 + 1 - 1 + \cdots$$
Hence
$$G_n = 0 \text{ when } n \text{ is even,}$$
$$= 1 \text{ when } n \text{ is odd.}$$
Thus G_n does not converge at all as $n \doteq \infty$.

Hence G is divergent in this case.

When the series
$$A = a_1 + a_2 + a_3 + \cdots$$
is such that
$$\lim_{n=\infty} A_n = +\infty,$$
it is sometimes convenient to indicate this fact by the notation
$$A = +\infty.$$
Similarly if
$$\lim_{n=\infty} A_n = -\infty,$$
we may write
$$A = -\infty.$$

Returning to the geometric series, we see at once that when $g > 1$, $G_n \doteq +\infty$; while when $g < -1$, G_n oscillates between ever larger limits. We have thus the theorem: —

The geometric series 1) *is convergent when* $|g| < 1$. *It diverges when* $|g| \geq 1$. *When convergent, its sum is*
$$G = \frac{1}{1-g}.$$

12. The Harmonic Series. This is
$$H = 1 + \tfrac{1}{2} + \tfrac{1}{3} + \tfrac{1}{4} + \cdots \tag{1}$$
We show that
$$H = +\infty \tag{2}$$
and is therefore divergent.

In fact
$$\tfrac{1}{3} + \tfrac{1}{4} > \tfrac{1}{2}$$
$$\tfrac{1}{5} + \tfrac{1}{6} + \tfrac{1}{7} + \tfrac{1}{8} > \tfrac{1}{2}$$
$$\tfrac{1}{9} + \tfrac{1}{10} + \cdots + \tfrac{1}{16} > \tfrac{1}{2}$$
etc. Thus $H_2 > \frac{1}{2}$, $H_{2^2} > \frac{1}{2} + \frac{1}{2}$, $H_{2^3} > \frac{1}{2} + \frac{1}{2} + \frac{1}{2}$

and in general
$$H_{2^m} > m \cdot \tfrac{1}{2}.$$

Thus, however large the positive number G is taken

$$H_n > G,$$

if n is greater than some integer ν. Thus

$$\lim H_n = +\infty,$$

which establishes 2).

13. Fundamental Postulate. In order to go on with our work we need to use a fact which the reader will admit as soon as understood.

Suppose a variable v steadily increases as in Fig. 1, and yet always remains less than a fixed number G. Then obviously v must tend to a limit V. This limit may be less than G but it certainly cannot be greater than G. We have then

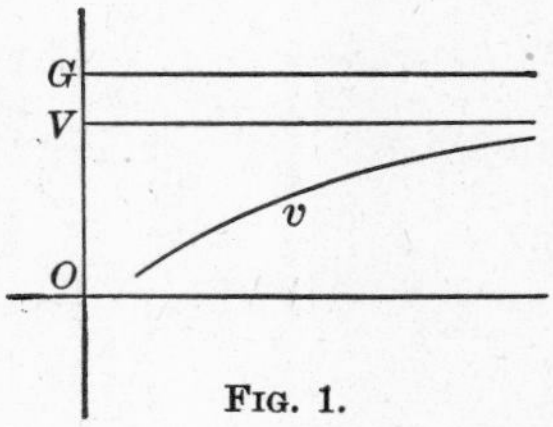

FIG. 1.

$$V = \lim v \leq G. \tag{1}$$

Similarly suppose a variable w steadily decreases as in Fig. 2, and yet always remains greater than a fixed number G. Then manifestly w must tend to a limit W and

$$W = \lim w \geq G. \tag{2}$$

We take it that these two facts are self-evident and require no proof.

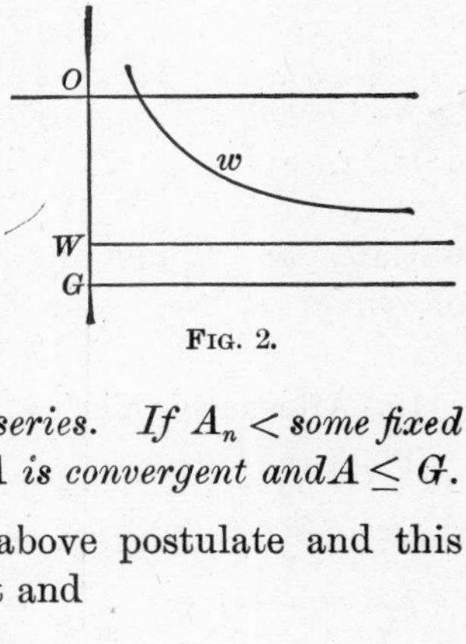

FIG. 2.

2. By means of this postulate we can establish a theorem of great importance in the theory of series :

Let $A = a_1 + a_2 + \cdots$ be a positive term series. If $A_n <$ some fixed number G, however large n is taken, then A is convergent and $A \leq G$.

For as $A_n < G$, $\lim A_n$ exists by the above postulate and this limit is $\leq G$. But then A is convergent and

$$A = \lim A_n \leq G.$$

14. The Hyperharmonic Series. This is

$$S = 1 + \frac{1}{2^s} + \frac{1}{3^s} + \frac{1}{4^s} + \cdots \tag{1}$$

We establish now the following theorem:

The series S is convergent if $s > 1$, and divergent if $s \leq 1$.

For when $s = 1$, S becomes the harmonic series H, which is divergent as we saw in 12. When $s < 1$, each term $\frac{1}{n^s}$ is greater than the corresponding term $\frac{1}{n}$ in H.

Thus

$$S_n > H_n.$$

As $H_n \doteq +\infty$, so does $S_n \doteq +\infty$, and S is divergent in this case.

Let now $s > 1$. Then

$$\frac{1}{2^s} + \frac{1}{3^s} < \frac{1}{2^s} + \frac{1}{2^s} = \frac{2}{2^s} = \frac{1}{2^{s-1}} = g, \text{ say.}$$

As $s > 1$, g is < 1. Similarly

$$\frac{1}{4^s} + \frac{1}{5^s} + \frac{1}{6^s} + \frac{1}{7^s} < \frac{1}{4^s} + \frac{1}{4^s} + \frac{1}{4^s} + \frac{1}{4^s} = \frac{4}{4^s} = \frac{1}{4^{s-1}} = g^2,$$

$$\frac{1}{8^s} + \frac{1}{9^s} + \cdots + \frac{1}{15^s} > \frac{8}{8^s} = \frac{1}{8^{s-1}} = g^3, \text{ etc.}$$

Thus however large m is taken there exists an integer n such that

$$S_m < 1 + g + g^2 + \cdots + g^{n-1} = G_n. \quad (2$$

As here $g < 1$, the geometric series G is convergent and $G_n < G$. Thus 2) gives

$$S_m < G$$

for any m. Thus by the theorem in 13, S is convergent, and moreover

$$S < G. \quad (3$$

15. Alternating Series. 1. Let $a_1 > a_2 > a_3 > \cdots \doteq 0$. Then the series

$$A = a_1 - a_2 + a_3 - a_4 + \cdots \quad (1$$

is an *alternating* series.

Examples.

$$1 - \tfrac{1}{2} + \tfrac{1}{3} - \tfrac{1}{4} + \cdots$$

$$1 - \frac{x^2}{2!} + \frac{x^4}{4!} - \cdots \quad 0 < x < 1.$$

$$\frac{x}{1} - \frac{x^3}{3!} + \frac{x^5}{5!} - \cdots \quad 0 < x < 1.$$

The last two series are the developments of $\cos x$, $\sin x$ as we observed in 9.

We prove now the theorem :

The alternating series 1) *is convergent. Its sum A is* > 0, *and the remainder after n terms $\bar{A}_n$ is numerically* $< a_{n+1}$.

For
$$A_{2n+1} = (a_1 - a_2) + (a_3 - a_4) + \cdots + (a_{2n-1} - a_{2n}) + a_{2n+1}.$$

Thus $A_{2n+1} > a_1 - a_2 > 0$. We also have
$$A_{2n+1} = a_1 - (a_2 - a_3) - (a_4 - a_5) - \cdots$$

Thus A_{2n+1} is steadily decreasing and $< a_1 - (a_2 - a_3) < a_1$. Hence by the fundamental postulate 13,
$$\lim_{n=\infty} A_{2n+1}$$
exists and is $\leq a_1 - a_2$ and $\leq a_1 - (a_2 - a_3)$.

Next we note that
$$A_{2n+1} = A_{2n} + a_{2n+1}.$$

As $\lim a_{2n+1} = 0$, by hypothesis we have
$$\lim A_{2n} = \lim A_{2n+1}.$$
Hence
$$\lim_{m=\infty} A_m \text{ exists.}$$

Thus A is convergent and
$$0 < A < a_1. \tag{2}$$

Finally we note that the series
$$P = a_{n+1} - a_{n+2} + a_{n+3} - \cdots$$
is an alternating series ; it is therefore convergent and therefore analogous to 2),
$$0 < P < a_{n+1}. \tag{3}$$

But obviously the series P and the residual series $\bar{A}_n$ differ at most by their sign ; hence
$$\bar{A}_n = \pm P.$$
Thus using 3)
$$|\bar{A}_n| < a_{n+1}.$$

2. The fact that the remainder after n terms in an alternating series is numerically less than the next term enables us to estimate the error in calculating such a series and stopping the summation at the nth term.

Example. Let us compute sin 10°, using the development

$$\sin x = \frac{x}{1\,!} - \frac{x^3}{3\,!} + \frac{x^5}{5\,!} - \cdots \tag{4}$$

We first convert 10° into circular measure and find

$$x = .1745329.$$

$$\log x = 9.2418774.$$

$$\log x^3 = 7.7256322 \quad , \quad x^3 = .0053165.$$

$$\log x^5 = 6.2093870 \quad , \quad x^5 = .0001619.$$

$$\frac{x^3}{3\,!} = .0008861.$$

$$\frac{x^5}{5\,!} = .00000135.$$

$$\frac{x^7}{7\,!} < .00000001.$$

Thus the first two terms in 4) give sin 10° correct to 5 decimals, and the first three terms to 7 decimals. We have in fact

$$\frac{x}{1} - \frac{x^3}{3\,!} = .1736468.$$

$$\frac{x}{1} - \frac{x^3}{3\,!} + \frac{x^5}{5\,!} = .1736482.$$

From the tables we find

$$\sin 10° = .1736482.$$

16. The ϵ Notation. 1. Sooner or later the student must learn to use the ϵ notation. We propose to introduce it gradually, so that it will not seem difficult to him. The object of the notation is to enable one to think more easily and accurately when dealing with limits.

Suppose we have a sequence of real numbers

$$c_1, \; c_2, \; c_3 \cdots \tag{1}$$

What do we mean when we say $c_n \doteq a$

or

$$\lim_{n=\infty} c_n = c. \qquad (2$$

Let us plot the numbers 1) and the limit c on an axis. Let ϵ be a small positive number. The points $c-\epsilon$, $c+\epsilon$ determine an interval E of length 2ϵ as in the Figure. Then the limit 2) simply means that the c_n eventually lie within E no matter how small ϵ is taken.

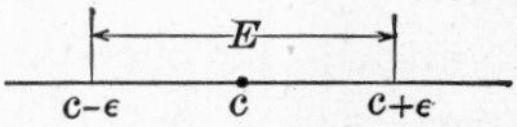

Put in more precise language, the limit 2) means that taking $\epsilon > 0$ small at pleasure and then fixing it, there exists an index m such that

$$c_{m+1},\ c_{m+2},\ c_{m+3} \cdots$$

all lie within E. The fact that these lie in E is expressed by the inequalities

$$|c - c_n| < \epsilon \quad , \quad n > m. \qquad (3$$

For the relation 3) merely states that whenever the index n is $> m$, the distance of c_n from c is $< \epsilon$.

It will be convenient to adopt a standard notation. To express that c is the limit of the c_n we shall write

$$\epsilon > 0,\ m,\ |c - c_n| < \epsilon \quad , \quad n > m. \qquad (4$$

This we will read as follows:

For each positive ϵ there exists an index m, such that $|c - c_n| < \epsilon$ for all $n > m$.

Conversely if 4) holds, we know that 2) does.

This may sound elaborate and formidable to the beginner and quite unnecessary to express a very simple fact. This is indeed so if we never deal with but very simple limits ; or never employ but very simple reasoning on limits. Now the fact is that the function theory is founded on the notion of limits. We are constantly reasoning on limits. The same is true in the calculus. But in a first course in the calculus the student is too immature to pay much attention to a rigorous treatment of limits. His main object should be to seize the spirit of the methods of the calculus and to learn how to use them easily. Then as he becomes more mature he can pay more attention to the demonstrations on which these methods are founded. In the present work we have no intention of insisting on rigor. Being a first course in the function theory, we shall endeavor to avoid all topics which require delicate handling. A demonstration of such matters is quite out of place in a first course. On the other hand, the student has advanced in maturity since his calculus days, and has reached the point when the subject of limits may be treated appropriately with more care.

2. Let us note that if $c_n \doteq 0$, then 4) becomes

$$\epsilon > 0, \quad m, \quad |c_n| < \epsilon, \quad n > m. \tag{5}$$

Conversely, if 5) holds, $\lim c_n = 0$.

3. A simple reflection will show that if $\lim c_n = c$ then not only does 4) hold, but we also may write

$$\epsilon > 0, \quad m, \quad |c - c_n| < \delta \quad , \quad n > m, \tag{6}$$

where δ may be any fixed positive number $< \epsilon$.

For the relation 6) merely says that we have replaced the interval E above, of length 2ϵ by another smaller interval of length 2δ.

We frequently have to deal with several inequalities of the type 6). In such cases we shall see that it is convenient to take $\delta = \frac{\epsilon}{2}$ or $\frac{\epsilon}{3}$, etc.

17. Necessary Conditions for Convergence. 1. When dealing with infinite series our first care is to see if the series in hand is convergent. As we never deal with divergent series in the elements of the function theory, if a series is found to be divergent it must be discarded. The following theorem is often useful :

For the series $A = a_1 + a_2 + \cdots$ *to converge it is necessary that* $a_n \doteq 0$.

For suppose A is convergent. Then by 16, 3 we have

$$\epsilon > 0, \quad m, \quad |A - A_n| < \frac{\epsilon}{2} \quad , \quad n > m.$$

Also
$$|A - A_{n+1}| < \frac{\epsilon}{2} \cdot$$

Hence by 5, 7)
$$|A_{n+1} - A_n| < \epsilon.$$
But
$$A_{n+1} - A_n = a_{n+1}.$$
Thus
$$|a_{n+1}| < \epsilon.$$
Hence by 16, 5) $\lim a_{n+1} = 0$, or what is the same, $\lim a_n = 0$.

2. Although it is necessary for $a_n \doteq 0$ when $A = a_1 + a_2 + \cdots$ is convergent, this condition is not sufficient as the following example shows.

The harmonic series
$$H = 1 + \tfrac{1}{2} + \tfrac{1}{3} + \cdots$$
is divergent as we saw in 12. Yet here
$$a_n = \frac{1}{n} \doteq 0.$$

3. *Let m be an arbitrary but fixed index. The two series* A, $\bar{A}_m$ *converge or diverge simultaneously. When convergent*
$$A = A_m + \bar{A}_m.$$

For when A is convergent $A = \lim A_n$. Let $n = m + s$. Then
$$A_n = A_m + \bar{A}_{m,s}.$$
When $n \doteq \infty$, so does s. As A_m is a constant, we see that when $\lim_{n=\infty} A_n$ exists, so does $\lim_{s=\infty} \bar{A}_{m,s}$, and conversely.

4. *If* A *is convergent,* $\lim_{n=\infty} \bar{A}_n = 0$.

For any n we have $A = A_n + \bar{A}_n$.

As A is convergent, $\lim A_n = A$. Thus
$$\bar{A}_n = A - A_n \doteq 0.$$

18. Adjoint Series. 1. In studying the convergence of a series
$$A = a_1 + a_2 + a_3 + \cdots \quad (1$$
it is convenient to consider the series obtained by replacing each term a_n by its numerical value $\alpha_n = |a_n|$. The resulting series
$$\mathfrak{A} = \alpha_1 + \alpha_2 + \alpha_3 + \cdots \quad (2$$

is called the *adjoint* of A. We write

$$\mathfrak{A} = \text{Adj}\, A.$$

In the function theory we often have to deal with the numerical or absolute values of numbers as $a, b, c \cdots$. It will often be convenient to denote them by the corresponding Greek letters $\alpha, \beta, \gamma \cdots$. Sometimes the Greek letter is so much like the Roman letter that the reader is apt to mistake it. We will replace it by the corresponding German letter. Thus Greek Α, Μ look like Roman A, M; we therefore replace them by $\mathfrak{A}, \mathfrak{M}$.

The following examples will illustrate the notion of a series and its adjoint.

Example 1.
$$A = 1 - \tfrac{1}{2} + \tfrac{1}{3} - \tfrac{1}{4} + \cdots$$
Its adjoint is
$$\mathfrak{A} = 1 + \tfrac{1}{2} + \tfrac{1}{3} + \tfrac{1}{4} + \cdots$$

Example 2.
$$A = 1 - \frac{x^2}{2\,!} + \frac{x^4}{4\,!} - \frac{x^6}{6\,!} + \cdots$$

Its adjoint is
$$\mathfrak{A} = 1 + \frac{\xi^2}{2\,!} + \frac{\xi^4}{4\,!} + \frac{\xi^6}{6\,!} + \cdots$$

where according to our notation $\xi = |x|$.

Should the terms of a series A be all positive, then A and $\mathfrak{A}$ are identical.

2. We prove now the fundamental theorem:

If $\mathfrak{A}$ converges, so does A.

For let
$$B = b_1 + b_2 + b_3 + \cdots$$

be the series formed of the positive terms of 1) taken in order, and

$$C = c_1 + c_2 + c_3 + \cdots$$

be the series formed of the negative terms of 1) taken, however, with positive signs. Then

$$B_n \leq \alpha_1 + \alpha_2 + \alpha_3 + \cdots = \mathfrak{A}$$

since B_n contains only a part of the terms of $\mathfrak{A}$. Hence B is convergent by 13, 2. Similarly $C_n < \mathfrak{A}$ and hence C is convergent.

Suppose A_n contains r positive terms and s negative terms. Then

$$A_n = B_r - C_s \quad , \quad r + s = n.$$

Let $n \doteq \infty$, then $B_r \doteq B$, $C_s \doteq C$, and hence

$$\lim A_n = \lim B_r - \lim C_s,$$

or

$$A = B - C.$$

Hence A is convergent.

3. A series may converge, although its adjoint does not.

Example.

$$A = 1 - \tfrac{1}{2} + \tfrac{1}{3} - \tfrac{1}{4} + \cdots$$

is convergent because it is an alternating series, by 15. Its adjoint

$$\mathfrak{A} = 1 + \tfrac{1}{2} + \tfrac{1}{3} + \tfrac{1}{4} + \cdots$$

is divergent since it is the harmonic series, by 12.

A series whose adjoint is convergent is called ***absolutely convergent.*** If A converges while $\mathfrak{A}$ does not, we say A is *simply convergent* when we wish to indicate that A does not converge absolutely. The greater part of the series employed in the elements of the function theory are absolutely convergent. We shall therefore have little to do with simply convergent series.

4. The following theorem is very useful in ascertaining if a given series is absolutely convergent :

Let $B = b_1 + b_2 + b_3 + \cdots$ converge and have all its terms > 0. Then the series $A = a_1 + a_2 + a_3 + \cdots$ is absolutely convergent if $\alpha_n \leq b_n$. Moreover $|A| \leq B$.

For passing to the adjoint of A, we have

$$\mathfrak{A}_n = \alpha_1 + \alpha_2 + \cdots + \alpha_n \leq b_1 + b_2 + \cdots + b_n < B.$$

Thus $\mathfrak{A}$ is convergent by 13, 2.

As

$$|A_n| \leq \mathfrak{A}_n \leq B$$

we have

$$|A| < B.$$

19. The Remainder Series. 1. Suppose we wish to compute the value of the convergent series

$$A = a_1 + a_2 + a_3 + \cdots \tag{1}$$

correct to a certain number of decimals, say to p decimals. We compute successively

$$A_1 = a_1$$
$$A_2 = a_1 + a_2$$
$$A_3 = a_1 + a_2 + a_3$$

etc. In order to know if we may stop at A_n we must know if the remainder $\bar{A}_n$ affects the pth decimal in A_n. We must know, therefore, if

$$|\bar{A}_n| < 10^{-p}.$$

In case that A is an alternate series the theorem of 15 shows that we may take n so that

$$|a_{n+1}| < 10^{-p}.$$

For we showed that

$$|\bar{A}_n| < a_{n+1}.$$

When the series 1) is not alternate, it is not so easy to estimate the magnitude of the remainder. The theorem of 18, 4 may sometimes be applied with advantage to $\bar{A}_n$. In fact if $a_n \leq b_n$ we have

$$|\bar{A}_n| < B_n < B.$$

2. *Example.* Let us use the theorem of 18, 4 to show that exponential series

$$E = 1 + \frac{x}{1\,!} + \frac{x^2}{2\,!} + \frac{x^3}{3\,!} + \cdots \tag{2}$$

is convergent for $x > 0$, and to estimate the magnitude of the remainder $\bar{E}_n$.

Let us take x large at pleasure and then fix it. We next take m so large that $m + 1 > x$. Then

$$g = \frac{x}{m+1} < 1. \tag{3}$$

Let us set

$$M = \frac{x^m}{m\,!}.$$

As x and m are fixed, M is a constant. Then

$$\frac{x^{m+s}}{(m+s)!} = \frac{x^m}{m\,!} \cdot \frac{x^s}{(m+1)\cdots(m+s)} < Mg^s.$$

Thus each term of

$$\bar{E}_m = \frac{x^m}{m\,!} + \frac{x^{m+1}}{(m+1)!} + \frac{x^{m+2}}{(m+2)\,!} + \cdots$$

after the first is less than the corresponding term of the convergent geometric series

$$M + Mg + Mg^2 + \cdots = M(1 + g + g^2 + \cdots)$$
$$= \frac{M}{1-g}.$$

Hence the remainder series $\overline{E}_m$ is convergent. Thus E is convergent and

$$\overline{E}_m < \frac{M}{1-g} \tag{4}$$

where g is given by 3).

Positive Term Series

20. Theorems of Comparison. Series whose terms are all positive are of especial importance for deducing tests of convergence. To ascertain if a given positive term series A is convergent it is generally advantageous to compare it with some other positive term series B whose convergence or divergence is known. We begin therefore by establishing two theorems of comparison.

2. *Let* $A = a_1 + a_2 + \cdots$, $B = b_1 + b_2 + \cdots$ *be positive term series. Let* r, s *be positive constants.*

If 1°
$$r \leq \frac{a_n}{b_n} \leq s \quad , \quad n = 1, 2, 3 \cdots$$

or 2°
$$\lim \frac{a_n}{b_n} \textit{ exists and is } \neq 0,$$

then A *and* B *converge or diverge simultaneously.*

For *on the* 1° *hypothesis* $a_n \leq sb_n$; hence if B converges, $A_n \leq sB_n < sB$. Thus A converges by 13, 2. Also $a_n \geq rb_n$; hence $A_n \geq rB_n$. Thus if B is divergent, so is A.

On the 2° *hypothesis*, let

$$\frac{a_n}{b_n} \doteq l \text{ and } l > 0.$$

Then as n increases, $\frac{a_n}{b_n}$ gets nearer and nearer l. Hence for a sufficiently large m, there exist two positive numbers r, s such that

$$r < \frac{a_n}{b_n} < s, \quad n > m.$$

Thus the terms of the series

$$\bar{A}_m = a_{m+1} + a_{m+2} + \cdots$$

satisfy condition 1° above. Thus this 2° case is reduced to the preceding.

Example 1.

$$A = \frac{1}{1 \cdot 2} + \frac{1}{2 \cdot 3} + \frac{1}{3 \cdot 4} + \cdots$$

Here

$$a_n = \frac{1}{n(n+1)} < \frac{1}{n^2}.$$

Thus each term of A is less than the corresponding term of the convergent series

$$\frac{1}{1^2} + \frac{1}{2^2} + \frac{1}{3^2} + \cdots$$

Hence A is convergent.

Example 2.

$$A = \frac{\cos x}{e^x} + \frac{\cos 2x}{e^{2x}} + \cdots \quad , \quad x > 0.$$

The adjoint series is

$$\mathfrak{A} = \frac{|\cos x|}{e^x} + \frac{|\cos 2x|}{e^{2x}} + \cdots$$

As $|\cos u| \leq 1$, each term of this series is $\leq$ the corresponding term of the convergent geometric series

$$\frac{1}{e^x} + \frac{1}{e^{2x}} + \frac{1}{e^{3x}} + \cdots$$

Hence $\mathfrak{A}$ is convergent, and thus A is absolutely convergent.

Example 3.

$$A = \Sigma a_n = \Sigma \log\left(1 + \frac{\mu}{n} + \frac{\theta_n}{n^r}\right) \quad , \quad r > 1$$

where μ is a constant and

$$|\theta_n| < \text{some } G.$$

By the calculus we have, setting $r = 1 + s$,

$$a_n = \frac{1}{n}\left(\mu + \frac{\theta_n}{n^s}\right) - \frac{\sigma_n}{n^2}\left(\mu + \frac{\theta_n}{n^s}\right)^2 \quad , \quad 0 < \sigma_n < 1.$$

If $\mu = 0$, we have

$$a_n = \frac{\theta_n}{n^r}\left(1 - \frac{\sigma_n \theta_n}{n^r}\right)$$

which is comparable with the convergent series

$$\sum \frac{1}{n^r} \quad , \quad r > 1.$$

Thus A is convergent in this case.

If $\mu \neq 0$, we see that $na_n \doteq \mu$. Thus A is comparable with the divergent series

$$H = 1 + \tfrac{1}{2} + \tfrac{1}{3} + \tfrac{1}{4} + \cdots.$$

When $\mu > 0$, we see the terms of A finally become positive and $A = +\infty$. When $\mu < 0$, the terms finally become negative and $A = -\infty$.

Example 4. $C = \sum\limits_1^\infty \left\{ \frac{1}{n} - \log\left(1 + \frac{1}{n}\right) \right\} = \Sigma c_n.$

This series is convergent. For if $n > 1$, by the law of the mean,

$$\log\left(1 + \frac{1}{n}\right) = \frac{1}{n} + M_n \cdot \frac{1}{n^2} \quad , \quad |M_n| < \text{some } M.$$

Thus

$$|c_n| < \frac{M}{n^2}.$$

The adjoint of C is thus comparable with the convergent series

$$M \sum \frac{1}{n^2}.$$

The series C is therefore absolutely convergent. Its sum is called the *Eulerian constant.* By calculation we find

$$C = .57721566\ldots$$

3. The second theorem of comparison is :

Let $\quad A = a_1 + a_2 + a_3 + \cdots \quad , \quad B = b_1 + b_2 + b_3 + \cdots$

be positive term series. If B is convergent and

$$\frac{a_{n+1}}{a_n} \leq \frac{b_{n+1}}{b_n} \quad , \quad n = 1, 2, \cdots$$

A is convergent. If B is divergent and

$$\frac{a_{n+1}}{a_n} \geq \frac{b_{n+1}}{b_n},$$

A is divergent.

For *on the* 1° *hypothesis*,

$$\frac{a_{n+1}}{b_{n+1}} \leq \frac{a_n}{b_n} \leq \cdots \leq \frac{a_1}{b_1} = q, \text{ say.}$$

Thus

$$\frac{a_n}{b_n} \leq q,$$

and we may apply 2.

On the 2° *hypothesis* we have

$$\frac{a_n}{b_n} \geq q$$

and may again apply 2.

21. D'Alembert's Test 1. As an application of the second theorem of comparison 20, 3, we will establish a test for convergence or divergence of a positive term series which is perhaps more often used than any other. It is called *D'Alembert's test.*

The positive term series $A = a_1 + a_2 + \cdots$ *converges if there exists a constant* $r < 1$ *for which*

$$\frac{a_{n+1}}{a_n} \leq r, \text{ or } \lim \frac{a_{n+1}}{a_n} = r.$$

The series A diverges if

$$\frac{a_{n+1}}{a_n} \geq 1, \text{ or if } \lim \frac{a_{n+1}}{a_n} > 1.$$

Let us suppose that

$$\frac{a_{n+1}}{a_n} \leq r.$$

We compare A with the convergent geometric series

$$R = 1 + r + r^2 + \cdots$$

and apply 20, 3.

Let us next suppose that

$$\lim \frac{a_{n+1}}{a_n} = r. \qquad (1$$

Then we may choose $\epsilon > 0$ so small that $s = r + \epsilon$ is also < 1. Then 1) states that there exists an m such that

$$\frac{a_{n+1}}{a_n} \leq s \quad , \quad n > m.$$

Thus we are led back to the former case. In a similar manner we may treat the divergence part of the theorem.

Example 1.
$$A = a + 2\,a^2 + 3\,a^3 + \cdots$$

is convergent if $0 \leq a < 1$. For the ratio of two terms

$$\frac{a_{n+1}}{a_n} = \frac{n+1}{n} \cdot a \doteq a < 1.$$

Example 2. Let us show that the exponential series

$$E = 1 + \frac{x}{1\,!} + \frac{x^2}{2\,!} + \cdots$$

converges absolutely for any x. To this end we consider its adjoint

$$\mathfrak{E} = 1 + \frac{\xi}{1!} + \frac{\xi^2}{2!} + \cdots$$

The ratio of the $n+1^{st}$ term to the nth is

$$\frac{\xi^n}{n!} : \frac{\xi^{n-1}}{(n-1)!} = \frac{\xi}{n} \doteq 0$$

for any given ξ. Thus in this case $r = 0$ in D'Alembert's test. Hence $\mathfrak{E}$ converges, and thus E converges absolutely for any x.

Example 3. Let us consider the convergence of the series which are the developments of the cosine and sine, viz.:

$$C = 1 - \frac{x^2}{2!} + \frac{x^4}{4!} - \cdots$$

$$S = \frac{x}{1!} - \frac{x^3}{3!} + \frac{x^5}{5!} - \cdots$$

The adjoints of these are

$$\mathfrak{C} = 1 + \frac{\xi^2}{2!} + \frac{\xi^4}{4!} + \cdots$$

$$\mathfrak{S} = \frac{\xi}{1!} + \frac{\xi^3}{3!} + \frac{\xi^5}{5!} + \cdots$$

The terms of these series form a part of the series $\mathfrak{E}$ considered in Example 2. Thus

$$\mathfrak{C} < \mathfrak{E} \quad , \quad \mathfrak{S} < \mathfrak{E}$$

and hence $\mathfrak{C}$, $\mathfrak{S}$ converge for any ξ since $\mathfrak{E}$ does. *Thus C and S converge absolutely for any x.*

This result may also be obtained directly from D'Alembert's test. For the ratio of two successive terms of $\mathfrak{C}$ is

$$\frac{\xi^{2n}}{(2n)!} : \frac{\xi^{2n-2}}{(2n-2)!} = \frac{\xi^2}{2n(2n-1)} \doteq 0.$$

Hence $\mathfrak{C}$ converges for any ξ, and a similar result holds for $\mathfrak{S}$.

Example 4. Let us show that the logarithmic series

$$L = \frac{x}{1} - \frac{x^2}{2} + \frac{x^3}{3} - \cdots$$

converges absolutely for any $|x| < 1$ *and diverges for* $|x| > 1$. In fact the adjoint series is

$$\mathfrak{L} = \frac{\xi}{1} + \frac{\xi^2}{2} + \frac{\xi^3}{3} + \cdots$$

The ratio of two successive terms is

$$\frac{\xi^{n+1}}{n+1} : \frac{\xi^n}{n} = \frac{n}{n+1} \cdot \xi \doteq \xi.$$

Here the limit r in D'Alembert's test is ξ.

2. We must note that *when in D'Alembert's test the limit*

$$\lim \frac{a_{n+1}}{a_n} = 1,$$

we can neither conclude that A converges or that it diverges, as the following example shows.

Example. Let $A = \frac{1}{1^s} + \frac{1}{2^s} + \frac{1}{3^s} + \cdots$

Here $$\frac{a_{n+1}}{a_n} = \frac{n^s}{(n+1)^s} = \frac{1}{\left(1 + \frac{1}{n}\right)^s} \doteq 1.$$

Now when $s > 1$, A is convergent, while when $s < 1$, A is divergent.

22. Cauchy's Integral Test. 1. This is a test of great power; it is expressed in the theorem:

Let $f(x)$ be a steadily decreasing positive function such that

$$f(n) \geq a_n.$$

Then the positive term series

$$A = a_1 + a_2 + a_3 + \cdots$$

is convergent if

$$J = \int_m^{\infty} f(x)dx$$

is convergent.

For on the ordinates $x = n$, in Fig. 1, let us lay off the values of a_n. Then A_n = area of the shaded region from $x = 0$ to $x = n$. But the curve belonging to $y = f(x)$ lies above this shaded region. Thus

$$\bar{A}_{m,n} = a_{m+1} + a_{m+2} + \cdots + a_{m+n} < J.$$

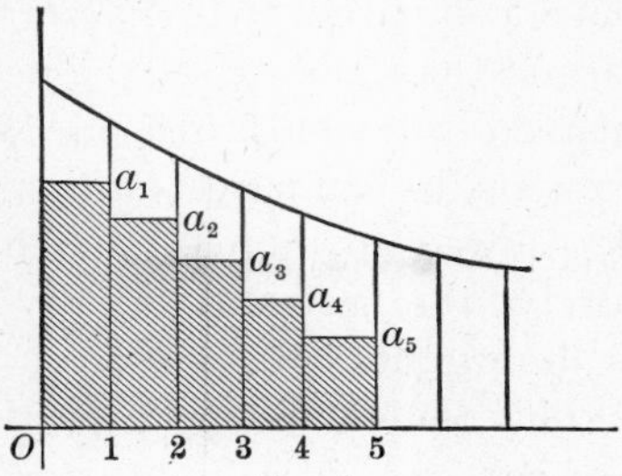

FIG. 1.

Hence $\bar{A}_m$ is convergent, and hence A is.

2. Similarly we have a *divergent test:*

Let $f(x)$ be a steadily decreasing positive function such that $a_n \geq f(n)$. Then the positive term series

$$A = a_1 + a_2 + \cdots$$

is divergent if

$$K = \int_m^{\infty} f(x)dx$$

is divergent.

For consulting Fig. 2 we see that

$$\bar{A}_{m,n} = a_{m+1} + a_{m+2} + \cdots a_{m+n} > \int_{m+1}^{m+n+1} f(x)dx$$

Let now $n \doteq \infty$. The integral on the right $\doteq +\infty$ by hypothesis; hence $\bar{A}_m$ is divergent, hence A is divergent.

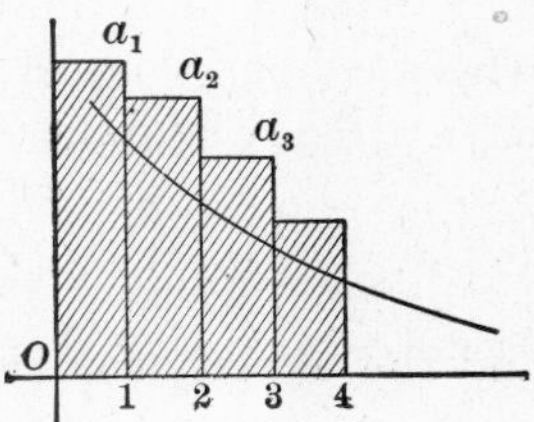

FIG. 2.

3. In the last section the student might be tempted to reason as follows. $\bar{A}_m$ is the area of the rectangles from $x = m$ to ∞. This is greater than the area of the curve from $x = m$ to ∞. Thus one would have at once

$$\bar{A}_m > K. \tag{2}$$

As the integral $K = \infty$, so is A_m, hence $A = \infty$.

Against this form of reasoning one can urge the objection that one is dealing with ∞ as if it were an ordinary number. It is true that in a first course in the calculus the student often falls into this habit. At times this is quite convenient, at other times it can create great confusion. To avoid such loose reasoning mathematicians to-day do not operate on infinite quantities as if they were finite. For example in the present case we wish to show that $\overline{A}_m$ is divergent. To this end we have compared two *infinite* areas in 2) and asserted that one is larger than the other. The modern mathematician avoids this; instead he would reason as in the foregoing section 2. The relation 1) compares *finite* areas. In this relation the variable n is allowed to increase indefinitely. Since $\overline{A}_{m,n}$ increases indefinitely, the series $\overline{A}_m$ is divergent by definition. Hence also A is divergent.

The reader will perhaps think this a very small point. In the present case it is indeed trivial. We have chosen it however to illustrate a great principle :

The student must avoid operating on infinite quantities as if they were finite. All operations must be performed on finite quantities, except in the single operation of passing to the limit.

23. The Logarithmic Scale. 1. As we have already remarked, the convergence or divergence of a positive term series

$$A = a_1 + a_2 + a_3 + \cdots$$

may often be determined readily by comparing A with some series whose convergence or divergence is known. Two such series we have already found. The geometric series

$$G = 1 + g + g^2 + g^3 + \cdots \tag{1}$$

and the hyperharmonic series

$$S = 1 + \frac{1}{2^s} + \frac{1}{3^s} + \frac{1}{4^s} + \cdots \tag{2}$$

We propose now to use Cauchy's integral test to show that *the series*

$$\sum \frac{1}{nl_1^s n} \tag{3}$$

$$\sum \frac{1}{nl_1 nl_2^s n} \tag{4}$$

$$\sum \frac{1}{nl_1 nl_2 nl_3^s n} \tag{5}$$

$$\cdot \quad \cdot \quad \cdot \quad \cdot \quad \cdot$$

all converge when $s > 1$ and diverge when $s \leq 1$.

For brevity we have set

$$l_1 n = \log n \quad , \quad l_2 n = \log(\log n) \quad , \quad \cdots$$

We must note that in the domain of real numbers, $\log x$ does not exist for $x \leq 0$. Thus the summation in the series 3), 4) $\cdots$ must begin with a value of n for which $l_m n$ exists.

Let us consider the series 3), or

$$L = \frac{1}{2 \log^s 2} + \frac{1}{3 \log^s 3} + \frac{1}{4 \log^s 4} + \cdots \tag{6}$$

when $s > 1$.

From the calculus we have

$$\frac{d \log^{1-s} x}{dx} = \frac{1-s}{x \log^s x}.$$

Thus

$$\int_\alpha^\beta \frac{dx}{x \log^s x} = \frac{1}{s-1} \left\{ \frac{1}{\log^{s-1} \alpha} - \frac{1}{\log^{s-1} \beta} \right\} \quad , \quad 0 < \alpha < \beta.$$

Hence

$$\int_\alpha^\infty \frac{dx}{x \log^s x} = \frac{1}{s-1} \frac{1}{\log^{s-1} \alpha}$$

is convergent. Hence by Cauchy's test 6) is convergent when $s > 1$.

Let us now take $s = 1$. From the calculus we have

$$\frac{dl_2 x}{dx} = \frac{d}{dx} \log(\log x) = \frac{1}{x \log x}.$$

Hence

$$\int_\alpha^\beta \frac{dx}{x \log x} = \log(\log \beta) - \log(\log \alpha) \quad , \quad 0 < \alpha < \beta.$$

Thus
$$\int^{\infty} \frac{dx}{x \log x} = +\infty.$$

Hence by Cauchy's test 6) is divergent for $s=1$. Hence *à fortiori* it diverges for $s<1$.

To treat the general case we would employ the function

$$f(x) = \frac{1}{xl_1xl_2x \cdots l_{m-1}xl_m{}^sx}.$$

2. The series 3), 4), 5), ⋯ form a *scale*. That is when $s>1$ each converges more slowly than the foregoing. When $s=1$ each diverges more slowly than the foregoing. To apply this scale to test the convergence or divergence of a given positive term series A we begin by comparing the terms of A with those of 3). If no test results, we next employ the series 4), and so on.

24. Kummer's Test. 1. This is embodied in the following theorem:

Let $A = a_1 + a_2 + \cdots$ be a positive term series. Let $k_1, k_2 \cdots$ be a set of positive numbers chosen at pleasure. A is convergent if for some constant $k>0$.

$$K_n = k_n \cdot \frac{a_n}{a_{n+1}} - k_{n+1} \geq k \quad , \quad n = 1, 2, \cdots \tag{1}$$

A is divergent if
$$D = \frac{1}{k_1} + \frac{1}{k_2} + \cdots \tag{2}$$

is divergent and $K_n \leq 0,\ n = 1, 2, \cdots$

For on the first hypothesis

$$a_2 \leq \frac{1}{k}(k_1a_1 - k_2a_2).$$

$$a_3 \leq \frac{1}{k}(k_2a_2 - k_3a_3).$$

. . . .

$$a_n \leq \frac{1}{k}(k_{n-1}a_{n-1} - k_na_n).$$

Hence adding these

$$0 \leq A_n \leq a_1 + \frac{1}{k}(k_1 a_1 - k_n a_n) < a_1\left(1 + \frac{k_1}{k}\right).$$

Thus A is convergent by 13, 2.

On the Second Hypothesis

$$\frac{a_n}{a_{n+1}} \leq \frac{k_{n+1}}{k_n},$$

or

$$\frac{a_{n+1}}{a_n} \geq \frac{k_{n+1}^{-1}}{k_n^{-1}}.$$

Thus A is divergent by 20, 3.

2. We shall call the divergent series 2) *Kummer's series.*

25. Raabe's and Cahen's Tests. 1. From Kummer's test we may deduce a set of tests of great usefulness. Thus if we take

$$k_1 = k_2 = \cdots = 1$$

we get D'Alembert's test 21.

If we take

$$k_1 = 1,\ k_2 = 2,\ k_3 = 3 \cdots$$

we get:

Raabe's Test. The positive term series $A = a_1 + a_2 + \cdots$ is convergent if

$$\lambda_0(n) = n\left(\frac{a_n}{a_{n+1}} - 1\right) \geq l \quad , \quad l > 1. \tag{1}$$

A is divergent if

$$\lambda_0(n) \leq 1. \tag{2}$$

For here

$$K_n = n\frac{a_n}{a_{n+1}} - (n+1) \geq k > 0$$

if 1) holds. On the other hand

$$K_n \leq 0$$

if 2) holds.

2. In the foregoing we have used the divergent series

$$D = \tfrac{1}{1} + \tfrac{1}{1} + \tfrac{1}{1} + \cdots$$

and

$$D = \tfrac{1}{1} + \tfrac{1}{2} + \tfrac{1}{3} + \cdots$$

to get D'Alembert's and Raabe's tests. If we use the scale of divergent logarithmic series considered in

$$\sum \frac{1}{nl_1x},$$

$$\sum \frac{1}{nl_1xl_2x},$$

$$\cdots\cdots$$

we get a set of tests which may be stated as follows:

Let $A = a_1 + a_2 + \cdots$ *be a positive term series. Let*

$$\lambda_1(n) = l_1 n\left\{n\left(\frac{a_n}{a_{n+1}} - 1\right) - 1\right\} = l_1 n\{\lambda_0(n) - 1\}, \tag{3}$$

$$\lambda_2(n) = l_2 n\left\{l_1 n\left[n\left(\frac{a_n}{a_{n+1}} - 1\right) - 1\right] - 1\right\} = l_2 n\{\lambda_1(n) - 1\}.$$

$$\cdots\cdots\cdots\cdots\cdots\cdots\cdots\cdots$$

Then A *converges if there exists an* s *such that*

$$\lambda_s(n) \geq \delta > 1 \quad \textit{for some } n > m;$$

A diverges if

$$\lambda_s(n) \leq 1 \quad \textit{for } n > m.$$

Let us prove the first test 3) in this set. The others are proved similarly. We take here

$$k_n = n \log n.$$

Then A converges if

$$K_n = n \log n \frac{a_n}{a_{n+1}} - (n+1)\log(n+1) \geq k > 0.$$

As

$$n + 1 = n\left(1 + \frac{1}{n}\right),$$

$$K_n = \lambda_1(n) - \log\left(1 + \frac{1}{n}\right)^n - \log\left(1 + \frac{1}{n}\right),$$

$$= \lambda_1(n) - \log\left(1 + \frac{1}{n}\right)^{n+1},$$

$$= \lambda_1(n) - (1 + \alpha) \quad , \quad \alpha > 0.$$

Thus A converges if

$$\lambda_1(n) \geq \delta > 1 \quad \text{for } n > \text{some } m.$$

In this way we see also that A diverges if

$$\lambda_1(n) \leq 1 \quad \text{for } n > \text{some } m.$$

3. From 3) we deduce

Cahen's Test. If the positive term series $A = a_1 + a_2 + \cdots$ *is such that for every* n

$$C_n = n\left\{n\left(\frac{a_n}{a_{n+1}} - 1\right) - 1\right\} \leq \text{some } G,$$

then A *is divergent.*

For

$$\lambda_1(n) \leq \frac{\log n}{n} \cdot G.$$

Here the right side $\doteq 0$. Hence $\lambda_1(n) \leq 1$ for $n >$ some m, and A is divergent by 2.

26. Gauss' Test. *Let* $A = a_1 + a_2 + \cdots$ *be a positive term series such that*

$$\frac{a_n}{a_{n+1}} = \frac{n^s + \alpha_1 n^{s-1} + \cdots + \alpha_s}{n^s + \beta_1 n^{s-1} + \cdots + \beta_s}, \tag{1}$$

where $s, \alpha_1, \alpha_2 \cdots \beta_1, \beta_2 \cdots$ *do not depend on* n. *Then* A *is convergent if*

$$\alpha_1 - \beta_1 > 1,$$

and divergent if

$$\alpha_1 - \beta_1 \leq 1.$$

This may be deduced from 25 as follows. Here

$$\lambda_0(n) = n\left(\frac{a_n}{a_{n+1}} - 1\right) = \frac{\alpha_1 - \beta_1 + \frac{1}{n}\{\alpha_2 - \beta_2 + \cdots\}}{1 + \frac{1}{n}\{\beta_1 + \cdots\}}. \tag{2}$$

Thus

$$\lim \lambda_0(n) = \alpha_1 - \beta_1.$$

Hence if $\alpha_1 - \beta_1 > 1$, certainly there exists some $l > 1$ such that

$$n\left(\frac{a_n}{a_{n+1}} - 1\right) \geq l \quad \text{for all } n > \text{some } m.$$

Thus Raabe's test shows that A is convergent. If $\alpha_1 - \beta_1 = 1$, Raabe's test does not always apply. To dispose of this case we may apply the $\lambda_1(n)$ test of 25, 2. Or, more simply, we may apply Cahen's test. We find at once

$$\lim C_n = \alpha_2 - \beta_2 - \beta_1.$$

Thus

$$C_n < \text{some } G$$

and A is divergent.

27. A test similar to Gauss' test in 26 is the following:

Let $A = a_1 + a_2 + \cdots$ be a positive term series such that

$$\frac{a_n}{a_{n+1}} = 1 + \frac{\alpha}{n} + \frac{\beta_n}{n^\mu},$$

where $\mu > 1$, and $\beta_n <$ some G. Then A is convergent if $\alpha > 1$, and divergent if $\alpha \leq 1$.

For here

$$\lambda_0(n) = n\left(\frac{a_n}{a_{n+1}} - 1\right) = \alpha + \frac{\beta_n}{n^{\mu-1}} \doteq \alpha.$$

Thus A is convergent if $\alpha > 1$, and divergent if $\alpha < 1$. If $\alpha = 1$, we have

$$\lambda_1(n) = l_1 n\{\lambda_0(n) - 1\} = \frac{l_1 n}{n^{\mu-1}} \cdot \beta_n \doteq 0,$$

and A is divergent.

28. Binomial Series. This is

$$B = 1 + \mu x + \frac{\mu \cdot \mu - 1}{1 \cdot 2} x^2 + \frac{\mu \cdot \mu - 1 \cdot \mu - 2}{1 \cdot 2 \cdot 3} x^3 + \cdots$$

$$= 1 + \binom{\mu}{1} x + \binom{\mu}{2} x^2 + \binom{\mu}{3} x^3 + \cdots \qquad (1$$

This series arises when we develop $(1+x)^\mu$ by Taylor's theorem; here we wish merely to consider the convergence of the series as an application of the foregoing tests.

If μ is a positive integer, B is a polynomial of degree μ. If $\mu = 0$, $B = 1$. We now exclude these exceptional values of μ.

Applying D'Alembert's test to the adjoint of 1), we find

$$\frac{\alpha_{n+1}}{\alpha_n} = \left|\frac{\mu - n + 1}{n}\right| \cdot |x| \doteq |x|.$$

Thus B converges absolutely for $|x| < 1$, and diverges if $|x| > 1$.

Let $x = 1$. Then

$$B = 1 + \mu + \frac{\mu \cdot \mu - 1}{1 \cdot 2} + \cdots$$

Then
$$\frac{\alpha_{n+1}}{\alpha_n} = \frac{|\mu - n + 1|}{n} \doteq 1.$$

As D'Alembert's test gives us no information in this case, we apply Raabe's test. Here

$$\lambda_0(n) = n\left(\frac{\alpha_n}{\alpha_{n+1}} - 1\right) = \frac{1 + \mu}{1 - \frac{1 + \mu}{n}}$$

for n sufficiently large. Thus

$$\lambda_0(n) \doteq 1 + \mu.$$

Hence B converges absolutely if $\mu > 0$, and its adjoint diverges if $\mu < 0$.

But in this case we note that the terms of B are alternately positive and negative. Also

$$\frac{\alpha_{n+1}}{\alpha_n} = \left|1 - \frac{1 + \mu}{n}\right|,$$

so that α_n form a decreasing sequence from a certain term, provided $\mu > -1$, when $\alpha_n \doteq 0$. Thus B converges when $\mu > -1$ and diverges when $\mu \leq -1$.

Let $x = -1$. Then

$$B = 1 - \mu + \frac{\mu \cdot \mu - 1}{1 \cdot 2} - \cdots$$

If $\mu > 0$, the terms of B finally have one sign and $\lambda_0(n) \doteq 1 + \mu$. Hence B converges absolutely.

If $\mu < 0$, let $\mu = -\lambda$. Then B becomes

$$1 + \lambda + \frac{\lambda \cdot \lambda + 1}{1 \cdot 2} + \frac{\lambda \cdot \lambda + 1 \cdot \lambda + 2}{1 \cdot 2 \cdot 3} + \cdots$$

Here
$$\lambda_0(n) = \frac{1 - \lambda}{1 + \frac{\lambda - 1}{n}} \doteq 1 - \lambda,$$

and B therefore diverges in this case. To sum up, we have the theorem :

The binomial series 1) *converges absolutely for* $|x|<1$, *and diverges for* $|x|>1$. *When* $x=1$, *it converges for* $\mu>-1$ *and diverges for* $\mu\le -1$; *it converges absolutely only for* $\mu>0$. *When* $x=-1$, *it converges absolutely for* $\mu>0$ *and diverges for* $\mu<0$.

29. The Hypergeometric Series. This is

$$F(\alpha, \beta, \gamma, x) = 1 + \frac{\alpha\cdot\beta}{1\cdot\gamma}x + \frac{\alpha\cdot\alpha+1\cdot\beta\cdot\beta+1}{1\cdot 2\cdot\gamma\cdot\gamma+1}x^2 + \frac{\alpha\cdot\alpha+1\cdot\alpha+2\cdot\beta\cdot\beta+1\cdot\beta+2}{1\cdot 2\cdot 3\cdot\gamma\cdot\gamma+1\cdot\gamma+2}x^3+\cdots \qquad (1$$

Let us find when this very important series converges. Passing to the adjoint series, we find

$$\frac{a_{n+2}}{a_{n+1}} = \left|\frac{(\alpha+n)(\beta+n)}{(n+1)(\gamma+n)}\right|\cdot|x| \doteq |x|. \qquad (2$$

Thus F converges absolutely for $|x|<1$ and diverges for $|x|>1$.

Let $x=1$. The terms of F finally have one sign and

$$\frac{a_{n+1}}{a_{n+2}} = \frac{n^2+n(1+\gamma)+\gamma}{n^2+n(\alpha+\beta)+\alpha\beta}.$$

Applying Gauss' test, 26, we find F converges when and only when

$$\alpha+\beta-\gamma<0.$$

Let $x=-1$. The terms finally alternate in sign. We may write $F=a_1-a_2+a_3-\cdots$. Let us find when $a_n\doteq 0$. We have

$$a_{n+2} = \frac{\alpha\beta}{\gamma}\cdot\frac{(\alpha+1)\cdots(\alpha+n)(\beta+1)\cdots(\beta+n)}{(1+1)\cdots(1+n)(\gamma+1)\cdots(\gamma+n)}.$$

Now

$$\alpha+m = m\left(1+\frac{\alpha}{m}\right), \quad \beta+m = m\left(1+\frac{\beta}{m}\right),$$

$$1+m = m\left(1+\frac{1}{m}\right), \quad \gamma+m = m\left(1+\frac{\gamma}{m}\right).$$

Thus

$$a_{n+2} = \prod_1^n \frac{\alpha\beta}{\gamma}\cdot\frac{\left(1+\frac{\alpha}{m}\right)\left(1+\frac{\beta}{m}\right)}{\left(1+\frac{1}{m}\right)\left(1+\frac{\gamma}{m}\right)}.$$

But
$$\frac{1}{1+\frac{1}{m}}=1-\frac{1}{m}+\frac{\sigma_m}{m^2} \quad ; \quad \frac{1}{1+\frac{\gamma}{m}}=1-\frac{\gamma}{m}+\frac{\tau_m}{m^2},$$
where
$$\sigma_m \doteq 1 \quad , \quad \tau_m \doteq \gamma^2 \quad \text{as } r \doteq \infty.$$
Hence
$$a_{n+2}=\prod_1^n\left(1+\frac{\alpha}{m}\right)\left(1+\frac{\beta}{m}\right)\left(1-\frac{1}{m}+\frac{\sigma_m}{m^2}\right)\left(1-\frac{\gamma}{m}+\frac{\tau_m}{m^2}\right)$$
$$=\prod_1^n\left(1+\frac{\alpha+\beta-\gamma-1}{m}+\frac{\eta_m}{m^2}\right).$$
Hence
$$\log a_{n+2}=\sum_1^n \log\left(1+\frac{\alpha+\beta-\gamma-1}{m}+\frac{\eta_m}{m^2}\right)$$
$$=\sum_1^n l_m = L_n.$$
Thus
$$L=\lim_{n=\infty} \log a_{n+2}=\sum_1^\infty l_m.$$

Now for a_n to $\doteq 0$ it is necessary that $L_n \doteq -\infty$. In 20, Ex. 3, we saw that this takes place only when $\alpha+\beta-\gamma-1<0$.

Let us now see if L is an alternating series. If so, we must also have $a_n > a_{n+1} < \cdots$. From 2) we have
$$\frac{a_{n+2}}{a_{n+1}}=1+\frac{\alpha+\beta-\gamma-1}{n}+\frac{\delta_n}{n^2}.$$

Thus when $\alpha+\beta-\gamma-1<0$ the L series is alternating.

Summing up, we have the following theorem :

The hypergeometric series F converges absolutely when $|x|<1$, and diverges when $|x|>1$. When $x=1$, F converges only when $\alpha+\beta-\gamma<0$, and then absolutely. When $x=-1$, F converges only when $\alpha+\beta-\gamma-1<0$, and absolutely if $\alpha+\beta-\gamma<0$.

CHAPTER III

SERIES WITH COMPLEX TERMS

30. 1. Having discussed series whose terms are real, we now consider those whose terms are complex numbers. As heretofore such series will be represented by

$$A = a_1 + a_2 + a_3 + \cdots \tag{1}$$

the sum of the first n terms by A_n, and the residual series by $\bar{A}_n$. If we replace each term of A by its numerical value $\alpha_n = |a_n|$, the resulting series

$$\mathfrak{A} = \alpha_1 + \alpha_2 + \alpha_3 + \cdots$$

will be the adjoint series.

Before defining the sum of 1) we must define what we mean by the phrase "A_n converges to a number L as n increases indefinitely," or in symbols $A_n \doteq L$ as $n \doteq \infty$, or

$$\lim_{n=\infty} A_n = L. \tag{2}$$

Suppose we plot the points associated with the complex numbers, $A_1, A_2, A_3 \cdots$ and L. Then when we say $A_n \doteq L$, we mean that these points get nearer and nearer L. More precisely this idea may be expressed as follows:

About L describe a circle of radius ϵ as small as we choose. Then all the points

$$A_{m+1},\ A_{m+2},\ A_{m+3},$$

fall within this circle for some m, as in the figure. In other words, there exists an index m such that

$$|L - A_n| < \epsilon \quad \text{for all } n > m. \tag{3}$$

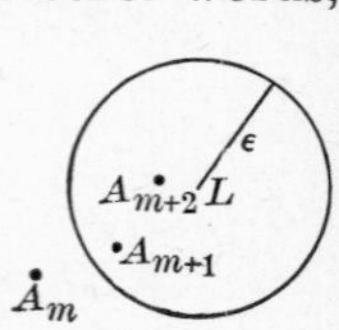

If the reader will turn to 16, he will see that this is a natural extension of the term limit when the numbers considered were real.

We are now ready to give a final definition. We say 2) holds when for each positive ϵ there exists an m such that 3) holds.

This definition applies to the limit of any sequence of complex numbers as

$$c_1 \quad , \quad c_2 \quad , \quad c_3 \quad \cdots$$

To express that c is the limit of c_n we shall write

$$\epsilon > 0 \quad , \quad m \quad , \quad |c - c_n| < \epsilon \quad , \quad n > m. \qquad (4$$

This we read as in 16, viz.: For each positive ϵ there exists an index m, such that $|c - c_n| < \epsilon$ for all $n > m$.

Having now defined the term limit we may extend the terms *convergent*, *divergent*, *sum*, defined in 10, without further comment to the series 1) whose terms are complex. Thus when $\lim A_n$ exists, we say A is convergent. The limit of A_n is the sum of 1). If $\lim A_n$ does not exist, A is divergent.

A number of results established in the last chapter hold for series whose terms are complex. In fact the reader will see that the demonstration applies equally well to complex terms. For the convenience of the reader we state some of them here.

2. Let $A = a_1 + a_2 + \cdots$ be a series with complex terms. Then A and the residual series $\overline{A}_m$ both converge or both diverge. If A is convergent, $\overline{A}_n \doteq 0$, also $a_n \doteq 0$ as $n \doteq \infty$. If A converges, $B = ka_1 + ka_2 + \cdots$ converges and $B = kA$, $k \neq 0$.

3. We have just noted that when A is convergent, a_n must $\doteq 0$. From this we draw the obvious yet important conclusion:

If $A = a_1 + a_2 + \cdots$ *is convergent, then*

$$|a_n| \leq \textit{some } G \quad , \quad n = 1, 2, 3, \qquad (5$$

For, describe a circle C about the origin. Then since $a_n \doteq 0$, all the terms $a_{m+1}, a_{m+2} \cdots$ lie within C for some definite m. Let us now describe another circle D about the origin so large that it contains the m points $a_1, a_2 \cdots a_m$ and also C. If G is the radius of D, the relation 5) holds obviously.

4. The reader should note that although the terms $a_1, a_2 \cdots$ of the series 1) are complex, it does not follow that they may not be real. The class of complex numbers contains the class of real

numbers as a subclass. It follows therefore that any theorem established for series with complex terms must necessarily hold when the terms of the series are all real.

31. Absolute Convergence. 1. The terms of the series

$$A = a_1 + a_2 + a_3 + \cdots \tag{1}$$

being complex, let us set

$$a_n = b_n + ic_n \quad , \quad n = 1, 2, \cdots \tag{2}$$

Let

$$B = b_1 + b_2 + b_3 + \cdots \tag{3}$$

$$C = c_1 + c_2 + c_3 + \cdots \tag{4}$$

Then

$$A_n = B_n + iC_n. \tag{5}$$

We show now that:

If B, C converge, so does A, and $A = B + iC$. Conversely, if A converges, both B and C converge.

For if B, C are convergent, we have from 5)

$$\lim A_n = \lim B_n + i \lim C_n,$$

or

$$A = B + iC.$$

Conversely, let 1) be convergent. Let its sum be $A = \beta + i\gamma$. Then Fig. 1 shows that as $A_n \doteq A$, then $B_n \doteq \beta$ and $C_n \doteq \gamma$.

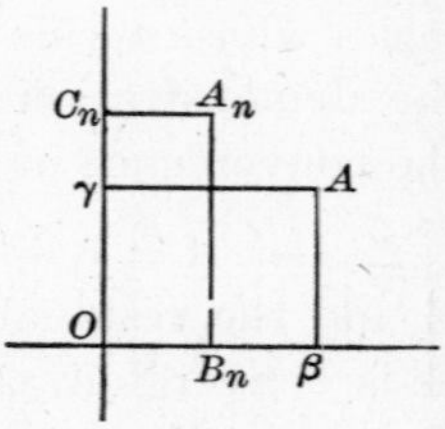

FIG. 1.

2. As already remarked the adjoint of 1) is

$$\mathfrak{A} = \alpha_1 + \alpha_2 + \alpha_3 + \cdots$$

where $|a_n| = \alpha_n$. From Fig. 2 we see that

$$\beta_n = |b_n| \leq \alpha_n \quad , \quad \gamma_n = |c_n| \leq \alpha_n.$$

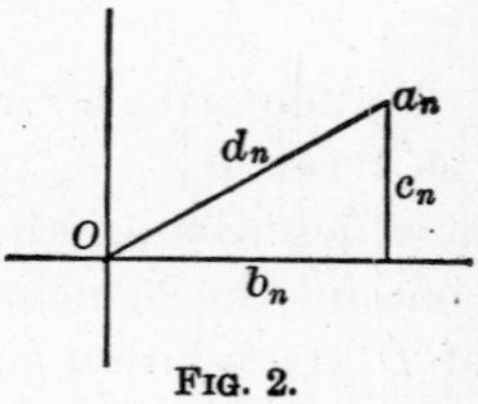

FIG. 2.

Similarly the adjoints of B and C are

$$\mathfrak{B} = \beta_1 + \beta_2 + \cdots$$

$$\mathfrak{C} = \gamma_1 + \gamma_2 + \cdots$$

We now prove the important theorem:

If the adjoint of A converges, A is convergent.

For obviously $\mathfrak{B}_n \leq \mathfrak{A}_n < \mathfrak{A}$, hence $\mathfrak{B}$ is convergent, and therefore B converges absolutely. Similarly $\mathfrak{C}_n \leq \mathfrak{A}_n < \mathfrak{A}$ and hence C converges absolutely. The theorem now follows from 1.

3. When the adjoint of A converges, we say A converges *absolutely*.

The great importance of the last theorem is obvious. It enables us in nearly every case in practice to reduce the problem of determining whether the series A is convergent or not to the same problem relative to the adjoint series $\mathfrak{A}$. But the terms of $\mathfrak{A}$ are real positive numbers, and the convergence, of such series was treated in the last chapter.

4. Having established the last theorem, the reader will note that the reasoning of 18, 4 holds for complex terms. Hence the theorem:

If each term of $A = a_1 + a_2 + \cdots$ *is numerically* $<$ *the corresponding term of the convergent positive term series* $B = b_1 + b_2 + \cdots$ *then* A *is absolutely convergent and*

$$|A| \leq B.$$

5. Returning to 2, let us note that the reasoning there shows that:

For 1) *to converge absolutely, it is necessary and sufficient that the two real series* 3), 4) *converge absolutely.*

32. Addition and Subtraction. From the two series

$$A = a_1 + a_2 + a_3 + \cdots$$
$$B = b_1 + b_2 + b_3 + \cdots$$

let us form the series

$$C = (a_1 + b_1) + (a_2 + b_2) + (a_3 + b_3) + \cdots$$

We now show that:

If A, B *are convergent,* C *is convergent and its sum is* $A + B$.

For
$$C_n = (a_1 + b_1) + \cdots + (a_n + b_n)$$
$$= A_n + B_n.$$

Now
$$\lim A_n = A \quad , \quad \lim B_n = B.$$

Hence
$$C = \lim C_n = A + B.$$

Similarly we prove:

The series

$$D = (a_1 - b_1) + (a_2 - b_2) + \cdots$$

converges if A, B *converge and* $D = A - B$.

33. Multiplication. 1. Suppose we have two polynomials

$$P = p_1 + p_2 + \cdots + p_m = \sum_1^m p_i,$$

$$Q = q_1 + q_2 + \cdots + q_n = \sum_1^n q_j.$$

Then from algebra we know that

$$\begin{aligned} PQ = q_1p_1 + q_1p_2 + \cdots + q_1p_m, \\ + q_2p_1 + q_2p_2 + \cdots + q_2p_m, \\ \cdot \quad \cdot \quad \cdot \quad \cdot \quad \cdot \quad \cdot \quad \cdot \quad \cdot \\ + q_np_1 + q_np_2 + \cdots + q_np_m. \end{aligned}$$

The general term of the product is p_iq_j. We may thus write

$$PQ = \sum_{i,j} p_iq_j \qquad \begin{aligned} i &= 1, 2, \cdots m \\ j &= 1, 2, \cdots n. \end{aligned} \tag{1}$$

Instead of two polynomials P, Q let us take two infinite series

$$A = a_1 + a_2 + \cdots \quad , \quad B = b_1 + b_2 + \cdots \tag{2}$$

and from them form the series

$$C = \sum_{i,j} a_ib_j \tag{3}$$

which contains all possible terms a_ib_j without repetition. We prove now the theorem:

If the series A, B *are absolutely convergent, so is* C *and* $C = A \cdot B$.

We begin by considering the adjoint series

$$\mathfrak{A} = \Sigma\alpha_i \quad \mathfrak{B} = \Sigma\beta_i \quad \mathfrak{C} = \Sigma\alpha_i\beta_j.$$

Let us look at the product $\mathfrak{A}_m\mathfrak{B}_m$; it contains all terms $\alpha_i\beta_j$ whose indices i, j are both $\leq m$. Let us now take n so large that the sum of the first n terms of $\mathfrak{C}$, that is $\mathfrak{C}_n$, contains all the terms of $\mathfrak{A}_m\mathfrak{B}_m$. In general $\mathfrak{C}_n$ contains *other* terms of the type $\alpha_r\beta_s$

where r, s are not both $\leq m$. On the other hand let no term $\alpha_r \beta_s$ have an index $> \nu$. Then

$$\begin{aligned}\mathfrak{C}_n - \mathfrak{A}_m\mathfrak{B}_m \leq\ & \alpha_1\beta_{m+1} + \alpha_1\beta_{m+2} + \cdots + \alpha_1\beta_\nu \\ & + \alpha_2\beta_{m+1} + \alpha_2\beta_{m+2} + \cdots + \alpha_2\beta_\nu \\ & + \quad \cdots \qquad \cdots \qquad \cdots \\ & + \alpha_\nu\beta_{m+1} + \alpha_\nu\beta_{m+2} + \cdots + \alpha_\nu\beta_\nu \\ & + \beta_1\alpha_{m+1} + \beta_1\alpha_{m+2} + \cdots + \beta_1\alpha_\nu \\ & + \quad \cdots \qquad \cdots \qquad \cdots \\ & + \beta_\nu\alpha_{m+1} + \beta_\nu\alpha_{m+2} + \cdots + \beta_\nu\alpha_\nu.\end{aligned}$$

For every possible term $\alpha_r\beta_s$ which $\mathfrak{C}_n - \mathfrak{A}_m\mathfrak{B}_m$ can contain is to be found among the terms on the right. Moreover all the terms involved are positive numbers.

Now the first row on the right gives

$$\alpha_1(\beta_{m+1} + \beta_{m+2} + \cdots + \beta_\nu) < \alpha_1\overline{\mathfrak{B}}_m,$$

and a similar relation holds for the other rows. Thus

$$\begin{aligned}\mathfrak{C}_n - \mathfrak{A}_m\mathfrak{B}_m &< \alpha_1\overline{\mathfrak{B}}_m + \cdots + \alpha_\nu\overline{\mathfrak{B}}_m \\ &\quad + \beta_1\overline{\mathfrak{A}}_m + \cdots + \beta_\nu\overline{\mathfrak{A}}_m \\ &< (\alpha_1 + \cdots + \alpha_\nu)\overline{\mathfrak{B}}_m + (\beta_1 + \cdots + \beta_\nu)\overline{\mathfrak{A}}_m \\ &< \mathfrak{A}\overline{\mathfrak{B}}_m + \mathfrak{B}\overline{\mathfrak{A}}_m.\end{aligned}$$

Let now $m \doteq \infty$. Then $\overline{\mathfrak{A}}_m \doteq 0$, $\overline{\mathfrak{B}}_m \doteq 0$ by 17, 4. Thus the left side $\doteq 0$. But

$$\lim \mathfrak{A}_m\mathfrak{B}_m = \lim \mathfrak{A}_m \lim \mathfrak{B}_m = \mathfrak{A} \cdot \mathfrak{B}.$$

Hence $\mathfrak{C}$ is convergent and

$$\mathfrak{C} = \mathfrak{A} \cdot \mathfrak{B}.$$

This shows that the C series is absolutely convergent. To show that $C = A \cdot B$, let m, n have the same meaning as before only now referred to the A, B, C series. Then $C_n - A_mB_m$ is numerically $\leq$ the sum of the corresponding terms in $\mathfrak{C}_n - \mathfrak{A}_m\mathfrak{B}_m$. Hence

$$| C_n - A_mB_m | \leq \mathfrak{C}_n - \mathfrak{A}_m\mathfrak{B}_m.$$

Now when $m = \infty$, the right side $\doteq 0$. Thus

$$\lim (C_n - A_m B_m) = 0.$$

As $\lim A_m B_m = AB$, this gives $C = AB$.

2. In forming the product series 3) it is well to have a definite law in order that no term $a_i b_j$ is omitted, and no term is repeated. Such a law is expressed as follows:

$$\begin{aligned} C = a_1 b_1 + (a_1 b_2 + a_2 b_1) + (a_1 b_3 + a_2 b_2 + a_3 b_1) \\ + (a_1 b_4 + a_2 b_3 + a_3 b_2 + a_4 b_1) + \cdots \end{aligned} \qquad (4$$

We notice that the sum of the indices $i + j$ is 2 in the first term, it is 3 in the second term, 4 in the third term, etc. Also in each term the index i increases while j decreases. In this way it is possible to form all the terms $a_i b_j$ in 3) without repetition or omission. Of course there are many other simple ways of doing this, but this is in general the most convenient.

34. Cauchy's Paradox. 1. At this point we are face to face with a paradox. One would expect that if the series A and B converge, the series C in 33, 4) would converge and have as sum $A \cdot B$. In case that A, B converge absolutely, we have just seen that this is indeed true. We now exhibit an example due to *Cauchy* which shows that if A, B are convergent but not absolutely convergent, then the series C may not even converge.

In fact, let

$$A = \frac{1}{\sqrt{1}} - \frac{1}{\sqrt{2}} + \frac{1}{\sqrt{3}} - \frac{1}{\sqrt{4}} + \cdots$$

$$B = \frac{1}{\sqrt{1}} - \frac{1}{\sqrt{2}} + \frac{1}{\sqrt{3}} - \frac{1}{\sqrt{4}} + \cdots = A.$$

The series A being an alternating series, is convergent by 15, 1. Its adjoint is divergent by 14 since here $s = \frac{1}{2}$.

Let us now form the series C in 33, 4).

We have

$$\begin{aligned} C &= \frac{1}{\sqrt{1}}\frac{1}{\sqrt{1}} - \left(\frac{1}{\sqrt{1}\sqrt{2}} + \frac{1}{\sqrt{2}}\frac{1}{\sqrt{1}}\right) \\ &\quad + \left(\frac{1}{\sqrt{1}}\frac{1}{\sqrt{3}} + \frac{1}{\sqrt{2}}\frac{1}{\sqrt{2}} + \frac{1}{\sqrt{3}}\frac{1}{\sqrt{1}}\right) - \cdots \\ &= c_2 + c_3 + c_4 + \cdots \end{aligned}$$

Here

$$|c_n| = \frac{1}{\sqrt{1}} \frac{1}{\sqrt{n-1}} + \frac{1}{\sqrt{2}} \frac{1}{\sqrt{n-2}} + \cdots + \frac{1}{\sqrt{n-1}} \cdot \frac{1}{\sqrt{1}} = \gamma_{n+1}.$$

Now from algebra we have

$$\sqrt{m(n-m)} \leq \tfrac{1}{2} n \quad , \quad n \geq m > 0.$$

Hence

$$\frac{1}{\sqrt{m(n-m)}} \geq \frac{2}{n} \quad , \quad \gamma_{n+1} > \frac{2(n-1)}{n}.$$

Thus C is divergent since c_n does not $\doteq 0$, as it must if C were convergent, by 17, 1.

2. The foregoing paradox arises from the *tacit assumption* that the earlier mathematicians made and which students to-day are too prone to make; viz. that infinite series have the properties of finite sums. The sum of an infinite series is the *limit* of a sum of a finite number of terms, in symbols

$$A = \lim_{n=\infty} A_n.$$

Now it does not follow that the properties which each A_n may possess also hold in the limit. In other words we must learn to discredit the dictum: what is true of the variable is true of the limit. In general this dictum is valid; there are, however, countless cases where it is not. In particular it is true that infinite series have many properties in common with finite sums, but they do not have all their properties, witness the foregoing paradox. It is helpful indeed in our reasoning to remember that in general infinite series do behave as finite sums. It is also extremely helpful to remember that very often what is true of the variable is true of the limit. Such partial truths are of great value in exploring the way and in seeking for proofs that are really rigorous. Their value is *heuristic* and every student should employ them freely. He must, however, learn to replace reasoning founded upon them by proofs of a more binding character.

3. Let us note a few cases where the student is apt to go astray unless warned.

Example 1. Let us plot a finite number of real positive numbers, $a_1, a_2 \cdots a_m$, no two of which are equal. Then there is always *one* point which is nearest the origin. This is true for any m. Is it true for an infinite sequence of such numbers

$$a_1 \quad , \quad a_2 \quad , \quad a_3 \quad \cdots$$

Not always, as the sequence

$$1 \quad , \quad \tfrac{1}{2} \quad , \quad \tfrac{1}{3} \quad , \quad \tfrac{1}{4} \quad \cdots$$

shows. Obviously there is no $a_s = \frac{1}{s}$ which is nearest the origin. For $a_{s+1} = \frac{1}{s+1}$ is nearer 0 than a_s.

Example 2. Similarly in any finite set of different numbers there is always one which is greatest. In an infinite set this is not always true. Thus the set

$$\tfrac{3}{4} \quad , \quad \tfrac{7}{8} \quad , \quad \tfrac{15}{16} \quad , \quad \tfrac{31}{32} \quad \cdots$$

has no greatest.

Example 3. In the interval (0, 1) formed of the point x such that $0 \leq x \leq 1$ there is a first point $x = 0$ and a last point $x = 1$. On the other hand, in the set of points x such that

$$0 < x < 1$$

there is no first point, and no last point.

35. Associative and Commutative Properties. In any sum of a finite number of terms as

$$S = a + (b + c) + d + e, \tag{1}$$

we may leave out parentheses or put them in wherever we choose. This is called the *associative property* of sums. Thus the sum 1) may be written

$$S = (a + b) + (c + d) + e$$
$$= a + b + c + (d + e),$$

etc. Also the value of 1) is not changed when its terms are rearranged in any way. Thus

$$S = b + a + d + c + e$$
$$= e + c + d + a + b,$$

etc. This is called the *commutative* property. The student is so used to making these transformations that he does it almost without thought. It is natural for him to extend these properties to infinite series. Yet simple examples will show him that this is not always permissible.

Example 1. Let

$$A = 1 + (1-1) + (1-1) + (1-1) + \cdots \qquad (2$$
$$= a_1 + a_2 + a_3 + a_4 + \cdots$$

Here,

$$A_n = a_1 + \cdots + a_n$$
$$= 1 + (1-1) + \cdots + (1-1) \quad , \quad n \text{ terms}$$
$$= 1.$$

Hence

$$\lim A_n = 1.$$

Thus 2) is convergent and its sum is 1.

If we remove the parentheses from 2), we get the series

$$B = 1 + 1 - 1 + 1 - 1 + 1 - 1 + \cdots$$
$$= b_1 + b_2 + b_3 + \cdots$$

Here,

$$B_{2n} = 2 \quad , \quad B_{2n+1} = 1.$$

Hence $\lim\limits_{m=\infty} B_m$ does not exist and B is not convergent.

Example 2. (*Dirichlet.*) Let

$$A = 1 - \tfrac{1}{2} + \tfrac{1}{3} - \tfrac{1}{4} + \cdots \qquad (3$$

This we saw is convergent. We shall show directly that we may group the terms of A by twos or by fours without changing its value. Let us admit this fact for a moment. Then we have

$$A = (1 - \tfrac{1}{2}) + (\tfrac{1}{3} - \tfrac{1}{4}) + (\tfrac{1}{5} - \tfrac{1}{6}) + \cdots \qquad (4$$
$$= (1 - \tfrac{1}{2} + \tfrac{1}{3} - \tfrac{1}{4}) + (\tfrac{1}{5} - \tfrac{1}{6} + \tfrac{1}{7} - \tfrac{1}{8}) + \cdots \qquad (5$$

From 4) we have

$$\tfrac{1}{2} A = (\tfrac{1}{2} - \tfrac{1}{4}) + (\tfrac{1}{6} - \tfrac{1}{8}) + (\tfrac{1}{10} - \tfrac{1}{12}) + \cdots$$

Adding this to 5) gives

$$\tfrac{3}{2} A = (1 + \tfrac{1}{3} - \tfrac{1}{2}) + (\tfrac{1}{5} + \tfrac{1}{7} - \tfrac{1}{4}) + \cdots \qquad (6$$

We shall show directly that it is permissible to remove the parentheses in 6) without changing the value of the series. Thus

$$\tfrac{3}{2}A = 1 + \tfrac{1}{3} - \tfrac{1}{2} + \tfrac{1}{5} + \tfrac{1}{7} - \tfrac{1}{4} + \cdots \tag{7}$$

Let us now compare the two series 3) and 7). We notice that 7) is obtained from 3) by taking two positive terms of 3) to one negative. Each term of 3) is to be found somewhere in 7) and no term is repeated. Thus the series 7) is merely a *rearrangement* of 3). If now all infinite series enjoyed the commutative property, the rearrangement of the terms of 3) would not affect its value. But the left side of 7) shows that the sum of 7) is $\frac{3}{2}$ times greater than the sum of 3). Thus not all infinite series are commutative.

36. Since it is often convenient to put in or to leave out parentheses in a series and also to rearrange its terms, it becomes necessary to ascertain when this is permissible. To this end we establish the following theorems :

1. *Absolutely convergent series are commutative.* For let

$$A = a_1 + a_2 + a_3 + \cdots$$

be absolutely convergent. Let

$$B = b_1 + b_2 + b_3 + \cdots$$

be a series obtained from A by rearranging its terms. We wish to show that B is convergent and that its sum is A.

Since the adjoint series

$$\mathfrak{A} = \alpha_1 + \alpha_2 + \alpha_3 + \cdots$$

is convergent, we may take m so large that

$$\overline{\mathfrak{A}}_m < \epsilon. \tag{1}$$

We may then take n so large that B_n contains all the terms of A_m, and ν so large that A_ν contains all the terms of B_n.

Then

$$A_\nu - B_n \tag{2}$$

contains no term of index $\leq m$ and the terms of the sum 2), each taken in absolute value, lie among the terms of the residual series $\overline{\mathfrak{A}}_m$. Hence

$$|A_\nu - B_n| < \overline{\mathfrak{A}}_m,$$

or, using 1),

$$< \epsilon.$$

Thus B is convergent and

$$\lim B_n = A.$$

2. Let us now turn to the *associative* property. We begin by showing that we may insert parentheses at pleasure in any convergent series, a fact we embody in the following theorem :

Let $A = a_1 + a_2 + a_3 + \cdots$ *be convergent. Let*

$$b_1 = a_1 + \cdots + a_{m_1} \quad , \quad b_2 = a_{m_1+1} + \cdots + a_{m_2} \quad , \quad \cdots$$

Then the series

$$B = (a_1 + \cdots + a_{m_1}) + (a_{m_1+1} + \cdots + a_{m_2}) + \cdots$$
$$= b_1 + b_2 + \cdots$$

is convergent and $A = B$. *Moreover the number of terms which* b_n *embraces may increase indefinitely with* n.

For

$$B_n = A_{m_n}. \qquad (3$$

Since A is convergent,

$$\lim_{n=\infty} A_{m_n} = A.$$

Thus passing to the limit $n = \infty$ in 3) gives

$$B = A.$$

3. The next theorem relates to removing parentheses from a series. Thus if we remove the parentheses from the series

$$B = (a_1 + a_2 + \cdots + a_{m_1}) + (a_{m_1+1} + \cdots +_{m_2}) + \cdots$$
$$= b_1 + b_2 + \cdots \qquad (4$$

we get the series

$$A = a_1 + a_2 + a_3 + \cdots \qquad (5$$

We show now that in the following three cases the parentheses may be removed from the series 4).

1° If A is convergent, B converges and $A = B$.

2° If A is a positive term series and B converges, then A is convergent and $A = B$.

3° If the number of terms in each parenthesis in 4) is $\leq$ a fixed number p, and if $a_n \doteq 0$, then A converges if B does and $A = B$.

For *on the* 1° *hypothesis*, we have only to apply 2 to show that B converges and $A = B$.

On the 2° *hypothesis*, we have

$$\epsilon < 0 \quad , \quad m \quad , \quad \bar{B}_n < \epsilon, \quad n > m. \tag{6}$$

If now we take $s > m_n$, $B - A_s$ will contain only terms in the residual series $\bar{B}_n$. As the terms a_n are positive, we have from 6)

$$B - A_s < \epsilon.$$

Thus

$$A_s \doteq B \text{ or } A = B.$$

On the 3° *hypothesis*, we note that the terms of A_n will embrace a certain number of terms of B, say B_m, and in general a part of the next term of B. We may therefore write

$$A_n = B_m + b'_{m+1}, \tag{7}$$

where b'_{m+1} is a part of b_{m+1}. Since b_{m+1} contains at most p terms a_n and as by hypothesis $a_n \doteq 0$, we see that

$$b'_m \doteq 0.$$

Passing to the limit in 7) we see that

$$A_n \doteq B.$$

4. Let us now return to verify the statements made in 35, Ex. 2. Since the series 3) in that article is convergent, we may indeed group its terms by twos or by fours without changing its value. In the series 6) we see that $p = 3$ and that in 3)

$$a_n = (-1)^{n+1} \cdot \frac{1}{n} \doteq 0.$$

Hence this series falls under the 3° case of the theorem 3 above. Hence if we remove the parentheses from 6), the resulting series 7) has the same value as 6). Thus the series 3) is not commutative. It is also not absolutely convergent and the theorem 1 does not apply.

37. Riemann on Simply Convergent Series. 1. It will interest the reader to see that a simply convergent real term series may be rearranged so as to give a series whose sum is any desired real number.

Let the given series be

$$A = a_1 + a_2 + a_3 + \cdots \tag{1}$$

Let

$$B = b_1 + b_2 + b_3 + \cdots \tag{2}$$

be the series formed of the positive terms of 1), keeping their relative order in 1). Let

$$C = c_1 + c_2 + c_3 + \cdots \tag{3}$$

be the negative terms of 1) with their signs all changed. We begin by establishing the following theorem :

If A is a real term simply convergent series, both B and C are divergent, i.e.

$$B = +\infty \quad , \quad C = +\infty.$$

For in the first place B and C must both have an infinite number of terms. Otherwise some residual series $\bar{A}_m$ would have terms with only one sign. As A is convergent, $\bar{A}_m$ would converge absolutely. Hence A would be absolutely convergent, which is contrary to hypothesis.

Let us thus suppose that A_n contains r terms of B and s terms of C. Then

$$\mathfrak{A}_n = B_r + C_s \quad , \quad n = r + s.$$

If now B and C converge, we see that $\mathfrak{A}$ also converges and thus A is absolutely convergent. On the other hand

$$A_n = B_r - C_s$$

shows that if B or C were convergent, both would converge, since $A_n \doteq A$ by hypothesis.

2. We can now establish

Riemann's Theorem. If A is a simply convergent series with real terms, it is possible to rearrange the terms of A forming a series S for which lim S_n is any prescribed number l, or $\pm\infty$.

To fix the ideas let l be a positive number; the demonstration of the other cases is similar. Since by 1, $B_n \doteq +\infty$, there exists an m such that

$$b_1 + b_2 + \cdots + b_{m_1} > l. \tag{4}$$

Let m_1 be the least index for which 4) holds. Since also $C_n \doteq +\infty$, there exists an index m such that

$$(b_1 + \cdots + b_{m_1}) - (c_1 + \cdots + c_{m_2}) < l. \tag{5}$$

Let m_2 be the least index for which 5) holds. Continuing, we take just enough terms, say m_3 terms, of B so that

$$(b_1 + \cdots + b_{m_1}) - (c_1 + \cdots + c_{m_2}) + (b_{m_1+1} + \cdots + b_{m_1+m_3}) > l.$$

In this way we may form the series

$$T = (b_1 + \cdots + b_{m_1}) - (c_1 + \cdots + c_{m_2}) + (\quad) - (\quad) + \cdots$$

It is easy now to show that

$$\lim T_n = l.$$

For since A is convergent, $a_n \doteq 0$. Moreover we choose our terms in T so that T_n differs from l by an amount $<$ some a_ν of A. Thus

$$T_n - l \doteq 0.$$

Let now S be the series T with the parentheses removed. Since the terms in the parenthesis are positive, the series S is convergent and has T as sum.

3. The foregoing theorem shows that Dirichlet's example considered in 35 does not illustrate an exceptional case, but the rule. This remarkable behavior of non-absolutely convergent series should make the reader more careful in dealing with infinite series. On the other hand, it would be a great misfortune if he became afraid of them. Let him consider infinite series just as if they were finite sums when striving to prove a theorem or solve a problem. Only he must not neglect at the end to go back over his steps and justify them carefully.

4. Let us make an obvious extension of the foregoing result to series whose terms are complex. If

$$A = a_1 + a_2 + a_3 + \cdots$$

where

$$a_n = b_n + ic_n,$$

we saw in 31, 1 that

$$A = B + iC$$

when A is convergent; while we saw in 31, 5 that if A does not converge absolutely, at least one of the series B, C is not absolutely convergent.

Suppose the series B is simply convergent, then B is not commutative. Hence A cannot be commutative. Thus we have the theorem:

No simply convergent series of complex terms can enjoy the commutative property.

Power Series

38. The series

$$A = a_0 + a_1 z + a_2 z^2 + a_3 z^3 + \cdots \tag{1}$$

is a *power series.* Here the coefficients a_0, a_1, $a_2 \cdots$ and z may be complex numbers. Such series are of utmost importance in the function theory. Indeed one is tempted to say they form the most important class of series. Special cases of such series are the series afforded by Taylor's development in the calculus. In fact Taylor's series

$$f(0) + \frac{f'(0)}{1!}x + \frac{f''(0)}{2!}x^2 + \cdots$$

is only a power series as is seen by setting

$$a_0 = f(0) \quad , \quad a_n = \frac{f^{(n)}(0)}{n!}.$$

Thus the developments of $\sin x$, $\cos x$, e^x, etc., given in 9 are power series. The variable x is there real, of course.

A slightly more general form of 1) is

$$a_0 + a_1(z-a) + a_2(z-a)^2 + a_3(z-a)^3 + \cdots \tag{2}$$

Since the series 2) goes over into 1) on replacing $z - a$ by z we may reason on 1) without loss of generality.

39. Circle of Convergence. 1. A fundamental theorem in the theory of power series is the following:

Let the series

$$A = a_0 + a_1 z + a_2 z^2 + \cdots \tag{1}$$

converge for $z=b$. Then it converges absolutely for any c within the circle K through b with the origin as center. If A diverges for $z=b$, it diverges for any point d without K.

For the adjoint series corresponding to $z = c$ is

$$\mathfrak{A} = \alpha_0 + \alpha_1 \gamma + \alpha_2 \gamma^2 + \cdots \tag{2}$$

where $\alpha_n = |a_n|$, $\gamma = |c|$. To show that this converges we observe that by hypothesis

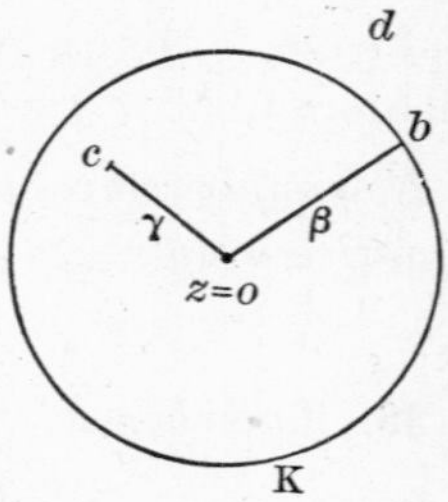

$$a_0 + a_1 b + a_2 b^2 + \cdots \tag{3}$$

converges. Thus by 30, 3,

$$\alpha_0 \quad , \quad \alpha_1 \beta \quad , \quad \alpha_2 \beta^2 \quad , \quad \cdots$$

are all $<$ some g. We now write $\mathfrak{A}$ thus:

$$\mathfrak{A} = \alpha_0 + \alpha_1 \beta \left(\frac{\gamma}{\beta}\right) + \alpha_2 \beta^2 \left(\frac{\gamma}{\beta}\right)^2 + \alpha_3 \beta^3 \left(\frac{\gamma}{\beta}\right)^3 + \cdots \tag{4}$$

Comparing this with the convergent geometric series

$$G = g + g\left(\frac{\gamma}{\beta}\right) + g\left(\frac{\gamma}{\beta}\right)^2 + \cdots, \quad \frac{\gamma}{\beta} < 1 \tag{5}$$

we see each term of 4) is $<$ the corresponding term of 5). Thus 2) is convergent and A converges absolutely for $z = c$.

Suppose now A diverges for $z = b$. Then it diverges at any point d without K. For if it converges at d, it must converge, as we have just seen, at all points within a circle $\mathfrak{K}$ passing through d and having O as center. Thus A would converge at $z = b$, which is contrary to hypothesis.

2. If the circle C whose center is $z=0$ and whose radius is R is such that 1) converges for every point within C and diverges for every point without C, this circle is called the *circle of convergence* of the power series 1).

Nothing is said about the convergence of 1) at points on C. It may or may not converge at a given point on C.

3. Let us note before passing on that the series 4), 5) enable us to give a rough estimate of the numerical value of the series 1) at a point $z = c$. For let A_c denote the sum of 1) for the point $z = c$. Then

$$|A_c| < \mathfrak{A}$$

by 31, 4. But we saw that $\mathfrak{A}$, or what is the same the sum of 4), is less than the sum of 5). But the sum of this series is

$$\frac{g}{1 - \frac{\gamma}{\beta}}.$$

Thus

$$|A_c| < \frac{g}{1 - \frac{\gamma}{\beta}}, \tag{6}$$

which is the relation we had in view.

4. Let us find the circle of convergence of certain series which we shall employ later. The value of the radius R is placed at the right.

1) $$e^z = 1 + \frac{z}{1!} + \frac{z^2}{2!} + \frac{z^3}{3!} + \cdots \qquad R = \infty$$

2) $$\cos z = 1 - \frac{z^2}{2!} + \frac{z^4}{4!} - \cdots \qquad R = \infty$$

3) $$\sin z = \frac{z}{1!} - \frac{z^3}{3!} + \frac{z^5}{5!} - \cdots \qquad R = \infty$$

4) $$(1+z)^\mu = 1 + \frac{\mu}{1} z + \frac{\mu \cdot \mu - 1}{1 \cdot 2} z^2 + \frac{\mu \cdot \mu - 1 \cdot \mu - 2}{1 \cdot 2 \cdot 3} z^3 + \cdots \qquad R = 1$$

5) $$\log(1 + z) = z - \frac{z^2}{2} + \frac{z^3}{3} - \frac{z^4}{4} + \cdots \qquad R = 1$$

6) $$\sinh z = z + \frac{z^3}{3!} + \frac{z^5}{5!} + \cdots \qquad R = \infty$$

7) $$\cosh z = 1 + \frac{z^2}{2!} + \frac{z^4}{4!} + \cdots \qquad R = \infty$$

8) $$F(\alpha, \beta, \gamma, z) = 1 + \frac{\alpha \cdot \beta}{1 \cdot \gamma} z + \frac{\alpha \cdot \alpha + 1 \cdot \beta \cdot \beta + 1}{1 \cdot 2 \cdot \gamma \cdot \gamma + 1} z^2 + \cdots \qquad R = 1$$

9) $$J_n(z) = \frac{z^n}{2^n n!} \left\{ 1 - \frac{z^2}{2(2n+2)} + \frac{z^4}{2 \cdot 4(2n+2)(2n+4)} + \cdots \right\}. \qquad R = \infty$$

For convenience of reference we have added on the left side their values as functions of the complex variable z. For the present the reader should consider the series on the right merely as series whose circles of convergence are to be found. Since these circles all have $z = 0$ as center, it is the radius R which we seek.

Suppose now that the adjoint of one of these series, call it A, converges for $|z| = \gamma$. Then R is certainly as great as γ. If, on the other hand, A diverges for $|z| = \gamma$, R is certainly no greater than γ. Finally, if A converges for $|x| < \gamma$ while it diverges for $|x| > \gamma$, then the radius of convergence R is $= \gamma$.

Now the series 1), 2), 3), 4), 5), 8) we have already considered for real values of z. In 21, Ex. 2, we saw that 1) converges for any real x. Thus for this series $R = \infty$.

Similarly 21, Ex. 3, shows that $R = \infty$ for the series 2), 3).

In 28 we saw that 4) converges for real x such that $|x| < 1$ and diverges when $|x| > 1$. Thus $R = 1$ for this series.

Similarly 21, Ex. 4, shows that $R = 1$ for the series 5).

Finally in 29 we saw that 8) converges for real x such that $|x| < 1$ and diverges for $|x| > 1$. Thus $R = 1$ for this series.

Thus there remain only the series 6), 7), 9). The first two are at once disposed of. For the terms of their adjoint series form a part of the adjoint series of 1). Thus $R = \infty$ for both 6) and 7).

As to 9), the ratio of two successive terms of its adjoint is

$$\frac{\alpha_{n+1}}{\alpha_n} = \frac{\zeta^2}{2^2(s+1)(n+s+1)} \doteq 0$$

for any given ζ. Thus $R = \infty$ for this series.

5. The following development we shall use later

$$\frac{1}{u-z} = \frac{1}{u-a}\left\{1 + \frac{z-a}{u-a} + \left(\frac{z-a}{u-a}\right)^2 + \cdots\right\} \tag{10}$$

valid for $|z-a| < |u-a|$.

To prove it we note that

$$\begin{aligned} u - z &= (u-a) - (z-a) \\ &= (u-a)\left\{1 - \frac{z-a}{u-a}\right\} \\ &= (u-a)(1-v). \end{aligned}$$

Now

$$\frac{1}{1-v} = 1 + v + v^2 + \cdots \quad , \quad |v| < 1. \tag{11}$$

Thus

$$\frac{1}{u-z} = \frac{1}{u-a} \cdot \frac{1}{1-v}$$

gives 10) on using 11).

40. Two-way Series. 1. In the series considered up to the present

$$a_1 + a_2 + a_3 + \cdots = \sum_1^\infty a_n$$

the index takes on only positive values. It is sometimes convenient to consider series in which n takes on both positive and negative values. This leads to the symbol

$$\cdots + a_{-3} + a_{-2} + a_{-1} + a_0 + a_1 + a_2 + a_3 + \cdots \tag{1}$$

or

$$\sum_{-\infty}^{\infty} a_n.$$

We call 1) a *two-way series.*

Example 1. We shall see that in certain cases a function of z can be developed in the form

$$a_0 + a_1 z + a_2 z^2 + \cdots$$
$$+ \frac{b_1}{z} + \frac{b_2}{z^2} + \frac{b_3}{z^3} + \cdots$$

If we set $b_n = a_{-n}$, this can be written

$$\sum_{-\infty}^{\infty} a_n z^n. \tag{2}$$

Example 2. In the elliptic functions we consider series of the type

$$1 + qe^{2\pi iz} + q^4 e^{2 \cdot 2\pi iz} + q^9 e^{3 \cdot 2\pi iz} + \cdots$$
$$+ \frac{q}{e^{2\pi iz}} + \frac{q^4}{e^{2 \cdot 2\pi iz}} + \frac{q^9}{e^{3 \cdot 2\pi iz}} + \cdots$$

which may be represented by

$$\sum_{-\infty}^{\infty} q^{n^2} e^{2\pi inz}. \tag{3}$$

2. With the series 1) we associate the two series

$$B = \sum_0^\infty a_n \quad , \quad C = \sum_1^\infty a_{-n}. \tag{4}$$

If these two series converge, we say A is *convergent* and its *sum* is

$$A = B + C.$$

If either or both the series 4) are divergent, we say A is *divergent.*

Thus the theory of the two-way series is made to depend on the two one-way series 4).

Instead of the series 4) we could use any two other series obtained from 1) by breaking it at any other index m. Obviously the same results would be obtained with these as with the series 4).

If the adjoint series

$$\mathfrak{A} = \sum_{-\infty}^{\infty} \alpha_n \quad , \quad \alpha_n = | a_n |$$

converges, we say that A converges *absolutely.* Thus if B and C converge absolutely, A is also absolutely convergent.

3. Another definition of convergence and sum of the series 1) is the following. Let

$$A_{m,n} = a_{-m} + a_{-m+1} + \cdots + a_{-1} + a_0 + a_1 + \cdots + a_n. \qquad (5$$

Suppose that as $m, n \doteq \infty$ independently of each other, $A_{m,n}$ converges to some fixed number which we denote by

$$\lim_{m,\, n=\infty} A_{m,n} \qquad (6$$

or more briefly by l; that is, suppose that for each $\epsilon > 0$ there exists an r such that $A_{m,n}$ differs from l by an amount $< \epsilon$ for all m and $n > r$. In this case we say that A is convergent and its sum is the limit 6). This definition leads to that given in 2, but we do not wish to urge this point.

4. As an *example* let us show that 3) converges absolutely for any given $z = x + iy$ when $r = |q| < 1$. For, assuming for the moment that

$$e^{u+iv} = e^u e^{iv},$$

we have

$$e^{2\pi i n z} = e^{2\pi i n x} \cdot e^{-2\pi n y}.$$

Hence

$$| e^{2\pi i n z} | = e^{-2\pi n y}.$$

The adjoints of the B and C series defined in 4) are here

$$\mathfrak{B} = \sum_0^{\infty} r^{n^2} e^{-2\pi n y} \quad , \quad \mathfrak{C} = \sum_1^{\infty} r^{n^2} e^{2\pi n y}.$$

The ratio of two successive terms in $\mathfrak{B}$ is

$$\frac{r^{(n+1)^2}}{r^{n^2}} \cdot e^{-2\pi y} = r^{2n+1}e^{-2\pi y} \doteq 0$$

as $n \doteq \infty$. Thus B converges absolutely; similarly C also.

5. *Two-way Power Series.* Let us consider the series

$$\frac{a_1}{z} + \frac{a_2}{z^2} + \frac{a_3}{z^3} + \cdots \tag{7}$$

If we set

$$z = \frac{1}{u},$$

it becomes

$$a_1 u + a_2 u^2 + a_3 u^3 + \cdots$$

If this series converges for $u = c$, it converges absolutely for all $|u| < |c|$. Hence if 7) converges for $z = b$, it converges absolutely for all $|z| > |b|$.

Let C be a circle about the origin such that 7) converges for every z without C and diverges for every z within C. Then C is called the *circle of convergence* of 7).

Let us now consider the two-way series

$$\begin{aligned} &a_0 + a_1 z + a_2 z^2 + \cdots \\ &+ \frac{b_1}{z} + \frac{b_2}{z^2} + \cdots = P + Q, \end{aligned} \tag{8}$$

where P is the series in the first line. If C is the circle of convergence of P, and D that of Q, the ring $R = C - D$ lying between these two circles is called the *ring of convergence* of 8.

The radius of C may be infinite.

41. Double Series. 1. A point whose coördinates x, y are integers or zero is called a *lattice point.* Any set of such points is a *lattice set.* Let $a_{m,n}$ be given numbers, the indices m, n corresponding to points of some lattice set. The symbol

$$A = \Sigma a_{m,n} \tag{1}$$

is called a *double series.* With 1) we may associate a series

$$B = \Sigma b_r \tag{2}$$

where b_r is some term $a_{m,n}$ of 1) and where each term $a_{p,q}$ of 1) is some b_s of 2). If 2) converges absolutely, all these B series, being merely rearrangements of one of them, have the same sum. In this case we say 1) is *convergent* and its *sum* is that of 2). As heretofore it is often convenient to denote the sum of the series A when convergent by the same letter. When the series 2) does not converge absolutely, we shall say 1) is divergent.

The series

$$\mathfrak{A} = \Sigma \alpha_{m,n} \quad , \quad \alpha_{m,n} = | a_{m,n} |$$

is called the *adjoint* of 1). From our definition of convergence it follows that $\mathfrak{A}$ converges when A does, and conversely.

2. Let us note that the multiplication of two simple series

$$A = \sum_1^\infty a_m \quad , \quad B = \sum_1^\infty b_n$$

leads to double series. In fact let us set

$$c_{m,n} = a_m b_n.$$

Then

$$C = \Sigma c_{m,n} \tag{3}$$

is a double series, and when A and B are absolutely convergent, we saw that C is convergent and $A \cdot B = C$. In the series 3) the indices m, n range over the lattice points in the first quadrant, excluding those on the x or y axes as for these m or n would have the value 0.

3. We have seen that

$$\frac{1}{1-a} = 1 + a + a^2 + \cdots \quad , \quad |a| < 1,$$

$$\frac{1}{1-b} = 1 + b + b^2 + \cdots \quad , \quad |b| < 1.$$

Thus

$$\frac{1}{(1-a)(1-b)} = \sum_{m,n=0}^\infty a^m b^n = \Sigma c_{m,n} \tag{4}$$

where m, n range over all lattice points in the first quadrant, including those which lie on the x and y axes.

4. In studying the double series 1) it is often convenient to suppose the terms a_{mn} placed at the lattice points m, n. From this point of view any simple series

$$A = \sum_1^\infty a_m$$

may be converted into a double series as follows. Choose an infinite lattice set $\mathfrak{L}$ at pleasure, *e.g.* the points in the first quadrant. Put each term a_m at some lattice point r, s, so that each point of $\mathfrak{L}$ bears one term of A. If a_m lies at the point r, s, we may denote it by $b_{r,s}$, so that $b_{r,s}$ is only another symbol for a_m. In this way we get a double series

$$B = \Sigma b_{r,s}.$$

5. *Example.* Let a, b be any two complex numbers, such that the three points $0, a, b$ are not collinear. If m, n range over all lattice points, the origin excluded,

$$ma + nb$$

will be the vertices of a set of congruent parallelograms, as in the figure, which completely cover the plane.

The series

$$A = \sum \frac{1}{(ma + nb)^p} \tag{5}$$

is important in the elliptic functions and will be employed later. We now establish the theorem:

The series 5) *converges when* $p > 2$ *and diverges when* $p \leq 2$.

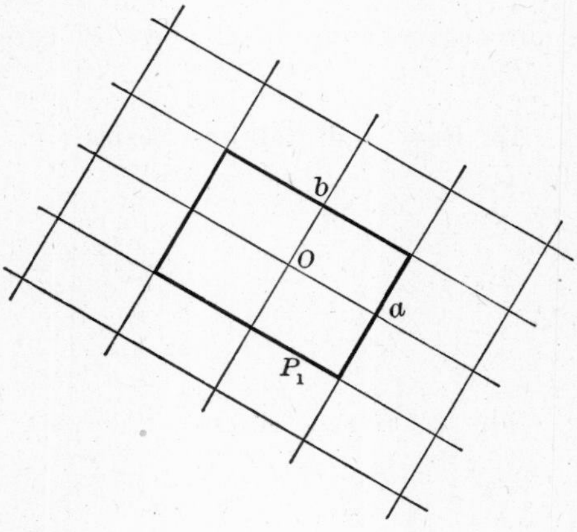

For brevity let us set

$$\omega_{mn} = ma + nb.$$

The adjoint of 5) is thus

$$\mathfrak{A} = \sum \frac{1}{|\omega_{mn}|^p}. \tag{6}$$

Then by definition 5) and 6) converge simultaneously.

We replace 6) by the simple series

$$\mathfrak{B} = \Sigma \beta_s,$$

where β_1 denotes the sum of the terms of 6) whose indices m, n correspond to points on the first parallelogram P_1 whose center is the origin O; β_2 is the sum of the terms of 6) whose indices lie on the second parallelogram P_2 about O, etc.

Let d and D be the least and greatest distances of the sides of P_1 from O. Then each of the 8 numbers $\omega_{m,n}$ which lie on P_1 satisfy the relation

$$d \leq |\omega_{mn}| < D.$$

Similarly each of the $2 \cdot 8$ numbers ω_{mn} which lie on P_2 satisfy the relation

$$2\,d \leq |\omega_{mn}| \leq 2\,D, \text{ etc.}$$

Thus

$$\frac{8}{D^p} \leq \beta_1 < \frac{8}{d^p},$$

$$\frac{2 \cdot 8}{(2\,D)^p} \leq \beta_2 \leq \frac{2 \cdot 8}{(2\,d)^p}, \text{ etc.}$$

Thus

$$\sum \frac{8\,s}{(sD)^p} \leq \Sigma \beta_s \leq \sum \frac{8\,s}{(sd)^p},$$

or

$$\frac{8}{D^p} \sum \frac{1}{s^{p-1}} \leq \mathfrak{B} \leq \frac{8}{d^p} \sum \frac{1}{s^{p-1}}.$$

As

$$\sum \frac{1}{s^{p-1}}$$

converges when $p > 2$ and diverges when $p \leq 2$, the theorem is proved.

42. Row and Column Series. 1. Let us consider the double series

$$\begin{aligned} A &= a_{11} + a_{12} + a_{13} + \cdots \\ &+ a_{21} + a_{22} + a_{23} + \cdots \\ &+ \quad . \quad . \quad . \quad . \quad . \\ &= \Sigma a_{m,n} \qquad m, n = 1, 2, \cdots \end{aligned} \tag{1}$$

The mth row of A gives a series

$$r_m = \sum_{n=1}^{\infty} a_{m,n} = a_{m1} + a_{m2} + \cdots \tag{2}$$

and from these we can form a series

$$R = r_1 + r_2 + \cdots = \sum_{m=1}^{\infty} r_m \tag{3}$$

$$= \sum_{m=1}^{\infty} \sum_{n=1}^{\infty} a_{m,n},$$

putting in the value of r_m as given by 2). We say the series R is obtained by *summing* 1) *by rows.*

Similarly the nth column of A gives a series

$$c_n = \sum_{m=1}^{\infty} a_{m,n} = a_{1n} + a_{2n} + \cdots \tag{4}$$

and from these we can form a series

$$C = c_1 + c_2 + \cdots = \sum_{n=1}^{\infty} c_n$$

$$= \sum_{n=1}^{\infty} \sum_{m=1}^{\infty} a_{m,n}. \tag{5}$$

We say the series C is obtained by *summing* 1) *by columns.*

2. To sum a double series A which is known to be convergent, we may often use the following theorem with advantage :

If A is convergent, each series r_m, c_n is absolutely convergent. The series R and C both converge absolutely and

$$A = R = C. \tag{6}$$

For let

$$B = b_1 + b_2 + \cdots = \Sigma b_s \tag{7}$$

be one of the simple series associated with the double series A. Since A is convergent, B converges absolutely by definition, and $A = B$. Let $|a_{mn}| = \alpha_{mn}$. The adjoint of A is

$$\mathfrak{A} = \Sigma \alpha_{mn}.$$

Let us denote the series formed from $\mathfrak{A}$ analogous to

$$r_m \ , \ c_m \ , \ R \ , \ C \ , \ b_m$$

by

$$\rho_m \ , \ \gamma_m \ , \ \mathfrak{R} \ , \ \mathfrak{C} \ , \ \beta_m.$$

To show that r_m is absolutely convergent we observe that we can take s so large that each term of

$$\rho_{m,p} = \alpha_{m,1} + \alpha_{m,2} + \cdots + \alpha_{m,p}$$

lies in $\mathfrak{B}_s$. Hence

$$\rho_{m,p} \leq \mathfrak{B}_s \leq \mathfrak{B}.$$

Thus

$$\rho_m = \lim_{p=\infty} \rho_{m,p} \leq \mathfrak{B}.$$

Hence the series ρ_m is convergent and r_m is therefore absolutely convergent. The same holds for c_n.

To show that R is absolutely convergent let us consider

$$\mathfrak{R} = \rho_1 + \rho_2 + \cdots = \lim_{n=\infty} \mathfrak{R}_m$$

$$= \lim_{m=\infty} (\rho_1 + \rho_2 + \cdots + \rho_m).$$

But

$$\rho_m = \alpha_{m1} + \alpha_{m2} + \cdots$$

$$= \lim_{n=\infty} \rho_{m,\,n} = \lim_{n=\infty} (\alpha_{m1} + \alpha_{m2} + \cdots + \alpha_{mn}).$$

If therefore we set

$$\begin{aligned} \mathfrak{A}_{m,\,n} = \alpha_{11} + \alpha_{12} + \cdots + \alpha_{1n} \\ + \alpha_{21} + \alpha_{22} + \cdots + \alpha_{2n} \\ + \quad . \quad . \quad . \quad . \quad . \quad . \\ + \alpha_{m1} + \alpha_{m2} + \cdots \alpha_{mn}, \end{aligned}$$

we get

$$\lim_{n=\infty} \mathfrak{A}_{mn} = \mathfrak{R}_m,$$

and hence

$$\mathfrak{R} = \lim_{m=\infty} \lim_{n=\infty} \mathfrak{A}_{m,\,n}.$$

Now let us take s so large that each term of $\mathfrak{A}_{m,\,n}$ lies in $\mathfrak{B}_s$. Then

$$\mathfrak{A}_{mn} \leq \mathfrak{B}_s < \mathfrak{B}.$$

Passing to the limit $n = \infty$ gives

$$\mathfrak{R}_m \leq \mathfrak{B}.$$

Passing to the limit $m = \infty$ shows that $\mathfrak{R} \leq \mathfrak{B}$. Hence $\mathfrak{R}$ is convergent. As each

$$|r_m| \leq \rho_m,$$

we see that R is absolutely convergent.

To show that $R = A$ we begin by taking s so large that

$$\overline{\mathfrak{B}}_s < \epsilon.$$

Next we take p, q so large that every term of $\mathfrak{A}$ not in $\mathfrak{A}_{p,q}$ lies in $\bar{\mathfrak{B}}_s$. Then

$$\mathfrak{B} - \mathfrak{A}_{mn}$$

contains only terms of $\bar{\mathfrak{B}}_s$ when $m > p$, $n > q$. Thus

$$\mathfrak{B} - \mathfrak{A}_{mn} < \epsilon.$$

Now the numerical value of $B - A_{mn}$ is $\leq$ the sum of the numerical values of the terms of this series. Thus

$$|B - A_{mn}| \leq \mathfrak{B} - \mathfrak{A}_{mn} \leq \epsilon.$$

Letting now $n \doteq \infty$, we get

$$|B - R_m| \leq \epsilon.$$

Letting $m \doteq \infty$, we get

$$|B - R| \leq \epsilon.$$

As $\epsilon > 0$ is small at pleasure, this gives

$$B = R. \quad \therefore A = R.$$ Q.E.D.

Similarly we show that C is absolutely convergent and $A = C$.

3. Let us now show conversely :

If the $\mathfrak{R}$ or the $\mathfrak{C}$ series converges, A is convergent.

Let us suppose that $\mathfrak{R}$ is convergent. Taking s at pleasure, we may take m, n so large that the terms of $\mathfrak{B}_s$ lie in $\mathfrak{A}_{mn}$. Hence

$$\mathfrak{B}_s \leq \mathfrak{A}_{mn} \leq \mathfrak{R}_m \leq \mathfrak{R}.$$

Thus $\mathfrak{B}$ is convergent by 13, 2. Hence A is convergent by definition.

4. The following example will show that double series cannot be treated as if they were finite sums. They are the limits of such sums and often illustrate the fact that what is true of the variable is not necessarily true of the limit. Consider the series

$$\begin{aligned} A = 1 - a + \frac{a^2}{2\,!} - \frac{a^3}{3\,!} + \cdots \\ + 1 - 2a + \frac{(2a)^2}{2\,!} - \frac{(2a)^3}{3\,!} + \cdots \\ + 1 - 3a + \frac{(3a)^2}{2\,!} - \frac{(3a)^3}{3\,!} + \cdots \\ + \cdot \quad \cdot \quad \cdot \quad \cdot \quad \cdot \quad \cdot \quad \cdot \quad \cdot \quad \cdot \quad \cdot \end{aligned}$$

where $a > 0$.

The mth row has here the sum

$$r_m = e^{-ma}.$$

Thus summing A by rows we get

$$R = r_1 + r_2 + \cdots$$
$$= e^{-a} + e^{-2a} + e^{-3a} + \cdots$$

This is a geometric series and converges absolutely since $a > 0$. We cannot infer, however, that A is convergent or that if it were its sum $= R$. In fact A is divergent. For if it were convergent each c_n series must be convergent by 2. This is not so, for

$$c_1 = 1 + 1 + 1 + \cdots$$

is divergent.

43. Application to Power Series. We wish to apply the foregoing theorem to obtain a result which we shall use later. Let the power series

$$P(z) = a_0 + a_1 z + a_2 z^2 + \cdots \qquad (1$$

have $\mathfrak{C}$ as a circle of convergence. About any point z within $\mathfrak{C}$ let us describe a circle $\mathfrak{c}$ of radius ρ which also lies within $\mathfrak{C}$. The point $z + h$ will lie in $\mathfrak{c}$ if $|h| \leq \rho$. Hence the series 1) converges absolutely when we replace z by $z + h$; that is

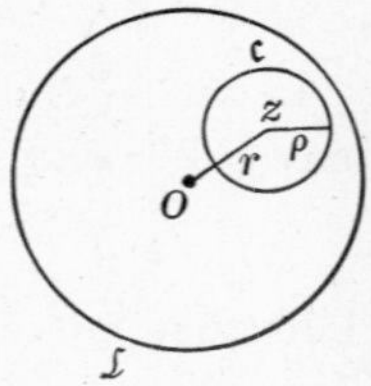

$$P(z + h) = a_0 + a_1(z + h) + a_2(z + h)^2 + \cdots \qquad (2$$

is an absolutely convergent series. Let us expand the terms of 2) and write the result as a double series. We get

$$\begin{aligned} A = &\ a_0 + 0 + 0 + 0 + \cdots \\ &+ a_1 z + a_1 h + 0 + 0 + \cdots \\ &+ a_2 z^2 + 2\, a_2 z h + a_2 h^2 + 0 + \cdots \\ &+ a_3 z^3 + 3\, a_3 z^2 h + 3\, a_3 z h^2 + h^3 + \cdots \\ &+ \cdot \quad \cdot \quad \cdot \quad \cdot \quad \cdot \quad \cdot \quad \cdot \quad \cdot \quad \cdot \quad \cdot \end{aligned} \qquad (3$$

If we sum 3) by rows, we get the absolutely convergent series 2). From this we cannot infer that 3) is convergent as we saw in 42, 4

The series A is, however, convergent, as we may easily see as follows. Let us set $|z| = r$. Then 1) converges absolutely for $z = r + \rho$ since this point lies within $\mathfrak{C}$. Thus

$$\begin{aligned} &\alpha_0 + \alpha_1(r+\rho) + \alpha_2(r+\rho)^2 + \cdots \\ &= \alpha_0 + \alpha_1 r + \alpha_1\rho + \alpha_2 r^2 + 2\,\alpha_2 r\rho + \alpha_2\rho^2 + \cdots \end{aligned} \tag{4}$$

is convergent. Thus the simple series

$$B = a_0 + a_1 z + a_1 h + a_1 z^2 + 2\,a_2 zh + a_2 h^2 + \cdots$$

is absolutely convergent since each of its terms is numerically $\geq$ the corresponding term of 4). Thus A is convergent and we can sum it by rows or by columns. Summing by rows gives

$$A = P(z+h).$$

Summing by columns we get, since the result is the same as before,

$$P(x+h) = P(z) + hP_1(z) + \frac{1}{2!}h^2P_2(z) + \frac{1}{3!}h^3P_3(z) + \cdots \quad (5$$

where

$$P_1 = a_1 + 2\,a_2 z + 3\,a_3 z + \cdots$$

$$P_2 = 2\,a_2 + 2\cdot 3\,a_3 z + 3\cdot 4\,a_4 z^2 + \cdots$$

. . . .

CHAPTER IV

THE ELEMENTARY FUNCTIONS

44. 1. The functions employed in elementary mathematics are the following:

Integral rational functions.
Rational functions.
Algebraic functions.
Circular functions.
Exponential functions.
Hyperbolic functions.
Inverse circular functions.
Logarithmic functions.

Except in case of the algebraic functions the independent variable x is usually real.

We propose in this chapter to define these functions for complex values of the variable, and to study a few of their simplest and most useful properties.

2. The reader is perfectly familiar with all these functions, the variable being real, except possibly the hyperbolic functions. For such as have not used these functions in the calculus we add the following. They are defined by

$$\cosh x = \frac{e^x + e^{-x}}{2} \quad , \quad \sinh x = \frac{e^x - e^{-x}}{2} \cdot \qquad (1$$

The left sides are read "hyperbolic cosine of x" and "hyperbolic sine of x." We see that they are merely linear combinations of e^x and e^{-x}.

These functions have been computed and tabulated, so that one is as free to use them as $\sin x$, $\cos x$. The reader is referred for example to

B. O. Peirce, A Short Table of Integrals.
Ginn and Company, Boston, 1899.

Jahnke and Emde. Funktionentafeln.
Teubner, Leipzig, 1909.

By means of these tables we may draw the graph of these functions which we herewith give. The graph of $\cosh x$ is the familiar *catenary*, that is, the form of a chain supported at two points on the same level. It is important to note that:

$\cosh x$ never vanishes, while $\sinh x$ vanishes just once, viz: for $x = 0$.

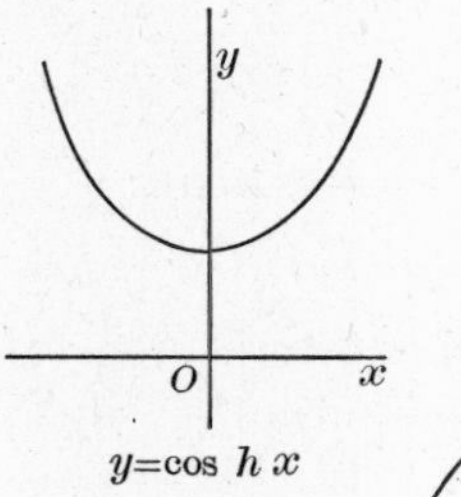

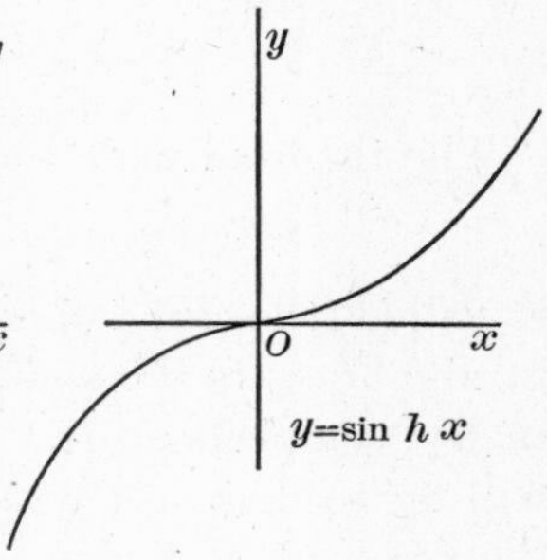

We note also that $\cosh x$ is symmetric with respect to the y-axis, and $\sinh x$ with respect to the origin.

If we express e^x, e^{-x} as series we find

$$\cosh x = 1 + \frac{x^2}{2!} + \frac{x^4}{4!} + \cdots \tag{2}$$

$$\sinh x = \frac{x}{1!} + \frac{x^3}{3!} + \frac{x^5}{5!} + \cdots \tag{3}$$

From 1) we find at once that

$$\cosh^2 x - \sinh^2 x = 1. \tag{4}$$

45. The Integral Rational Function. These functions have the form

$$a_0 + a_1 z + a_2 z^2 + \cdots + a_m z^m, \tag{1}$$

where the coefficients $a_0, a_1, \cdots a_m$ are any given complex numbers and the independent variable z is free to take on all complex values, or as we say is free to range over the whole z-plane. The exponent m is an integer ≥ 0, and is called the *degree* of 1). Such functions are called polynomials in algebra. Since 1) involves only the operations of addition and multiplication of complex numbers, its value can be calculated for any given value of z.

In algebra we learn that 1) vanishes for just m values of z, say

$$z_1\ ,\ z_2\ \cdots\ z_m, \tag{2}$$

some of which however may be equal. We call 2) the *roots* or *zeros* of 1). Knowing the roots 2) and denoting the expression 1) by w, it is shown in algebra that

$$w = a_m(z - z_1)(z - z_2) \cdots (z - z_m). \tag{3}$$

The theorem which states that:

Every polynomial of degree m has m roots

is called the fundamental theorem of algebra. As often given in algebras, its demonstration is long and difficult. Few students really comprehend it. It is a luxury which most students are willing to dispense with. And quite rightly, for it is far beyond their powers at that time. Later we shall give two proofs of this important theorem which the student *will comprehend;* one is so simple that he will not need to set pen to paper to follow it.

46. Rational Functions. The quotient of two integral rational functions of z is a rational function. Such functions have the form

$$\frac{a_0 + a_1 z + \cdots + a_m z^m}{b_0 + b_1 z + \cdots + b_n z^n}, \tag{1}$$

where the coefficients $a_0, a_1 \cdots b_0, b_1 \cdots$ are constants and m, n are integers ≥ 0. The expression 1) involves division by 0 for those values of z for which the denominator vanishes. Let these be

$$z_1 \ , \ z_2 \ \cdots \ z_n. \tag{2}$$

For any value of the complex variable z not included in 2) the value of the expression 1) may be computed by rational operations. These values of z form the *domain of definition* of the expression 1). We may thus state:

The domain of definition of a rational function of z is the whole z-plane excepting the zeros of the denominator.

The *degree* of 1) is the greater of the two exponents m, n, supposing of course that a_m, b_n are $\neq 0$.

When 1) is of the first degree, it is said to be *linear.* The type of a linear rational function of z is therefore

$$\frac{a + bz}{c + dz}. \tag{3}$$

The rational functions include the integral rational functions as a subclass. In fact let the numerator of 1) be exactly divisible by the denominator; then 1) reduces to a polynomial. This takes place in particular when the denominator reduces to a constant, that is when $n = 0$.

47. Algebraic Functions. 1. We say w is an algebraic function of z when it satisfies an equation of the type

$$w^n + R_1(z)w^{n-1} + R_2(z)w^{n-2} + \cdots + R_n(z) = 0, \qquad (1$$

where the coefficients R_1, $R_2 \cdots$ are given rational functions of z, and n is a positive integer. The *degree* of w is n.

Let us give to z a definite value, real or complex, say $z = a$. If a is a zero for one of the denominators of the coefficients, we shall say that the point corresponding to this value of a is an *exceptional point.* Obviously 1) has no meaning at such a point. Suppose now that a is not such a point. Then all the coefficients in 1) can be calculated, and 1) reduces to an equation with constant coefficients. But such an equation admits n roots, which in general are unequal,

$$w_1 \ , \ w_2 \ , \ \cdots \ w_n. \qquad (2$$

Thus the equation 1) defines an n-valued function w of z for all values of z not included among the exceptional points of the coefficients. These values of z, or, using our geometric language, the points in the z-plane corresponding to these non-exceptional points, constitute the *domain of definition* of the algebraic function w.

The number of exceptional points is finite. For the highest degree of any coefficient R_1, $R_2 \cdots$ being say h, no coefficient has more than h exceptional points. As there are only n coefficients, there are at most hn exceptional points. Hence:

The domain of definition of an algebraic function of z embraces the whole z-plane, excepting possibly a finite number of points.

2. Let us note in passing that the class of algebraic functions embraces the rational functions as a subclass.

For let $n = 1$ in 1); it reduces to

$$w + R_1(z) = 0,$$

or

$$w = - R_1(z), \text{ a rational function.}$$

3. We have said that the roots 2) are in general unequal. Let us denote the equation 1) by $F(w, z) = 0$. If we eliminate w from the two relations

$$F = 0 \quad , \quad \frac{\partial F}{\partial w} = 0$$

we will get an *algebraic* equation in z, say

$$G(z) = 0, \tag{3}$$

of degree m, let us say. It is shown now in algebra that the roots 2) are all distinct at a point $z = c$ when c is not a root of 3). We may call the roots of 3) *critical points;* they are finite in number. The exceptional and critical points together may be called *singular points.* All the other points may be called *ordinary.*

48. Explicit Algebraic Functions. 1. The two roots of the algebraic equation

$$w^2 + R_1(z)w + R_2(z) = 0, \tag{1}$$

where R_1, R_2 are rational functions of z, are

$$w = -\tfrac{1}{2} R_1 \pm \tfrac{1}{2}\sqrt{R_1^2 - 4 R_2}. \tag{2}$$

Since 2) satisfies 1), it is an algebraic function of z. To calculate this function we have to perform, besides the rational operations, the operation of extracting a square root of a known quantity.

2. The three roots of the algebraic equation

$$w^3 + R_1(z)w + R_2(z) = 0, \tag{3}$$

where R_1, R_2 are rational functions of z, are given by

$$w = \sqrt[3]{-\tfrac{1}{2} R_2 + \sqrt{\tfrac{1}{4} R_2^2 + \tfrac{1}{27} R_1^3}} + \sqrt[3]{-\tfrac{1}{2} R_2 - \sqrt{\tfrac{1}{4} R_2^2 + \tfrac{1}{27} R_1^3}}. \tag{4}$$

Since 4) satisfies 3) it is an algebraic function of z. The right side of 4) exhibits this function by means of *roots* of quantities which can be successively calculated by rational operations. We say 2) and 4) are explicit algebraic functions of z.

In general we say w is an explicit algebraic function of 2) when its expression involves the extraction of roots of rational functions of z, or the extraction of roots of such roots, or the rational operations on such roots, each operation performed only a finite number of times. This definition is clumsy, but its idea is very simple. The expressions 2) and 4) will serve as illustrations.

3. It is shown in algebra that every explicit algebraic function of z is a root of an equation of the type 47, 1). The demonstration is simple but will not be given here.

On the other hand it is not true that every algebraic function of z is an explicit algebraic function. The demonstration of this fact is anything but simple. The solution of the cubic and biquadratic equations was effected by the Italian algebraists in the first half of the sixteenth century. The algebraic solution of the quintic was then sought. This became one of the celebrated problems of the seventeenth and eighteenth centuries. The greatest mathematicians of their time sought its solution, but in vain. At last Abel in 1826 demonstrated that the roots of the general equation of the fifth and higher degrees cannot be expressed as explicit algebraic functions of their coefficients, in other words that these equations do not admit an algebraic solution.

If then the roots of the general equation of fifth degree cannot be expressed in terms of radicals, in terms of what functions can they be expressed? In 1858 the illustrious French mathematician *Hermite* showed that these roots may be expressed in terms of the elliptic modular functions. This will be referred to again when we take up the study of elliptic functions.

49. Study of $\sqrt{z}$. 1. Let $z = r(\cos\phi + i\sin\phi)$, then as we saw in 7, 3 the two values of $\sqrt{z}$ are

$$w_1 = \sqrt{r}\left(\cos\frac{\phi}{2} + i\sin\frac{\phi}{2}\right), \quad w_2 = -w_1. \tag{1}$$

If we let z describe a curve in the z-plane, the two roots w_1, w_2 will describe curves in the w-plane.

For example, let z describe a circle $\mathfrak{C}$ of radius r as in Fig. 1. When z is at A, $\phi = 0$, hence $w_1 = \sqrt{r}$, $w_2 = -\sqrt{r}$. Thus w_1 is at α and w_2 is at δ. Let z describe the quadrant AB. Then ϕ increases from 0° to 90° while r remains constant. From 1) we see that the argument $\frac{1}{2}\phi$ of w_1 increases only half as fast while its modulus $\sqrt{r}$ remains constant. Thus when z describes the quadrant AB, w_1 describes the octant $\alpha\beta$. Since $w_2 = - w_1$, we see that at the same time w_2 describes the octant $\delta\epsilon$. Let now z describe the second quadrant BC. At C, $\phi = 180°$, hence $\frac{1}{2}\phi = 90°$.

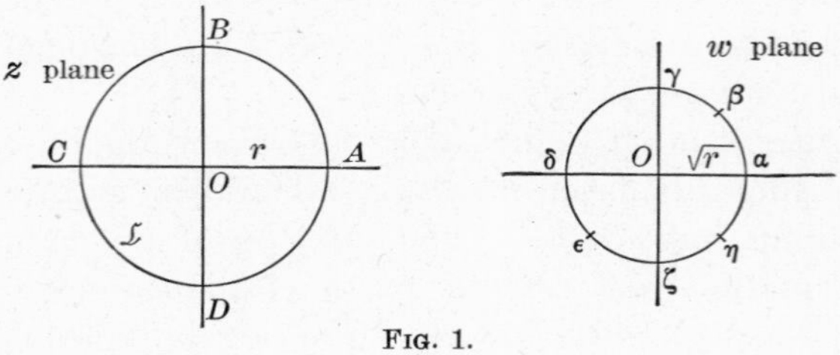

FIG. 1.

Thus when z has reached C, w_1 has arrived at γ, while w_2 has got to ζ. Continuing, we see that when z has gone all around the circle, $\phi = 360°$, hence $\frac{1}{2}\phi = 180°$, and hence w_1 is at δ. Meantime w_2 has moved from ζ to α. Now when we began, w_1 was at α, and w_2 at δ. After the circuit, w_1 is at δ and w_2 at α. The two roots have been interchanged.

2. We will now let z describe any closed curve $\mathfrak{K}$ about the origin as in Fig. 2.

To any point P on $\mathfrak{K}$ whose polar coördinates are r, ϕ will correspond a value of w_1 given by 1), and the point in the w-plane corresponding to this value w_1 has the polar coördinates $\sqrt{r}$, $\frac{1}{2}\phi$.

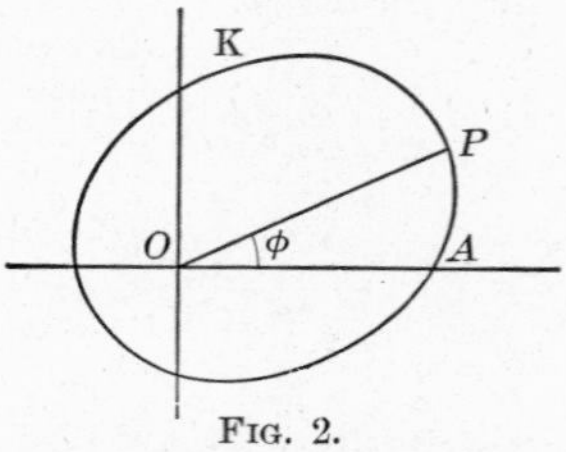

FIG. 2.

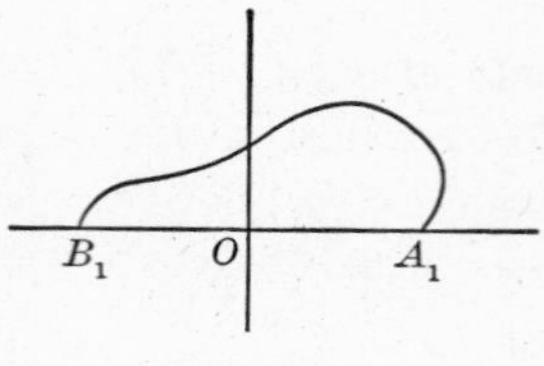

FIG. 3.

As z describes $\mathfrak{K}$ starting from A, ϕ will increase steadily from $\phi = 0°$ to $\phi = 360°$ when z will have returned to A. The modulus r varies continuously from its original value, say $r = a$, sometimes increasing, sometimes decreasing, but finally returning to its original value a. From this we see that the argument $\frac{1}{2}\phi$ of w_1 will increase steadily from 0° to 180° while the modulus $\sqrt{r}$

will vary continuously. Thus w_1 will describe a continuous curve as in Fig. 3, whose end points A_1, B_1 lie on the real axis at the distance $\sqrt{a}$ from the origin in the w-plane. Moreover, as $w_2 = -w_1$ we see that w_2 will describe a symmetric curve on the other side of the origin. Hence when z has completed its circuit about the origin of the z-plane, w_1 and w_2 have interchanged positions in the w-plane.

Thus we see that this more general case behaves in an entirely analogous manner to the simple case considered in 1. The main facts to remember are these :

1° When z describes a circuit about the origin, w_1 and w_2 each describes a curve, but not a closed curve.

2° At the end of the circuit, w_1 and w_2 have interchanged values. In other words, a circuit about the origin effects the substitution

$$\begin{pmatrix} w_1 & w_2 \\ w_2 & w_1 \end{pmatrix}.$$

For this reason the point $z = 0$ is called a *branch point*.

3. Let now z describe a closed curve, as in Fig. 4, which does not enclose the origin 0. Let the polar coördinates of

	A	B	C	D	E
be	$a, \alpha;$	$b, \beta;$	$c, \gamma;$	$d, \delta;$	$e, \epsilon.$

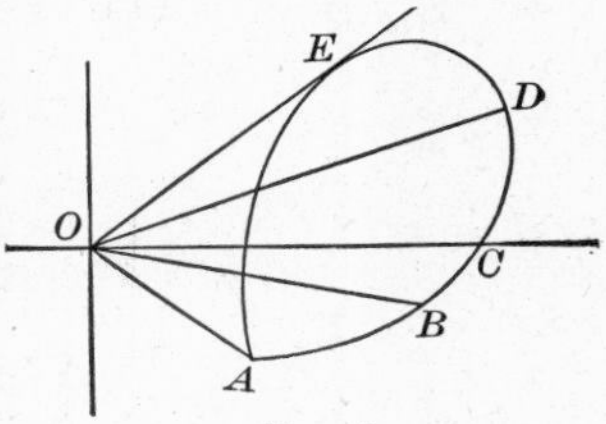

FIG. 4.

The value of w_1 at the point A is thus, by 1),

$$w_1 = \sqrt{a}\,(\cos \tfrac{1}{2}\alpha + i \sin \tfrac{1}{2}\alpha).$$

The point A_1 in Fig. 5, corresponding to this, has the polar coördinates $\sqrt{a}$, $\frac{1}{2}\alpha$. Let now z move along the arc $ABC \cdots$. Its argument ϕ steadily increases till the radius vector becomes tangent to the curve at E; that is ϕ increases from $\phi = \alpha$ to $\phi = \epsilon$. Thus the argument $\frac{1}{2}\phi$ of w_1 steadily increases from $\frac{1}{2}\alpha$ to $\frac{1}{2}\epsilon$, as w_1 moves from A_1 to E_1 in Fig. 5. The modulus r of z increases from $r = a$ to $r = d$ as it moves from A to a point D in Fig. 4, when it begins to decrease.

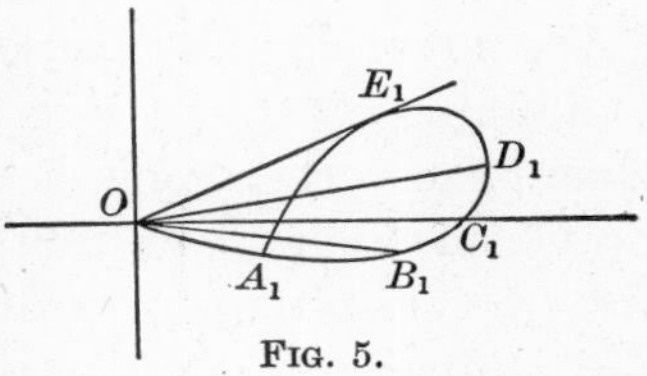

FIG. 5.

Similarly, if to fix the ideas we suppose $r > 1$, the modulus $\sqrt{r}$ of w_1 will increase from $\sqrt{a}$ to $\sqrt{d}$ as w_1 moves from A_1 to a point D_1 in Fig. 5. As z moves from E back to A and so completes the circuit, ϕ decreases from ϵ back to its original value α. The modulus r also assumes its original value $r = a$, at the close of the circuit. Thus w_1 also comes back to its point of departure A_1. Hence:

When z describes a closed curve not including the origin, w_1 describes a closed curve also.

Since $w_2 = -w_1$ we see that w_2 will describe a symmetric closed curve on the other side of the origin.

4. When z describes a circuit about $z = 0$ we have seen that the two values of $w = \sqrt{z}$ are permuted; on the other hand, we have seen that if z describes a circuit about any other point, which does not include the origin, the two values of w are unaltered at the end of this circuit. We therefore say that $z = 0$ is the only branch point of w.

50. Study of $w = \sqrt{(z-a)(z-b)}$. 1. Let

$$z - a = \alpha(\cos\theta + i\sin\theta),$$

$$z - b = \beta(\cos\phi + i\sin\phi).$$

Let

$$u_1 = \sqrt{\alpha}(\cos\tfrac{1}{2}\theta + i\sin\tfrac{1}{2}\theta) \quad , \quad u_2 = -u_1, \tag{1}$$

$$v_1 = \sqrt{\beta}(\cos\tfrac{1}{2}\phi + i\sin\tfrac{1}{2}\phi) \quad , \quad v_2 = -v_1. \tag{2}$$

Then the two values of w are

$$w_1 = u_1 v_1 \quad , \quad w_2 = -u_1 v_1.$$

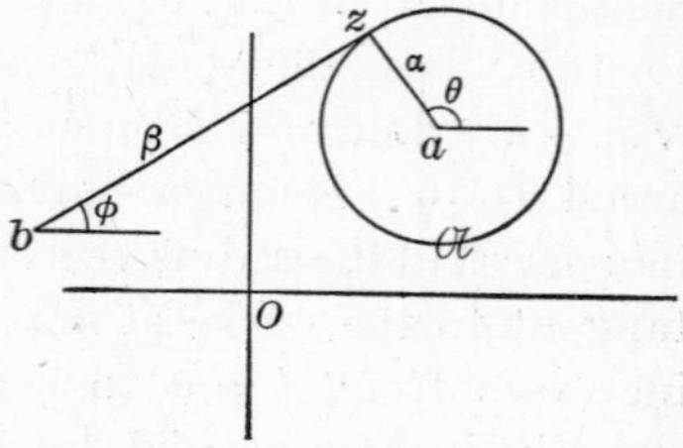

We note that the expressions 1), 2) defining u_1, v_1 have precisely the same form as that defining w_1 in 49. From this it follows that when z describes a circuit $\mathfrak{A}$ about a, u_1 will go over into $u_2 = -u_1$. On the other hand the curve $\mathfrak{A}$ lies outside of b, and hence by 49, 3, when z describes $\mathfrak{A}$, v_1 returns to its original value at the close. Thus v_1 is unchanged. Hence the effect of the circuit $\mathfrak{A}$ on w_1 is to change it into $-u_1v_1$ or w_2. As $w_2 = -w_1$, we see that the same circuit converts w_2 into w_1. Thus a circuit of z about a effects the substitution

$$\begin{pmatrix} w_1 & w_2 \\ w_2 & w_1 \end{pmatrix}.$$

Similarly if z describes a circuit $\mathfrak{B}$ about b, but excluding a, the roots w_1, w_2 are also permuted.

For this reason the points $z = a$, $z = b$ are called *branch points*.

The same reasoning shows that if z describes a circuit about a or b, but in the opposite direction, the two roots w_1, w_2 are permuted also.

Next let z describe a closed curve $\mathfrak{C}$ which does not include either a or b. Then 49 shows that both u_1, v_1 return after the circuit to their original values and hence $w_1 = u_1v_1$ also returns to its original value.

2. Let z move from c to d over the path $\mathfrak{L}$. If it describes the same path in the opposite direction, *i.e.* from d to c, we may denote it by $\mathfrak{L}^{-1}$. Let $\mathfrak{M}$ denote the other path from c to d as in the figure. Then $\mathfrak{L}\mathfrak{M}^{-1}$ will denote the closed curve from c over $\mathfrak{L}$ to d and back to c over the curve $\mathfrak{M}$.

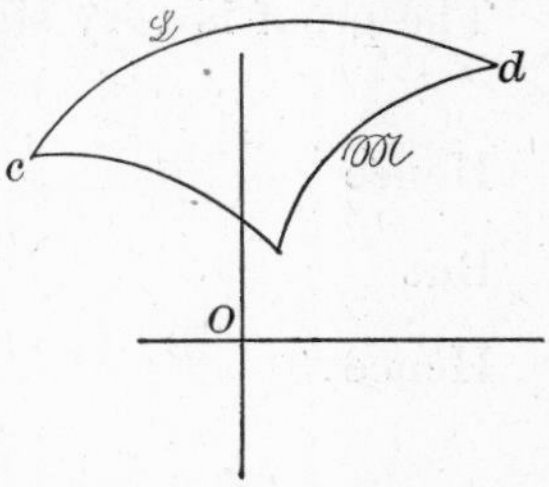

At each point z, the algebraic function

$$w = \sqrt{(z-a)(z-b)}$$

has two values. The values of w for $z = c$ let us call γ and $-\gamma$. When z ranges over the curve $\mathfrak{L}$, the different values that w has group themselves into two curves or *branches* which we may call L_1 and L_2. An end point of one of these curves, say L_1, is γ. Let δ be the other end point of L_1. *If $\mathfrak{L}$ does not pass through one of the branch points $z = a$, $z = b$*, the two values that w has for each value of z are distinct. In this case the two branches L_1, L_2 have no point in common. We may thus distinguish the two branches L_1, L_2 by giving one of their points. Thus the branch L_1 is determined by the fact that it passes through γ, or through δ.

Suppose now we allow z to range from c to d over $\mathfrak{L}$. If we start with $w = \gamma$, what value will we have when z reaches d if, as we pass over $\mathfrak{L}$, we always choose that determination of w which will form *a continuous set of values?* Now at $z = d$, w has two values $w = \delta$, and $w = -\delta$. From the foregoing the value we must choose is obviously $w = \delta$. Let us indicate this by the notation

$$\gamma_{\mathfrak{L}} = \delta,$$

whereby we mean that if we start from $z = c$ with that value of w which is $= \gamma$ and allow z to range over the path $\mathfrak{L}$, the value that w has at the other end of $\mathfrak{L}$ is δ.

Suppose that we next allow z to move from c to d over the path $\mathfrak{M}$. We prove now the important fact:

If $\mathfrak{L}$, $\mathfrak{M}$ do not pass through or enclose a branch point,

$$\gamma_{\mathfrak{L}} = \gamma_{\mathfrak{M}} = \delta.$$

In other words, if we start with the same determination of w at $z = c$ we arrive at the same value of w at $z = d$, whatever path we choose, provided no two paths pass through or enclose a branch point.

The proof is very simple. For by 1,

$$\gamma_{\mathfrak{L}\mathfrak{M}^{-1}} = \gamma.$$

Hence

$$\gamma_{\mathfrak{L}\mathfrak{M}^{-1}\mathfrak{M}} = \gamma_{\mathfrak{M}}.$$

But

$$\gamma_{\mathfrak{L}\mathfrak{M}^{-1}\mathfrak{M}} = \gamma_{\mathfrak{L}}.$$

Hence

$$\gamma_{\mathfrak{L}} = \gamma_{\mathfrak{M}}.$$

3. Suppose we start at $z = c$ with the determination of $w = \gamma$. We allow z to describe the circle $\mathfrak{C}$ as in the figure. We ask what is the value of w when z returns to c? As w has only two values at c we have

$$\gamma_{\mathfrak{C}} = \gamma \quad \text{or} \quad \gamma_{\mathfrak{C}} = -\gamma.$$

To determine which, we introduce the paths

$$dc \text{ and } ce.$$

Then

$$\gamma_{\mathfrak{C}} = \gamma_{cd \cdot dc \cdot ec}.$$

As the two paths de and $dc \cdot ce$ do not include a branch point,

$$\gamma_{\mathfrak{C}} = \gamma_{cd \cdot dc \cdot ce \cdot ec}.$$

Now $cd \cdot dc$ is a circuit about the branch point $z = a$. Hence

$$\gamma_{cd \cdot dc} = -\gamma,$$

and thus

$$\gamma_{\mathfrak{C}} = (-\gamma)_{ce \cdot ec}.$$

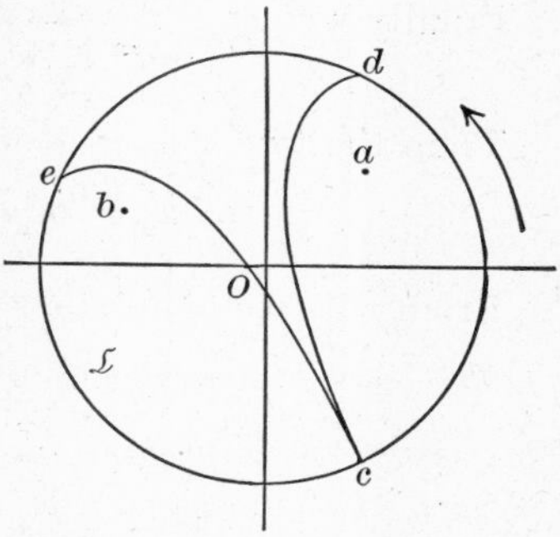

Also $ce \cdot ec$ is a circuit about the branch point $z = b$. Hence

$$(-\gamma)_{ce \cdot ec} = \gamma.$$

Thus finally

$$\gamma_{\mathfrak{C}} = \gamma.$$

51. The Elliptic Radicals. 1. When we take up the elliptic functions, we shall find that two radicals

$$w = \sqrt{4(z - e_1)(z - e_2)(z - e_3)} \qquad (1$$

and

$$w = \sqrt{(1 - z^2)(1 - k^2 z^2)} \qquad (2$$

figure very prominently. Let us consider first 1). If we set

$$z - e_m = r_m(\cos \theta_m + i \sin \theta_m)$$

and

$$u_m = \sqrt{r_m}(\cos \tfrac{1}{2}\theta_m + i \sin \tfrac{1}{2}\theta_m), \qquad m = 1, 2, 3,$$

the two values of w in 1) are

$$w_1 = u_1 u_2 u_3 \quad , \quad w_2 = -w_1.$$

Now the radicals $u_m = \sqrt{z - e_m}$ have the same form as those considered in 50 and we may therefore conclude at once:

The branch points of 1) *are* e_1, e_2, e_3. *When* z *describes a circuit about one of them,* w_1 *and* w_2 *are interchanged. A circuit which includes two of the branch points leaves* w_1, w_2 *unchanged; a circuit which includes all three branch points interchanges* w_1, w_2. *Finally a circuit which includes none of the branch points leaves* w_1, w_2 *unaltered.*

2. Let us now turn to the radical 2). Since

$$(1 - z^2)(1 - k^2 z^2) = k^2(z - 1)(z + 1)\left(z - \frac{1}{k}\right)\left(z + \frac{1}{k}\right),$$

we set

$$z - 1 = r_1(\cos \theta_1 + i \sin \theta_1) \quad , \quad z + 1 = r_2(\cos \theta_2 + i \sin \theta_2),$$

$$z - \frac{1}{k} = r_3(\cos \theta_3 + i \sin \theta_3) \quad , \quad z + \frac{1}{k} = r_4(\cos \theta_4 + i \sin \theta_4).$$

Finally we set $u_m = \sqrt{r_m}(\cos \frac{1}{2}\theta_m + i \sin \frac{1}{2}\theta_m), \qquad m = 1, 2, 3, 4.$

Then the two values of w in 2) are

$$w_1 = ku_1u_2u_3u_4 \quad , \quad w_2 = -w_1.$$

From this we conclude:

The branch points of the radical 2) *are* $1, -1, \frac{1}{k}, -\frac{1}{k}$. *When* x *describes a circuit which includes no branch point or an even number of them, the values of* w_1, w_2 *are each the same at the end of the circuit as at the start. If the circuit contains an odd number of the branch points, the values of* w_1, w_2 *are interchanged after the circuit.*

52. Study of $w = \sqrt[3]{\frac{z-a}{z-b}}$. The method we adopt to study this radical is the same as that employed in 49, 50, and 51. We set

$$z - a = \alpha(\cos\theta + i\sin\theta) \quad , \quad z - b = \beta(\cos\phi + i\sin\phi)$$

and introduce the cube root of unity

$$\omega = \cos\frac{2\pi}{3} + i\sin\frac{2\pi}{3}.$$

We also set

$$u_1 = \sqrt[3]{\alpha}\left(\cos\frac{\theta}{3} + i\sin\frac{\theta}{3}\right) \quad , \quad u_2 = \omega u_1 \quad , \quad u_3 = \omega^2 u_1,$$

$$v_1 = \sqrt[3]{\beta}\left(\cos\frac{\phi}{3} + i\sin\frac{\phi}{3}\right) \quad , \quad v_2 = \omega v_1 \quad , \quad v_3 = \omega^2 v_1.$$

Then the three values of w are

$$w_1 = \frac{u_2}{v_1} \quad , \quad w_2 = \omega\frac{u_1}{v_1} \quad , \quad w_3 = \omega^2\frac{u_1}{v_1}. \tag{1}$$

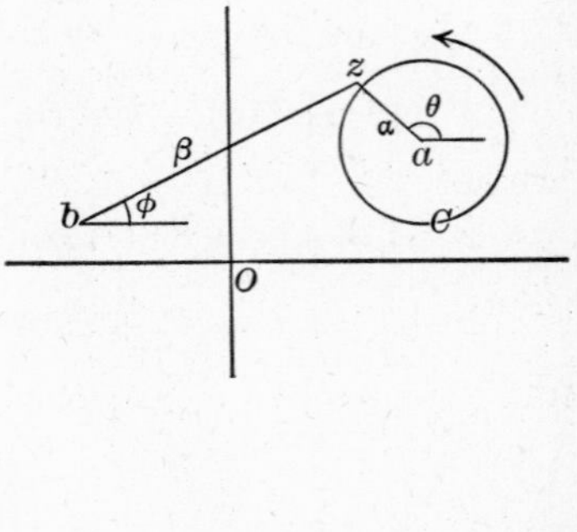

Let now z describe a circle C about $z = a$, as in the figure. Then θ increases from say $\theta = t$ to $\theta = t + 2\pi$, while ϕ returns to its original value. At the beginning of the circuit

$$u_1 = \sqrt[3]{\alpha}(\cos\tfrac{1}{3}t + i\sin\tfrac{1}{3}t). \tag{2}$$

At the end of the circuit, u_1 has acquired the value

$$(u_1)_C = \sqrt[3]{a}(\cos \tfrac{1}{3}(t + 2\pi)\ i \sin \tfrac{1}{3}(t + 2\pi))$$
$$= \omega u_1.$$

Thus
$$(u_2)_C = \omega(u_1)_C = \omega^2 u_1 = u_3,$$
$$(u_3)_C = \omega^2(u_1)_C = \omega^3 u_1 = u_1.$$

The effect of C is to convert

$$u_1 \quad , \quad u_2 \quad , \quad u_3$$

into
$$u_2 \quad , \quad u_3 \quad , \quad u_1.$$

As v_1 remains unaltered by the circuit C, the relation 1) shows that after the circuit

$$w_1 \quad , \quad w_2 \quad , \quad w_3$$

go over into
$$w_2 \quad , \quad w_3 \quad , \quad w_1.$$

The circuit thus effects the substitution

$$A = \begin{pmatrix} w_1 & w_2 & w_3 \\ w_2 & w_3 & w_1 \end{pmatrix}.$$

Let z now describe a circle D about $z = b$ in the positive direction. The same considerations show that ϕ increases from say $\phi = p$ to $\phi = p + 2\pi$. On the other hand, θ returns to its original value. Thus at the beginning of the circuit D,

$$v_1 = \sqrt[3]{\beta}\,(\cos \tfrac{1}{3}p + i \sin \tfrac{1}{3}p).$$

At the end of D, v_1 has acquired the value

$$(v_1)_D = \sqrt[3]{\beta}(\cos \tfrac{1}{3}(p + 2\pi) + i \sin \tfrac{1}{3}(p + 2\pi))$$
$$= \omega v_1.$$

Similarly
$$(v_2)_D = \omega v_2 = v_3 \quad ; \quad v_3 = \omega v_3 = v_1.$$

As u_1 remains unaltered by the circuit D we have

$$(w_1)_D = \left(\frac{u_1}{v_1}\right)_D = \frac{u_1}{\omega v_1} = \omega^2 \frac{u_1}{v_1} = \omega^2 w_1 = w_3.$$

Similarly w_2 goes over into w_1 and w_3 into w_2 after D. Thus the circuit D effects the substitution

$$B = \begin{pmatrix} w_1 & w_2 & w_3 \\ w_3 & w_1 & w_2 \end{pmatrix}.$$

We notice $A^2 = B$; that is, going around $z = a$ twice in the positive direction produces the substitution B. If we go around a three times, $w_1\ w_2\ w_3$ take on their original values, or

$$A^3 = \begin{pmatrix} w_1 & w_2 & w_3 \\ w_1 & w_2 & w_3 \end{pmatrix}.$$

A substitution which effects no change in the roots is called the identical substitution and is denoted by 1. Thus

$$A^3 = 1.$$

Let us now see what happens when z describes the circuit C in the negative direction. This path according to our agreement is represented by C^{-1}. In this case θ decreases from say $\theta = t$ to $\theta = t - 2\pi$. At the end of the circuit C^{-1}, u_1 as given by 2) has acquired the value

$$(u_1)_{C^{-1}} = \sqrt[3]{\alpha}(\cos \tfrac{1}{3}(t - 2\pi) + i \sin \tfrac{1}{3}(t - 2\pi))$$
$$= \omega^{-1}u_1 = \omega^2 u_1 = u_3.$$

Similarly $(u_2)_{C^{-1}} = u_1$ and $(u_3)_{C^{-1}} = u_2$.

As v_1 is unaltered by this circuit, we see that C^{-1} produces the substitution

$$A^{-1} = \begin{pmatrix} w_1 & w_2 & w_3 \\ w_3 & w_1 & w_2 \end{pmatrix} = B.$$

Since the circuit C^{-1} just undoes what C does, we should have $AA^{-1} = 1$ and this we see is indeed so.

Similarly the circuit D^{-1} produces the substitution $B^{-1} = A$.

We notice that A, B combine as products.

53. 1. One and Many Valued Functions. The integral rational function,

$$w = a_0 + a_1 z + \cdots + a_m z^m,$$

assigns for each value of z, a single value to w. It is a *one-valued function* of z. Let $w = b$ for $z = a$. If we allow z to describe some curve in the z-plane returning to its point of departure $z = a$, w will describe a curve in the w-plane which starts from $w = b$, and returns to this point.

2. On the other hand the function

$$w = \sqrt{z - a}$$

assigns to w two values for each value of z except $z = a$ where w has only one value $w = 0$. This function is a *two-valued* function.

For a similar reason

$$w = \sqrt[3]{\frac{z-a}{z-b}}$$

is a *three-valued* function.

3. Since the equation

$$w^n + R_1 w^{n-1} + \cdots + R_n = 0 \qquad (1$$

considered in 47 has in general n distinct roots, the function w of z defined by this relation is called an *n-valued* function.

Let $z = a$ be an ordinary point [47, 3]. If now z describes a curve C which does not pass through a singular point, the n values which w has at each point of C can be grouped together

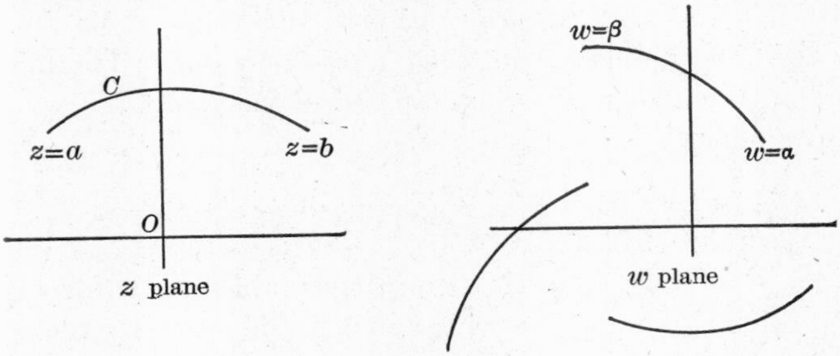

so as to form n curves or *branches*. If $w = \alpha$ is one of the roots of 1) for $z = a$, one and only one of these branches will pass through the point $w = \alpha$. It thus serves to characterize this branch.

Now when dealing with many-valued functions we very often have to solve this problem:

We take one of the values as $w = \alpha$ which w has at the ordinary point $z = a$ and ask what value of w do we get when z describes some curve C leading to $z = b$ and avoiding all singular points. The many values which w has for the points of C will be distributed over certain continuous curves or *branches* and the value of w we *always* want is that value of w for $z=b$ which lies on the branch passing through the point $w=\alpha$.

This general problem we have studied in several simple cases in 49–52.

If this value of w is $w=\beta$, we say that branch of w which takes on the value $w=\alpha$ for $z=a$, has the value $w=\beta$ at $z=b$, when z describes the curve C. We have used the notation

$$(\alpha)_C=\beta$$

to denote this fact.

If z describes some other curve D not passing through a singular point and leading from $z=a$ to $z=b$, the end value of this branch will not be in general β. In any case it must be one of the many values which w takes on for $z=b$.

The Exponential Function

54. Addition Theorem. 1. In the foregoing articles we have considered the algebraic functions which include as special cases the rational and the integral rational functions. All functions which are not algebraic are called *transcendental*. The first such function we shall study is the *exponential function*.

It is defined by the series

$$1+\frac{z}{1!}+\frac{z^2}{2!}+\frac{z^3}{3!}+\cdots \tag{1}$$

In 39, 4 we saw that this converges absolutely for every z. Thus it defines a function of z which is denoted by the symbol

$$e^z \quad \text{or} \quad \text{Exp}\, z.$$

The domain of definition of this function is the whole z-plane. When z has a real value x, 1) reduces to the well-known exponential function

$$e^x=1+\frac{x}{1!}+\frac{x^2}{2!}+\frac{x^3}{3!}+\cdots$$

studied in algebra and the calculus.

A most important property of e^x is the *addition theorem*, as it is called, viz.:

$$e^xe^y=e^{x+y}.$$

Let us show that the relation holds for complex values. Let u, v be complex numbers. Then by definition

$$e^u = 1 + \frac{u}{1!} + \frac{u^2}{2!} + \frac{u^3}{3!} + \cdots$$

$$e^v = 1 + \frac{v}{1!} + \frac{v^2}{2!} + \frac{v^3}{3!} + \cdots$$

If we multiply these absolutely convergent series, as shown in 33, 2, we get

$$e^u e^v = 1 + \left(\frac{u}{1!} + \frac{v}{1!}\right) + \left(\frac{u^2}{2!} + \frac{u}{1!}\frac{v}{1!} + \frac{v^2}{2!}\right)$$

$$+ \left(\frac{u^3}{3!} + \frac{u^2}{2!}\frac{v}{1!} + \frac{u}{1!}\frac{v^2}{2!} + \frac{v^3}{3!}\right) + \cdots$$

$$= 1 + \frac{1}{1!}(u+v) + \frac{1}{2!}(u+v)^2 + \frac{1}{3!}(u+v)^3 + \cdots$$

$$= e^{u+v}.$$

Thus
$$e^u e^v = e^{u+v} \tag{2}$$
holds for any complex numbers u v.

2. From the addition theorem we can show how to calculate e^z for any

$$z = x + iy \quad , \quad x, y \text{ real}$$

by using our ordinary logarithmic tables. We have in fact

$$e^z = e^{x+iy} = e^x e^{iy}. \tag{3}$$

Now
$$e^{iy} = 1 + \frac{iy}{1!} + \frac{(iy)^2}{2!} + \frac{(iy)^3}{3!} + \cdots$$

$$= 1 - \frac{y^2}{2!} + \frac{y^4}{4!} - \cdots$$

$$+ i\left(\frac{y}{1!} - \frac{y^3}{3!} + \frac{y^5}{5!} - \cdots\right).$$

Hence
$$e^{iy} = \cos y + i \sin y. \tag{4}$$

Thus from 3) we have
$$e^z = e^x(\cos y + i \sin y). \tag{5}$$

The relation 5) is an expression of the complex number e^z, which is nothing but the sum of the series 1), in its polar form $r(\cos\theta + i\sin\theta)$. Thus the modulus of e^z is e^x, and its argument is y. In symbols

$$|e^z| = e^x \quad , \quad \text{Arg } e^z = y. \tag{6}$$

Thus to plot the value of $w = e^z = e^x e^{iy}$ we first describe a circle of unit radius about the origin of the w-plane and then lay off on this an arc of length $= y$ as in the figure. On a radius through the end of this arc we now lay off a length $= e^x$. The end point of this segment is w.

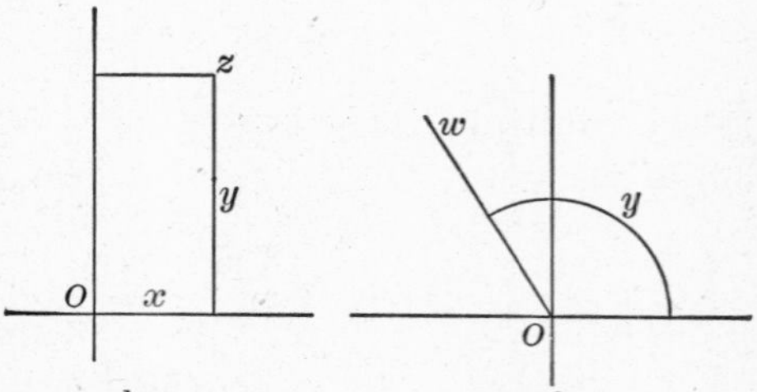

z plane w plane

To calculate e^z by the tables we first compute

$$r = e^x.$$

Then we convert the arc y into degrees, getting an angle θ. Then

$$w = e^z = r(\cos\theta + i\sin\theta). \tag{7}$$

If we wish to reduce w to the rectangular form

$$w = u + iv$$

we have, comparing with 7),

$$u = r\cos\theta \quad , \quad v = r\sin\theta. \tag{8}$$

Let us note in passing the important theorem :

The exponential function e vanishes for no value of z.

For e^z cannot $= 0$ unless its modulus $e^x = 0$. But e^x vanishes for no real x.

3. As an *example* let us compute $w = e^z$ for

$$z = -1.6 - 2\cdot 8\,i.$$

Here $$x = -1.6, \quad y = -2{\cdot}8.$$

Hence $$r = e^x = e^{-1.6}.$$

Let us set $$s = e^{1.6};$$

then $$\log s = 1.6 \log e = t, \text{ say.}$$

Here the symbol log stands for the logarithm whose base is 10.

$$\log e = 0.43429$$
$$\log(\log e) = 9.63778$$
$$\log 1.6 = 0.20412$$
$$\log t = 9.84190$$
$$\log s = 0.69487$$
$$\log r = 9.30513, \quad r = .20190$$

We now convert y into degrees. From our tables we have

$$2^{\text{rad}}_{.} = 114° \, 35' \, 30''$$
$$0.8^{\text{rad}}_{.} = 45 \quad 50 \quad 12$$

Hence

$$\theta = -\,160° \, 25' \, 42'',$$

or adding 360°

$$\theta = 199° \, 34' \, 18''.$$

To simplify our calculation let us take

$$\theta = 199° \, 34'$$
$$\log(-\cos\theta) = 9.97417$$
$$\log(-\sin\theta) = 9.52492$$
$$\log r = 9.30513$$
$$\log(-u) = 9.27930 \qquad u = -\,.19024$$
$$\log(-v) = 8.83005 \qquad v = -\,.067616$$

As a *check* for our work we should have

$$\tan\theta = \frac{v}{u}.$$

But

$$\log\frac{v}{u} = 9.55075$$

or

$$\theta = 199° \, 34'$$

as before. As a final result we have therefore

$$w = -\,.19024 - .06762\,i$$
$$|w| = .20190 \quad , \quad \text{Arg } w = 199° \, 34'.$$

4. Since the function e^x for real x often occurs in calculations, tables of this function have been prepared. We mention those of B. O. Peirce and those of Jahnke and Emde already referred to in 44.

From Peirce's Tables, p. 114, we have

$$\log e^{-1} = 9.56571$$
$$\log e^{-.6} = 9.73942.$$

Hence $$\log e^{-1.6} = 9.30513 \quad , \quad e^{-1.6} = .20190,$$

which agrees with its value obtained in 3. In the Tables of Jahnke and Emde we may take out the value of $e^{-1.6}$ directly from the table on p. 6.

55. 1. *Euler's Formula.* Let us suppose the real angle ϕ is expressed in circular measure. Then 54, 4), gives Euler's celebrated formula

$$e^{i\phi} = \cos\phi + i\sin\phi, \qquad (1$$

which we referred to in 1, 3). The point in the z-plane associated with this number lies on the unit circle, *i.e.* a circle about the origin of unit radius. It lies on the radius making an angle ϕ with the real axis. Since every complex number can be expressed in polar form

$$z = r(\cos\phi + i\sin\phi), \qquad (2$$

we have, using 1)

$$z = re^{i\phi}. \qquad (3$$

We call this the *exponential form* of z. Thus we have three ways of representing a complex number: the rectangular form $x + iy$, the polar form given by 2), and the exponential form given by 3). Each way of expressing z is useful at times.

From 1) we have

$$e^{\frac{\pi i}{2}} = i \quad , \quad e^{\pi i} = -1 \quad , \quad e^{\frac{3\pi}{2}i} = -i \quad , \quad e^{2\pi i} = 1. \qquad (4$$

The n roots of unity are represented by

$$1 \; , \; e^{\frac{2\pi i}{n}} \; , \; e^{2\cdot\frac{2\pi i}{n}} \; , \; e^{3\cdot\frac{2\pi i}{n}} \; , \; \cdots e^{(n-1)\frac{2\pi i}{n}}. \qquad (5$$

The n roots of

$$a = r(\cos\theta + i\sin\theta)$$

are

$$z_0 = \sqrt[n]{r}\, e^{\frac{i\theta}{n}} \quad , \quad z_1 = \sqrt[n]{r}\, e^{i\left(\frac{\theta}{n}+\frac{2\pi}{n}\right)} \cdots z_{n-1} = \sqrt[n]{r}\, e^{i\left(\frac{\theta}{n}+(n-1)\frac{2\pi}{n}\right)} \qquad (6$$

Or if ω is the first imaginary n^{th} root in 5)

$$z_0 = \sqrt[n]{e}^{\,i\frac{\theta}{n}} \quad , \quad z_1 = \omega z_0 \quad , \quad \cdots z_{n-1} = \omega^{n-1} z_0. \qquad (7$$

2. In plane trigonometry the two formulae

$$\cos(\theta + \phi) = \cos\theta \cos\phi - \sin\theta \sin\phi \tag{8}$$

$$\sin(\theta + \phi) = \sin\theta \cos\phi + \cos\theta \sin\phi \tag{9}$$

are of fundamental importance. They express the *addition theorem* of the cosine and sine functions. Let us show how they may be derived from Euler's formula.

From 1) we have

$$e^{-i\phi} = \cos\phi - i \sin\phi. \tag{10}$$

From 1), 10), we have, adding and subtracting,

$$\cos\phi = \tfrac{1}{2}(e^{i\phi} + e^{-i\phi}) \tag{11}$$

and

$$\sin\phi = \frac{1}{2i}(e^{i\phi} - e^{-i\phi}). \tag{12}$$

These last two formulae expressing the cosine and sine as exponentials are often useful.

Let us now multiply 1) by

$$e^{i\theta} = \cos\theta + i \sin\theta.$$

We get

$$\begin{aligned} e^{i\theta}e^{i\phi} = e^{i(\theta+\phi)} &= \cos(\theta + \phi) + i \sin(\theta + \phi) \qquad (13 \\ &= \cos\theta \cos\phi - \sin\theta \sin\phi + i(\cos\theta \sin\phi + \sin\theta \cos\phi). \end{aligned}$$

Equating the real and imaginary parts of this equation gives 8) and 9) at once.

3. Let us show how the powers of $\sin\theta$, $\cos\theta$ may be expressed in terms of the sine and cosine of multiple angles. To this end we set

$$u = e^{i\phi} \quad , \quad v = e^{-i\phi}.$$

Then 11) and 12) give

$$\begin{aligned} (2\cos\phi)^m = (u + v)^m &= u^m + \binom{m}{1}u^{m-1}v + \binom{m}{2}u^{m-2}v^2 + \cdots \\ &= (u^m + v^m) + \binom{m}{1}(u^{m-2} + v^{m-2})uv \\ &\quad + \binom{m}{2}(u^{m-4} + v^{m-4})u^2v^2 + \cdots \qquad (14 \end{aligned}$$

Now

$$uv = e^{i\phi}e^{-i\phi} = 1.$$

Also

$$u^m + v^m = e^{mi\phi} + e^{-mi\phi} = 2\cos m\phi.$$

Thus 14) gives for $m = 2, 3, \cdots$

$$2\cos^2\phi = \cos 2\phi + 1$$
$$4\cos^3\phi = \cos 3\phi + 3\cos\phi \qquad (15$$
$$8\cos^4\phi = \cos 4\phi + 4\cos 2\phi + 3$$
$$\cdots\cdots\cdots$$

Similarly
$$(2i\sin\phi)^m = (u - v)^m$$
gives
$$-2\sin^2\phi = \cos 2\phi - 1$$
$$-4\sin^3\phi = \sin 3\phi - 3\sin\phi$$
$$+8\sin^4\phi = \cos 4\phi - 4\cos 2\phi + 3 \qquad (16$$
$$\cdots\cdots\cdots$$

56. Period of e^z. We are familiar with the fact that
$$\sin(x + 2\pi) = \sin x$$
for any real x. We say $\sin x$ is periodic and has the period 2π.

It is easy to show that e^z admits the period $2\pi i$, that is,
$$e^{z+2\pi i} = e^z$$
for all values of z. For $e^{z+2\pi i} = e^z \cdot e^{2\pi i}$ by 54, 3)
$$= e^z.$$

In the same way we see that e^z admits $2m\pi i$ as period, where m is an integer.

We say any complex number α is a *period* of e^z when
$$e^{z+\alpha} = e^z \qquad (1$$
holds for all values of z. Let us show that e^z has only the periods $2m\pi i$ just given.

For let $\alpha = a + ib$ be a period. Then 1), holding for every value of z, will hold for $z = 0$, and we have
$$e^\alpha = e^0 = 1,$$
or putting in the value of α
$$e^{a+ib} = 1 = e^a e^{ib}.$$

Thus
$$e^a = 1,\ \ b = 2k\pi,\ k \text{ an integer}.$$

Hence $a = 0$. Thus any period must have the form $2k\pi i$. But these we have already seen are periods.

We call $2\pi i$ the *primitive* period of e^z, since all its periods can be expressed as multiples of this period.

57. 1. Graphical Study of e^z. In the calculus the student has become thoroughly familiar with the notion of the graph of a function, and has seen on many occasions how useful it may be. In the function theory of a complex variable, the graph of a function is also most serviceable at times. Let us study the graph of

$$w = e^z = e^x e^{iy} = e^x(\cos y + i \sin y) \tag{1}$$

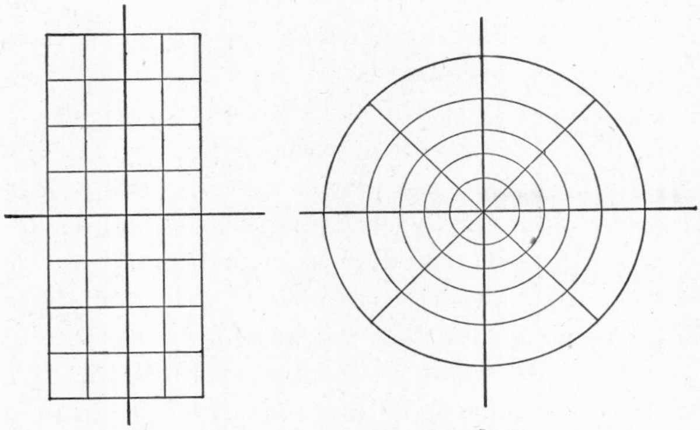

We have seen that when the variable z describes some curve C in the z-plane w will describe a curve $\mathfrak{C}$ in the w-plane, and we call $\mathfrak{C}$ the *image* of C.

Let z range over a line parallel to the x-axis. Then $z = x + ib$, where x ranges from $-\infty$ to $+\infty$, and b is constant. Let us call this parallel l. The value of w corresponding to such a z is, by 1),

$$w = e^x e^{ib}.$$

As

$$|w| = e^x \quad , \quad \text{Arg. } w = b,$$

as moreover

$$\lim_{x=-\infty} e^x = 0, \quad \lim_{x=+\infty} e^x = +\infty,$$

we see that w describes a straight line or ray $\mathfrak{r}$ issuing from $w = 0$, and making the angle b with the real axis in the w-plane. Thus to each point on l corresponds some point on $\mathfrak{r}$. As b increases from 0 to 2π, that is, as l moves parallel to itself through the distance 2π, the corresponding $\mathfrak{r}$ rotates through an angle 2π.

Let z now range over a parallel λ to the y-axis. Then $z = a + iy$, where a is constant and y ranges from $-\infty$ to $+\infty$. From 1) the value of w corresponding to such a z is

$$w = e^a e^{iy}$$

As
$$|w| = e^a \quad , \quad \text{Arg. } w = y$$

we see that the corresponding points in the w-plane lie on a circle $\mathfrak{c}$. When z moves over a segment of length 2π on the line λ, y moves over an angle of 2π, and hence w goes once around the circle $\mathfrak{c}$.

The parallels l, λ divide the z-plane into a set of rectangles R. To each such R_m corresponds in the w-plane a curvilinear rectangle $\mathfrak{R}_m$ bounded by the rays $\mathfrak{r}$ and the circles $\mathfrak{c}$. When z lies in R_m, the corresponding value of w lies in $\mathfrak{R}_m$. In this way the relation between z and the corresponding value of w is roughly given. The smaller we take the rectangles R the more accurately we will know the value of w corresponding to a given z.

Suppose now that z describes a curve C. To find approximately the curve $\mathfrak{C}$ which w describes we have only to note the points $a_1, a_2 \cdots$ where z enters and leaves the rectangles R. Then $\mathfrak{C}$ will enter and leave the corresponding rectangles $\mathfrak{R}$ at points which may be estimated roughly by proportion. The smaller we take the R, the more accurately we will be able to plot $\mathfrak{C}$.

2. Let us draw the lines

$$y = 2m\pi \quad , \quad m = \pm 1, \pm 2, \cdots$$

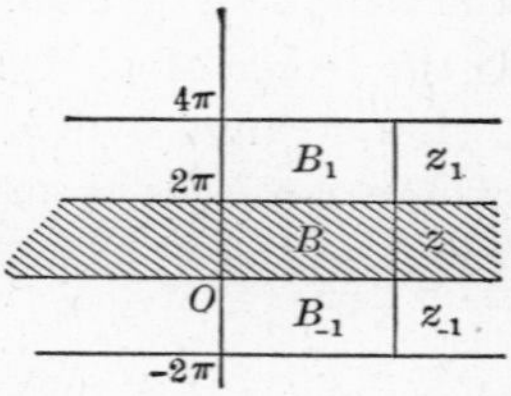

parallel to the x-axis. This divides the z-plane into a system of bands B, B_1, B_{-1}, B_2, $B_{-2} \cdots$

If we take a point $z = x + iy$ in B, the point $z_m = z + 2m\pi i$ will have the same position relative to B_m as z does to B. We say z_m is *congruent* to z. On account of the periodicity of e^z

$$e^{z_m} = e^{z+2m\pi i} = e^z.$$

Thus w has the same value at z_m as it has at z. For this reason we call these bands, *bands of periodicity*.

All the values that w can take on at any point, it takes on in any one of these bands as B. Let us show that:

The function $w = e^z$ does not take on the same value twice in B.

For say

$$z_1 = a + ib \quad , \quad z_2 = \alpha + i\beta$$

are two points in B for which $e^{z_1} = e^{z_2}$.

Then

$$e^{a+ib} = e^{\alpha+i\beta}$$

or

$$e^a e^{ib} = e^\alpha e^{i\beta}.$$

This requires that

$$e^a = e^\alpha \quad \text{or} \quad a = \alpha;$$

also that

$$b = \beta + 2\,m\pi.$$

As z_1, z_2 both lie in B we must take $m = 0$. Thus $b = \beta$. Hence $z_1 = z_2$.

Thus to each point z in B corresponds one point in the w-plane, and conversely to each point w in the w-plane corresponds just one point in B, if we agree to reckon only one of its two edges as belonging to B.

For this reason B is called a *fundamental domain* of e^z, that is, a domain in which e^z takes on every value it can take on, once and only once.

The Circular Functions

58. 1. **Addition Theorem.** We wish now to extend the definition of the circular functions to complex values. In the calculus we learn that the developments

$$\cos x = 1 - \frac{x^2}{2!} + \frac{x^4}{4!} - \cdots$$

$$\sin x = \frac{x}{1!} - \frac{x^3}{3!} + \frac{x^5}{5!} - \cdots$$

are valid for all real x. If we replace x by the complex variable z, the series on the right converge absolutely for every value of z, as we saw in 39, 4.

This affords a natural extension of the circular functions when we wish to pass from the domain of real to complex numbers. We thus set

$$\cos z = 1 - \frac{z^2}{2!} + \frac{z^4}{4!} - \cdots \tag{1}$$

$$\sin z = \frac{z}{1!} - \frac{z^3}{3!} + \frac{z^5}{5!} - \cdots \tag{2}$$

The domain of definition of these functions is the whole z-plane. When z becomes real, $\cos z$, $\sin z$ reduce to the familiar $\cos x$, $\sin x$. For real values of z therefore, $\cos z$, $\sin z$ have the properties of $\cos x$, $\sin x$.

We wish now to show that these properties still hold for complex z. The most important of all these is the *addition theorem*

$$\sin (u+v) = \sin u \cos v + \cos u \sin v, \tag{3}$$

$$\cos (u+v) = \cos u \cos v - \sin u \sin v. \tag{4}$$

Here u, v are any complex numbers. Let us establish 3). The reader may prove 4) in the same way as an exercise.

From 1), 2) we have on multiplying

$$\sin u \cos v = u - \left(\frac{u^3}{3!} + \frac{uv^2}{2!}\right) + \left(\frac{u^5}{5!} + \frac{u^3v^2}{3!\,2!} + \frac{uv^4}{1!\,4!}\right)$$

$$- \left(\frac{u^7}{7!} + \frac{u^5v^2}{5!\,2!} + \frac{u^3v^4}{3!\,4!} + \frac{uv^6}{1!\,6!}\right) + \cdots$$

$$\cos u \sin v = v - \left(\frac{v^3}{3!} + \frac{u^2v}{2!}\right) + \left(\frac{v^5}{5!} + \frac{v^3u^2}{3!\,2!} + \frac{vu^4}{1!\,4!}\right)$$

$$- \left(\frac{v^7}{7!} + \frac{v^5u^2}{5!\,2!} + \frac{v^3u^4}{3!\,4!} + \frac{vu^6}{1!\,6!}\right) + \cdots$$

Adding we get

$$\sin u \cos v + \cos u \sin v = (u+v) - \frac{1}{3!}(u+v)^3 + \frac{1}{5!}(u+v)^5 - \cdots$$

$$= \sin (u+v)$$

which is 3).

2. Since we have now defined

$$e^z \quad , \quad \cos z \quad , \quad \sin z$$

for all values of z, let us note that the relation 54, 4) holds whether y is real or not. We therefore have

$$e^{iu} = \cos u + i \sin u \tag{5}$$

for any complex u. Hence also

$$e^{u+iv} = e^u(\cos v + i \sin v) \tag{6}$$

holds for all complex u and v.

We note that 5) is a generalization of Euler's Formula, 55, 1).

Since 5) holds for complex u, we see that we may also generalize 55, 11), 12). We thus have

$$\cos u = \frac{e^{iu} + e^{-iu}}{2} \tag{7}$$

$$\sin u = \frac{e^{iu} - e^{-iu}}{2i} \tag{8}$$

and these relations hold for any complex u.

Let us set $u = z + \frac{\pi}{2}$ in 8); then

$$\sin\left(z + \frac{\pi}{2}\right) = \frac{1}{2i}\left\{e^{i\left(z+\frac{\pi}{2}\right)} - e^{-i\left(z+\frac{\pi}{2}\right)}\right\}$$

$$= \frac{1}{2i}\left\{e^{\frac{\pi i}{2}} e^{iz} - e^{-\frac{\pi i}{2}} e^{-iz}\right\}$$

$$= \tfrac{1}{2}(e^{iz} + e^{-iz}), \quad \text{by 55, 4)}$$

$$= \cos z, \quad \text{by 7)}.$$

Thus

$$\sin\left(z + \frac{\pi}{2}\right) = \cos z \quad , \quad \sin(z + \pi) = -\sin z. \tag{9}$$

etc., as for real values of z.

3. From the addition theorem we can show how to calculate $\cos z$, $\sin z$ for any complex

$$z = x + iy$$

by using ordinary logarithmic tables. We have in fact from 3)

$$\sin z = \sin(x + iy) = \sin x \cos iy + \cos x \sin iy \tag{10}$$

Now

$$\cos iy = 1 - \frac{(iy)^2}{2\,!} + \frac{(iy)^4}{4\,!} - \cdots$$

$$= 1 + \frac{y^2}{2\,!} + \frac{y^4}{4\,!} + \cdots$$

$$= \cosh y \quad \text{by 44, 2)}.$$

Thus

$$\cos iy = \cosh y \tag{11}$$

Similarly

$$\sin iy = \frac{iy}{1\,!} - \frac{(iy)^3}{3\,!} + \frac{(iy)^5}{5\,!} - \cdots$$

$$= i\left(\frac{y}{1\,!} + \frac{y^3}{3\,!} + \frac{y^5}{5\,!} + \cdots\right)$$

$$= i \sinh y, \quad \text{by 44, 3)}$$

Thus

$$\sin iy = i \sinh y. \tag{12}$$

Putting 11), 12) in 10) we get

$$\sin z = \sin(x+iy) = \sin x \cosh y + i \cos x \sinh y. \qquad (13$$

Similarly we get

$$\cos z = \cos(x+iy) = \cos x \cosh y - i \sin x \sinh y. \qquad (14$$

The formulæ 13) 14) express $\sin z$, $\cos z$ in the rectangular form $u+iv$, where u, v are known.

4. As an example let us compute

$$w = \cos z = u + iv$$

for

$$z = -1.6002 - 2.8\,i.$$

Here

$$x = -1.6002 \quad , \quad y = -2.8.$$

We first reduce x to degrees. From our tables we have

$$1^{\text{rad}} = 57^\circ\ 17'\ 45''$$

$$.6002 = 34\ \ 23\ \ 20$$

Thus

$$-x = 91^\circ\ 41' \quad \text{approximately.}$$

$$\log|\cos x| = 8.4680$$

$$\log|\sin x| = 9.9998$$

$$\log \cosh y = 0.9166$$

$$\log|\sinh y| = 0.9134$$

$$\log|u| = 9.3846 \qquad u = -.2424$$

$$\log v = 0.9132 \qquad v = 8.188$$

Hence

$$\cos z = -.2424 + 8.188\,i, \quad \text{approx.}$$

5. As an exercise in multiplying series, let us show that

$$\sin^2 z + \cos^2 z = 1. \qquad (15$$

From 1) and 2) we have

$$\sin^2 z = \frac{z^2}{1!} - z^4\left(\frac{1}{3!}+\frac{1}{3!}\right) + z^6\left(\frac{1}{5!}+\frac{1}{3!}\frac{1}{3!}+\frac{1}{5!}\right)$$

$$- z^8\left(\frac{1}{7!}+\frac{1}{3!}\frac{1}{5!}+\frac{1}{5!}\frac{1}{3!}+\frac{1}{7!}\right)+\cdots$$

$$\cos^2 z = 1 - z^2\left(\frac{1}{2!}+\frac{1}{2!}\right) + z^4\left(\frac{1}{4!}+\frac{1}{2!}\frac{1}{2!}+\frac{1}{4!}\right)$$

$$- z^6\left(\frac{1}{6!}+\frac{1}{4!}\frac{1}{2!}+\frac{1}{2!}\frac{1}{4!}+\frac{1}{6!}\right)$$

$$+ z^8\left(\frac{1}{8!}+\frac{1}{6!}\frac{1}{2!}+\frac{1}{4!}\frac{1}{4!}+\frac{1}{6!}\frac{1}{2!}+\frac{1}{8!}\right)-\cdots$$

Thus
$$\sin^2 z + \cos^2 z = 1 - \frac{z^2}{2!}\left\{1 - \binom{2}{1} + 1\right\}$$
$$+ \frac{z^4}{4!}\left\{1 - \binom{4}{1} + \binom{4}{2} - \binom{4}{3} + 1\right\} \qquad (16$$
$$- \frac{z^6}{6!}\left\{1 - \binom{6}{1} + \binom{6}{2} - \binom{6}{3} + \binom{6}{4} - \binom{6}{5} + 1\right\} + \cdots$$

Now from elementary algebra we have for a positive integer m

$$(a+b)^m = a^m + \binom{m}{1}a^{m-1}b + \binom{m}{2}a^{m-2}b^2 + \cdots + \binom{m}{m-1}ab^{m-1} + b^m. \qquad (17$$

If we set here $a = 1$, $b = -1$, it gives

$$0 = 1 - \binom{m}{1} + \binom{m}{2} - \binom{m}{3} + \cdots + (-1)^m. \qquad (18$$

This relation shows that all the $\{\cdots\}$ in 16) vanish. Thus the right side of 16) reduces to its first term, and establishes 15).

6. When a function $f(z)$ is such that

$$f(-z) = -f(z) \qquad (19$$

for all values of z for which $f(z)$ is defined we say f is an *odd function* of z. Similarly if

$$f(-z) = f(z) \qquad (20$$

we say f is an *even function*.

Since 1) involves only even powers, and 2) involves only odd powers, we have:

The function $\cos z$ is an even function, and $\sin z$ is an odd function of z.

7. Let us now define the other circular functions for complex z. This we do as in trigonometry. We set

$$\tan z = \frac{\sin z}{\cos z}, \quad \cot z = \frac{\cos z}{\sin z}, \quad \sec z = \frac{1}{\cos z}, \quad \operatorname{cosec} z = \frac{1}{\sin z}.$$

These functions are defined for all values of z for which their respective denominators do not vanish.

59. Zeros and Periodicity. 1. Let us find for what values

$$\sin z = 0. \tag{1}$$

We already know that such values are

$$z = m\pi \quad , \quad m = 0 \quad , \quad \pm 1 \quad , \quad \pm 2 \quad , \quad \cdots \tag{2}$$

We show that there are no others. Suppose in fact that

$$\sin (a + ib) = 0.$$

Then by the addition theorem 58, 13)

$$\sin a \cosh b + i \cos a \sinh b = 0.$$

Hence

$$\sin a \cosh b = 0, \tag{3}$$

$$\cos a \sinh b = 0. \tag{4}$$

Now when a product $\alpha\beta = 0$, either α or β must $= 0$. Thus in 3) since $\cosh b$ does not vanish at all [44, 2], we must have $\sin a = 0$. Thus $a = m\pi$. Putting this value of a in 4) it gives

$$\sinh b = 0.$$

But this requires [44, 2] that $b = 0$. We thus get the important result :

The function $\sin z$ has the same zeros as the real function $\sin x$; they are given by 2).

From 58, 9) we see that the zeros of $\cos z$ are

$$\frac{\pi}{2} + m\pi \quad , \quad m = 0 \quad , \quad \pm 1 \quad , \quad \pm 2 \cdots$$

as for real $\cos x$.

2. Let us now investigate the *periodicity* of

$$w = \sin z.$$

From 58, 9) we have

$$\sin (z + 2\, m\pi) = \sin z \quad , \quad m = \pm 1 \quad , \quad \pm 2 \quad , \quad \cdots$$

Thus $2\, m\pi$ are periods. Let us show that there are no others. For say $a + ib$ were a period. Then for all values of z we would have

$$\sin (z + a + ib) = \sin z.$$

In this relation set $z = 0$; it gives

$$\sin(a + ib) = 0.$$

But this equation is satisfied, as we saw in 1, only when

$$a = n\pi \quad , \quad b = 0.$$

Thus all the periods of $\sin z$ must be included among the numbers $n\pi$. But among these we know only those are periods for which n is even, or $n = 2m$. We have thus established:

The periods of $\sin z$ are $2m\pi$. $m = \pm 1, \pm 2, \cdots$

Since all of these are multiples of 2π, this is called the *primitive period.*

60. Graphical Study of $w = \sin z$. Let z describe a parallel l to the x-axis. Then $z = x + ib$ where b is constant. Then

$$\begin{aligned} w &= \sin(x + ib) = \sin x \cosh b + i \cos x \sinh b \\ &= u + iv. \end{aligned}$$

Thus to the point z whose coördinates are x, b corresponds in the w-plane a point whose coördinates are

$$u = \sin x \cosh b, \quad v = \cos x \sinh b. \tag{1}$$

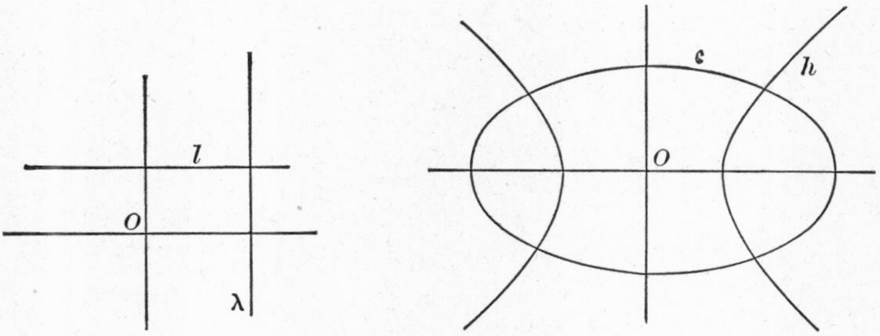

Thus the image $\mathfrak{e}$ of the line l is the curve whose equations in parameter form are 1). As $\sin x$, $\cos x$ have the period 2π, we see that when z describes a segment of l of length 2π, w comes back to its original position in the w-plane. The curve 1) is thus closed. It is in fact an ellipse. For

$$\begin{aligned} \frac{u^2}{\cosh^2 b} + \frac{v^2}{\sinh^2 b} &= \sin^2 x + \cos^2 x \\ &= 1. \end{aligned} \tag{2}$$

Next we let z range over a parallel λ to the y-axis. Then $z = a + iy$, where a is constant. As before we have

$$w = \sin(a + iy) = \sin a \cosh y + i \cos a \sinh y$$
$$= u + iv$$

so that

$$u = \sin a \cosh y, \qquad v = \cos a \sinh y. \tag{3}$$

As z ranges over λ, w will describe a curve $\mathfrak{h}$ whose parametric equations are 3). As before we have

$$\frac{u^2}{\sin^2 a} - \frac{v^2}{\cos^2 a} = \cosh^2 y - \sinh^2 y$$
$$= 1, \text{ by 44, 4)}. \tag{4}$$

Thus $\mathfrak{h}$ is a hyperbola.

The ellipses 2) and the hyperbolas 4) are confocal and hence cut each other orthogonally.

The parallels l, λ divide the z-plane into a set of rectangles R, to which corresponds a set of curvilinear rectangles $\mathfrak{R}$. When z lies in some R_m, the corresponding value of w will lie in the image $\mathfrak{R}_m$ of R_m. Thus the smaller the rectangles R are taken the smaller the rectangles $\mathfrak{R}$ become and therefore the more accurate is our knowledge of the true value of w.

The Hyperbolic Functions

61. For any complex z we define

$$\cosh z = \frac{e^z + e^{-z}}{2} = 1 + \frac{z^2}{2!} + \frac{z^4}{4!} + \cdots \tag{1}$$

$$\sinh z = \frac{e^z - e^{-z}}{2} = \frac{z}{1!} + \frac{z^3}{3!} + \frac{z^5}{5!} + \cdots \tag{2}$$

From these we further define

$$\tanh z = \frac{\sinh z}{\cosh x}, \quad \coth z = \frac{\cosh z}{\sinh z}, \tag{3}$$

$$\operatorname{sech} z = \frac{1}{\cosh z}, \quad \operatorname{cosech} z = \frac{1}{\sinh z}. \tag{4}$$

We saw in 39, 4 that the series 1), 2) converge absolutely for every value of z. The domain of definition of $\sinh z$, $\cosh z$ is therefore the whole z-plane. That of the four functions 3) 4) is the whole z-plane except those points for which their respective denominators vanish.

Since we have now defined

$$\sin z \quad , \quad \cos z \quad , \quad \sinh z \quad , \quad \cosh z$$

for all values of z, the relations 58, 11), 12) are not restricted to real y as we easily see, but hold for any complex value.

We have therefore the important relations connecting the circular and hyperbolic functions, viz.:

$$\cos iz = \cosh z, \tag{5}$$

$$\sin iz = i \sinh z, \tag{6}$$

$$\tan iz = i \tanh z, \text{ etc.} \tag{7}$$

These relations show that all the analytical properties of the hyperbolic functions may be deduced from the corresponding relations between the circular functions.

Thus the addition theorem

$$\sin(u + v) = \sin u \cos v + \cos u \sin v$$

gives

$$\begin{aligned} \sin i(u + v) &= i \sinh(u + v) \\ &= \sin iu \cos iv + \cos iu \sin iv \\ &= i \sinh u \cosh v + i \cosh u \sinh v, \end{aligned}$$

or dividing by i,

$$\sinh(u + v) = \sinh u \cosh v + \cosh u \sinh v. \tag{8}$$

Similarly

$$\cos(u + v) = \cos u \cos v - \sin u \sin v$$

gives

$$\cosh(u + v) = \cosh u \cosh v + \sinh u \sinh v. \tag{9}$$

The formulæ 8), 9) express the *addition theorem* of the sinh and cosh functions.

Again the relation

$$\sin^2 u + \cos^2 u = 1$$

becomes on replacing u by iu

$$\sin^2 iu + \cos^2 iu = 1,$$

or

$$\cosh^2 u - \sinh^2 u = 1, \tag{10}$$

and so on.

In a similar manner, when we have considered differentiation and integration, we shall see that all formulæ involving these operations on circular functions go over into corresponding formulæ for the hyperbolic functions on using the relations 5), 6).

A student of a new subject is naturally eager to see its usefulness made manifest as soon as possible. We submit the results just obtained as an example. As another example we recall the treatment of analytic trigonometry founded on Euler's formula which we indicated in 55. We adduce also the elegant manner of establishing the formulæ of 6. Other examples will occur as we advance.

Logarithms

62. 1. In the equation

$$e^w = z \tag{1}$$

let us find the values of w corresponding to a given z. We set

$$w = u + iv \quad , \quad z = re^{i\theta}. \tag{2}$$

Here r, θ are known, and we are to find u, v. Putting 2) in 1) gives

$$e^u e^{iv} = re^{i\theta}. \tag{3}$$

Equating moduli, we have $e^u = r$, whence

$$u = \log r. \tag{4}$$

Equating arguments in 3) gives

$$v = \theta + 2\,\pi m \quad , \quad m \text{ an integer.} \tag{5}$$

This shows that all values of w which satisfy 1) must have the form

$$w = \log r + i\theta + 2\,m\pi i. \tag{6}$$

If we set these values of w in 1) we see that they do in fact satisfy it. Thus 6) is the solution of 1). We call it the logarithm of z, and write

$$w = \log z. \tag{7}$$

There is a slight ambiguity which custom and usefulness sanction. In 6) the symbol $\log r$ means the logarithm of algebra. For each positive r, $\log r$ has one and only one value. On the other hand the symbol $\log z$ has an infinity of values, viz. those given in 6). As the reader is never seriously in doubt which of the two meanings the symbol *log* has, there is no need of denoting w by a new symbol, as $\operatorname{Log} z$ for example.

2. In algebra $y = \log x$ is defined by

$$e^y = x. \tag{8}$$

But here x is restricted to positive values. By enlarging our number system, the equation 8) admits a solution whatever value x has, the value $x = 0$ excepted. In doing this we find, however, not one but an infinity of solutions as given in 6). If we allow z to range over a curve, the corresponding values of w will trace out an infinity of congruent curves or *branches*. Each value of $m = 0, \pm 1, \pm 2, \cdots$ in 6) will give one of these branches. The branch corresponding to $m = 0$ we will call the *principal branch*. The branch belonging to a special value of m as n, say, we may denote by $\log_n z$.

Thus

$$w_n = \log_n z = \log r + i\theta + 2\,n\pi i. \tag{9}$$

3. The relation

$$\log xy = \log x + \log y \tag{10}$$

established in algebra for positive x, y is called the *addition theorem* of logarithms. It is an immediate consequence of

$$e^x e^y = e^{x+y}$$

A similar relation holds in the complex domain. For let

$$u = re^{i\theta} \quad , \quad v = se^{i\phi}.$$

Then

$$uv = rse^{i(\theta+\phi)}.$$

Hence by 2) and 6)

$$\begin{aligned} \log uv &= \log (rs) + i(\theta + \phi) + 2\,n\pi i \qquad (11 \\ &= (\log r + i\theta + 2\,n'\pi i) + (\log s + i\phi + 2\,n''\pi i) \end{aligned}$$

when n', n'' are any two integers such that

$$n' + n'' = n.$$

Thus 11) may be written, using 9)

$$\log_n(uv) = \log_{n'} u + \log_{n''} v. \tag{12}$$

If we leave the symbol *log* undetermined, we may write 11)

$$\log uv = \log u + \log v. \tag{13}$$

The relations 12), 13) express the *addition theorem* of the logarithm in the complex domain. They are the generalization of 10).

4. Let us find the *zeros of log z*. If we set

$$w = \log z = u + iv,$$

we have

$$|w| = \sqrt{u^2 + v^2}$$
$$= \sqrt{\log^2 r + (\theta + 2m\pi)^2}.$$

This being the sum of two squares cannot vanish unless

$$\log r = 0 \quad , \quad \theta + 2m\pi = 0,$$

or unless

$$r = 1 \quad , \quad \theta = -2m\pi,$$

that is,

$$z = 1.$$

Since $\log 1 = 0$ this shows that: —

The function log z has one and only one zero, viz.: $z = 1$.

5. *Branch Points.* Let z describe in the positive direction a circle of radius r about the origin. Then r in 2) remains constant while θ increases from say $\theta = \theta_0$ to $\theta = \theta_0 + 2\pi$. If we start with the value of w corresponding to $\theta = \theta_0$ in 9), w_n will acquire at the end of the circuit the value

$$\overline{w}_n = \log r + i(\theta_0 + 2\pi) + 2n\pi i$$
$$= \log r + i\theta_0 + 2(n+1)\pi i$$
$$= w_{n+1}.$$

Thus a circuit about the origin in the positive direction converts each branch w_n into w_{n+1}.

Suppose now that z passes around C in the negative direction. Then θ decreases from say $\theta = \theta_0$ to $\theta = \theta_0 - 2\pi$. Thus w_n will have at the end of the circuit the value

$$w_n = \log r + i(\theta_0 - 2\pi) + 2n\pi i$$
$$= \log r + i\theta_0 + 2(n-1)\pi i$$
$$= w_{n-1}.$$

Thus a circuit about the origin in the negative direction converts each branch w_n into w_{n-1}.

Finally, let z describe a closed curve $\mathfrak{C}$ which does not include the origin as in the Figure. In this case both r and θ vary as z moves over $\mathfrak{C}$. But if z starts from the point $z = z_0$ for which $r = r_0$, $\theta = \theta_0$ as in the Figure, obviously r and θ acquire these same values when z has returned to z_0. Thus if we start out with the value of w corresponding to $r = r_0$, $\theta = \theta_0$ in 9), w_n will have this same value when z has returned to z_0. Hence each w_n remains unaltered when z describes a closed curve which does not enclose the origin $z = 0$.

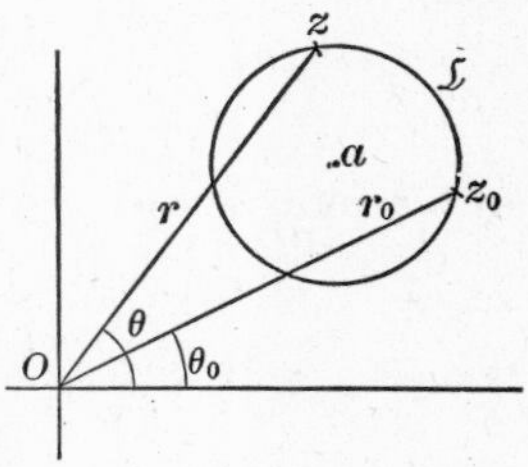

Since the branches w_n permute when z describes a circuit about the origin $z = 0$, this point is called a *branch point*. There is no other point in the z-plane having this property; that is, $z = 0$ is the only branch point of the logarithmic function $w = \log z$.

Since $\log x$ in the real domain is not defined for $x = 0$, it follows that the formula 6) has no meaning for $r = 0$; that is, when $z = 0$. Thus the domain of definition of w is the whole z-plane excepting $z = 0$.

63. The Function z^μ. 1. Letting μ denote any complex number, we define the symbol

$$z^\mu \text{ by } z^\mu = e^{\mu \log z} \tag{1}$$

Let

$$z = re^{i\phi},$$

then

$$\log z = \log r + i\phi + 2\, s\pi i, \qquad s \text{ an integer.}$$

Hence 1) gives

$$z^\mu = e^{\mu \log r} e^{\mu i \phi} e^{2 s \mu \pi i}. \tag{2}$$

Let us consider special cases of the exponent μ.

1° *μ a positive integer m.* As

$$e^{2ms\pi i} = 1,$$

2) becomes

$$z^m = e^{m \log r} e^{m i \phi}.$$

But by algebra,

$$e^{m \log r} = r^m.$$

Hence

$$z^m = r^m e^{m i \phi} \tag{3}$$

$$= z \cdot z \cdot \cdots z, \quad m \text{ times},$$

which agrees with 4, 4).

2° *μ a negative integer.* Let $\mu = -n$. Then we find

$$z^{-n} = r^{-n}e^{-ni\phi} = \frac{1}{z^n},$$

as in algebra.

3° $\mu = \frac{m}{n}$, *a fraction.* Here

$$e^{2s\mu\pi i} = e^{s\cdot\frac{m}{n}\cdot 2\pi i} = \omega,$$

an nth root of unity by 55, 5).

Also

$$e^{\mu\log r} = e^{\frac{m}{n}\log r} = \sqrt[n]{r^m}.$$

Hence

$$z^{\frac{m}{n}} = \sqrt[n]{r^m}\cdot\omega\cdot e^{\frac{m\phi}{n}i}, \tag{4}$$

as in algebra. Here the radical

$$\sqrt[n]{r^m}$$

has the value heretofore assigned to it; that is, it is the positive real root of the positive real number r^m. One often denotes the right side of 4) by

$$\sqrt[n]{z^m}.$$

4° *μ a real number not a fraction, and z real and positive.* Let us denote this value of z by a. Here $\phi = 0$, $r = a$. Then

$$e^{\mu\log r} = e^{\mu\log a} = a^\mu,$$

as is shown in algebra. Then 2) gives

$$z^\mu = a^\mu e^{2s\mu\pi i} \quad , \quad s = 0, \pm 1, \pm 2 \cdots \tag{5}$$

This shows that in this case z^μ has an infinity of values, each differing from the others by a factor of the form

$$e^{2s\mu\pi i}.$$

For

$$s = 0 \quad , \quad z^\mu = a^\mu.$$

2. From the foregoing it follows that the function 1) is in general infinite-valued, as the logarithm is. If we give to $\log z$ a definite one of its many values, the exponent on the right side of 1) takes on a definite value, as v, say. Then 1) gives z^μ as the absolutely convergent series

$$z^\mu = 1 + \frac{v}{1!} + \frac{v^2}{2!} + \frac{v^3}{3!} + \cdots$$

Its value is thus completely determined.

3. Suppose μ is not a positive or negative integer or 0. Then $z = 0$ is a branch point of z^μ. For if we start at $z = a$ with one of the many values of $w = z^\mu$, w will not have this value when z describes a circuit about the origin.

Since $z = 0$ is the only branch point of $\log z$, the only branch point of w is also $z = 0$. That is to say, if we start at $z = a$ with one of the many values of w, as w_a, and allow z to describe a closed curve, which does not enclose the origin, w will return to its original value w_a when z returns to $z = a$.

Inverse Circular Functions

64. 1. In trigonometry we learn that the equation

$$\sin y = x \tag{1}$$

has two sets of solutions y when $0 \leq x \leq 1$. If $y = y_0$ is one solution of 1), all solutions are given by

$$\begin{aligned} y &= y_0 + 2\,m\pi, \\ y &= \pi - y_0 + 2\,n\pi, \end{aligned} \qquad m, n = 0, \pm 1, \pm 2, \cdots \tag{2}$$

Thus 1) defines an infinite-valued function which is denoted by

$$y = \sin^{-1} x \text{ or } y = \text{arc} \sin x.$$

Of these two, we shall employ the latter only.

Let us now pass to the domain of complex numbers. We seek the solution w of

$$\sin w = z \tag{3}$$

where z is any given complex number.

Now by 58, 8)

$$\sin w = \frac{e^{iw} - e^{-iw}}{2\,i}.$$

This in 3) gives

$$e^{2iw} - 2\,ize^{iw} = 1,$$

or setting

$$t = e^{iw},$$

we get

$$t^2 - 2\,izt = 1.$$

Solving this for t, we get

$$e^{iw} = iz + \sqrt{1 - z^2}, \tag{4}$$

where the radical may have either of its two values. From 4) we have, taking the logarithm of both sides,

$$w = \frac{1}{i} \log \{iz + \sqrt{1 - z^2}\}. \tag{5}$$

As the log is infinite-valued and as the radical may have either sign, we see that 3) admits a twofold infinity of solutions. If we denote these solutions by arc sin z, we have

$$w = \text{arc} \sin z = \frac{1}{i} \log \{iz + \sqrt{1 - z^2}\}. \tag{6}$$

2. Let us show that the relations 2) still hold for complex values. Let us set

$$iz + \sqrt{1 - z^2} = Z_1,$$

$$iz - \sqrt{1 - z^2} = Z_2.$$

Then if

$$L_1 = \log Z_1$$

is one of the determinations of log Z_1, all the other determinations of log Z_1 are given by

$$L_1 + 2\, m\pi i,$$

as we saw in 62. Thus if

$$u = \frac{1}{i} \log_r \{iz + \sqrt{1 - z^2}\} = \frac{1}{i} \log Z_1$$

is one of the values of 5) when the radical is taken with the positive sign, all the other values of 5) for this determination of the radical are given by

$$u + 2\, m\pi \quad , \quad m \text{ an integer.} \tag{7}$$

Similarly if

$$v = \frac{1}{i} \log_s \{iz - \sqrt{1 - z^2}\} = \frac{1}{i} \log Z_2$$

is one of the values of 5) when the radical has the negative sign, all the other values of 5) for this determination of the radical are given by

$$v + 2\, m\pi \quad , \quad m \text{ an integer.} \tag{8}$$

Now

$$u + v = \frac{1}{i} \log Z_1 Z_2, \tag{9}$$

the logarithm on the right being properly determined. But

$$Z_1 Z_2 = -1$$

and

$$\log(-1) = \pi i + 2n\pi i.$$

Thus 9) gives

$$u + v = \pi + 2n\pi,$$

or

$$v = \pi - u + \text{a multiple of } 2\pi.$$

Putting this value of v in 8) it becomes

$$\pi - u + 2s\pi \quad , \quad s \text{ an integer.} \tag{10}$$

Thus all the values 6), that is, of arc sin z, are given by 7) and 10). We have therefore shown:

If $w = w_0$ is a solution of 3), all solutions of 3) are given by

$$w = w_0 + 2m\pi \quad , \quad w = \pi - w_0 + 2m\pi, \tag{11}$$

where

$$m = 0 \quad , \quad \pm 1, \pm 2 \cdots$$

3. Since $z = 1$, $z = -1$ are branch points of

$$\sqrt{1 - z^2} = \sqrt{-(z-1)(z+1)},$$

we see that when z describes a small circuit C about one of them, Z_1 and Z_2 permute. Thus if at $z = z_0$ we start out with one of the values of w at this point, say $w = w_0$, and allow z to pass around C, w will not return to its original value w_0 when z returns to z_0. Thus $z = 1$, and $z = -1$ are branch points of w.

Let us see if there are any other branch points for $w =$ arc sin z. Since $z = 1$, $z = -1$ are the only branch points of

$$Z = iz + \sqrt{1 - z^2},$$

the only other branch points of w must be branch points of log Z, that is, points $z = a$ for which $Z = 0$. But the relation

$$ia + \sqrt{1 - a^2} = 0$$

gives

$$-a^2 = 1 - a^2,$$

or

$$1 = 0,$$

which is absurd. We have thus shown that:

The branch points of the function

$$w = \text{arc sin } z$$

are the points $z = 1$, $z = -1$, and only these.

4. In a precisely similar manner we may define and study the other inverse circular functions

$$\text{arc}\cos z \quad , \quad \text{arc}\tan z \quad , \quad \text{etc.}$$

We will not take space to do this, as it is all too obvious. We note, however, that the solution of the equation

$$\tan w = z \tag{12}$$

is

$$w = \frac{1}{2i}\log\frac{1+iz}{1-iz} = \text{arc}\tan z. \tag{13}$$

Its branch points are

$$z = i \text{ and } z = -i.$$

CHAPTER V

REAL VARIABLES

65. Many readers of this book have studied the calculus chiefly with the view of learning its technique and of applying it to geometry, mechanics, physics, etc. Such students have little time to spend on demonstrations, and it is natural that their ideas of the limiting processes which lie at the base of all the principles and method of the calculus are often vague. It seems best, therefore, to insert a chapter at this point whose object is to briefly treat such topics of the calculus as we shall need in the course of this work. It will be our purpose rather to refresh the reader's memory and to illuminate the subject than to repeat demonstrations or to discuss delicate points. One may therefore, turn over the following pages, reading such parts as are not quite familiar; or he may pass at once to the next chapter and return to this one when further explanations are necessary.

66. Notion of a Function. 1. The functions used in the calculus are usually made up of simple combinations of the elementary functions, as

$$y = \sin x + \frac{1+\sqrt{1-x^2}}{\log x}, \tag{1}$$

$$u = \frac{e^{x+y^2}\sin xy}{\tan(x+y)} + \sqrt{\sin y}. \tag{2}$$

Or they are defined implicitly by equations between such functions, as for example,

$$\frac{x^2}{a^2} + \frac{y^2}{b^2} - 1 = 0. \tag{3}$$

The equation 1) defines y as a function of the independent variable x. But when $x \leq 0$, $\log x$ has no sense, the variables being real. Also $\sqrt{1-x^2}$ is not real when $x^2 > 1$. Finally, when $x=1$, $\log x = 0$, and the denominator in 1) vanishes. Thus 1) defines y only for $0 < x < 1$. These values of x form the *domain of definition* of y.

2. Let us turn now to 2). This relation defines u as a function of two variables x, y. We note that the denominator either $=0$ or is not defined when the point x, y lies on one of the lines,

$$x + y = m \cdot \frac{\pi}{2}, \qquad m = 0, \pm 1, \pm 2 \cdots \tag{4}$$

Also the radical $\sqrt{\sin y}$ is not real when $\sin y$ is negative, that is, when

$$(2n-1)\pi < y < 2n\pi, \qquad n = 0, \pm 1, \pm 2 \cdots \tag{5}$$

The domain of definition of u embraces thus that part of x, y plane after removing the lines 4) and the bands 5) which are parallel to the x-axis and of width π.

3. It is convenient to generalize our definition of a function. To fix the ideas, let us take a single independent variable x. Let us mark a certain set of points on the x-axis and denote them by $\mathfrak{A}$. At each value of x in $\mathfrak{A}$, let us assign to y one or more values according to some law. Then we call y a function of x, and we call $\mathfrak{A}$ its domain of definition.

To illustrate this let us take the function 1). For the point set $\mathfrak{A}$ we take the values of x such that $0 < x < 1$, that is, the interval $(0, 1)$ except the end points. The value we assign to y for a given x in $\mathfrak{A}$ is the value that the right side of 1) has for this value of x.

Another illustration would be the temperature y at a given place at a given time x. If we were concerned only with temperatures from the time $x = a$, to the time $x = b$, these would define y as a function of x in the interval $\mathfrak{A} = (a, b)$, and this would be its domain of definition. This would be an example of a function which is not defined by an analytic expression as in 1).

As an illustration of a function of two variables not defined by an analytic expression we may take the following. Let x denote the latitude and y the longitude expressed in circular measure of a point on the earth's surface. Let u denote the temperature at the earth's surface at one and the same instant. As the latitude is restricted to lie between $-\frac{\pi}{2}$ and $\frac{\pi}{2}$, and the longitude between $-\pi$ and π, we see the domain of definition of u is the rectangle

$$-\frac{\pi}{2} \leq x \leq \frac{\pi}{2} \quad , \quad -\pi \leq y \leq \pi.$$

67. Limits. 1. We have already discussed the notion of a limit of a sequence of numbers

$$a_1, a_2, a_3, \cdots \tag{1}$$

when studying series. In the calculus we use the notion of limit also in another way. Thus in defining the derivative of a function $y = f(x)$ we form the difference quotient

$$\frac{\Delta y}{\Delta x} = \frac{f(x+h) - f(x)}{h} \tag{2}$$

and allow the increment $h = \Delta x$ to converge to 0 by passing over all values near $h = 0$. The value $h = 0$ is excluded, since this would make the denominator in 2) vanish. What do we mean by the limit of 2) as $h \doteq 0$? The value of x being fixed, the quotient 2) is a function of h; let us denote this by $q(h)$. If now $q(h)$ converges to some fixed value l as $h \doteq 0$, we mean that q may be made to differ from l by an amount as small as we please, say by $< \epsilon$, provided h remains numerically $<$ some positive number δ.

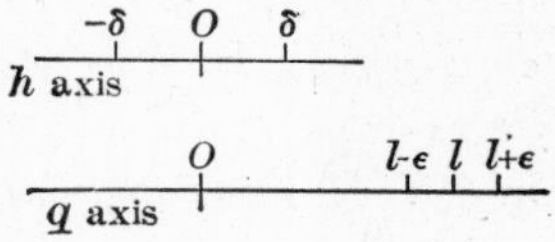

Graphically we may state this as follows. Let us plot the values of q for values of h near $h = 0$, on an axis which we may call the q-axis. With l as a center we may lay off an interval of length 2ϵ. Then if $q \doteq l$ as $h \doteq 0$, there must exist an interval $(-\delta, \delta)$ on the h-axis such that q falls within the ϵ interval when $h \neq 0$ is restricted to lie within the δ interval.

This graphical formulation of the notion of a limit may be put in analytic form. By the phrase $q(h) \doteq l$ as $h \doteq 0$ we mean that for each $\epsilon > 0$, there exists a $\delta > 0$ such that

$$|q(h) - l| < \epsilon$$

provided $$0 < |h| < \delta.$$

The reader should think this over carefully and see that this analytic formulation exactly represents the above graphical formulation.

2. This notion of the limit is used in many other parts of the calculus. We will therefore state the definition quite generally.

Let the function $y = f(x)$ be one-valued about the point $x = a$. When we say $f(x) \doteq l$ as $x \doteq a$ or otherwise expressed that the limit of $f(x) = l$ for $x = a$, in symbols

$$\lim_{x=a} f(x) = l, \tag{3}$$

we mean this:

For each $\epsilon > 0$ *there exists a* $\delta > 0$ *such that* $|f(x) - l| < \epsilon$ *provided* $0 < |x - a| < \delta$.

The last sentence will be expressed more briefly by a line of symbols,

$$\epsilon > 0 \quad , \quad \delta > 0 \quad , \quad |f(x) - l| < \epsilon \quad , \quad 0 < |x - a| < \delta, \tag{4}$$

and such a line of symbols is to be read as the sentence above in italics.

3. The reader will note the similarity of this definition and that employed in 16.

Almost all students dislike this ϵ form of the definition when first presented to them. It seems so much easier to think of $f(x)$ converging to l as x converges to a. Why bother about these ϵ's and δ's? In reply we refer the student to the remarks made in 16. Fortunately the intuitive form of the definition of f converging to its limit is usually quite sufficient, and we shall avoid the ϵ's as much as possible. When we do employ them, it will be to aid clear thinking. When the reader can think clearly without the ϵ's, let him do without them.

4. The reader should note that when the limit 3) exists, $f(x) \doteq l$ when x converges to a from the right side, or when it converges to a from the left. For by the definition given in 2, the only restriction on x is to remain in the δ interval, excluding, of course, the value $x = a$. It can therefore approach a from either side, and $f(x)$ must $\doteq l$ in either case.

5. From the definition of a limit we conclude that when 3) holds, we may write

$$f(x) = l + \epsilon' \tag{5}$$

and know that $|\epsilon'| < \epsilon$ provided x lies in some δ interval. We may also say in this case that $\epsilon' \doteq 0$ as $x \doteq a$.

68. Limits for Two Variables. Let us now consider limits of a function of two variables. Suppose the one-valued function is defined in a certain domain $\mathfrak{A}$. Let $x = a$, $y = b$ be a point α of $\mathfrak{A}$ Then $u(a, b)$ is the value of u at the point α. More briefly we may denote this value by $u(\alpha)$.

Let us describe a circle of radius δ about α. The points x, y within this circle may be called the *domain* of this point of *norm* δ, and denoted by any one of the symbols

$$D_\delta(a, b) \quad , \quad D(a, b) \quad , \quad D_\delta(\alpha) \quad , \quad D(\alpha).$$

The simpler forms may be used when no ambiguity can arise.

When the center α of this domain is *excluded*, we indicate this fact by a star, thus D^*.

What now do we mean when we say: u converges to l as the point $\xi = x, y$ converges to $\alpha = a, b$? In symbols

$$u \doteq l \quad , \quad \text{as } \xi \doteq \alpha.$$

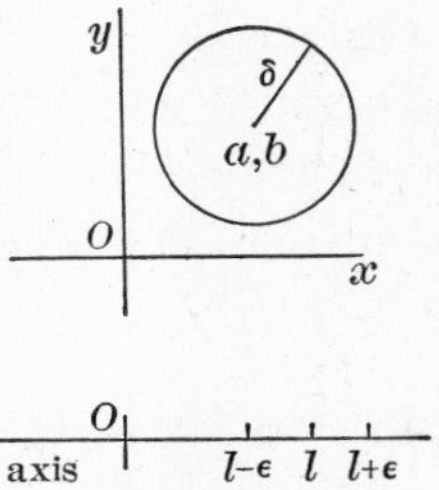

We mean just this: Let us plot the values of u on an axis, the u-axis. With l as a center we lay off the ϵ interval as in the figure. About the point $\alpha = a, b$ we describe the δ circle in the x, y plane of radius δ as in the figure. Then for each ϵ interval there must exist a δ circle such that u remains within this interval when the point x, y remains within this circle, the center a, b excluded.

Analytically we may formulate this as follows:

The limit of $u(x, y)$ for $x = a$, $y = b$ is l, or in symbols,

$$\lim_{x=a,\, y=b} u(x, y) = l$$

when for each $\epsilon > 0$, there exists a $\delta > 0$ such that

$$|u(x, y) - l| < \epsilon$$

when x, y lies in $D_\delta^*(a, b)$.

The reader will note that the definition of a limit for a single variable is a special case of the one just given, the domain of the point $\alpha = a, b$ reducing to an interval.

He should also notice that in passing to the limit the point x, y is never allowed to become $\alpha = a, b$; that is, x, y ranges in $D^*(\alpha)$ and not in $D(\alpha)$.

69. Continuity. 1. Let $y=f(x)$ be a one-valued function in the interval $\mathfrak{A} = (p, q)$ whose graph is given in Fig. 1. The graph shows that y is continuous in $\mathfrak{A}$ except at the point $x = b$. Let us formulate the notion of continuity analytically. To this end we note how $f(x)$ behaves at a point of continuity as $x = a$, and about the point of discontinuity $x = b$.

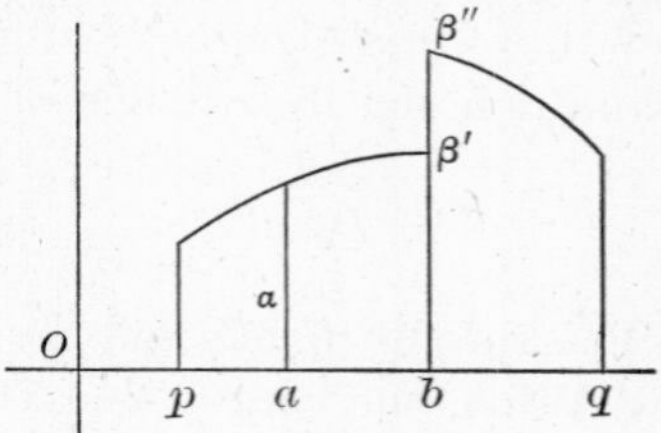

FIG. 1.

Let $f(x)$ have the value α at $x = a$. Then as $x \doteq a$, we see that $y \doteq \alpha$; in symbols

$$\lim_{x=a} f(x) = f(a) = \alpha.$$

On the other hand, at the point $x = b$, the ordinate does not converge to a definite value. For when $x = b$ on the left $y \doteq \beta'$; when $x \doteq b$ on the right, $y \doteq \beta''$. But if the reader will turn back to 67, 4, he will see that when

$$\lim_{x=b} f(x)$$

exists, $f(x)$ must converge to the same value whether $x \doteq b$ on one side or on the other.

Another case of discontinuity is illustrated by Fig. 2. Here $y = f(x)$ is a one-valued function whose value at $x = a$ is defined to be $y = \alpha$. The figure shows that

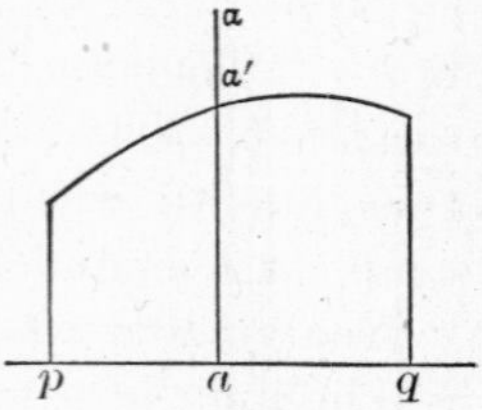

FIG. 2.

$$\lim_{x=a} f(x) = \alpha'.$$

Here the limit exists, but its value is not the value that $f(x)$ has assigned to it at this point which is α.

These considerations lead us to say:

The function $f(x)$ is continuous at $x = a$ when and only when $f(x)$ converges to the value of f at a, that is, when

$$\lim_{x=a} f(x) = f(a).$$

Therefore if $\lim f(x)$ does not exist at $x = a$, or if it exists but has a value different from the value $f(a)$, then we must say that f is *discontinuous* at $x = a$. If $f(x)$ is continuous at each point of an interval $\mathfrak{A} = (p, q)$ we say f is *continuous in* $\mathfrak{A}$.

2. When $f(x)$ is continuous at $x = a$, we know that the value of $f(x)$ differs from its value at $x = a$ by an amount as small as we please if x is only kept sufficiently near a. In symbols

$$f(x) = f(a) + \epsilon' \qquad (1$$

where $\epsilon' \doteq 0$ as $x \doteq a$. This is the same as saying that

$$|\epsilon'| < \epsilon \quad , \quad \text{providing } |x - a| < \text{ some } \delta. \qquad (2$$

3. Let $f(x)$ be continuous in $\mathfrak{A} = (p, q)$. Let us take $\epsilon > 0$ at pleasure and fix it. At any point $x = a$ we lay off the δ interval about a as in Fig. 3 such that the ϵ' in 1) satisfies the inequality 2). Let us pass to another point b in $\mathfrak{A}$ and lay off the corresponding δ interval about b, such that ϵ' again satisfies 2). At the point $x = b$ the curve is steeper than at a, and therefore the δ interval at b is shorter than at a, that is, the value of δ at b is less than at a. The reader will note, however, that as a ranges from p to q the value of δ corresponding to the different values of a will never sink below some positive number η. In other words, for the value of ϵ that we have been using, there exists an $\eta > 0$ such that $f(x)$ differs from $f(a)$ by an amount $< \epsilon$ when $|x - a| < \eta$; and here a is any point in $\mathfrak{A}$.

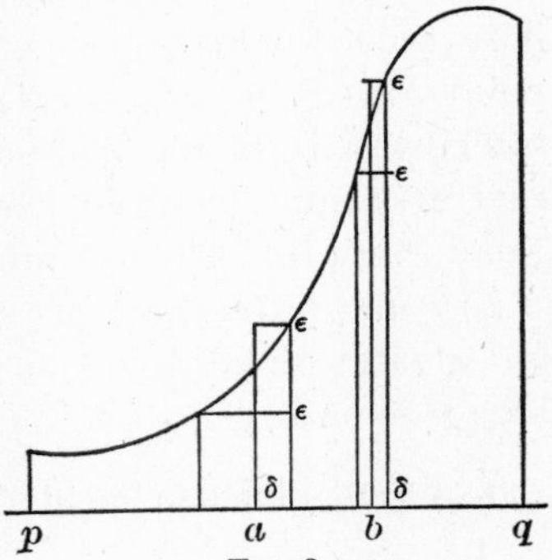

FIG. 3.

If we expressed this in symbols, we would say that for each $\epsilon > 0$, and for any and all points a in $\mathfrak{A}$, there exists a fixed $\eta > 0$ such that

$$|f(x) - f(a)| < \epsilon \quad , \quad \text{provided } |x - a| < \eta. \qquad (3$$

Or what is the same,

$$f(x) = f(a) + \epsilon',$$

where

$$|\epsilon'| < \epsilon \quad \text{provided} \quad |x - a| < \eta. \qquad (4$$

This important property of a continuous function in an interval $\mathfrak{A}$ is expressed by saying that $f(x)$ converges uniformly to $f(a)$ in $\mathfrak{A}$; or in symbols

$$f(x) \doteq f(a) \text{ uniformly in } \mathfrak{A}.$$

The reader should remember that here a is a variable point in the interval $\mathfrak{A}$.

4. When $f(x)$ has a point of discontinuity in $\mathfrak{A} = (p, q)$ as at $x = e$ in Fig. 4, the reader will see at once that taking $\epsilon > 0$ small enough and then fixing it, there is no corresponding $\eta > 0$ such that 3) or 4) holds wherever a is taken in $\mathfrak{A}$. To make this perfectly clear we have taken ϵ as in Fig. 4, and laid off the corresponding δ interval at a point a.

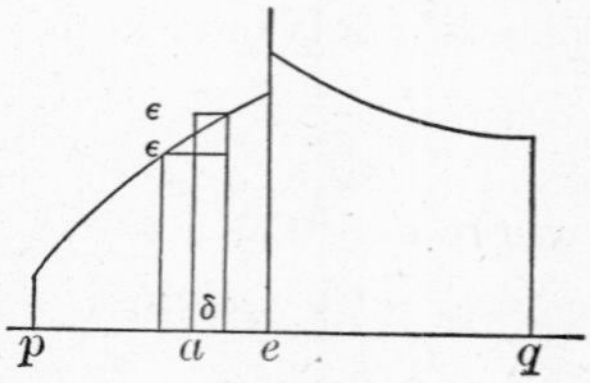

FIG. 4.

The reader will see at once that for a point b very near e, the length of the δ interval will be determined by the fact that it cannot contain the point $x = e$. For in any interval containing this point $f(x)$ could differ from $f(b)$ by an amount far greater than the small quantity ϵ, as Fig. 5 shows.

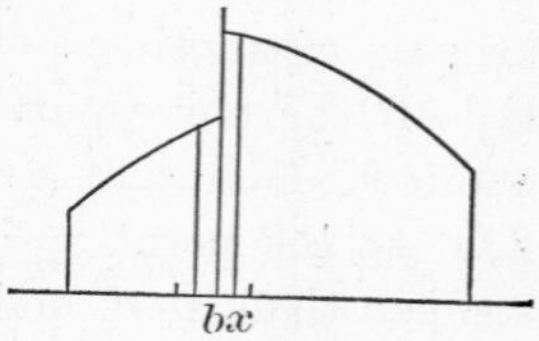

FIG. 5.

5. Finally let us consider the function

$$f(x) = \tan x.$$

This is defined for all x not included in the point set

$$\pm \pi \quad , \quad \pm \frac{3}{2}\pi \quad , \quad \pm \frac{5}{2}\pi \quad \cdots$$

Let x range over the point set $\mathfrak{A}$ defined by $0 \geq x < \frac{\pi}{2}$. This may be denoted by $\left(0, \frac{\pi}{2}^*\right)$, the star * indicating that the end point $\frac{\pi}{2}$ is omitted. We call such a set an *incomplete* interval.

Obviously $f(x)$ is continuous at each point $x = a$ of $\mathfrak{A}$, for

$$\lim_{x=a} \tan x = \tan a.$$

It is not uniformly continuous in $\mathfrak{A}$. For in the relation 2) we see that δ must $\doteq 0$ as the point a approaches $\frac{\pi}{2}$. There exists therefore no $\eta > 0$ such that 3) or 4) holds.

6. The analytic definition of continuity can be extended at once to functions of any number of variables. For clearness let us take two.

Let the one-valued function $u(x, y)$ be defined in some domain D about the point $x = a$, $y = b$. Then u is continuous at this point when $u(x, y)$ converges to $u(a, b)$ as the point x, y converges to the point a, b; in symbols when

$$\lim_{x=a,\ y=b} u(x, y) = u(a, b).$$

If $u(x, y)$ is continuous at each point belonging to some point set $\mathfrak{A}$, we say u is *continuous in* $\mathfrak{A}$.

7. Let $u(x, y)$ be continuous at the point a, b. If

$$c = u(a, b) \neq 0,$$

there exists a domain $D_\delta(a, b)$ about a, b such that in it $u(x, y)$ has the same sign as c.

For since u is continuous at a, b there exists a $\delta > 0$ such that

$$|u(x, y) - c| < \epsilon \tag{5}$$

when x, y is restricted to $D_\delta(a, b)$. But 5) is equivalent to

$$c - \epsilon < u(x, y) < c + \epsilon. \tag{6}$$

Obviously as c is $\neq 0$ we may make $\epsilon > 0$ so small that $c - \epsilon$ and $c + \epsilon$ have the same sign as c.

8. If $u(x, y)$ is continuous at a, b

$$|u(x, y)| < \text{some } G \tag{7}$$

in $D_\delta(a, b)$ for a sufficiently small $\delta > 0$.

This follows at once from 6).

70. Geometric Terms. 1. At this point it will be convenient to introduce some geometric terms which we shall need constantly. We begin by considering the point set $\mathfrak{A}$ formed of the points *within* a circle $\mathfrak{K}$, that is, in the interior of $\mathfrak{K}$. Any point a of $\mathfrak{A}$ is such that we may describe a circle $\mathfrak{c}$ about it as center, and all the points within $\mathfrak{c}$ form a part of $\mathfrak{A}$. In other words, $\mathfrak{A}$ is such that any point a of it is surrounded by some domain $D_\delta(a)$ which also lies in $\mathfrak{A}$. As a approaches $\mathfrak{K}$, $\delta \doteq 0$. But for each given a, δ is >0.

We may now generalize. Let $\mathfrak{A}$ denote any set of points in the plane. If $\mathfrak{A}$ is such that each of its points a has a domain $D(a)$ which also lies in $\mathfrak{A}$, we call the point set $\mathfrak{A}$ a *region*.

For example, the two curves C_1, C_2 in Fig. 1 define a ring $\mathfrak{R}$ whose boundary or edge $\mathfrak{E}$ is formed by them. The set of points $\mathfrak{A}$ in the ring $\mathfrak{R}$ but not on its edge $\mathfrak{E}$ form a region.

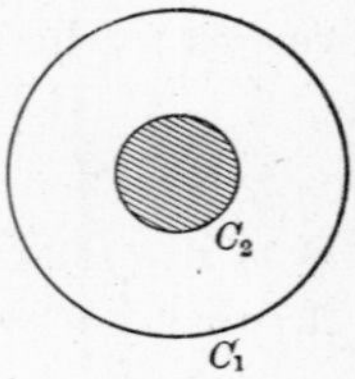

FIG. 1.

Let us look at the set of points $\mathfrak{B}$ formed of $\mathfrak{A}$ and the curve C_1, in symbols the point set

$$\mathfrak{B} = \mathfrak{A} + C_1.$$

The set $\mathfrak{B}$ is not a region. For let e be a point of C_1 as in Fig. 2. Then however $\mathfrak{c}$ is taken it will contain points of $\mathfrak{B}$ and points not in $\mathfrak{B}$.

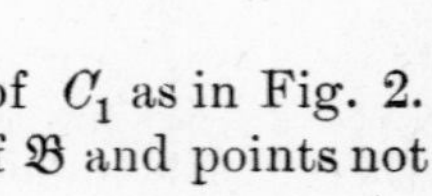

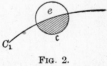

FIG. 2.

As another example of a region, let $\mathfrak{A}$ be the point set formed of all the points of the x, y plane except the points lying on a finite number of ordinary curves, and also a finite number of isolated points. Obviously $\mathfrak{A}$ is a region.

We say a region $\mathfrak{A}$ is *connected* when any two of its points can be joined by a curve lying in $\mathfrak{A}$.

If the boundary of a connected region is a closed curve without double point, we call it a *simple* region.

2. Let $\mathfrak{A}$ be a connected region whose boundary or edge $\mathfrak{E}$ is formed of a finite number of ordinary closed curves or points. The point set $\mathfrak{C}$ formed of $\mathfrak{A}$ and $\mathfrak{E}$, that is, $\mathfrak{C} = \mathfrak{A} + \mathfrak{E}$, we call a *connex*. If $\mathfrak{A}$ is a simple region, the corresponding connex $\mathfrak{C}$ is called *simple* also.

3. The reader will note that the definition of continuity given in 69, 6 requires that if $u(x, y)$ is continuous in a connex $\mathfrak{C}$, it must be continuous at each point of its edge, and this requires that u is defined as a one-valued function for all points in some $D(e)$ of e.

4. Let $\mathfrak{A}$ be a connex or a connected region. Let P be any point; it may or may not lie in $\mathfrak{A}$. Let r be the radius vector joining P to a point z of $\mathfrak{A}$. If z can describe a continuous curve lying in $\mathfrak{A}$ such that r describes a complete revolution about P, we say that $\mathfrak{A}$ is *cyclic* relative to P, otherwise *acyclic*

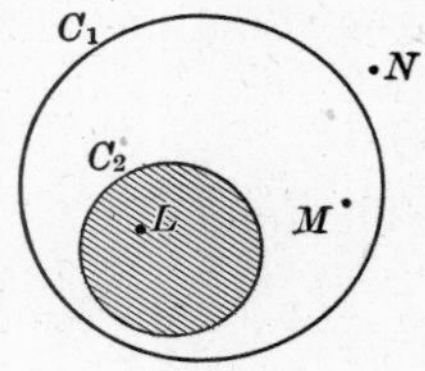

FIG. 3.

Thus in Fig. 3 let $\mathfrak{A}$ be the ring-shaped figure bounded by C_1, C_2. Then $\mathfrak{A}$ is cyclic relative to L and M, but acyclic relative to N.

71. Uniform Continuity. Let us now show that if $u(x, y)$ is continuous in a connex $\mathfrak{C}$ it is uniformly continuous. By this we mean the following. Since u is continuous at a point a, b of $\mathfrak{A}$ we have

$$u(x, y) = u(a, b) + \epsilon' \quad , \quad |\epsilon'| < \epsilon, \tag{1}$$

if only x, y lies in some domain $D_\delta(a, b)$ of the point a, b. We say now that the point set $\mathfrak{C}$ being a connex, δ cannot sink below some minimum value $\eta > 0$, as the point a, b ranges over $\mathfrak{C}$.

For say that as a, b converges to some point α, β of $\mathfrak{C}$, $\delta \doteq 0$. Since u is continuous at α, β,

$$|\epsilon'| < \frac{\epsilon}{2},$$

if x, y lies in some $D_\sigma(\alpha, \beta)$.

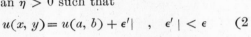

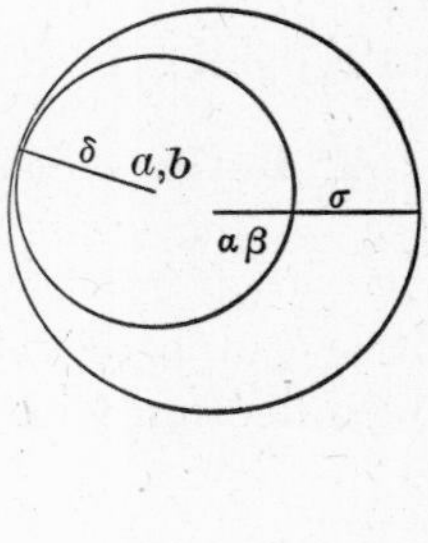

But then δ cannot $\doteq 0$, for as the point a, b converges to the point α, β, the figure shows $\delta \doteq \sigma$, and not to 0. Since therefore δ cannot $\doteq 0$ as a, b ranges over $\mathfrak{C}$, it follows that there exists an $\eta > 0$ such that

$$u(x, y) = u(a, b) + \epsilon' \quad , \quad |\epsilon'| < \epsilon \tag{2}$$

wherever the point a, b is taken in $\mathfrak{C}$, provided x, y lies in $D_\eta(a, b)$, the norm η being the same wherever a, b may be in $\mathfrak{C}$.

We may thus state the following theorem, which for our further development is of utmost importance:

If $u(x, y)$ is continuous in a connex $\mathfrak{C}$, it is uniformly continuous in $\mathfrak{C}$; or in other words the relation 2) holds in $\mathfrak{C}$.

72. Differentiation. 1. We touched on this subject by way of illustration in 67. We wish now to discuss it more fully. Let $y = f(x)$ be a one-valued function in the interval $\mathfrak{A} = (a, b)$ whose graph is given in Fig. 1. If we give to x an increment $h = \Delta x$, the function receives an increment

$$\Delta y = f(x + h) - f(x).$$

The quotient

$$\frac{\Delta y}{\Delta x} = \frac{f(x + h) - f(x)}{h} \qquad (1$$

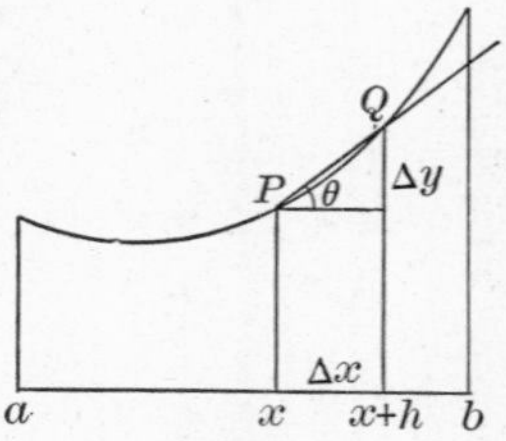

FIG. 1.

is called the *difference quotient*. From the figure we see

$$\frac{\Delta y}{\Delta x} = \tan\theta. \qquad (2$$

As $\Delta x \doteq 0$, the secant PQ converges to a limiting position, viz. the tangent at P.

We call the limit of 1) when $h \doteq 0$ the differential coefficient at the point x and write

$$\frac{dy}{dx} = f'(x) = \lim_{h=0} \frac{f(x + h) - f(x)}{h}. \qquad (3$$

If f has a differential coefficient at each point of some interval A, we say f has a derivative in A; the value of this derivative at a point x of A is given by 3).

2. Let us consider the function

$$y = (x - 1)^{\frac{1}{3}}. \qquad (4$$

The graph of this function is given in Fig. 2. It has a point of inflection with a vertical tangent at $x = 1$. We see here that the secant PQ converges to a vertical position. The difference quotient

$$\frac{\Delta y}{\Delta x} = \frac{1}{(\Delta x)^{\frac{2}{3}}}$$

is always > 0 and increases indefinitely as $\Delta x \doteq 0$. We say its limit is $+\infty$ and write

$$\frac{dy}{dx} = f'(x) = +\infty \quad \text{for} \quad x = 1.$$

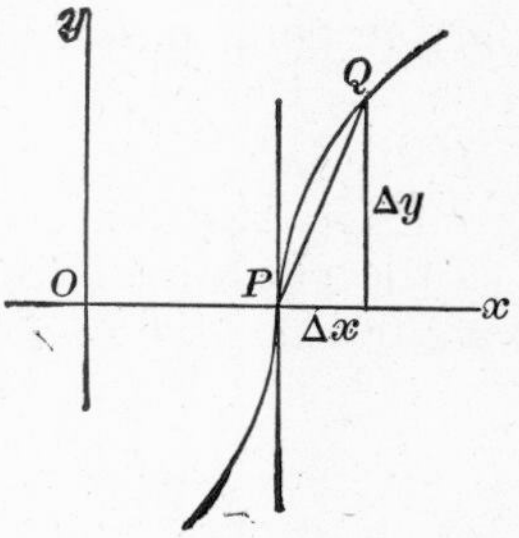

FIG. 2.

To say that a variable q has the limit $+\infty$ as $x \doteq a$ is only a short way of saying q has no limit at $x = a$, but that it increases without limit as $x \doteq a$.

Strictly speaking the function 4) has no differential coefficient at $x = 1$. Usage, however, permits us to say its differential coefficient is $+\infty$ at this point. We also say the derivative $f'(x)$ is *definitely infinite* at this point, meaning thereby that the difference quotient does not change its sign about $x = 1$.

3. Let us consider the function

$$y = (x-1)^{\frac{2}{3}} \quad , \quad \text{radical with positive sign.} \tag{5}$$

The graph of this function, Fig. 3, has a vertical cusp at $x = 1$.

At this point

$$\frac{\Delta y}{\Delta x} = \frac{(\Delta x)^{\frac{2}{3}}}{\Delta x} \tag{6}$$

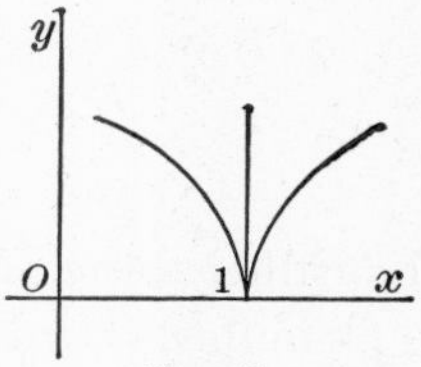

FIG. 3.

It is thus positive for positive Δx, and negative when Δx is negative. Thus

$$\frac{\Delta y}{\Delta x} \doteq +\infty \quad \text{as } \Delta x \doteq 0 \quad \text{on the right,}$$
$$\doteq -\infty \quad \cdot \cdot \cdot \cdot \cdot \cdot \cdot \quad \text{left.}$$

Here we cannot say that the difference quotient $\Delta y/\Delta x$ converges to any value, not even to an improper limit as $+\infty$, or $-\infty$, since it changes its sign in any interval about $x = 1$.

4. Let us now consider the differentiation of a function of several variables. For clearness let us take a function $u(x, y)$ of two variables which we suppose is one-valued in some domain D

of the point a, b. Then, as the reader knows,

$$\lim_{h=0} \frac{u(a+h, b)-u(a, b)}{h} = u'_x(a, b) = \frac{\partial u}{\partial a} \tag{7}$$

is the partial differential coefficient of u with respect to x at the point a, b, and a similar definition holds for

$$u'_y(a, b) = \frac{\partial u}{\partial b}.$$

The values of 7) as the point a, b ranges over some set of points $\mathfrak{A}$ define the first partial derivative of u with respect to x; this we denote by

$$u'_x(x, y) \text{ or } u'_x \text{ or } \frac{\partial u}{\partial x}. \tag{8}$$

A similar definition holds for

$$u'_y(x, y) \text{ or } u'_y \text{ or } \frac{\partial u}{\partial y}. \tag{9}$$

The derivatives 8), 9) are also functions of x, y and so in general possess partial derivatives

$$u''_{xx} = \frac{\partial^2 u}{\partial x^2}, \quad u''_{xy} = \frac{\partial^2 u}{\partial x \partial y}, \quad \text{etc.}$$

5. Suppose u possesses first partial derivatives for the points x, y of some point set $\mathfrak{A}$. The expression

$$du = \frac{\partial u}{\partial x} h + \frac{\partial u}{\partial y} k \tag{10}$$

is called the *first differential of u.*

Similarly, if u has second partial derivatives,

$$d^2u = \frac{\partial^2 u}{\partial x^2} h^2 + 2 \frac{\partial^2 u}{\partial x \partial y} hk + \frac{\partial^2 u}{\partial y^2} k^2 \tag{11}$$

is the *second differential of u*, etc.

We note that the right side of 11) may be written symbolically

$$\left(h \frac{\partial}{\partial x} + k \frac{\partial}{\partial y}\right)^2 u. \tag{12}$$

To deduce 11) from 12) we expand 12) as in algebra and replace

$$\left(\frac{\partial}{\partial x}\right)^2 u \text{ by } \frac{\partial^2 u}{\partial x^2}, \text{ etc.}$$

In general, suppose u has all partial derivatives of order $\leq n$ for all points x, y in some set $\mathfrak{A}$. Then

$$d^n u = \left(h\frac{\partial}{\partial x} + k\frac{\partial}{\partial y}\right)^n u, \qquad (13$$

when after expanding the right side we replace

$$\left(\frac{\partial}{\partial x}\right)^m \left(\frac{\partial}{\partial y}\right)^{n-m} u \text{ by } \frac{\partial^n u}{\partial x^m \partial y^{n-m}}.$$

73. Law of the Mean. 1. Let the graph of the one-valued function $y = f(x)$ be as in the figure. Let the secant PQ make the angle ϕ with the x-axis. At each point x let us draw the tangent to the curve. It makes an angle θ with the x-axis. Let now x start at a and move toward b. The tangent changes its inclination from point to point. If the reader will reflect a few moments, he will see that it is altogether impossible to pass from a to b without somewhere the tangent being parallel to the secant PQ. Let this be the case for $x = c$. Now

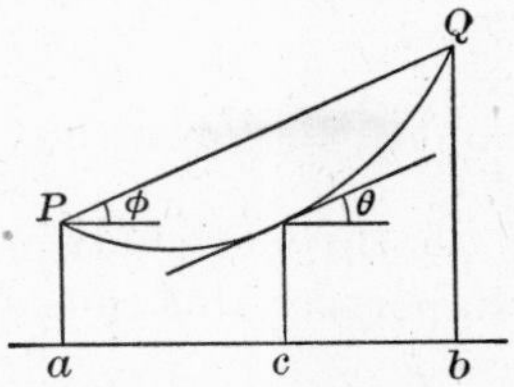

$$\tan\phi = \frac{f(b) - f(a)}{b - a},$$

$$\tan\theta = \frac{dy}{dx} = f'(x) \cdot$$

Since $\phi = \theta$ at the point c, we have, on equating these two expressions,

$$f(b) - f(a) = (b - a)f'(c) \quad , \quad a < c < b.$$

This is the celebrated Law of the Mean. It is one of the most important theorems in the whole calculus.

The foregoing considerations do not form an analytic proof of this law. They do, however, make the reader feel in the most convincing manner that this law is true, and this is all that he needs at this stage. On account of its importance let us formulate it as follows:

If $f(x)$ is one-valued and continuous in the interval $\mathfrak{A} = (a, b)$ and if $f'(x)$ is finite or definitely infinite within $\mathfrak{A}$, then for some point $a < c < b$

$$f(b) - f(a) = (b - a)f'(c). \qquad (1$$

2. Let $a \leq x \leq b$, $f(x+h) - f(x) = \Delta f$. Then the law of the mean 1) gives, setting $h = \Delta x$,

$$\frac{\Delta f}{\Delta x} = f'(u) \quad , \quad x < u < x + h. \tag{2}$$

Suppose now that $f'(x)$ is continuous in the interval $\mathfrak{A}$. Then

$$f'(u) = f'(x) + \epsilon' \quad , \quad |\epsilon'| < \epsilon, \tag{3}$$

provided $|\Delta x| <$ some fixed δ, wherever the point x is chosen in $\mathfrak{A}$. This in 2) gives

$$\frac{\Delta f}{\Delta x} = f'(x) + \epsilon' \tag{4}$$

and $\epsilon' \doteq 0$ uniformly in $\mathfrak{A}$.

3. From the law of the mean it is easy to establish another very important theorem, viz.:

Taylor's Development in Finite Form. In the interval $\mathfrak{A} = (a, b)$ let $f(x)$ and its first $n-1$ derivatives be continuous. Let $f^{(n)}(x)$ be finite or definitely infinite within $\mathfrak{A}$. Then for any x within $\mathfrak{A}$

$$f(x) = f(a) + \frac{x-a}{1!} f'(a) + \frac{(x-a)^2}{2!} f''(a) + \cdots$$

$$+ \frac{(x-a)^{n-1}}{(n-1)!} f^{(n-1)}(a) + \frac{(x-a)^n}{n!} f^{(n)}(v) \quad , \quad a < v < x. \tag{5}$$

As this is not a work on the calculus we do not intend to prove this theorem ; we have quoted it in order to state precisely conditions for its validity.

4. From the law of the mean we can draw an important conclusion which we shall need later. Suppose $u(x, y)$ has continuous first partial derivatives about the point a, b. When we pass from this point to the neighboring point $a+h, b+k$, u receives the increment

$$\Delta u = u(a+h, b+k) - u(a, b).$$

But we have

$$\begin{aligned}\Delta u &= \{u(a+h, b+k) - u(a, b+k)\} + \{u(a, b+k) - u(a, b)\} \\ &= \Delta_1 + \Delta_2.\end{aligned}$$

By the law of the mean

$$\Delta_1 = hu'_x(c, b+k) \quad , \quad c \text{ between } a \text{ and } a+h$$
$$\Delta_2 = ku'_y(a, e) \quad , \quad e \text{ between } b \text{ and } b+k.$$

But u'_x, u'_y being continuous,

$$u'_x(c, b+k) = u'_x(a, b) + \alpha$$
$$u'_y(a, e) = u'_y(a, b) + \beta$$

where $\alpha \doteq 0$, $\beta \doteq 0$ as h and $k \doteq 0$. Hence we may state the theorem:

Let $u(x, y)$ have continuous first partial derivatives about the point a, b. Then the increment Δu differs from the differential du by a quantity of the form

$$\alpha h + \beta k$$

where α and $\beta \doteq 0$ as h and $k \doteq 0$. Thus

$$\Delta u = \frac{\partial u}{\partial x} h + \frac{\partial u}{\partial y} k + \alpha h + \beta k.$$

5. Suppose now that u'_x and u'_y are continuous functions of x, y in a connex $\mathfrak{C}$. Then, as observed in 71, α and β will converge uniformly to 0 in $\mathfrak{C}$. Hence in particular

$$|\alpha| < G \quad , \quad |\beta| < G,$$

provided $|h|$ and $|k|$ are $<$ some δ, and here δ is independent of the position of the point a, b in $\mathfrak{C}$.

6. Taylor's development 5) may be extended to a function of any number of variables. For clearness let us take a function $u(x, y)$ of two variables. Suppose u and all its partial derivates of orders $\leq n$ are continuous in some domain D about the point a, b. Let $a+h$, $b+k$ be any point in D. Let L be the segment joining these two points. Then any point x, y on L has the coördinates

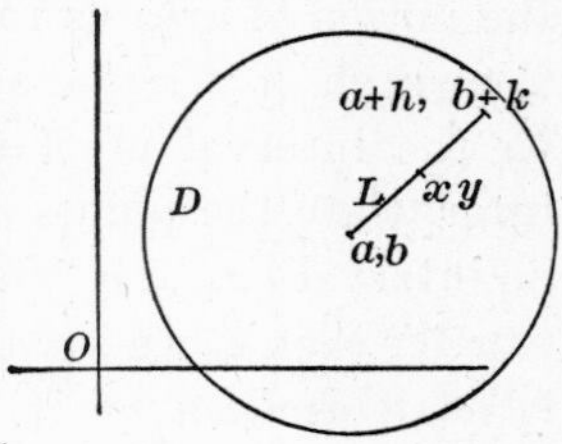

$$x = a + sh \quad , \quad y = b + sk \quad , \quad 0 \leq s \leq 1.$$

When s ranges over the interval $\mathfrak{S} = (0, 1)$, the point x, y ranges over L. Then

$$u(x, y) = u(a + sh, b + sk) = \phi(s)$$

is a function of s defined for values of s lying in $\mathfrak{S}$. But

$$\phi'(s) = \frac{\partial u}{\partial x} h + \frac{\partial u}{\partial y} k = du(x, y),$$

$$\phi''(s) = \frac{\partial^2 u}{\partial x^2} h^2 + 2 \frac{\partial^2 u}{\partial x \partial y} hk + \frac{\partial^2 u}{\partial y^2} k^2 = d^2u(x, y),$$

. . . .

Hence $\phi'(s), \phi''(s) \cdots \phi^{(n)}(s)$ are continuous in $\mathfrak{S}$ and we may apply 2 to the function $\phi(s)$. Doing this and then setting $s = 1$, we get

$$u(a + h, b + k) = u(a, b) + \frac{1}{1!} du(a, b) + \frac{1}{2!} d^2(a, b) + \cdots$$
$$+ \frac{1}{n!} d^n u(a + \theta h, b + \theta h) \qquad (6$$

where $0 < \theta < 1$.

For convenience of reference we note that

$$du(a, b) = \frac{\partial u}{\partial a} h + \frac{\partial u}{\partial b} k,$$

$$d^2u(a, b) = \frac{\partial^2 u}{\partial a^2} h^2 + 2 \frac{\partial^2 u}{\partial a \partial b} hk + \frac{\partial^2 u}{\partial b^2} k^2.$$

Integration

74. 1. The integral

$$\int_a^b f(x)dx \qquad (1$$

may be defined in connection with the notion of area as follows. Let the graph of $f(x)$ be as in Fig. 1. In the interval of $\mathfrak{A} = (a, b)$ we interpolate the points $a_1, a_2 \cdots$ If no interval (a_{m-1}, a_m) has a length greater than δ, we say these points *effect a division of* $\mathfrak{A}$ *of norm* δ.

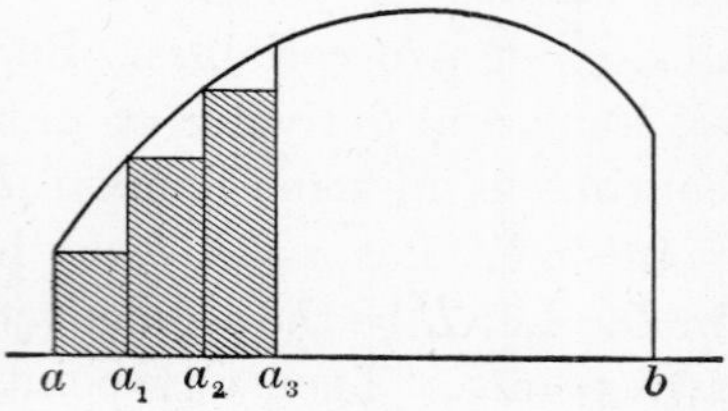

FIG. 1.

We set

$$\delta_m = a_m - a_{m-1} = \Delta x_m$$

and form the sum

$$f(a_1)\,\Delta x_1 + f(a_2)\,\Delta x_2 + \cdots = \Sigma f(a_m)\Delta x_m. \tag{2}$$

The value of this sum is the area of the shaded rectangles in the figure. If now $\delta \doteq 0$, this sum obviously converges to the area under the curve. Thus when $f(x)$ is a one-valued continuous function of x in the interval $\mathfrak{A}$, the sum 2) has a limit as $\delta \doteq 0$. This limit is the value of the symbol 1). This symbol we also denote sometimes by

$$\int_{\mathfrak{A}} f(x)\,dx.$$

2. These geometric considerations enable us to take a more general definition of 1). In the intervals δ_m let us take at pleasure a point α_m. If $f(\alpha_m) = \beta_m$, let us construct the rectangles of base δ_m and height β_m, as in Fig. 2. We now form the sum

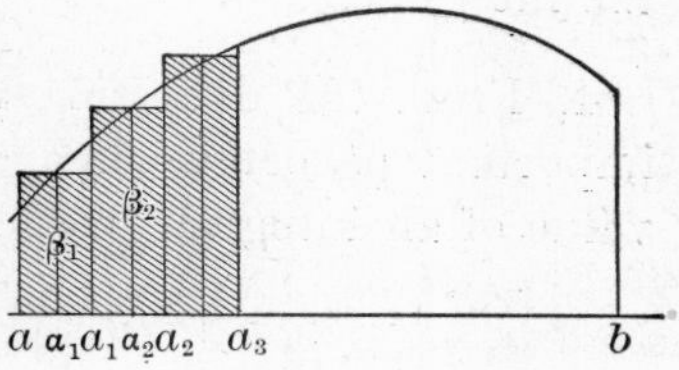

FIG. 2.

$$f(\alpha_1)\,\Delta x_1 + f(\alpha_2)\,\Delta x_2 + \cdots = \Sigma f(\alpha_m)\,\Delta x_m. \tag{3}$$

The value of this sum is the area of the shaded rectangles. If now $\delta \doteq 0$, the sum obviously converges to the area under the curve and therefore has the same value as before.

Let us state this in a theorem:

If $f(x)$ is continuous in the interval (a, b),

$$\lim_{\delta=0} \Sigma f(\alpha_m)\Delta x_m \tag{4}$$

exists and this limit is the value of the integral 1).

3. With this definition we can establish the following fundamental theorem:

In the interval (a, b) let $F(x)$ be one-valued and have the continuous derivative $f(x)$. Then

$$\int_a^b f(x)\,dx = F(b) - F(a). \tag{5}$$

For, using the points $a_1, a_2 \cdots a_{n-1}$ introduced in 1, we have by the law of the mean

$$F(a_1) - F(a) = f(\alpha_1)\Delta x_1$$
$$F(a_2) - F(a_1) = f(\alpha_2)\Delta x_2$$
$$\cdot \quad \cdot \quad \cdot \quad \cdot \quad \cdot \quad \cdot \quad \cdot \quad \cdot$$
$$F(b) - F(a_{n-1}) = f(\alpha_n)\Delta x_n$$

where α_m is some point in the interval Δx_m.

Adding these equations gives

$$F(b) - F(a) = \Sigma f(\alpha_m)\Delta x_m.$$

Now by 2 the limit of the right side as $\delta \doteq 0$ exists and equals the integral in 5).

4. From the definition of an integral given in 1) follows an important property which is useful in estimating the numerical value of an integral. Since

$$|\Sigma f(a_m)\Delta x_m| \leq \Sigma |f(a_m)| \Delta x_m,$$

we have, on passing to the limit $\delta = 0$,

$$\left| \int_a^b f(x)\, dx \right| \leq \int_a^b |f(x)|\, dx \quad , \quad a \leq b. \qquad (6$$

Also let $\quad |f(x)| \leq \phi(x)$ in the interval (a, b).

Then similarly we have

$$\left| \int_a^b f(x)\, dx \right| \leq \int_a^b \phi(x) dx \quad , \quad a \leq b. \qquad (7$$

5. Another property of importance is that:

$$J(x) = \int^x f(x) dx \quad , \quad a \leq x \leq b$$

considered as a function of its upper limit x is a continuous function of x such that

$$\frac{dJ}{dx} = f(x),$$

the integrand $f(x)$ being continuous in (a, b).

75. Surface Integrals. 1. Let $u = f(x, y)$ be a one-valued continuous function of x, y in a field $\mathfrak{A}$ bounded by a finite set of ordinary curves. As x, y ranges over $\mathfrak{A}$, the end points of the ordinate through x, y will describe a surface S, while the points of the ordinates will constitute a solid of volume V lying between S and the x, y plane under S.

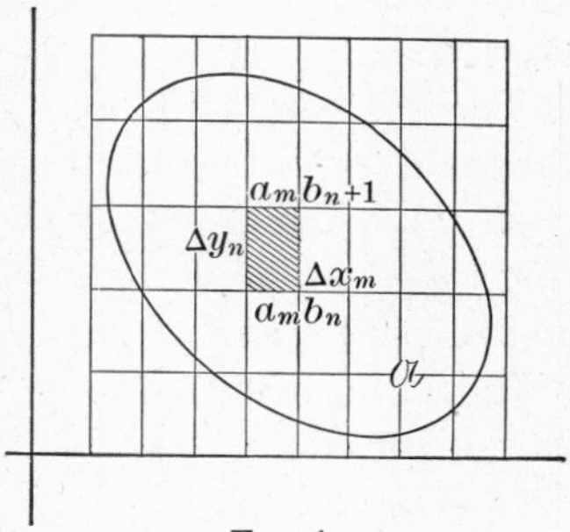

FIG. 1.

Let us draw a set of parallels to the x, y axes in the x, y plane as in Fig. 1. This effects a division of the plane into rectangles R. If their sides Δx, Δy are all $\leq \delta$, we say the norm of this division is δ. Let us now form the sum analogous to 74, 2),

$$\Sigma f(a_m, b_n) \Delta x_m \Delta y_n, \tag{1}$$

extended over all rectangles containing a point of $\mathfrak{A}$. The points a_m, b_n are the vertices of these rectangles.

The sum 1) is obviously the volume of the set of prisms whose bases are the rectangles $\Delta x_m \Delta y_n$ and whose heights are the ordinates of the surface S at the points $x = a_m$, $y = b_n$. We take it as geometrically evident that the sum 1) converges to the volume V as $\delta \doteq 0$. This limit we use to define the symbol

$$\int_{\mathfrak{A}} f(x, y) dx dy. \tag{2}$$

2. To calculate this integral it is usual to express it as an iterated integral

$$\int_{\mathfrak{B}} dx \int_{\mathfrak{C}} f(x, y) dy. \tag{3}$$

Here the symbol $\mathfrak{B}$ denotes the projection of the field $\mathfrak{A}$ on the x-axis. Let x be a point of $\mathfrak{B}$. The line through x parallel to the y-axis will partly lie in $\mathfrak{A}$. This section we denote by $\mathfrak{C}_x$ or more shortly by $\mathfrak{C}$. Thus to calculate 3) we give x a fixed value in $\mathfrak{B}$ and calculate

$$\int_{\mathfrak{C}} f(x, y) dy, \tag{4}$$

the field of integration being the section $\mathfrak{C}$ of $\mathfrak{A}$ corresponding to the value of x chosen. This integral itself is a function of x. This we now integrate relative to x over the field $\mathfrak{B}$, getting in this way 3).

To illustrate, suppose the field of integration $\mathfrak{A}$ in 2) is bounded by the three outer curves and the two inner curves of Fig. 2. Then the projection $\mathfrak{B}$ on the x-axis consists of the segments AB, CD. For a value of x corresponding to E, the section $\mathfrak{C}$ of $\mathfrak{A}$ is formed of the two segments marked $\mathfrak{C}$ in the figure. At F the section $\mathfrak{C}$ is made up of three segments, also marked $\mathfrak{C}$.

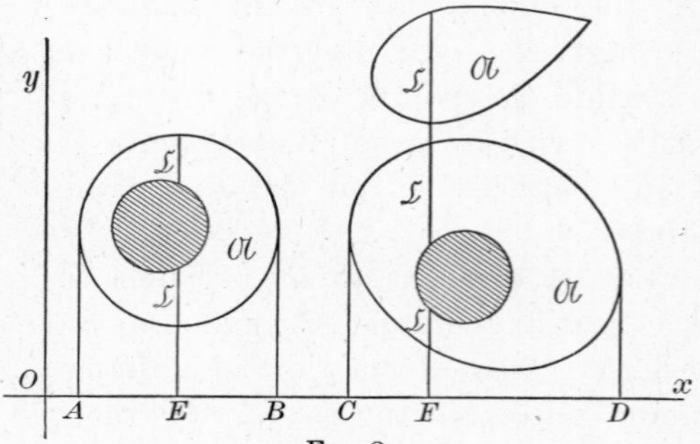

FIG. 2.

It is shown in the calculus that:

The two integrals 2) *and* 3) *are equal.*

The following geometrical considerations will make this apparent:

That slice of V which lies between the two planes

$$x = a_m \quad , \quad x = a_{m+1}$$

in Fig. 3 has approximately the volume

$$\Delta x_m \int_{\mathfrak{C}} f(a_m, y) dy,$$

as is seen from Fig. 3. The sum of these slices is

$$\sum \Delta x_m \int_{\mathfrak{C}} f(a_m, y) dy. \qquad (5$$

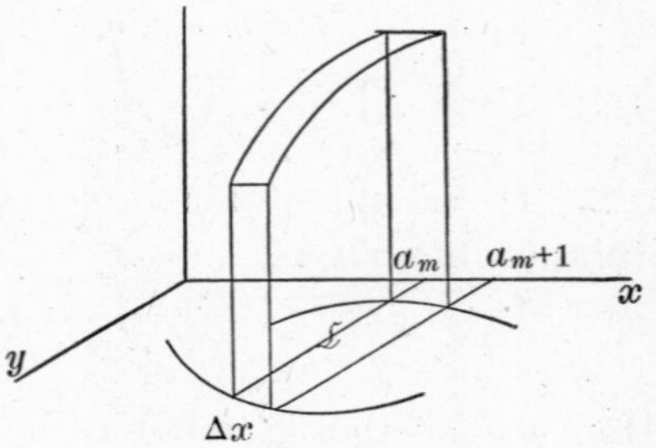

FIG. 3.

Thus the volume V is the limit of 5) or the iterated integral 3). Thus 2) and 3) are equal as they both $= V$.

76. Curvilinear Integrals. 1. Let us suppose that $f(x, y)$ is a one-valued continuous function of x, y at the points of a curve C

whose end points are a, b, as in Fig. 1. If we interpolate a set of points $a_1, a_2, a_3 \cdots$ such that the arcs $aa_1, a_1a_2, a_2a_3 \cdots$ are of length $\leq \delta$, we say these points $a_1, a_2 \cdots$ effect a division of norm δ.

Let x_m, y_m be the coördinates of a_m; let $\Delta x_m = x_{m+1} - x_m$. We now form the sum

$$\Sigma f(x_m, y_m)\Delta x_m. \quad (1$$

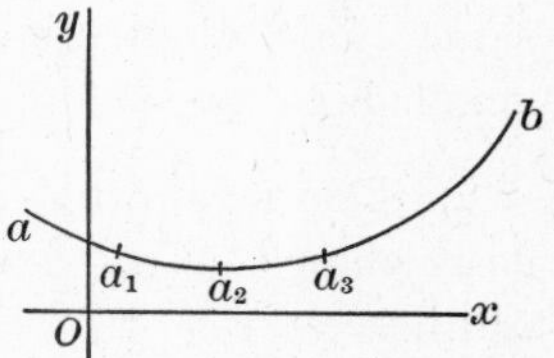

FIG. 1.

If we let $\delta \doteq 0$, this sum converges to a definite limit which we denote by

$$\int_C f(x, y)dx \text{ or by } \int_a^b f(x, y)dx \quad (2$$

and call it the *x-curvilinear integral* of $f(x, y)$.

When the curve C reduces to a segment of the x-axis, the integral 1) reduces to the ordinary integral considered in 74, since y is now constant.

Let us prove that the limit of 1) exists for the simple case that the equation of C is

$$y = \phi(x), \quad (3$$

ϕ being one-valued and continuous, the end points of C corresponding to $x = \alpha$, $x = \beta$. Then

$$f(x, y) = f[x, \phi(x)] = g(x),$$

and 1) becomes

$$\Sigma g(x_m)\Delta x_m. \quad (4$$

But $g(x)$ is continuous, hence the limit of 4) exists and is

$$\int_\alpha^\beta g(x)dx. \quad (5$$

Hence the limit of 1) exists and has the same value. We note that this form of proof not only establishes the existence of the limit of the sum 1) but determines its value.

Because 2) and 5) are equal, we may extend the properties of ordinary integrals to curvilinear integrals. Thus if c is some point on C between the end points a, b, we have

$$\int_a^b f(x, y)dx = \int_a^c f(x, y)dx + \int_c^b f(x, y)dx. \quad (6$$

Let us return to the sum 1). The factor $f(x_m, y_m)$ denotes the value of f at the end point of the arc $a_{m-1}a_m$. The same geometric considerations used in 74, 2 would show that 1) has the same limit when $x_m y_m$ denote *any* point in the arc $a_{m-1}a_m$. We shall make use of this fact in 3.

2. The foregoing proof applies to the case when C is the arc PQ of the circle of radius r in Fig. 2. For then

$$y = +\sqrt{r^2 - x^2} = \phi(x), \qquad (7$$

the radical being taken with the plus sign. It does not apply immediately if C is the arc PQS. For if $-s$ is the abscissa of S, y is two-valued in the interval $(-r, -s)$.

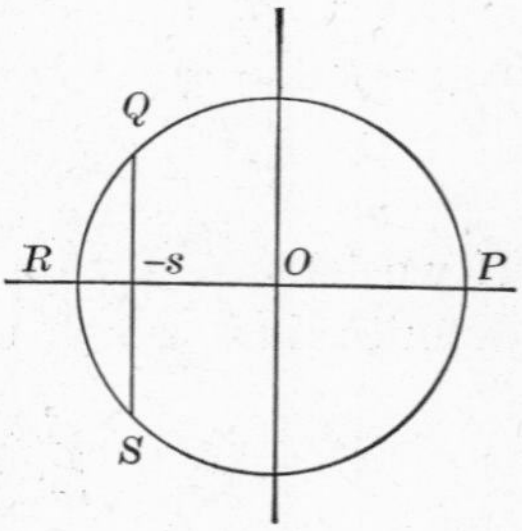

FIG. 2.

In this case we have only to break C into two arcs

$$C_1 = PQR \text{ and } C_2 = RS.$$

Then on C_1 we have ϕ determined as in 7), while on C_2 ϕ is determined by

$$y = -\sqrt{r^2 - x^2} = \phi(x),$$

the radical now having the negative sign.

Corresponding to this we would break 2) into two integrals

$$\int_{C_1} \text{ and } \int_{C_2}.$$

To each of these our proof applies.

3. In 2 we have taken the equation of the circle as

$$x^2 + y^2 = r^2, \qquad (8$$

which defines y as a two-valued function $\pm\sqrt{r^2 - x^2}$. Instead of the equation 8) we may use the equations of the circle in parameter form

$$x = r\cos u \quad , \quad y = r\sin u. \qquad (9$$

If we do this, we can avoid the radical and so deal from the start with one-valued functions.

In general, let

$$x = \phi(u) \quad , \quad y = \psi(u) \qquad (10$$

be the parametric equations of a curve C; that is, when u ranges from $u = \alpha$ to $u = \beta$, the point x, y defined by 10) describes the curve C. We suppose of course that ϕ, ψ are one-valued continuous functions in $\mathfrak{U} = (\alpha, \beta)$, with continuous first derivatives. Then

$$f(x, y) = f\{\phi(u), \psi(u)\} = g(u)$$

is a continuous function of u in $\mathfrak{U}$. Let us effect a division of $\mathfrak{U}$ of norm δ by interpolating the points $\alpha_1, \alpha_2 \cdots$. To them will correspond certain points $a_1, a_2 \cdots$ on C.

Then by the law of the mean

$$\Delta x_m = \phi(\alpha_m) - \phi(\alpha_{m-1}) = \phi'(v_m)\Delta u_m$$

where v_m is some point in the interval (α_{m-1}, α_m). To this point v_m will correspond x_m, y_m in the arc (a_{m-1}, a_m) on the curve C. Thus

$$\Sigma f(x_m, y_m)\Delta x_m = \Sigma g(v_m)\phi'(v_m)\Delta u_m.$$

If we let the norm $\delta \doteq 0$ in this relation, we get in the limit

$$\int_a^b f(x, y)\,dx = \int_\alpha^\beta g(u)\phi'(u)\,du. \qquad (11$$

4. In precisely the same manner the y-curvilinear integral gives

$$\int_a^b f(x, y)\,dy = \int_\alpha^\beta g(u)\psi'(u)\,du. \qquad (12$$

77. Work. 1. Let us show how the notion of curvilinear integrals presents itself naturally in mathematical physics. Suppose a particle is acted on by a force $\mathfrak{F}$ whose components are X and Y, as in Fig. 1. The work done in passing from P to a point Q near by on the curve C is

$$dW = \mathfrak{F} \cos\theta \cdot ds, \qquad (1$$

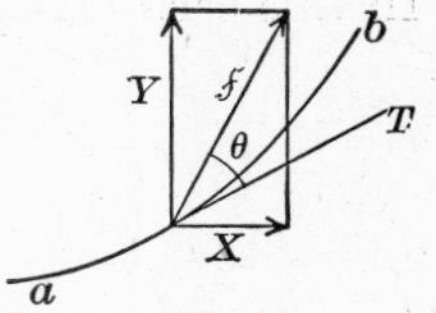

FIG. 1.

where θ is the angle between $\mathfrak{F}$ and the tangent T. If $\mathfrak{F}$ makes the angles α, β with the x and y axes, and T the angles α', β' with these axes, we have, from analytic geometry,

$$\cos\theta = \cos\alpha\cos\alpha' + \cos\beta\cos\beta'. \qquad (2$$

Now
$$\mathfrak{F} \cos \alpha = X \quad , \quad \mathfrak{F} \cos \beta = Y,$$
$$\frac{dx}{ds} = \cos \alpha' \quad , \quad \frac{dy}{ds} = \cos \beta'.$$

Thus 1) and 2) give
$$dW = Xdx + Ydy. \tag{3}$$

Thus the work done by the particle in passing from a to b along the curve C is
$$W = \int_a^b (Xdx + Ydy) \tag{4}$$
$$= \int_a^b Xdx + \int_a^b Ydy. \tag{5}$$

It is therefore the sum of two curvilinear integrals.

2. The relation 3) may be obtained more simply by referring to Fig. 2. The work performed in passing from P to a point Q very near is in general the same as if the particle took the route PR, RQ. The work done along PR is Xdx; the work done along RQ is Ydy. The total work dW is the sum of these or 3).

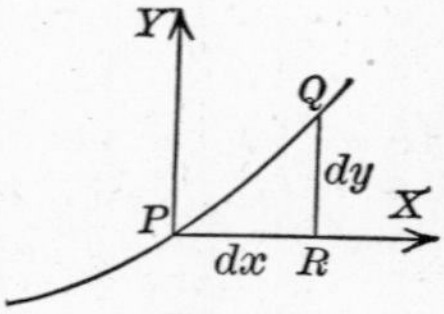

FIG. 2.

78. Potential. 1. In physics we often deal with forces $\mathfrak{F}$ whose components are the partial derivatives of some one-valued function $V(x, y)$, that is,
$$X = -\frac{\partial V}{\partial x} \quad , \quad Y = -\frac{\partial V}{\partial y}. \tag{1}$$

In this case 77, 3) gives
$$-dW = \frac{\partial V}{\partial x} dx + \frac{\partial V}{\partial y} dy = dV,$$

and the element of work is the total differential of the function V, with sign reversed.

Let us suppose that $\frac{\partial V}{\partial x}, \frac{\partial V}{\partial y}$ are continuous. We can then show that the work done in passing from a to b is independent of the path. For let us effect a division of norm δ of C by interpolating points $a_1, a_2, \cdots$ between a and b. Then by 73, 4

$$\Delta V = \frac{\partial V}{\partial x}\Delta x + \frac{\partial V}{\partial y}\Delta y + \alpha\Delta x + \beta\Delta y$$
$$= - X\Delta x - Y\Delta y + \alpha\Delta x + \beta\Delta y$$

where $\alpha, \beta \doteq 0$ with $\Delta x, \Delta y$. Thus we have

$$V(a) - V(a_1) = X_1\Delta x_1 + Y_1\Delta y_1 + \alpha_1\Delta x_1 + \beta\Delta y_1$$
$$V(a_1) - V(a_2) = X_2\Delta x_2 + Y_2\Delta y_2 + \alpha_2\Delta x_2 + \beta\Delta y_2$$
$$\cdots\cdots\cdots\cdots\cdots\cdots\cdots\cdots\cdots$$
$$V(a_{n-1}) - V(b) = X_n\Delta x_n + Y_n\Delta y_n + \alpha_n\Delta x_n + \beta_n\Delta x_n.$$

Now by 73, 5
$$|\alpha_m| \quad \text{and} \quad |\beta_m|$$

are all $<$ some ϵ for all norms $\delta <$ some δ_0. Thus, adding the foregoing equations, we get

$$V(a) - V(b) = \Sigma(X_m\Delta x_m + Y_m\Delta y_m) + \epsilon'$$

where $\epsilon' \doteq 0$ as $\delta \doteq 0$. Hence, letting $\delta \doteq 0$, the last relation gives

$$W = V(a) - V(b) = \int (Xdx + Ydy). \qquad (2$$

As $V(x, y)$ is one-valued, the value of the work done by the particle in moving from a to b is independent of the path taken, and depends thus only on the end points a, b.

2. It is sometimes useful to know that the relation 2) holds, in a certain sense, when V is not one-valued. In fact the foregoing reasoning is valid if $V(x, y)$ is only one-valued about each point of the curve C and possesses continuous first partial derivatives as before. Suppose then that V_a is the determination of $V(x, y)$ with which we start at a. If V_b denotes the value that V_a acquires on reaching b, passing over C, we see that we may write 2)

$$W = \int_C (Xdx + Ydy) = V_a - V_b. \qquad (3$$

3. The simplest case of a potential function is presented by several particles of masses $m_1, m_2, \cdots$.

A unit mass at P is attracted by m_1 by a force whose components are, as seen by the figure,

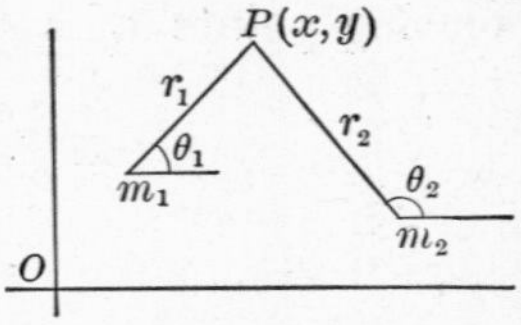

$$X_1 = \frac{m_1}{r_1^2}\cos\theta_1 \quad , \quad Y_1 = \frac{m_1}{r_1^2}\sin\theta_1.$$

Similar forces are exerted by m_2, m_3, $\cdots$. Thus the total force $\mathfrak{F}$ exerted on a unit mass at P has the components

$$X = \sum \frac{m_k}{r_k^2}\cos\theta_k \quad , \quad Y = \sum \frac{m_k}{r_k^2}\sin\theta_k. \tag{4}$$

Let us set

$$V = \sum \frac{m_k}{r_k}. \tag{5}$$

From

$$r^2 = x^2 + y^2$$

we have

$$rdr = xdx + ydy,$$

or

$$dr = \frac{x}{r}dx + \frac{y}{r}dy.$$

Hence

$$\frac{\partial r}{\partial x} = \frac{x}{r} = \cos\theta; \quad \frac{\partial r}{\partial y} = \frac{y}{r} = \sin\theta.$$

Thus

$$\frac{\partial}{\partial x}\left(\frac{1}{r}\right) = \frac{\partial}{\partial r}\left(\frac{1}{r}\right)\frac{\partial r}{\partial x} = -\frac{1}{r^2}\cos\theta,$$

$$\frac{\partial}{\partial y}\left(\frac{1}{r}\right) = -\frac{1}{r^2}\sin\theta.$$

Hence

$$\frac{\partial V}{\partial x} = \Sigma m_k \frac{\partial}{\partial x}\left(\frac{1}{r_k}\right) = -\Sigma m_k \frac{\cos\theta_k}{r_k^2} = -X.$$

We have therefore

$$X = -\frac{\partial V}{\partial x} \quad , \quad Y = -\frac{\partial V}{\partial y}, \tag{6}$$

and hence the function V is a potential function for the force $\mathfrak{F}$.

79. Electric Current. 1. Suppose a constant current of electricity is passing along the wire PQ. The lines of force generated by this current are circles C as in Fig. 1. The intensity of the force $\mathfrak{F}$ is given by

$$F = \frac{c}{r},$$

where c is proportional to the strength of the current. We have here, as shown in Fig. 2,

$$X = -F\sin\theta = -c\frac{y}{r^2} \quad , \quad Y = c\frac{x}{r^2}.$$

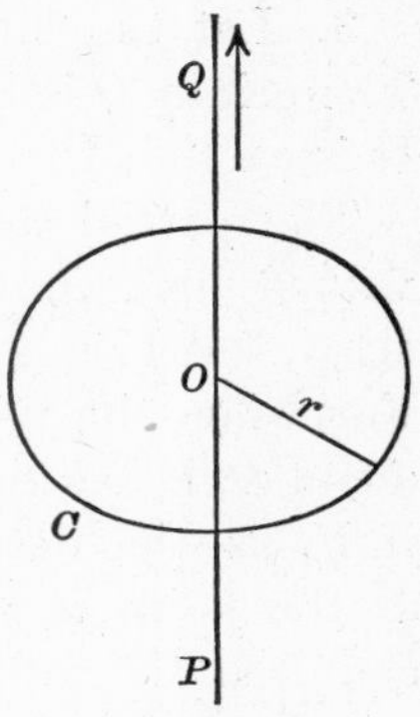

FIG. 1.

Suppose a unit mass of electricity to describe the circle C. Then

$$x = r\cos\theta \quad , \quad y = r\sin\theta,$$
$$dx = -r\sin\theta d\theta \quad , \quad dy = r\cos\theta d\theta.$$

The work is

$$W = \int_C (Xdx + Ydy)$$
$$= c\int_0^{2\pi}(\sin^2\theta + \cos^2\theta)d\theta = c\int_0^{2\pi} d\theta$$
$$= 2\pi c. \qquad (1$$

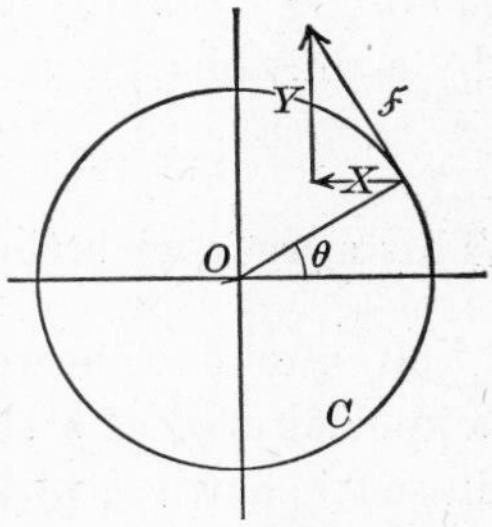

FIG. 2.

2. Let us now suppose that the unit mass is restricted to move in a connex $\mathfrak{A}$ acyclic with respect to O, as in Fig. 3. Let us set

$$V = -c\cdot\text{arc tan}\,\frac{y}{x}. \qquad (2$$

Then
$$\frac{\partial V}{\partial x} = \frac{cx^2}{x^2+y^2}\cdot\frac{y}{x^2} = c\frac{y}{r^2} = -X, \qquad (3$$

$$\frac{\partial V}{\partial y} = -c\frac{x}{r^2} = Y. \qquad (4$$

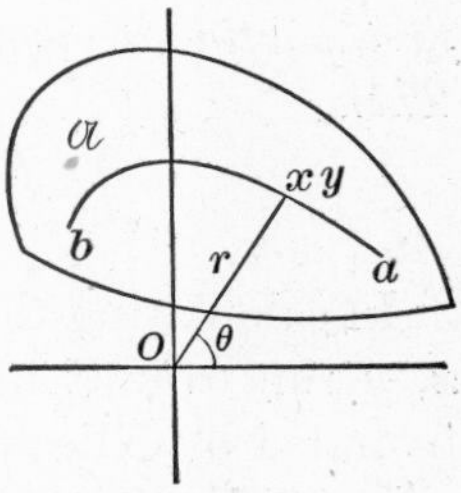

FIG. 3.

Thus V is one-valued in $\mathfrak{A}$ and has continuous first partial derivatives. We can therefore apply 78, 2), which gives as the work done by the unit charge moving from a to b,

$$W = c\left\{\text{arctg}\frac{x'}{y'} - \text{arctg}\frac{x''}{y''}\right\} \qquad (5$$

where $x'y'$, $x''y''$ are the coördinates of a, b.

The work W in moving from a to b is independent of the path between these points, provided only it lies in $\mathfrak{A}$.

3. Let the convex $\mathfrak{A}$ be cyclic with respect to O as in Fig. 4. The origin O is the point where the current pierces the x, y plane. It is excluded from $\mathfrak{A}$ by a small circle.

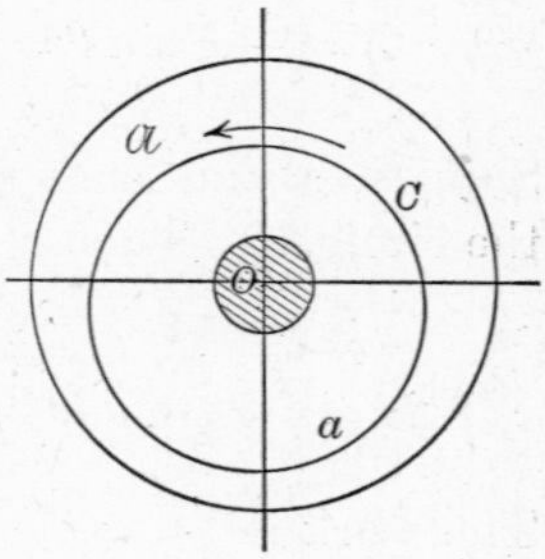

FIG. 4.

The partial derivatives of V are one-valued and continuous in $\mathfrak{A}$ as 3), 4) show, but V is no longer one-valued in $\mathfrak{A}$. For when the point x, y makes a circuit about O, V has increased by $-2c\pi$. Thus, if V_a is the determination of V chosen at the point a, after the circuit V_a has acquired the value

$$V_a - 2c\pi.$$

Thus, if we apply 78, 3), the work done by a unit charge moving around the circuit C is

$$W = 2c\pi.$$

This agrees with the result found directly in 1).

80. Stokes' Theorem. 1. The theorem we now wish to prove is a special case of a theorem due to Stokes and which is much used in mathematical physics. For our purposes it may be stated thus:

Let $F(x, y)$, $G(x, y)$ be one-valued functions having continuous first partial derivatives in a connex $\mathfrak{A}$ whose edge we denote by $\mathfrak{E}$. Then

$$\int_{\mathfrak{E}} (Fdx + Gdy) = \int_{\mathfrak{A}} \left(\frac{\partial G}{\partial x} - \frac{\partial F}{\partial y} \right) dxdy. \qquad (1$$

In calculating the curvilinear integral on the left we let the point x, y run over $\mathfrak{E}$ in the positive sense, that is so that the region bounded by $\mathfrak{E}$ lies to the left of the direction of motion as in Fig. 1.

Let $\mathfrak{B}$ be the projection of $\mathfrak{A}$ on the x-axis, and $\mathfrak{C}$ the section of $\mathfrak{A}$ at a point x of $\mathfrak{B}$. Then

$$\int_{\mathfrak{A}} \frac{\partial F}{\partial y} dxdy = \int_{\mathfrak{B}} dx \int_{\mathfrak{C}} \frac{\partial F}{\partial y} dy$$

as we saw in 75, 2.

At a point $x = \alpha$ in Fig. 1

$$\int_{\mathfrak{C}} \frac{\partial F}{\partial y} dy = (F_2 - F_3) + (F_4 - F_1) = (F_2 - F_1) + (F_4 - F_3),$$

where F_1 denotes the value of $F(x, y)$ at the point 1, etc. At a point as $x = \beta$ in Fig. 1 the right side becomes $F_2 - F_1$. Thus in any case

$$\int_{\mathfrak{C}} \frac{\partial F}{\partial y}\, dy = \Sigma\,(F_{s+1} - F_s),$$

and hence

$$\int_{\mathfrak{A}} \frac{\partial F}{\partial y}\, dx dy = \int_{\mathfrak{B}} dx \Sigma (F_{s+1} - F_s). \quad (2$$

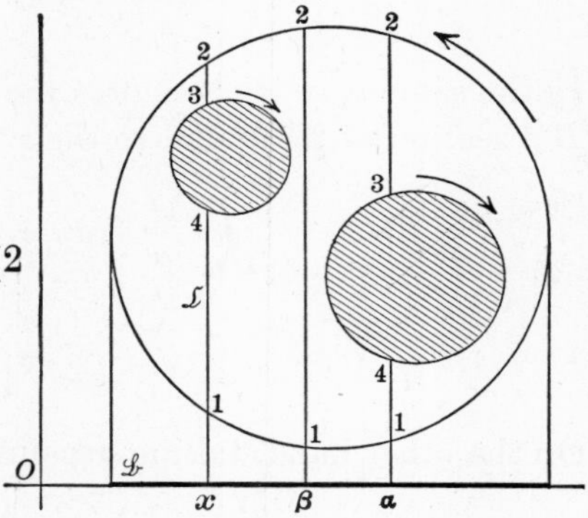

FIG. 1.

Let us show that the right side is equal to

$$-\int_{\mathfrak{C}} F dx. \quad (3$$

In fact to calculate 3) we break $\mathfrak{C}$ into a number of arcs such that for each arc y is a one-valued function of x. Along the lower arc AB of Fig. 2 let $y = y_1$, along the upper arc let $y = y_2$. Along the lower arcs CD, EF let $y = y_4$, and along the upper arcs let $y = y_3$. Thus

$$\int_{\mathfrak{C}} F dx = \int_a^b F(x, y_1) dx$$
$$+ \int_b^a F(x, y_2) dx$$
$$+ \int_c^d F(x, y_3) dx$$
$$+ \int_d^c F(x, y_4) dx$$
$$+ \int_e^f F(x, y_3) dx$$
$$+ \int_f^e F(x, y_4) dx.$$

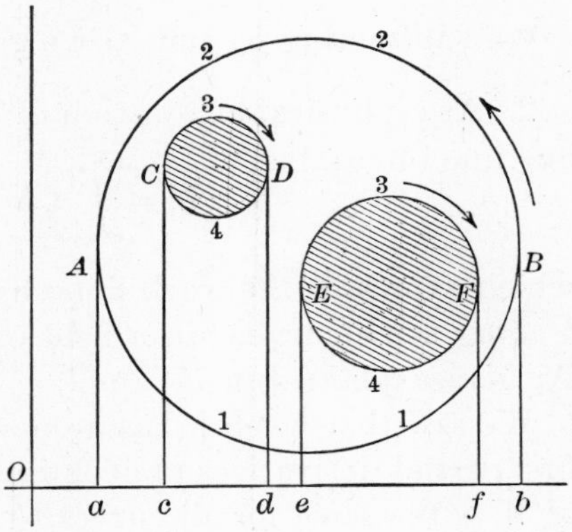

FIG. 2.

Hence

$$-\int_{\mathfrak{C}} F dx = \int_a^c (F_2 - F_1) dx + \int_c \{(F_2 - F_1) + (F_4 - F_3)\} dx + \cdots$$

$$= \int_{\mathfrak{B}} dx \Sigma (F_{s+1} - F_s) \quad (4$$

as in 2). Thus 2), 4) give

$$\int_{\mathfrak{A}} \frac{\partial F}{\partial y} dxdy = -\int_{\mathfrak{C}} Fdx. \tag{5}$$

In the same way if C denotes the projection of $\mathfrak{A}$ on the y-axis and B a section of $\mathfrak{A}$ parallel to the x-axis, we have

$$\int_{\mathfrak{A}} \frac{\partial G}{\partial y} dxdy = \int_C dy \int_B \frac{\partial G}{\partial x} dx$$

$$= \int_C dy \Sigma (G_{s+1} - G_s). \tag{6}$$

On the other hand, taking account of the positive direction of $\mathfrak{C}$

$$\int_{\mathfrak{C}} G dy = \int_C dx \Sigma (G_{s+1} - G_s). \tag{7}$$

Hence from 6), 7) we have

$$\int_{\mathfrak{A}} \frac{\partial G}{\partial x} dxdy = \int_{\mathfrak{C}} G dy. \tag{8}$$

On subtracting 5) and 8) we get 1).

2. As a physical application of Stokes' theorem let us return to our line integral

$$W = \int_a^b (Xdx + Ydy), \tag{9}$$

which expresses the work done by a unit mass moving from a to b along some curve C in a field of force $\mathfrak{F}$ whose components are X, Y as explained in 77.

We saw that when $\mathfrak{F}$ has a one-valued potential $V(x, y)$ whose first partial derivatives are continuous in some connex $\mathfrak{A}$, the value of W is the same for all curves C in $\mathfrak{A}$ leading from a to b. This condition is sufficient to make the value of W independent of the path C.

In this case

$$X = -\frac{\partial V}{\partial x}, \quad Y = -\frac{\partial V}{\partial y}. \tag{10}$$

If X, Y have continuous first partial derivatives, Stokes' theorem shows that if C_1, C_2 are two paths leading from a to b and $\mathfrak{K}$ the connex they bound, the work done in running over the boundary $\mathfrak{C} = C_1 + C_2^{-1}$ of $\mathfrak{R}$ is

$$W = \int_{\mathfrak{C}} (Xdx + Ydy) = \int_{C_1} - \int_{C_2}$$

$$= \int_{\mathfrak{R}} \left(\frac{\partial X}{\partial y} - \frac{\partial Y}{\partial x} \right) dxdy. \qquad (11$$

Now from 10)

$$\frac{\partial X}{\partial y} = \frac{\partial Y}{\partial x} = -\frac{\partial^2 V}{\partial x \partial y}.$$

Thus 11) gives

$$W = \int_{C_1} - \int_{C_2} = 0,$$

or the work performed along C_1 is the same as the work done along C_2, as it should be. This gives us nothing new.

But let us reverse our reasoning. Let us suppose that X, Y have continuous one-valued first partial derivatives in a certain connex $\mathfrak{A}$. We ask what condition must X, Y satisfy in order that W is independent of the path C?

The answer is that

$$\frac{\partial X}{\partial y} = \frac{\partial Y}{\partial x} \qquad (12$$

must hold at each point of $\mathfrak{A}$. For suppose it did not hold at a point c, in Fig. 3. Then within some domain D about c,

$$\frac{\partial X}{\partial y} - \frac{\partial Y}{\partial x},$$

being a continuous function of x, y, must have one sign, by 69, 7. Let γ be a circle with center c and lying in D. Then by Stokes' theorem

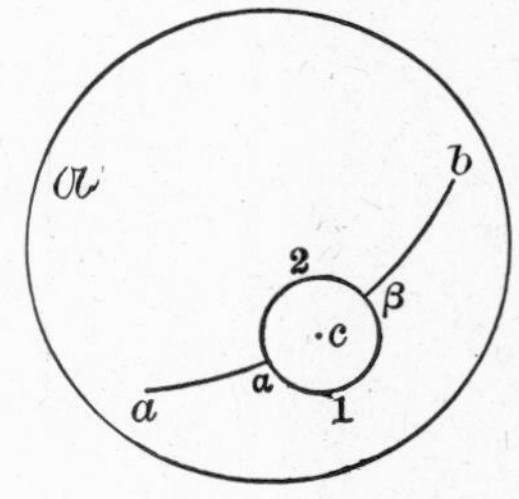

FIG. 3.

$$\int_{\gamma} (Xdx + Ydy) = \int_{\Gamma} \left(\frac{\partial X}{\partial y} - \frac{\partial Y}{\partial x} \right) dxdy,$$

where Γ is the region bounded by γ.

Now the right side cannot $= 0$ since the integrand has one sign in Γ. Thus the work done in going around γ is not 0, or

$$W_{\gamma} \neq 0. \qquad (13$$

Let us now go from a to b along opposite sides γ_1, γ_2 of γ. Suppose the work

$$W_{C_1} \quad , \quad W_{C_2}$$

for these two paths C_1, C_2 were the same. Then

$$W_{C_1 C_2^{-1}} = 0.$$

But

$$C_1 C_2^{-1} = a\alpha\gamma_1 \cdot \beta b \cdot b\beta \cdot \gamma_2^{-1}\alpha a.$$

Also

$$W_{a\alpha} = - W_{\alpha a} \quad , \quad W_{\beta b} = - W_{b\beta} \quad , \quad W_{\gamma_1 \gamma_2^{-1}} = W_{\gamma},$$

which contradicts 13).
Thus

$$W_{C_1 C_2^{-1}} = W_\gamma = 0,$$

which contradicts 13).

Stated in mathematical language these considerations give:

Let F, G be one-valued functions having continuous first partial derivatives in the connex $\mathfrak{A}$. In order that the value of

$$\int_a^b (Fdx + Gdy)$$

shall be the same for all paths in $\mathfrak{A}$ leading from a to b, it is necessary and sufficient that

$$\frac{\partial F}{\partial y} = \frac{\partial G}{\partial x} \text{ in } \mathfrak{A}. \qquad (14$$

CHAPTER VI

DIFFERENTIATION AND INTEGRATION

81. Résumé. Before going further, let us take a look back and see what we have accomplished so far. In Chapter I we have established the arithmetic of complex numbers. It is thus possible at this point to define algebraic functions of a complex variable z, since the definition involves only rational operations. The reader will recall that a rational function of z is defined by an expression of the type

$$R(z) = \frac{a_0 + a_1 z + \cdots + a_m z^m}{b_0 + b_1 z + \cdots b_n z^n}, \ m, n \text{ positive integers,}$$

which obviously involves only rational operations. An algebraic function w of z was defined by an equation of the type

$$w^n + R_1 w^{n-1} + \cdots + R_{n-1} w + R_n = 0,$$

where the coefficients are rational functions of z. Thus the definition also only involves the rational operations of addition, subtraction, multiplication, and division on the variable z.

The transcendental functions

$$e^z, \quad \sin z, \quad \log z, \quad \sinh z, \quad \text{arc} \sin z \cdots \qquad (1$$

cannot be defined in this simple manner. The definitions we have chosen as the most direct and simple employ infinite series. We have therefore developed the subject of series. Now the convergence of a given series A whose terms are any real or complex numbers is of prime importance because divergent series are not employed in elementary mathematics. To test the convergence of A we pass to the adjoint series $\mathfrak{A}$ when possible, because the terms of $\mathfrak{A}$ are real and positive. Thus we are led to consider first the theory of series whose terms are real, and especially those which are positive. This we did in Chapter II. In the next chapter we studied series whose terms are complex, and in particular the important subject of power series.

Having developed the theory of infinite series as much as needful we were in position to study in Chapter IV the elementary transcendental functions 1). At the same time we took a brief survey of the algebraic functions.

The next topic in order would be the *calculus* of these functions, that is, we should learn to differentiate and integrate these functions just as is done for a real variable x. In order to treat this subject clearly we have inserted a chapter, the foregoing one, whose object is to furbish up the reader's knowledge of the calculus and to emphasize certain points of theory which are usually passed over hurriedly in a first course. We also developed the notion of a curvilinear integral which is the foundation of the following chapters.

These matters having been looked after, we are now in a position to take up the differentiation and integration of functions of a complex variable z. But first let us define more explicitly a function of z.

82. Definition of a Function of z. 1. We have already defined a number of functions of the complex variable z, viz.: the algebraic functions, e^z, $\sin z$, $\log z$, etc. These we called the elementary functions. From these we can form more complicated functions of z as

$$w = \frac{3z^2+1}{1-z^4} + \sin z\sqrt{1+z^3}.$$

All such expressions will be called functions of z just as they would be in the calculus if z were replaced by the real variable x.

Any such relation establishes a relation between z and w as follows. For each value of z which belongs to a set of points $\mathfrak{A}$ in the z-plane, one or more values are assigned to w. We now generalize as in 66 in this manner. Let $\mathfrak{A}$ be a point set in the z-plane. Let a law be given which assigns to the variable w one or more values for each value of z in $\mathfrak{A}$. Then we say w is a function of z in $\mathfrak{A}$. If w has but one value for each z in $\mathfrak{A}$, w is a *one-valued* function in $\mathfrak{A}$, otherwise *many-valued*.

For example, the relation

$$w = \frac{\sqrt{z^2 - 1}}{\sin z} \tag{1}$$

assigns to w two values for each z not among

$$0, \ \pm\pi, \ \pm 2\pi, \ \cdots \tag{2}$$

except at $z = \pm 1$, where w has but a single value, $w = 0$. Thus w is a two-valued function in the point set $\mathfrak{A}$ which embraces the whole z-plane excluding the points 2).

The branch points of this function are $z = \pm 1$, that is, when z describes a circuit about one of these two points, the two values of w permute. By means of this two-valued function we can define a one-valued function of z. In fact let $\mathfrak{B}$ be an acyclic part of $\mathfrak{A}$ relative to the points $z = +1$, and $z = -1$. For example, let $\mathfrak{B}$ denote the points of $\mathfrak{A}$ which lie to the right of the parallel to the y-axis, $x = 1$. At the point $z = 2$, w has two values

$$\frac{\sqrt{3}}{\sin z} \quad \text{and} \quad \frac{-\sqrt{3}}{\sin z}.$$

Each of these may be used to define a branch of 1) and this branch is a one-valued function of z in $\mathfrak{B}$. If instead of $\mathfrak{B}$ we take a cyclic set $\mathfrak{C}$ relative to $+1$ or -1, the function of z just defined, which is one-valued in $\mathfrak{B}$, is two-valued in $\mathfrak{C}$.

Thus a function which is one-valued relative to one domain may be many-valued in some other. Conversely by taking on a part $\mathfrak{B}$ of the domain of definition $\mathfrak{A}$ of a many-valued function we may employ one of its branches to define a one-valued function of z relative to $\mathfrak{B}$.

2. It is important to remember that the functions we deal with in the following are one-valued in the domain $\mathfrak{A}$ under consideration unless the contrary is stated, or unless it is obvious from the matter in hand.

We make also another limitation. The domain for which a given function w is defined will always be a *region* [70, 1], unless the contrary is stated.

For example, the domain of definition $\mathfrak{A}$ of the function 1) is a region. For $z = a$ being any point of $\mathfrak{A}$ we may obviously describe a circle $\mathfrak{c}$ about a such that all points within $\mathfrak{c}$ belong to $\mathfrak{A}$. The reader will also note that the domain of definition of all the elementary functions defined in Chapter IV are regions.

For example, the domain of

$$w = \log z$$

is the point set $\mathfrak{A}$ formed of the whole z-plane excluding the origin $z = 0$. This function is infinite-valued in $\mathfrak{A}$; but any one of its branches is a one-valued function in a connex acyclic relative to $z = 0$.

As another example, the domain of definition of

$$w = \tan z = \frac{\sin z}{\cos z}$$

is a set $\mathfrak{A}$ embracing the whole z-plane excluding the points $\frac{\pi}{2} + m\pi$. Obviously, $\mathfrak{A}$ is a region.

3. Let w be a function of z defined over some point set $\mathfrak{A}$. To each point $z = x + iy$ in $\mathfrak{A}$, w will have one or more values,

$$w = u + iv. \tag{3}$$

The values of u, v will depend on the position of z in $\mathfrak{A}$, that is, on the values of x, y. Thus u, v are real functions of the two real independent variables x, y. If w is one-valued, so are u and v.

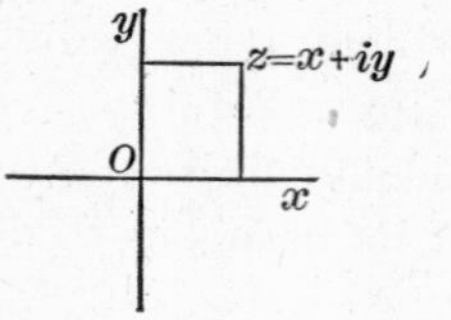

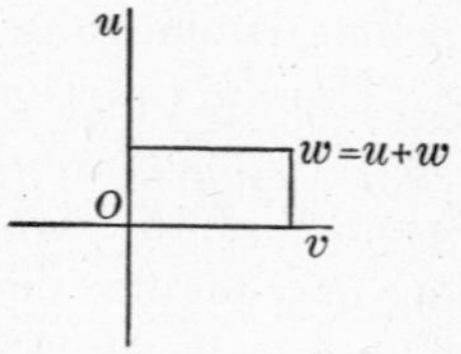

Conversely, let

$$u(x, y) \quad , \quad v(x, y)$$

be two real functions of the real variables x, y defined over some domain $\mathfrak{A}$. If we set

$$z = x + iy, \tag{4}$$

then to each point x, y of $\mathfrak{A}$ will correspond a value of z. By means of 3) we can now define a function w of z by stating that at the point z, w shall have the value 3) when u and v are given the values that they have at the point x, y corresponding to this value of z as defined in 4).

Example 1. Let

$$u = e^x \cos y \quad , \quad v = e^x \sin y. \tag{5}$$

To a given value of z, correspond a pair of values x, y determined by 4). For these values of x, y, the relations 5) define the values of u, v. These put in 3) determine the value w has for this value of z. Thus

$$w = e^x \cos y + ie^x \sin y$$

is a function of z. It happens to be the exponential function e^z [54, 5)].

Example 2. Let

$$u = x^2 + y^2 \quad , \quad v = -2\,xy.$$

Then we must consider from the foregoing definition

$$w = (x^2 + y^2) - i \cdot 2\,xy$$

as a function of z.

4. *Images.* Let

$$w = f(z) \tag{6}$$

be a function of z defined over a point set $\mathfrak{A}$. When z ranges over $\mathfrak{A}$, w will range over some point set, call it $\mathfrak{B}$, in the w-plane. It is convenient to call $\mathfrak{B}$ the *image* of $\mathfrak{A}$ afforded by 6). We write

$$\mathfrak{B} \sim \mathfrak{A}.$$

This we may read: $\mathfrak{B}$ is the image of $\mathfrak{A}$, or $\mathfrak{B}$ corresponds to $\mathfrak{A}$.

The relation 6) establishes thus a relation between the points of $\mathfrak{A}$ and $\mathfrak{B}$. If f is a one-valued function in $\mathfrak{A}$, to a point $z = a$ in $\mathfrak{A}$ will correspond but one point $w = b$ in $\mathfrak{B}$. If f is on the other hand a many-valued function in $\mathfrak{A}$, to $z = a$ will correspond more than one point in $\mathfrak{B}$, as b', b'', b''' $\cdots$. If $b^{(m)}$ is one of these points, we may write

$$b^{(m)} \sim a$$

which we read: $b^{(m)}$ corresponds to a.

When to each point a in $\mathfrak{A}$, there corresponds but one point b in $\mathfrak{B}$, and to each b in $\mathfrak{B}$ but one a in $\mathfrak{A}$, we say the correspondence between $\mathfrak{A}$ and $\mathfrak{B}$ is *one to one* or *unipunctual*. This we may write

$$\mathfrak{B} \sim \mathfrak{A} \quad , \quad \text{unipunctually}.$$

83. Limits, Continuity. 1. Let w be a one-valued function of z defined about $z = a$. Suppose as $z \doteq a$, that the values of w converge to some value l. We say l is the limit of w for $z = a$ and write

$$\lim_{z=a} w = l \quad ; \quad \text{or } w \doteq l \text{ as } z \doteq a. \tag{1}$$

Geometrically this means that having described an ϵ circle about the point l in the w-plane there exists a $\delta > 0$ such that when z is restricted to lie in a δ circle about $z = a$, the center excluded, the corresponding values of w fall in the ϵ circle.

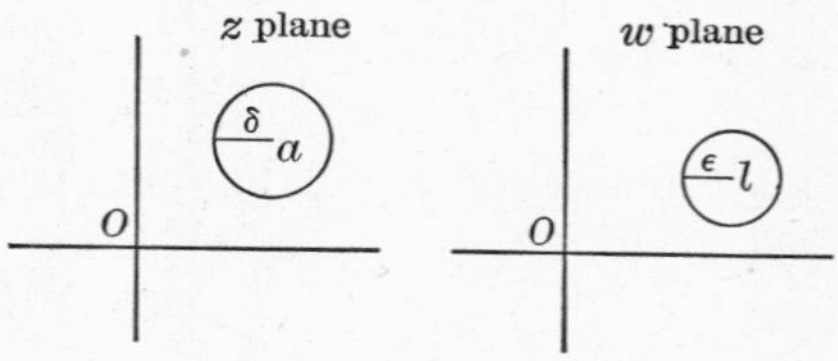

Expressed in ϵ language the relation 1) means that for each $\epsilon > 0$, there exists some $\delta > 0$ such that

$$|w - l| < \epsilon \quad \text{for all } 0 < |z - a| < \delta. \tag{2}$$

The reader will note the perfect analogy of this definition with the definition of a limit given in Chapter V where the variables are real. From this follows that the ordinary properties of limits employed in the calculus will also hold here.

Thus if

$$f(z) \doteq r \quad , \quad g(z) \doteq s \quad \text{as } z \doteq a,$$

then

$$\lim_{z=a}(f + g) = r + s,$$

$$\lim_{z=a} f \cdot g = r \cdot s.$$

If $|g(z)| \geq$ some $\gamma > 0$ near $z = a$,

$$\lim_{z=a} \frac{f}{g} = \frac{r}{s},$$

etc.

2. Suppose we write

$$w = u + iv \quad , \quad l = \lambda + i\mu \quad , \quad a = \alpha + i\beta,$$

where u, v are one-valued functions of x, y about the point α, β. Obviously if

$$u \doteq \lambda \quad , \quad v \doteq \mu \tag{3}$$

as x, y converges to the point α, β, then

$$w \doteq \lambda + i\mu = l \qquad \text{as } z \doteq a.$$

Conversely if

$$w \doteq l \qquad \text{as } z \doteq a,$$

necessarily 3) holds.

3. *Continuity*. Let z describe a continuous path P in the z-plane; if the corresponding values of w define a continuous curve in the w-plane, we say w is continuous.

To obtain an analytic formulation of this we have only to repeat the considerations of 69, with slight modifications. This leads us to define as follows:

Let w be a one-valued function of z defined about the point $z = a$. Let w have the value α at $z = a$. If

$$\lim_{z=a} w = \alpha,$$

we say w is *continuous at a*. If w is continuous at each point of some domain $\mathfrak{A}$, we say w is continuous in $\mathfrak{A}$.

4. As in 2, let $w = u + iv$. The same considerations show that for w to be continuous at $z = a = \alpha + i\beta$ it is necessary and sufficient that $u(x, y)$, $v(x, y)$ be continuous at the point α, β.

5. If w is continuous and $\neq 0$ at $z = a$, w is $\neq 0$ in some circle $\mathfrak{c}$ described about a.

For let $w = \alpha$ at $z = a$. Then for each $\epsilon > 0$ there exists a $\mathfrak{c}$ such that

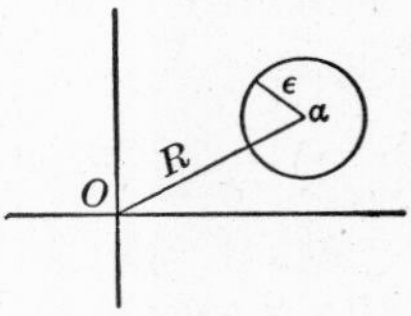

$$|w(z) - \alpha| < \epsilon \qquad \text{for any } z \text{ in } \mathfrak{c},$$

or what is the same,

$$\alpha - \epsilon < w(z) < \alpha + \epsilon. \tag{1}$$

If we take ϵ such that $\epsilon < |\alpha| = R$, this relation shows that

$$|w(z)| \geq \eta \qquad \text{where } \eta = |\alpha| - \epsilon > 0 \tag{2}$$

for all z in $\mathfrak{c}$.

6. If w is continuous at $z = a$,

$$|w(z)| < \text{some } G \tag{3}$$

for any z in some circle $\mathfrak{c}$ about a.

This follows at once from 1).

7. The inequalities 1), 2) may be extended to any connex $\mathfrak{C}$ as follows:

If w is continuous and $\neq 0$ in the connex $\mathfrak{C}$, the numerical value of w never sinks below some positive constant η in $\mathfrak{C}$, or

$$|w(z)| \geq \eta > 0 \qquad \text{in } \mathfrak{C}. \tag{4}$$

For suppose $w \doteq 0$ as z ranges over a set of points $a_1, a_2 \cdots$ in $\mathfrak{C}$ which converge to a. In symbols suppose

$$\lim_{n=\infty} w(a_n) = 0. \tag{5}$$

Now w being continuous,

$$w(a) = \lim_{n=\infty} w(a_n).$$

Thus $w = 0$ at $z = a$ by 5), and this contradicts the hypothesis that $w \neq 0$ in $\mathfrak{C}$.

8. If w is continuous in the connex $\mathfrak{C}$,

$$|w(z)| < \text{some } G \quad , \quad \text{in } \mathfrak{C}. \tag{6}$$

For if not, suppose $|w(z)| \doteq +\infty$ as z ranges over some set of points $a_1, a_2 \cdots$ in $\mathfrak{C}$ which $\doteq a$. But w being continuous at $z = a$, the relation 3) holds in c. But then

$$\lim_{n=\infty} |w(a_n)| \text{ cannot be } +\infty.$$

Thus if 6) does not hold, we are led to a contradiction.

Differentiation

84. 1. Let w be a one-valued function about the point $z = a$. When the independent variable z passes from $z = a$ to $z = a + h$, that is, when z receives an increment $h = \Delta z$, the function $w(z)$ receives an increment

$$\Delta w = w(a+h) - w(a).$$

The quotient

$$\frac{\Delta w}{\Delta z} = \frac{w(a+h) - w(a)}{h} \tag{1}$$

is called the difference quotient as in the calculus. If

$$\lim_{h=0} \frac{w(a+h) - w(a)}{h} \tag{2}$$

exists, we say w has a differential coefficient at $z = a$, whose value is the limit 2). It is denoted by $w'(a)$. If the limit 2) exists for each point z of a region $\mathfrak{A}$, it defines a function of z denoted by

$$\frac{dw}{dz} \text{ or by } w'(z)$$

and called the derivative of $w(z)$. The value of $w'(z)$ at $z=a$ is of course $w'(a)$.

2. The reader will note that this definition of the differential coefficient $w'(a)$ is entirely analogous to the definition when the variable is real, given in 72. The only difference lies in the fact that in the calculus, h is restricted to move on an axis about the point $h=0$, while in 2) h is any complex number $\neq 0$, in some circle about the point $h=0$.

3. Let us note that if w has a differential coefficient at $z=a$, w must be continuous at a.

For by hypothesis the limit 2) exists and is finite. As the denominator $h \doteq 0$, the numerator must also $\doteq 0$. But then

$$w(a+h) \doteq w(a),$$

which is the definition of continuity, 83, 3.

4. By reasoning exactly as in the calculus we can show that

$$\frac{d(f+g)}{dz} = f'(z) + g'(z), \tag{3}$$

$$\frac{d(fg)}{dz} = fg' + gf', \tag{4}$$

$$\frac{d}{dz}\left(\frac{f}{g}\right) = \frac{gf' - fg'}{g^2} \tag{5}$$

hold under the same conditions as when the variable is real. To illustrate this let us show that 5) *holds in any region* $\mathfrak{A}$ *in which* $g \neq 0$.

For let us set $h = \Delta z$,

$$w = \frac{f}{g}, \quad \bar{g} = g(z+h).$$

Then
$$\frac{\Delta w}{\Delta z} = \frac{g\Delta f - f\Delta g}{g\bar{g}\Delta z} = \frac{1}{\bar{g}}\frac{\Delta f}{\Delta z} - \frac{f}{g}\cdot\frac{1}{\bar{g}}\frac{\Delta g}{\Delta z}. \tag{6}$$

If Δz is taken so small at a given point z that $z+h$ lies in $\mathfrak{A}$, $\bar{g}$ is $\neq 0$. Next we note that

$$\lim_{\Delta z=0} g = \lim_{h=0} g(z+h) = g(z),$$

since g is continuous by 3. Passing now to the limit $\Delta z = 0$ in 6), we get 5).

5. By the aid of the foregoing we can find the derivative of a rational integral function

$$f = a_0 + a_1 z + a_2 z^2 + \cdots + a_m z^m.$$

For as in the calculus we show that

$$\frac{dz^n}{dz} = nz^{n-1}.$$

Thus by 3),
$$\frac{df}{dz} = a_1 + 2\,a_2 z + \cdots + ma_m z^{n-1}.$$

Also the derivative of a rational function

$$k = \frac{a_0 + a_1 z + \cdots + a_m z^m}{b_0 + b_1 z + \cdots + b_n z^n} = \frac{f}{g}$$

can be found by 5).

6. Let us prove here a theorem we shall need later.

If $w = f(z)$ has a differential coefficient $f'(a) \neq 0$ at $x = a$, there exists a $\delta > 0$ such that Δw does not vanish when $z = a + \Delta z$ is restricted to $D_\delta^*(a)$.

For as
$$\lim_{\Delta z=0} \frac{\Delta w}{\Delta z} = f'(a) \quad , \quad \text{at } z = a,$$

we have
$$\Delta w = \{f'(a) + \epsilon'\}\,\Delta z \tag{7}$$

where $|\,\epsilon'\,| < \epsilon$ if only $0 < |\,\Delta z\,| <$ some δ.

If now we take $0 < \epsilon < |f'(a)|$

we see that $f'(a) + \epsilon'$ cannot vanish when $0 < |\,\Delta z\,| < \delta$. Thus Δw cannot vanish under this restriction, as 7) shows.

85. The Derivative of a Power Series. 1. Let the power series

$$P(z) = a_0 + a_1 z + a_2 z^2 + \cdots \tag{1}$$

have $\mathfrak{C}$ as a circle of convergence. We show that P has a derivative within $\mathfrak{C}$, viz.:

$$P'(z) = a_1 + 2a_2 z + 3a_3 z^2 + \cdots \tag{2}$$

For by 43, 5)

$$P(z+h) = P(z) + hP_1(z) + \frac{1}{2!}h^2 P_2(z) + \cdots \tag{3}$$

where

$$P_1 = a_1 + 2a_2 z + 3a_3 z^2 + \cdots \tag{4}$$

which is the series on the right side of 2). As z is an arbitrary but fixed point, let us write 3)

$$P(z+h) = b_0 + b_1 h + b_2 h^2 + \cdots \tag{5}$$

This converges absolutely as long as the point $z + h$ lies within $\mathfrak{C}$, that is as long as

$$\eta = |h| \leq \text{some } \delta.$$

The adjoint of 5) is

$$\mathfrak{P} = \beta_0 + \beta_1 \eta + \beta_2 \eta^2 + \cdots$$

and as this converges for $\eta = \delta$,

$$\beta_0 + \beta_1 \delta + \beta_2 \delta^2 + \cdots = \beta_0 + \beta_1 \delta + \delta^2 \{\beta_2 + \beta_3 \delta + \beta_4 \delta^2 + \cdots\}$$

is convergent. Hence

$$\mathfrak{Q} = \beta_2 + \beta_3 \delta + \beta_4 \delta^2 + \cdots \tag{6}$$

is convergent.

From 3) and 5) we have

$$\frac{\Delta P}{\Delta z} = \frac{P(z+h) - P(z)}{h} = P_1(z) + h\{b_2 + b_3 h + \cdots\}$$

$$= P_1(z) + hQ. \tag{7}$$

Now each term of $Q = b_2 + b_3 h + b_4 h^2 + \cdots$

is numerically $\leq$ the corresponding term of the series 6) when $|h| < \delta$. Thus

$$|Q| < \mathfrak{Q}, \text{ a constant.}$$

Hence $hQ \doteq 0$ as $h \doteq 0$. Hence, passing to the limit $h = 0$ in 7), we get 2). We have thus this result:

The function of z defined by a power series 1) *has a derivative within its circle of convergence, which is obtained by differentiating* 1) *term by term.*

2. Let us show that :

The derivative series 2) *has the same circle of convergence* $\mathfrak{C}$ *as the series* 1).

For let z be any point within $\mathfrak{C}$; let b be any point within $\mathfrak{C}$ such that

$$\frac{\zeta}{\beta} < 1. \tag{8}$$

Since 1) is convergent at b,

$$\alpha_n \beta^n < \text{some } M \qquad n = 0, 1, 2 \cdots$$

by 30, 3. Let us now look at the adjoint of 2); it is

$$\alpha_1 + 2\,\alpha_2\zeta + 3\,\alpha_3\zeta^2 + \cdots \tag{9}$$

Its mth term is

$$m\alpha_m\zeta^{m-1} = \frac{m\alpha_m\beta^m}{\beta}\left(\frac{\zeta}{\beta}\right)^{m-1} < \frac{mM}{\beta}\left(\frac{\zeta}{\beta}\right)^{m-1}.$$

Thus each term of 9) is < the corresponding term of the series

$$\frac{M}{\beta}\sum_1^\infty m\left(\frac{\zeta}{\beta}\right)^{m-1}. \tag{10}$$

This last series is convergent by 21, Ex. 1 by virtue of 8). Hence 9) is convergent and hence 2) is absolutely convergent.

The series 2) cannot converge for any z without $\mathfrak{C}$. For then 9) would converge for some $\zeta >$ the radius of $\mathfrak{C}$. Thus

$$\alpha_0 + \alpha_1\zeta + 2\,\alpha_2\zeta^2 + 3\,\alpha_3\zeta^3 + \cdots$$

is convergent for this value of ζ. Hence *a fortiori*

$$\alpha_0 + \alpha_1\zeta + \alpha_2\zeta^2 + \alpha_3\zeta^3 + \cdots$$

is convergent, and thus 1) converges at a point without $\mathfrak{C}$, which is impossible.

3. Since

$$e^z = 1 + \frac{z}{1\,!} + \frac{z^2}{2\,!} + \cdots$$

$$\sin z = \frac{z}{1\,!} - \frac{z^3}{3\,!} + \frac{z^5}{5\,!} - \cdots$$

$$\cos z = 1 - \frac{z^2}{2\,!} + \frac{z^4}{4\,!} - \cdots$$

etc., we have, differentiating these series termwise,

$$\frac{de^z}{dz} = 1 + \frac{z}{1!} + \frac{z^2}{2!} + \cdots = e^z,$$

$$\frac{d \sin z}{dz} = 1 - \frac{z^2}{2!} + \frac{z^4}{4!} - \cdots = \cos z,$$

$$\frac{d \cos z}{dz} = -\frac{z}{1!} + \frac{z^3}{3!} - \cdots = -\sin z.$$

Similarly $$\frac{d \cdot \sinh z}{dz} = \cosh z \quad , \quad \frac{d \cdot \cosh z}{dz} = \sinh z.$$

86. The Cauchy-Riemann Equations. 1. In the foregoing article we have been able to find the derivatives of e^z, $\sin z$, $\sinh z \cdots$ because these functions are defined by means of power series. In other cases the following theorem is of great service ; it also has a deeper significance from a theoretical point of view.

Let $w = u + iv$ be a one-valued function of $z = x + iy$ in the domain $\mathfrak{A}$. Let u, v considered as functions of the real variables x, y have continuous first partial derivatives which satisfy

$$\frac{\partial u}{\partial x} = \frac{\partial v}{\partial y} \quad , \quad \frac{\partial u}{\partial y} = -\frac{\partial v}{\partial x} \tag{1}$$

in $\mathfrak{A}$. Then w has a derivative in $\mathfrak{A}$ and

$$\frac{dw}{dz} = \frac{\partial u}{\partial x} + i\frac{\partial v}{\partial x} = \frac{\partial v}{\partial y} + \frac{1}{i}\frac{\partial u}{\partial y}. \tag{2}$$

For
$$\frac{\Delta w}{\Delta z} = \frac{\Delta u}{\Delta z} + i\frac{\Delta v}{\Delta z}.$$

But by 73, 4,
$$\Delta u = \frac{\partial u}{\partial x}\Delta x + \frac{\partial u}{\partial y}\Delta y + \alpha\Delta x + \beta\Delta y, \tag{3}$$

$$\Delta v = \frac{\partial v}{\partial x}\Delta x + \frac{\partial v}{\partial y}\Delta y + \gamma\Delta x + \delta\Delta y, \tag{4}$$

where $|\alpha|$, $|\beta|$, $|\gamma|$, $|\delta|$ are all $< \frac{\epsilon}{4}$

if $0 < |\Delta z| <$ some η. Thus, using 1),

$$\frac{\Delta w}{\Delta z} = \frac{\frac{\partial u}{\partial x}(\Delta x + i\Delta y) + i\frac{\partial v}{\partial x}(\Delta x + i\Delta y)}{\Delta x + i\Delta y} + \epsilon'$$

$$= \frac{\partial u}{\partial x} + i\frac{\partial v}{\partial x} + \epsilon', \tag{5}$$

where $$\epsilon' = \frac{\alpha\Delta x + \beta\Delta y + i(\gamma\Delta x + \delta\Delta y)}{\Delta z}.$$

Now $$|\Delta x| \quad , \quad |\Delta y| \quad \text{are} \quad \leq |\Delta z|;$$

hence $$|\epsilon'| \leq |\alpha| + |\beta| + |\gamma| + |\delta| < \epsilon.$$

This says that $$\epsilon' \doteq 0 \quad \text{as} \quad \Delta z \doteq 0$$

Hence, passing to the limit $\Delta z = 0$ in 5), we get 2).

2. The equations 1) play a very important part in the theory of functions. They are called the Cauchy-Riemann equations.

From 5) we have, on using 2),

$$\Delta w = \{w'(z) + \epsilon'\}\,\Delta z, \tag{6}$$

where $\epsilon' \doteq 0$ with Δz.

For later use we note here an important property of ϵ':

Let $w(z)$ be one-valued about each point of a connex $\mathfrak{C}$, and let $w'(z)$ be continuous in $\mathfrak{C}$. Then $\epsilon' \doteq 0$ uniformly in $\mathfrak{C}$; that is, for each $\epsilon > 0$, there exists a $\delta > 0$ such that

$$|\epsilon'| < \epsilon \qquad \textit{provided } 0 < |\Delta z| < \delta;$$

moreover the same δ holds wherever z is taken in $\mathfrak{C}$.

For by 73, 5, $\alpha, \beta, \gamma, \delta \doteq 0$ uniformly in $\mathfrak{C}$.

87. Derivatives of the Elementary Functions. 1. Let us apply the theorem of 86, 1 to find the derivatives of the elementary transcendental functions. We have

$$w = e^z = e^x(\cos y + i \sin y)$$

so that here $$u = e^x \cos y \qquad v = e^x \sin y.$$

We have at once $$\frac{\partial u}{\partial x} = e^x \cos y = \frac{\partial v}{\partial y},$$

$$\frac{\partial u}{\partial y} = -e^x \sin y = -\frac{\partial v}{\partial x}.$$

As these are continuous functions of x, y in the whole x, y plane, the Cauchy-Riemann conditions are satisfied. We have, therefore, by 86, 2)

$$\frac{dw}{dz} = \frac{\partial u}{\partial x} + i\frac{\partial v}{\partial x} = e^x \cos y + ie^x \sin y$$

$$= e^x(\cos y + i \sin y)$$

$$= e^z. \qquad (1$$

This result agrees with that already found in 85, 3 by another method. The method just employed may be used to prove the more general relation

$$\frac{d \cdot e^{az}}{dz} = ae^{az}. \qquad (2$$

2. Similarly, we can show that

$$\frac{d \cdot \sin z}{dz} = \cos z. \qquad (3$$

For

$$w = \sin z = \sin (x + iy)$$

$$= \sin x \cosh y + i \cos x \sinh y, \text{ by 58, 13)}$$

$$= u + iv.$$

Here

$$\frac{\partial u}{\partial x} = \cos x \cosh y = \frac{\partial v}{\partial y},$$

$$\frac{\partial u}{\partial y} = \sin x \sinh y = -\frac{\partial v}{\partial x}.$$

These derivatives are continuous and satisfy the Cauchy-Riemann equations 86, 1). Hence

$$\frac{d \cdot \sin z}{dz} = \cos x \cosh y - i \sin x \sinh y$$

$$= \cos z, \text{ by 58, 14)},$$

which is 3).

Another way to establish 3) is to start from

$$\sin z = \frac{e^{iz} - e^{-iz}}{2\,i},$$

which we derived in 58, 8). Then by 2),

$$\frac{d \cdot \sin z}{dz} = \frac{ie^{iz} + ie^{-iz}}{2\,i} = \frac{e^{iz} + e^{-iz}}{2} = \cos z$$

by 58, 7).

3. Let us now show that

$$\frac{d \cdot \log z}{dz} = \frac{1}{z}, \tag{4}$$

taking one of the branches of $\log z$, say

$$\log z = \log r + i\phi + 2\,m\pi i.$$

Hence

$$u = \log r \quad , \quad v = \phi + 2\,m\pi,$$

where

$$r = \sqrt{x^2 + y^2} \quad , \quad \phi = \text{arctg}\,\frac{y}{x}.$$

Now at any point different from the origin

$$\frac{\partial u}{\partial x} = \frac{\partial u}{\partial r} \cdot \frac{\partial r}{\partial x} = \frac{1}{r} \cdot \frac{x}{r} = \frac{x}{r^2} = \frac{\partial v}{\partial y},$$

$$\frac{\partial u}{\partial y} = \frac{\partial u}{\partial r} \cdot \frac{\partial r}{\partial y} = \frac{1}{r} \cdot \frac{y}{r} = \frac{y}{r^2} = -\frac{\partial v}{\partial x}.$$

Thus the Cauchy-Riemann conditions are satisfied, and

$$\frac{d \cdot \log z}{dz} = \frac{\partial u}{\partial x} + i\frac{\partial v}{\partial x} = \frac{x}{r^2} - i\frac{y}{r^2}$$

$$= \frac{1}{r}(\cos\phi - i\sin\phi)$$

$$= \frac{1}{z},$$

which is 4).

4. In a similar manner we find :

$$\frac{d \cdot \text{arc}\sin z}{dz} = \frac{1}{\sqrt{1 - z^2}} \quad , \quad \frac{d\,\text{arctg}\,z}{dz} = \frac{1}{1 + z^2}, \tag{5}$$

$$\frac{d \cdot \sinh z}{dz} = \cosh z \quad , \quad \frac{d \cdot \cosh z}{dz} = \sinh z. \tag{6}$$

In the first equation of 5) we must choose the right branch of $\sqrt{1 - z^2}$ for the particular branch chosen for arc $\sin z$, just as in the calculus.

88. Inverse Functions. 1. Let w be a one-valued function of z in the domain $\mathfrak{A}$. As z ranges over $\mathfrak{A}$, let w range over a domain $\mathfrak{B}$, in such a way that to each point w in $\mathfrak{B}$ corresponds but a single point z in $\mathfrak{A}$. Then the relation

$$w = f(z) \tag{1}$$

may be used to define a one-valued function of w,

$$z = g(w) \tag{2}$$

in the domain $\mathfrak{B}$. We call this the *inverse function.* If, on the other hand, to several values of z in $\mathfrak{A}$ corresponds the same value of w in $\mathfrak{B}$, the relation 1) may be used to define a many-valued inverse function.

We have already had examples of inverse functions. Thus

$$w = e^z$$

defines the logarithmic function.

We note that $\mathfrak{B}$ is the image of $\mathfrak{A}$ afforded by 1). When the inverse function 2) is one-valued in $\mathfrak{B}$,

$$\mathfrak{B} \sim \mathfrak{A}, \text{ unipunctually.}$$

2. Let us now consider the derivative of the one-valued inverse function 2). We have the theorem:

If $\frac{dw}{dz}$ *is* $\neq 0$ *in* $\mathfrak{A}$, *the inverse function has a derivative*

$$\frac{dz}{dw} = \frac{1}{\frac{dw}{dz}} \quad \text{in } \mathfrak{B}. \tag{3}$$

For

$$\frac{\Delta z}{\Delta w} = \frac{1}{\frac{\Delta w}{\Delta z}}, \tag{4}$$

provided $\Delta w \neq 0$. Now by 84, 6, $\Delta w \neq 0$, if we take $0 < |\Delta z| <$ some δ. Thus, passing to the limit $\Delta z = 0$ in 4), we get 3).

3. We have already found the derivative of $\log z$ directly from its analytic expression

$$\log r + i\phi + 2\, m\pi i.$$

It may, however, be found much more easily from the theorem 2 above. We start from

$$w = e^z.$$

We have seen in 62 that $\log w$ is one-valued in any connected region $\mathfrak{B}$, acyclic relative to the branch point $w = 0$. While w

ranges over $\mathfrak{B}$, let z range over $\mathfrak{A}$. Since

$$\frac{dw}{dz} = e^z$$

never vanishes for any value of z by 54, 2, we have at once from 3),

$$\frac{dz}{dw} = \frac{1}{e^z} = \frac{1}{w}$$

or

$$\frac{d \cdot \log w}{dw} = \frac{1}{w}$$

which is the result obtained by another method in 87, 3, the letters w, z being of course interchanged.

4. Let us find the derivative of the arc sin function considered as the inverse of

$$w = \sin z.$$

We saw, 64, 3, that the branch points of

$$z = \text{arc} \sin w$$

are

$$w = \pm 1.$$

Thus in any connected region $\mathfrak{B}$ in the w-plane, which is acyclic relative to both of these points, any branch of the arc sin function, call it z, is a one-valued function of w. While w ranges over $\mathfrak{B}$, let z describe the set $\mathfrak{A}$. Then in $\mathfrak{A}$

$$\frac{dw}{dz} = \cos z$$

does not vanish. For $\cos z$ vanishes only for

$$z = \pm \frac{\pi}{2}, \quad \pm 3 \cdot \frac{\pi}{2} \quad \cdots$$

But for these points $w = \pm 1$, and these points are by hypothesis excluded from the region $\mathfrak{B}$.

Thus all the conditions of the theorem in 2 are satisfied. We have therefore

$$\frac{d \cdot \text{arc} \sin w}{dw} = \frac{dz}{dw} = \frac{1}{\frac{dw}{dz}} = \frac{1}{\cos z}$$

$$= \frac{1}{\sqrt{1 - w^2}}, \tag{5}$$

where the radical must have the sign of cos z at the point z which corresponds to the value of w in question.

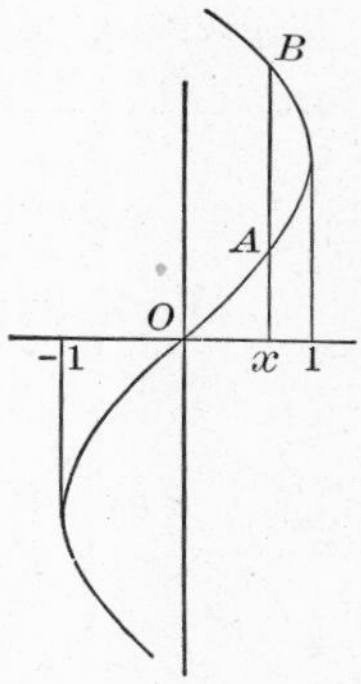

5. In the calculus we have

$$\frac{d \text{ arc } \sin x}{dx} = \frac{1}{\sqrt{1-x^2}}.$$

As the radical is two-valued, the sign to be taken depends on the branch of the function we employ. Thus if we take the branch which passes through A in the figure, we must take the + sign. If we take the branch which passes through B, the figure shows that we must take the − sign.

89. Function of a Function. 1. Let us now extend the familiar relation

$$\frac{dw}{dt} = \frac{dw}{dz} \cdot \frac{dz}{dt}$$

for complex values, under certain restrictions.

Let z be a function of t in some domain $\mathfrak{T}$. When t ranges over $\mathfrak{T}$ let z range over a domain $\mathfrak{Z}$ in the z-plane. Let w be a function of z in $\mathfrak{Z}$. Then w may be considered as a function of the variable t in $\mathfrak{T}$.

Example 1. Let

$$z = \sin t \quad , \quad w = e^z.$$

While t ranges over the whole t-plane $\mathfrak{T}$, z ranges over the whole z-plane $\mathfrak{Z}$. Thus

$$w = e^{\sin t}$$

is a function of t in $\mathfrak{T}$.

Example 2. Let

$$z = \sqrt{1-t^2},$$

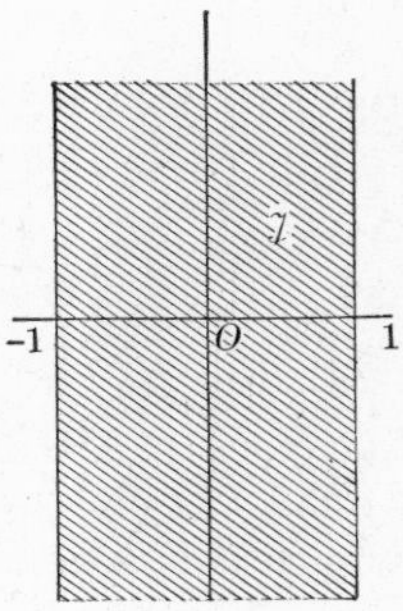

taking that branch which corresponds to $z = +1$ for $t = 0$. Then z is a one-valued function in any connected region $\mathfrak{T}$, which, as in the figure, is acyclic relative to the branch points $t = \pm 1$ of the radical. When t ranges over $\mathfrak{T}$, let z range over $\mathfrak{Z}$. Let

$$w = \log z,$$

taking that branch which $= 0$ for $z = 1$. Then w is a one-valued function of z in $\mathfrak{Z}$. Hence

$$w = \log\sqrt{1 - t^2}$$

is a one-valued function of t in $\mathfrak{T}$.

2. We now prove the following theorem:

Let z have the derivative $\frac{dz}{dt}$ in $\mathfrak{T}$, and w the derivative $\frac{dw}{dz}$ in $\mathfrak{Z}$. If $\frac{dz}{dt}$ does not vanish in $\mathfrak{T}$, then

$$\frac{dw}{dt} = \frac{dw}{dz} \cdot \frac{dz}{dt} \text{ in } \mathfrak{T}. \tag{1}$$

For

$$\frac{\Delta w}{\Delta t} = \frac{\Delta w}{\Delta z} \cdot \frac{\Delta z}{\Delta t}, \tag{2}$$

provided $\Delta z \neq 0$. But by 84, 6, this condition is satisfied if we take

$$0 < |\Delta t| < \text{some } \delta > 0$$

since by hypothesis $\frac{dz}{dt} \neq 0$ in $\mathfrak{T}$. Let now $\Delta t \doteq 0$, at the same time $\Delta w \doteq 0$. Thus, passing to the limit $\Delta t = 0$ in 2), we get 1).

3. We may use the relation 1) to calculate the derivative of complicated expressions, just as we do in the calculus. Thus, let

$$w = e^{\sin z}.$$

We set

$$w = e^u \quad , \quad u = \sin z.$$

Then

$$\frac{dw}{du} = e^u = e^{\sin z} \quad ; \quad \frac{du}{dz} = \cos z.$$

Hence

$$\frac{dw}{dz} = e^{\sin z} \cos z \tag{3}$$

for all z for which $\cos z \neq 0$.

For these exceptional values of z it is easy to show directly from $\frac{\Delta w}{\Delta z}$ that $\frac{dw}{dz} = 0$, so that the relation 3) holds even in this case.

4. Let us find the derivative of

$$w = (1 + z)^{\mu}, \tag{4}$$

where μ is a constant. Then by 63,

$$w = e^{\mu \log(1+z)}.$$

Let us set

$$u = \mu \log (1 + z) \quad , \quad w = e^u.$$

The only branch point of u is $z = -1$. Let then $\mathfrak{Z}$ be any connected acyclic region relative to this point. Let now u denote one of the branches of $\mu \log (1 + z)$; it is one-valued in $\mathfrak{Z}$, and

$$\frac{du}{dz} = \frac{\mu}{1+z}.$$

As this does not $= 0$ in $\mathfrak{Z}$ we have, from 1),

$$\frac{dw}{dz} = w \cdot \frac{\mu}{1+z} = \mu(1+z)^{\mu-1}. \tag{5}$$

5. We have proved the important relation 1) on the hypothesis that $\frac{dz}{dt}$ is $\neq 0$. This condition is imposed by the fact that our reasoning requires that Δz cannot $= 0$ as $\Delta t \doteq 0$. In 118, 9 we shall see that the relation 1) holds even when $\frac{dz}{dt} = 0$, *provided* $\frac{dz}{dt}$ *is a continuous function of* t.

90. Functions having a Derivative. 1. Let us return to 86 and prove the important converse theorem:

Let $f(z) = u + iv$ *be one-valued in the domain* $\mathfrak{A}$ *and have a derivative* $f'(z)$. *Then* u, v *satisfy the Cauchy-Riemann equations*

$$\frac{\partial u}{\partial x} = \frac{\partial v}{\partial y} \quad , \quad \frac{\partial u}{\partial y} = -\frac{\partial v}{\partial x} \tag{1}$$

at each point of $\mathfrak{A}$.

For at any point z of $\mathfrak{A}$

$$\frac{\Delta f}{\Delta z} = \frac{\Delta u}{\Delta z} + i\frac{\Delta v}{\Delta z}. \tag{2}$$

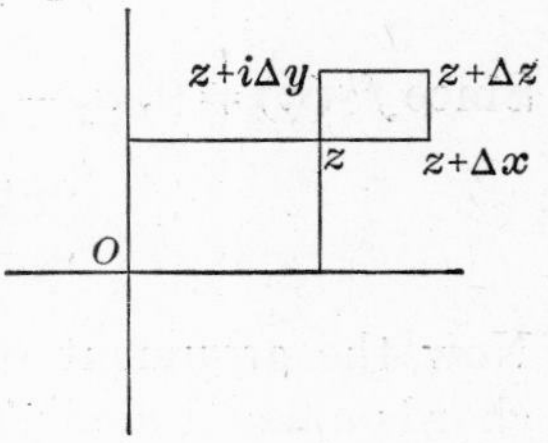

Since $f'(z)$ exists at z the left side of 1) must converge to $f'(z)$ however $z' = z + \Delta z$ converges to z. Suppose we allow z' to $\doteq z$ by making it approach z along a parallel to the x-axis. As in general

$$\Delta z = \Delta x + i\Delta y,$$

we see here that $\Delta y = 0$. Then 2) becomes

$$\frac{\Delta f}{\Delta z} = \frac{\Delta f}{\Delta x} = \frac{\Delta u}{\Delta x} + i\frac{\Delta v}{\Delta x}.$$

Passing to the limit, we get

$$f'(z) = \frac{\partial u}{\partial x} + i\frac{\partial v}{\partial x}. \tag{3}$$

Let us now allow $z' \doteq z$ by making it approach z along a parallel to the y-axis. Then $\Delta x = 0$ and hence $\Delta z = i\Delta y$. Thus 2) becomes

$$\frac{\Delta f}{\Delta z} = \frac{\Delta f}{i\Delta y} = \frac{1}{i}\frac{\Delta u}{\Delta y} + \frac{\Delta v}{\Delta y}.$$

Passing to the limit, we get

$$f'(z) = \frac{1}{i}\frac{\partial u}{\partial y} + \frac{\partial v}{\partial y}. \tag{4}$$

Comparing 3), 4) gives

$$\frac{\partial u}{\partial x} + i\frac{\partial v}{\partial x} = -i\frac{\partial u}{\partial y} + \frac{\partial v}{\partial y}.$$

Equating the real and imaginary parts gives 1).

2. *Conformal Representation. Let $w = f(z)$ be a one-valued function having a derivative in the connex $\mathfrak{A}$. Let C_1, C_2 be two curves within $\mathfrak{A}$ which meet at $z = a$, making the angle θ with each other. If $f'(a) \neq 0$, their images $\mathfrak{C}_1$, $\mathfrak{C}_2$ will cut at the same angle θ, at the point $\alpha \sim a$.*

For let a_1, a_2 be points on C_1, C_2 near a, as in the figure. Let $\alpha_1 = f(a_1)$, $\alpha_2 = f(a_2)$. Then

$$\alpha_1 - \alpha = \{f'(a) + \epsilon_1\}(a_1 - a),$$

$$\alpha_2 - \alpha = \{f'(a) + \epsilon_2\}(a_2 - a).$$

Since $f'(a) \neq 0$, $\alpha_2 - \alpha$ is $\neq 0$ if a_2 is sufficiently near a. Hence

$$\frac{\alpha_1 - \alpha}{\alpha_2 - \alpha} = \frac{a_1 - a}{a_2 - a} \cdot \frac{f'(a) + \epsilon_1}{f'(a) + \epsilon_2}. \tag{5}$$

Now the argument of the left side is the angle Φ between the chords $\alpha_1\alpha$ and $\alpha_2\alpha$. The argument of the first factor on the right of 5) is the angle Θ between the chords a_1a and a_2a. Since ϵ_1, ϵ_2 are numerically small, the argument of the second factor on the right of 5) is a small number δ. Thus, taking the arguments of both sides, we have

$$\Phi = \Theta + \delta$$

on choosing Θ properly. Now as a_1 and $a_2 \doteq a$, $\Theta \doteq \theta$ and $\delta \doteq 0$. Hence $\phi \doteq \theta$ also.

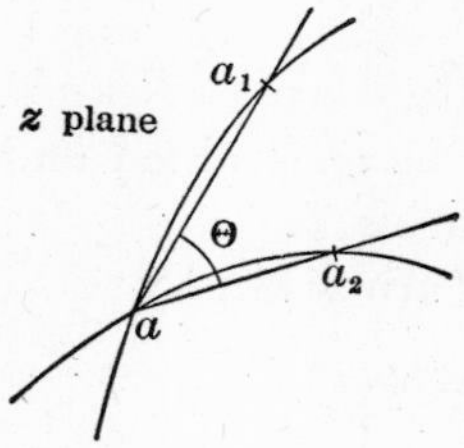

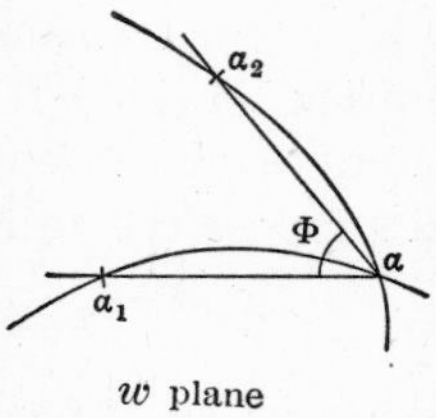

3. This property of the representation of the z-plane on the w-plane afforded by a function $w = f(z)$ having a derivative is of great importance in many applications of the function theory. We see that if $f'(z) \neq 0$ in circle $\mathfrak{C}$ about $z = a$, to any little triangle T in $\mathfrak{C}$ will correspond a triangle $\mathfrak{T}$ in the w-plane which is the more nearly similar to T, the smaller T is. This we may state briefly by saying: *The image of an infinitesimal triangle T, in which $f'(z) \neq 0$, is a similar infinitesimal triangle $\mathfrak{T}$ in the w-plane.*

For this reason the representation of the z-plane afforded by the function $w = f(z)$, is said to be *conformal*, where $f'(z) \neq 0$.

We have had examples of this conformality in studying the representations afforded by the exponential and the sine functions in 57 and 60.

Thus in the case of $w = e^z$, we divided the z-plane into a set of rectangles and found that their images are a set of circles and their radii which, of course, cut each other at right angles.

In the case of $w = \sin z$, the rectangles had as images a set of confocal ellipses and hyperbolas which also cut orthogonally.

4. The reader should note that if $f(z)$ is not one-valued or if $f'(z)$ is 0 or does not exist at $z = a$, the reasoning in 2 breaks down. We cannot say the representation is conformal at this point.

For example,

$$w = \sqrt{z},$$

which we studied in 49, is not one-valued at $z = 0$. Two radii in the z-plane passing through this point and making an angle θ with each other have as images two radii going through the point $w = 0$ and making an angle $\frac{1}{2}\theta$ with each other. Thus the representation is certainly not conformal at this point.

Integration

91. Definition. 1. Let $f(z) = u + iv$ be one-valued and continuous on the curve C whose end points are a, b.

We will suppose the equations of C are given by

$$x = \phi(t) \quad , \quad y = \psi(t), \tag{1}$$

as t ranges over an interval $\mathfrak{T} = (\alpha, \beta)$. We will suppose that $\phi'(t)$, $\psi'(t)$ are continuous in $\mathfrak{T}$; also that the correspondence between C and $\mathfrak{T}$ is unipunctual.

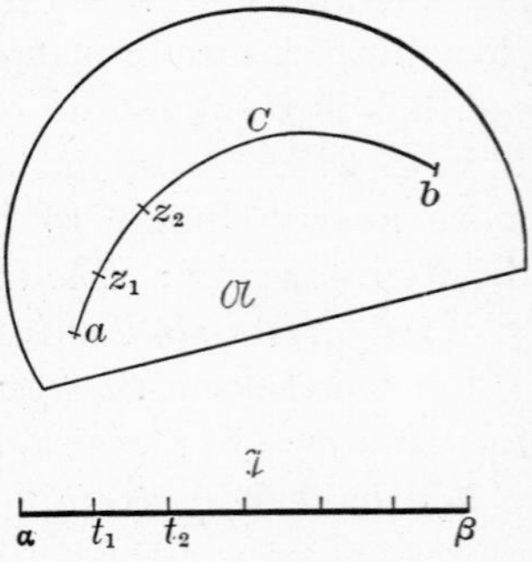

Let us effect a division of $\mathfrak{T}$ of norm η by interpolating the points

$$t_1, t_2, t_3 \cdots$$

To these points will correspond the points

$$z_1, z_2, z_3 \cdots \tag{D}$$

on C which effect a division D of norm δ, say, of C. Moreover

$$\delta \doteq 0, \text{ as } \eta \doteq 0.$$

Let us now calculate the sum

$$\Sigma f(z_m)\Delta z_m = f(z_1)(z_1 - a) + f(z_2)(z_2 - z_1) + \cdots \tag{2}$$

Since $\Delta z = \Delta x + i\Delta y$, we have

$$f(z)\Delta z = (u + iv)(\Delta x + i\Delta y) = u\Delta x - v\Delta y + i(u\Delta y + v\Delta x).$$

Thus

$$\Sigma f(z)\Delta z = \Sigma(u\Delta x - v\Delta y) + i\Sigma(u\Delta y + v\Delta x).$$

The sum 2) has, therefore, the value

$$\Sigma(u_m\Delta x_m - v_m\Delta y_m) + i\Sigma(u_m\Delta y_m + v_m\Delta x_m). \tag{3}$$

Suppose now we let $\delta \doteq 0$, the sums in 3) converge to curvilinear integrals. Thus the limit of 2) exists; we denote it by

$$\int_C f(z)dz \quad \text{or by} \quad \int_a^b f(z)dz. \qquad (4$$

We have, therefore,

$$\int_C f(z)dz = \lim_{\delta=0} \Sigma f(z_m)\Delta z_m$$

$$= \int_C (udx - vdy) + i\int_C (udy + vdx). \qquad (5$$

2. *Example*. Let us evaluate

$$\int_C z^2dz,$$

where C is an arc of the circle

$$x = r\cos t \quad , \quad y = r\sin t.$$

Here

$$f(z) = z^2 = (x+iy)^2 = x^2 - y^2 + 2\,xyi,$$

hence

$$u = x^2 - y^2 \quad , \quad v = 2\,xy,$$

$$dx = -\,r\sin tdt \quad , \quad dy = r\cos tdt,$$

$$udx = -\,r^3(\cos^2 t - \sin^2 t)\sin tdt = r^3(\sin^3 t - \cos^2 t\sin t)dt,$$

$$vdy = 2\,r^3\cos^2 t\sin tdt,$$

$$udy = r^3(\cos^2 t - \sin^2 t)\cos tdt,$$

$$vdx = -\,2\,r^3\cos t\sin^2 tdt.$$

Thus

$$\int_C fdz$$

$$= r^3\int_\alpha^\beta (\sin^3 t - 3\cos^2 t\sin t)dt + ir^3\int_\alpha^\beta (\cos^3 t - 3\sin^2 t\cos t)dt. \qquad (6$$

In particular, we note that if C is the whole circle, call it $\mathfrak{C}$,

$$\int_{\mathfrak{C}} z^2dz = 0. \qquad (7$$

92. Properties of Integrals. 1. The definition

$$\int_a^b f(z)dz = \lim_{\delta=0} \Sigma f(z_m)\Delta z_m \qquad (1$$

of an integral of a function of a complex variable is entirely analogous to the definition when the variable is real. The only difference is the path of integration; in one case it is a piece of the x-axis, in the other it is a curve C in the z-plane.

From this we conclude that many of the properties of integral developed in the calculus can be extended to the integral 1). Thus we have

$$\int_a^b f(z)dz = -\int_b^a f(z)dz \tag{2}$$

$$\int_a^b f(z)dz = \int_a^c fdz + \int_c^b fdz, \tag{3}$$

where c is a point on C.

$$\int_a^b (f+g)dz = \int_a^b fdz + \int_a^b gdz. \tag{4}$$

2. As an exercise let us prove the very important relation

$$\left|\int_C f(z)dz\right| \leq G\overline{C}, \tag{5}$$

where

$$|f(z)| \leq G \quad , \quad \text{on } C, \tag{6}$$

and $\overline{C}$ on the right of 5) stands for the length of the path of integration C. We have at once

$$|\Sigma f(z_m)\Delta z_m| \leq \Sigma |f(z_m)| \cdot |\Delta z_m| \leq G\Sigma |\Delta z_m| \tag{7}$$

on using 6). As

$$\Delta z_m = z_m - z_{m-1},$$

we see that $|\Delta z_m|$ is the length of the chord joining the points z_{m-1}, z_m on C. Thus, referring to the figure in 91,

$$\Sigma |\Delta z_m| \tag{8}$$

in 7) is the length of all the chords corresponding to the division D of norm δ. Now by definition the length of the curve C is the limit of 8) as $\delta \doteq 0$. Thus passing to the limit $\delta = 0$ in 7), we have 5).

3. From 5) we have the useful relation

$$\int_C \frac{f(z)dz}{(z-a)^n} \leq \frac{2\pi G}{R^{n-1}} \qquad n \text{ an integer} \tag{9}$$

where C is a circle of radius R about $z = a$, and

$$|f(z)| \leq G \qquad \text{on } C.$$

For the integrand is here

$$\frac{f(z)}{(z-a)^n} \qquad \text{which is numerically} \leq \frac{G}{R^n}$$

and the length of C is $2\pi R$.

93. Fundamental Integral Theorem. 1. In 91, 5) we have seen how the calculation of an integral may be reduced to that of two line integrals. In a great many cases it may be effected by a far simpler formula, as the following theorem shows.

Let $F(z)$ be one-valued about each point of a connex $\mathfrak{A}$, and have a continuous derivative $f(z)$. Then

$$\int_a^b f(z)dz = F(b) - F(a), \tag{1}$$

where if $F(z)$ is many valued in $\mathfrak{A}$, $F(b)$ is the value which $F(a)$ acquires as z ranges over the path of integration C.

For let us effect a division of C of norm δ by interpolating the points $z_1, z_2 \cdots z_{n-1}$. Then by 86, 6),

$$F(z_1) - F(a) = f(z_1)\Delta z_1 + \epsilon_1 \Delta z_1$$

$$F(z_2) - F(z_1) = f(z_2)\Delta z_2 + \epsilon_2 \Delta z_2$$

$$\cdot \quad \cdot \quad \cdot \quad \cdot \quad \cdot \quad \cdot \quad \cdot \quad \cdot \quad \cdot \quad \cdot \quad \cdot$$

$$F(b) - F(z_{n-1}) = f(z_n)\Delta z_n + \epsilon_n \Delta z_n.$$

Adding, we get

$$F(b) - F(a) = \Sigma f(z_m)\Delta z_m + \Sigma \epsilon_m \Delta z_m. \tag{2}$$

Now by the theorem in 86, 2, the $|\epsilon_m|$ are all $< \epsilon$ for any $\delta <$ some δ_0. Thus the last term in 2) is numerically

$$\leq \epsilon \Sigma |\Delta z_m| \leq \epsilon \overline{C},$$

where $\overline{C}$ is the length of C. This shows that the last term in 2) has the limit 0 as $\delta \doteq 0$. Thus passing to the limit $\delta = 0$ in 2), we get 1).

2. The relation 1) is merely an obvious extension of the similar relation in the integral calculus. It is just as useful in the function theory as it is in the calculus.

3. A particular case of the theorem 1 and one of especial value is:

Let $F(z)$ be one-valued in the connex $\mathfrak{A}$ and have a continuous derivative $f(z)$. Then

$$\int_C f(z)dz = 0 \tag{3}$$

for any closed curve C in $\mathfrak{A}$.

94. Examples. To make the reader feel perfectly at home with integration in the complex domain, we give now a number of examples.

Example 1. Let us evaluate

$$\int_a^b z^m dz \qquad m \text{ a positive integer.}$$

Here

$$f(z) = z^m \quad , \quad F(z) = \frac{1}{m+1} z^{m+1}.$$

Thus $F(z)$ is one-valued and $f(z)$ continuous in any connex. Hence for all a, b we have

$$\int_a^b f(z)dz = \frac{1}{m+1}\{b^{m+1} - a^{m+1}\}. \tag{1}$$

The reader will note that the integral considered in 91, 2 is a special case of 1).

Example 2.

$$\int_a^b \frac{dz}{z^m} \qquad m \text{ a positive integer} > 1.$$

Here

$$f(z) = \frac{1}{z^m}$$

is continuous in any connex $\mathfrak{A}$ which does not contain the origin, as for example the ring in Fig. 1.

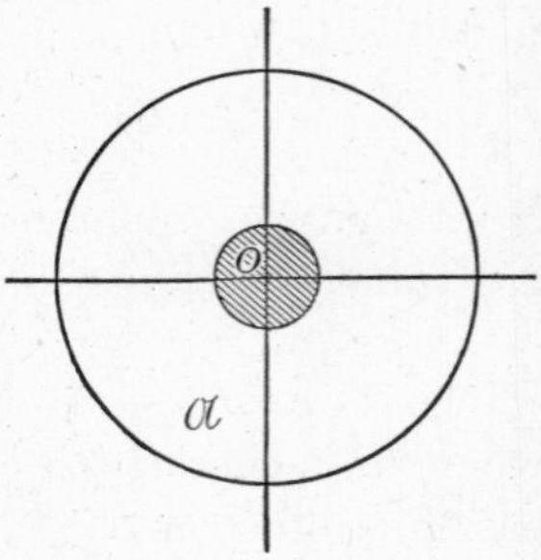

FIG. 1.

Also

$$F(z) = \frac{1}{1-m} \cdot \frac{1}{z^{m-1}}$$

is one-valued and has $f(z)$ as derivative in $\mathfrak{A}_i$.

Hence

$$\int_a^b \frac{dz}{z^m} = \frac{1}{1-m}\left\{\frac{1}{b^{m-1}} - \frac{1}{a^{m-1}}\right\}. \tag{2}$$

Example 3.

$$\int_a^b \frac{dz}{z}. \tag{3}$$

Here

$$f(z) = \frac{1}{z} \quad , \quad F(z) = \log z.$$

Thus $f(z)$ is continuous in any connex $\mathfrak{A}$ which does not contain the origin O. Unless $\mathfrak{A}$ is acyclic relative to O, $F(z)$ is many-valued. In fact if we start from $z = a$ with one of the determinations of $\log \epsilon$ at this point which we call F_a and allow z to describe a circuit $\mathfrak{K}$ about O in the positive sense, F_a will acquire the value $F_b = F_a + 2\pi i$ at the end of $\mathfrak{K}$.

Thus

$$\int_{\mathfrak{K}} \frac{dz}{z} = 2\pi i. \tag{4}$$

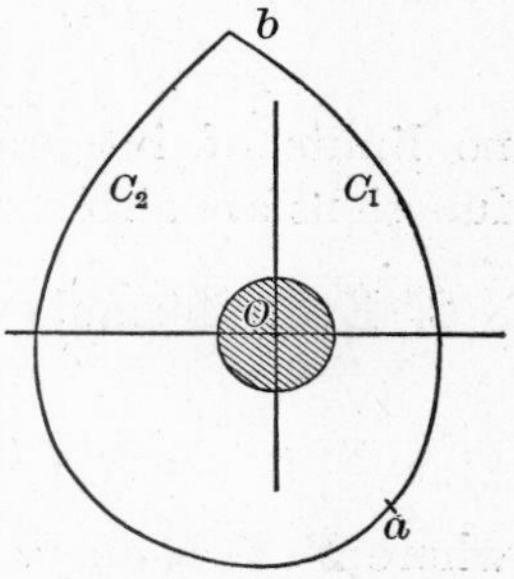

FIG. 2.

Let now J_1 be the value of 3) for the path C_1 in Fig. 2, and J_2 for the path C_2. Then

$$J_2 = J_1 - 2\pi i. \tag{5}$$

For $C_1 C_2$ forms a circuit $\mathfrak{K}$ about O. Hence by 4)

$$2\pi i = \int_{C_1 C_2 - 1} = \int_C + \int_{C_2^{-1}} = \int_{C_1} - \int_{C_2} = J_1 - J_2,$$

wnich proves 5).

Finally let $\mathfrak{B}$ be any connex, acyclic relative to the origin. Then any one of the branches of the logarithmic function is one-valued in $\mathfrak{B}$. Denoting this by $\log z$, we have

$$\int_a^b \frac{dz}{z} = \log b - \log a, \tag{6}$$

and this integral is independent of the path of integration, provided of course it remains in $\mathfrak{B}$.

95. The Indefinite Integral. 1. Returning to the relation 1) in 93, let us write it

$$\int_a^z f(z)dz = F(z) - F(a). \qquad (1$$

Let $G(z)$ be any other function of z which has the continuous derivative $f(z)$. Then similarly

$$\int_a^z f(z)dz = G(z) - G(a). \qquad (2$$

Comparing 1) and 2), we have

$$G(z) = F(z) + C,$$

where C is a constant. The functions F, G are called *primitive functions* of $f(z)$. They are denoted by

$$\int f(z)dz,$$

no limits of integration appearing in this symbol. Primitive functions are also called *indefinite integrals.*

2. Every formula of differentiation as

$$\frac{dF(z)}{dz} = f(z),$$

where $F(z)$ is one-valued and $f(z)$ is continuous in some connex $\mathfrak{A}$, gives rise to a formula of integration,

$$\int f(z)dz = F(z).$$

Thus any table of indefinite integrals given in the calculus may be extended to the complex variable z, provided z is restricted to a connex in which $F(z)$ is one-valued and $f(z)$ is continuous.

3. *Let the one-valued continuous function $f(z)$ be such that*

$$G(z) = \int_a^z f(z)dz \qquad (3$$

is also one-valued in the connex $\mathfrak{A}$. Then

$$\frac{dG}{dz} = f(z). \qquad (4$$

For let $z = u$ be some point of $\mathfrak{A}$. Then

$$\Delta G = G(u+h) - G(u) = \int_a^{u+h} f dz - \int_a^u f dz$$
$$= \int_u^{u+h} f dz.$$

As $f(z)$ is continuous,
$$f(z) = f(u) + \epsilon',$$

and $|\epsilon'| < \epsilon$ for $|h| <$ some δ. Thus

$$\frac{\Delta G}{\Delta z} = \frac{1}{h}\int_u^{u+h} \{f(u) + \epsilon'\} dz.$$

As u is a fixed value of z, $f(u)$ is constant. Hence

$$\frac{\Delta G}{\Delta z} = \frac{f(u)}{h}\int_u^{u+h} dz + \frac{1}{h}\int_u^{u+h} \epsilon' dz = J + K. \qquad (5$$

Obviously
$$J = f(u).$$

Also
$$\left|\int_u^{u+h} \epsilon' dz\right| < \epsilon |h|.$$

Hence
$$|K| < \epsilon.$$

Thus $K \doteq 0$ as $h \doteq 0$. Hence letting $h = \Delta z \doteq 0$ in 5), we get

$$G'(u) = f(u),$$

which is 4).

96. Change of Variable. 1. Every student of the calculus knows that a change of variable is often of great assistance in calculating an integral. It is equally useful in the function theory. To this end we establish the following theorem:

Let $f(z)$ be continuous on the curve C. When z ranges over C, let $u = \phi(z)$ range over a curve D which corresponds to C unipunctually. Let the inverse function $z = \psi(u)$ have a continuous derivative on D. Then

$$\int_C f(z) dz = \int_D f\{\psi(u)\}\psi'(u) du. \qquad (1$$

For let us effect a division of norm δ of D, by interpolating the points $u_1, u_2 \cdots$. To these points on D will correspond points

$z_1, z_2 \cdots$ on C which effect a division of norm, say γ, of C. Also

$$z_m - z_{m-1} = \Delta z_m = \psi'(u_m)\Delta u_m + \epsilon_m \Delta u_m,$$

where

$$|\epsilon_m| < \epsilon \qquad m = 1, 2, \cdots$$

provided $\delta <$ some δ_0. Thus

$$\Sigma f(z_m)\Delta z_m = \Sigma f\{\psi(u_m)\}\psi'(u_m)\Delta u_m + \Sigma f\epsilon_m \Delta u_m. \tag{2}$$

Now the last term on the right is numerically

$$< \epsilon G \Sigma |\Delta u_m| \leq \epsilon G \overline{D}, \tag{3}$$

where $\overline{D}$ is the length of the D curve, and $|f(z)| \leq G$. But 3) states that the last term of 2) has the limit 0 as $\delta \doteq 0$. Thus passing to the limit in 2), we get 1).

2. *Example.* Let us calculate

$$J = \int_a^b \frac{dz}{\sqrt{z^2 - c^2}} \quad , \quad c \neq 0 \tag{4}$$

along a curve C lying in a connex $\mathfrak{A}$ which is acyclic relative to the branch points $\pm c$ of the radical. We change the variable, setting

$$u = \phi(z) = z + \sqrt{z^2 - c^2}. \tag{5}$$

Then

$$z = \psi(u) = \frac{c^2 + u^2}{2u} \tag{6}$$

if $u \neq 0$. But u cannot vanish, for if it did, 5) gives

$$z + \sqrt{z^2 - c^2} = 0 \quad , \quad \text{or } z^2 = z^2 - c^2,$$

which requires $c = 0$, and this is contrary to hypothesis. From 6) we see that z is a one-valued function of u. To the end points of C correspond

$$\alpha = \phi(a) \quad , \quad \beta = \phi(b)$$

on the curve $D \sim C$.

From 6) we have

$$dz = \psi'(u)du = \frac{u^2 - c^2}{2u^2} du.$$

From 5), 6) we have

$$\sqrt{z^2 - c^2} = u - z = \frac{u^2 - c^2}{2u}.$$

Thus 4) becomes, on using 1),

$$J=\int_\alpha^\beta \frac{du}{u}=\log\frac{\beta}{\alpha}$$

$$=\log\frac{b+\sqrt{b^2-c^2}}{a+\sqrt{a^2-c^2}}. \qquad (7$$

97. Integration by Parts. 1. This is another important method for evaluating integrals. Analogous to the calculus we have the following theorem :

In the connex $\mathfrak{A}$, let the one-valued functions $f(z)$, $g(z)$ have continuous derivatives. Then

$$\int_a^b fg'\,dz=\Big[f(z)\,g(z)\Big]_a^b-\int_a^b gf'\,dz. \qquad (1$$

For let us set

$$h(z)=f\cdot g.$$

Then

$$h'(z)=fg'+gf'.$$

Hence by 93, 1),

$$\int_a^b(fg'+gf')dz=h(b)-h(a)=\Big[fg\Big]_a^b$$

or

$$\int_a^b fg'\,dz+\int_a^b gf'\,dz=\Big[fg\Big]_a^b,$$

which gives 1).

2. The relation 1) still holds when f and g are many-valued in the connex $\mathfrak{A}$, provided we take the right determinations of f, g and their derivatives along the path of integration as 91, 1 shows.

Example. Let us evaluate

$$J=\int z\log z dz. \qquad (2$$

We set

$$f(z)=\log z \quad , \quad g'(z)=z.$$

Then

$$f'(z)=\frac{1}{z} \quad , \quad g(z)=\frac{z^2}{2}.$$

Thus

$$J=\tfrac{1}{2}z^2\log z-\tfrac{1}{2}\int zdz$$

$$=\tfrac{1}{2}z^2(\log z-\tfrac{1}{2}). \qquad (3$$

98. Differentiation with Respect to a Parameter. 1. Let $g(z, u)$ be a one-valued continuous function of z on a curve C for each value of u in some connex $\mathfrak{U}$. Then the integral

$$\phi(u) = \int_C g(z, u)dz \tag{1}$$

defines a function of u over $\mathfrak{U}$.

For example, let

$$g(z, u) = \frac{f(z)}{(z-u)^n}, \quad n \text{ an integer,}$$

where $f(z)$ is a continuous function of z alone. Also for purposes of illustration let C be a simple closed curve, as a circle or an ellipse, and let the connex $\mathfrak{U}$ lie within C as in the figure. Then $z - u$ does not $= 0$ as z ranges over C, for any point u in $\mathfrak{U}$. Then

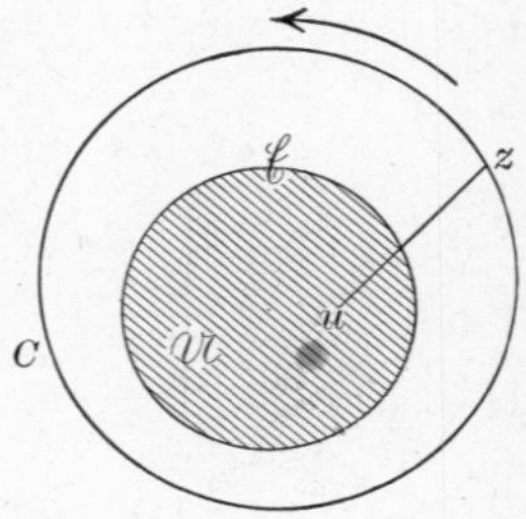

$$\int_C \frac{f(z)dz}{(z-u)^n} \tag{2}$$

defines a function of u over $\mathfrak{U}$. We shall see that the integrals of the type 2) are very important. Returning to the general integral 1), we prove the following theorem, which will be of great service later.

If $\frac{\partial g}{\partial u}$ *is a continuous function of* u *and* z *for each* u *in* $\mathfrak{U}$ *and* z *on* C, *we have*

$$\phi'(u) = \int_C \frac{\partial g}{\partial u} dz. \tag{3}$$

For by definition

$$\phi'(u) = \lim_{\Delta u = 0} \frac{\Delta \phi}{\Delta u}.$$

But

$$\Delta\phi = \phi(u+h) - \phi(u) \quad , \quad h = \Delta u$$

$$= \int_C g(z, u+h)\,dz - \int_C g(z, u)\,dz$$

$$= \int_C \{g(z, u+h) - g(z, u)\}\,dz. \tag{4}$$

Now as in 86, 2

$$g(z, u+h) - g(z, u) = \{g_u'(z, u) + \epsilon'\} \Delta u,$$

where $|\epsilon'| < \epsilon$ provided $0 < |\Delta u| <$ some δ; moreover this holds for every z on C.

Thus 4) gives

$$\frac{\Delta\phi}{\Delta u} = \int_C g_u'(z, u)\, dz + \int_C \epsilon'\, dz. \qquad (5$$

But

$$\left|\int_C \epsilon'\, dz\right| < \epsilon \bar{C},$$

as we have often seen. But this states that the last term of 5) has the limit 0 as $\delta \doteq 0$. Hence passing to the limit $\delta = 0$ in 5), we get 3).

Functions Defined by Series

99. Steady Convergence. 1. Let us consider series of the type

$$F = f_1(z) + f_2(z) + f_3(z) + \cdots = \sum_1^\infty f_m(z), \qquad (1$$

whose terms $f_m(z)$ are one-valued functions of z in some point set $\mathfrak{A}$, which may be unlimited. The simplest case of such series is power series

$$a_0 + a_1(z-a) + a_2(z-a)^2 + \cdots \qquad (2$$

or changing the variable by replacing $z - a$ by z,

$$a_0 + a_1 z + a_2 z^2 + \cdots \qquad (3$$

By means of such series we defined the functions e^z, $\sin z$, etc.

If the series 1) converges in $\mathfrak{A}$, it will define a one-valued function of z in $\mathfrak{A}$, which we denote by $F(z)$. We wish to study such functions relative to continuity, differentiation, and integration.

To this end we introduce the notion of steady convergence.

Suppose for all z in $\mathfrak{A}$ the mth term is such that

$$|f_m(z)| \leq g_m \qquad m = 1, 2, \cdots \qquad (4$$

where $g_1, g_2 \cdots$ are positive constants.

Let the series

$$G = g_1 + g_2 + g_3 + \cdots \qquad (5$$

converge. Obviously the series 1) converges absolutely for each z in $\mathfrak{A}$, by virtue of the relations 4). In this case we have compared a series whose terms are *functions of* z with a convergent series whose terms are *constant*. This kind of convergence we call *steady*. We therefore define:

The series 1) *converges steadily in* $\mathfrak{A}$ *when each term of* 1) *satisfies the relation* 4) *for all* z *in* $\mathfrak{A}$, *and when the corresponding constant term series* 5) *is convergent.*

2. An important property of steadily convergent series is the following:

If the series 1) *converges steadily in* $\mathfrak{A}$, *the remainder after* n *terms* $\overline{F}_n$ *is numerically* $<\epsilon$ *for any* $n >$ *some* m, *for every* z *in* $\mathfrak{A}$.

For the G series being convergent,

$$\overline{G}_m < \epsilon \quad , \quad \text{for some } m.$$

Hence as the g_m are positive

$$\overline{G}_n < \epsilon \qquad a \text{ fortiori for any } n > m.$$

But from 4),

$$|\overline{F}_n| \leq \overline{G}_n$$

for any z in $\mathfrak{A}$.

3. *Power Series. Let the circle of convergence of* 3) *be* C. *Let* D *be a circle lying within* C, *and having the origin as center. Then* 3) *converges steadily in* D.

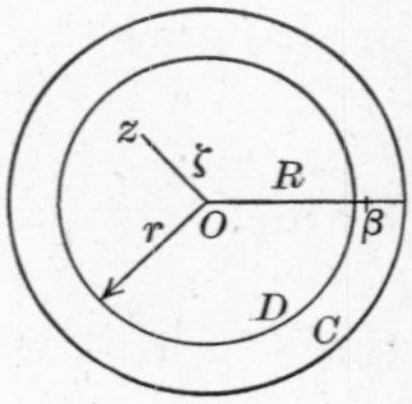

For, let $z = \beta > 0$ be a point lying between the two circles C, D on the real axis. Then as 3) converges absolutely at this point, the constant term series

$$\alpha_0 + \alpha_1\beta + \alpha_2\beta^2 + \cdots \qquad (6$$

is convergent. But for any z in D

$$|a_m z^m| \leq \alpha_m \beta^m \qquad m = 0, 1, 2 \cdots \qquad (7$$

Thus the terms of 3) satisfy the relations 4) for every z in D, and 3) converges steadily in D.

4. The definition of steady convergence may be extended at once to two-way series

$$\sum_{-\infty}^{\infty} f_m(z), \qquad (8$$

and to double series

$$\Sigma f_{r,s}(z). \qquad (9$$

Thus if for every z in some point set $\mathfrak{A}$

$$|f_{r,s}(z)| \leq g_{r,s},$$

and if

$$\Sigma g_{r,s}$$

is convergent, then 9) converges steadily in $\mathfrak{A}$.

5. *Example.* Let us consider the series

$$F = \sum \frac{1}{(z - \omega_{mn})^p}, \tag{10}$$

where p is an integer > 2 and

$$\omega_{mn} = ma + nb \tag{11}$$

as in 41, 5. These series, as we shall see, are very important in the elliptic functions.

Let us describe a circle $\mathfrak{K}$ about the origin and consider the series H formed only of terms of 10) for which the points 11) lie without $\mathfrak{K}$. We show that *the H series converges steadily in $\mathfrak{K}$.*

For

$$\left|\frac{z}{\omega_{mn}}\right| < k < 1$$

for any z in $\mathfrak{K}$ and for any ω_{mn} in H.

Now

$$\frac{1}{z - \omega_{mn}} = \frac{1}{\omega_{mn}} \frac{-1}{1 - \dfrac{z}{\omega_{mn}}}.$$

Hence

$$\left|\frac{1}{z - \omega_{mn}}\right| \leq \frac{C}{|\omega_{mn}|},$$

where C is some constant > 0.

Thus each term of the H series is $\leq$ the corresponding term of the positive constant term series

$$C \sum \frac{1}{|\omega_{mn}|^p},$$

which we saw converges in 41, 5. Thus H converges steadily in the circle $\mathfrak{K}$.

6. Let us show that:

A two-way power series

$$a_0 + a_1 z + a_2 z^2 + \cdots \tag{12}$$
$$+ \frac{b_1}{z} + \frac{b_2}{z^2} + \cdots$$

is steadily convergent in any ring $\mathfrak{R}$ lying within its ring of convergence R.

For let $R = C - D$, and $\mathfrak{R} = \mathfrak{C} - \mathfrak{D}$. Then the series in the first line of 12), call it P, converges steadily in $\mathfrak{C}$. Let now $z = \delta > 0$ be a point on the x-axis between the two circles D and $\mathfrak{D}$. Then the series Q formed of the second line in 12) converges absolutely for $z = \delta$, that is, the positive term series

$$\frac{\beta_1}{\delta} + \frac{\beta_2}{\delta^2} + \frac{\beta_3}{\delta^3} + \cdots \quad , \quad |b_n| = \beta_n \tag{13}$$

is convergent. Let now z be any point on the circle $\mathfrak{D}$ or without it. Then $|z| = \zeta > \delta$; hence each term of

$$Q = \frac{b_1}{z} + \frac{b_2}{z^2} + \frac{b_3}{z^3} + \cdots$$

is numerically $<$ the corresponding term in 13). Thus Q converges steadily for all points on and without $\mathfrak{D}$. Hence 12) converges steadily in the ring $\mathfrak{R}$ formed by $\mathfrak{C}$ and $\mathfrak{D}$.

100. Continuity. 1. It is quite important at times to know if the sum of a series of continuous functions is itself continuous. The following theorem is often useful.

Let the terms of the series

$$F = f_1(z) + f_2(z) + f_3(z) + \cdots \tag{1}$$

be continuous and one-valued about $z = a$. If 1) converges steadily in some circle $\mathfrak{C}$ about a, F is continuous at a.

To prove this we have only to show that

$$\lim_{h=0} F(a+h) = F(a). \tag{2}$$

Let

$$\Delta F = F(a+h) - F(a),$$

then 2) is equivalent to

$$\lim_{h=0} \Delta F = 0. \tag{3}$$

Let us write 1)

$$F = F_m + \overline{F}_m,$$

then

$$\Delta F = \Delta F_m + \Delta \overline{F}_m. \tag{4}$$

Since F converges steadily in $\mathfrak{C}$,

$$|\overline{F}_m(z)| < \frac{\epsilon}{2},$$

for some m and for any z in $\mathfrak{C}$ by 99, 2. Thus, in particular,

$$|\overline{F}_m(a)| < \frac{\epsilon}{2} \quad , \quad |\overline{F}_m(a+h)| < \frac{\epsilon}{2} \quad , \quad a+h \text{ in } \mathfrak{C}.$$

Hence subtracting,

$$|\Delta \overline{F}_m| < \epsilon \quad , \quad \text{or } \lim_{h=0} \Delta \overline{F}_m = 0. \qquad (5$$

Since F_m is the sum of m continuous functions, it is itself continuous. Hence

$$\lim_{h=0} \Delta F_m = 0. \qquad (6$$

Thus letting $h = \Delta z \doteq 0$ in 4), we get 3) on using 5), 6).

2. *The power series*

$$F = a_0 + a_1 z + a_2 z^2 + \cdots \qquad (7$$

is a continuous function of z at any point within its circle of convergence $\mathfrak{C}$.

For let $z = a$ be a point within $\mathfrak{C}$. Let $\mathfrak{K}$ be a circle about $z = 0$ which contains a in its interior. Then we can describe about $z = a$ a circle $\mathfrak{c}$ which lies in $\mathfrak{K}$. As 7) converges steadily in $\mathfrak{K}$ by 99, 3, it does in $\mathfrak{c}$ also, since this is a part of $\mathfrak{K}$. Hence F is continuous at $z = a$ by 1.

3. A property of power series often used is this:

Let the series

$$P = a_0 + a_1 z + a_2 z^2 + \cdots$$

converge about the origin. If $a_0 \neq 0$, P does not vanish in some circle $\mathfrak{c}$ about the origin.

This is an immediate consequence of 83, 5, since P is continuous at $z = 0$.

4. Closely connected with the property of continuity is the following theorem; it embraces 1, in fact, as a special case.

Let

$$F(z) = f_1(z) + f_2(z) + \cdots \qquad (8$$

converge steadily in some circle $\mathfrak{K}$ *about* $z = a$. *Let each*

$$f_n(z) \doteq c_n \quad , \quad as\ z \doteq a.$$

If

$$C = c_1 + c_2 + \cdots$$

is convergent, we have

$$\lim_{z=a} F(z) = \Sigma \lim_{z=a} f_n(z) = C. \tag{9}$$

For we may take m so large that

$$|\overline{F}_m(z)| < \frac{\epsilon}{3} \quad , \quad \overline{C}_m < \frac{\epsilon}{3} \quad , \quad z \text{ in } \mathfrak{K}. \tag{10}$$

Also we may take $\delta > 0$ so small that

$$|F_m(z) - C_m| < \frac{\epsilon}{3} \quad , \quad 0 < |z - a| < \delta, \tag{11}$$

since by hypothesis, $\quad F_m(z) \doteq C_m$ as $z \doteq a$.

Then the relation

$$F - C = F_m - C_m + \overline{F}_m - \overline{C}_m$$

gives

$$|F - C| \leq |F_m - C_m| + |\overline{F}_m| + |\overline{C}_m|$$

$$< \frac{\epsilon}{3} + \frac{\epsilon}{3} + \frac{\epsilon}{3} = \epsilon \qquad \text{by 10), 11)},$$

and this establishes 9).

101. Termwise Integration. 1. In order to integrate a series

$$F(z) = f_1(z) + f_2(z) + \cdots \tag{1}$$

it is usually most convenient to treat it as we would a finite sum and integrate it term by term, or as we say termwise. This method, which suggests itself at once to the reader, is permissible as follows:

Let each term of 1) *be one-valued and continuous in a connex* $\mathfrak{A}$. *If* 1) *converges steadily in* $\mathfrak{A}$, *we may integrate it termwise over any curve* C *in* $\mathfrak{A}$; *that is,*

$$\int_C F(z)dz = \int_C f_1 dz + \int_C f_2 dz + \cdots \tag{2}$$

For being steadily convergent,

$$F(z) = F_n + \overline{F}_n \tag{3}$$

and

$$|\overline{F}_n| < \epsilon \tag{4}$$

for all $n >$ some m, and for all z in $\mathfrak{A}$.

By 100, 1 F is continuous. As F_n is the sum of n continuous functions, it is continuous. Hence $\overline{F}_n$ is continuous. Thus 3) gives

$$\int_C F dz = \int_C F_n dz + \int_C \overline{F}_n dz. \tag{5}$$

By 92, 2,

$$\left| \int_C \overline{F}_n dz \right| < \epsilon \overline{C},$$

where $\overline{C}$ is the length of C. Thus the last term in 5) has the limit 0 as $n \doteq \infty$. Thus letting $n \doteq \infty$ in 5) we have

$$\int_C F dz = \lim_{n=\infty} \int_C F_n dz$$

$$= \lim_{n=\infty} \left\{ \int_C f_1 dz + \cdots + \int_C f_n dz \right\}. \tag{6}$$

Now for the series on the right of 2), that is,

$$\int_C f_1 dz + \int_C f_2 dz + \cdots$$

to converge it is necessary that the sum of its first n terms should converge to some limit. The relation 6) shows that this sum does converge and has as limit the member on the left. Thus 2) holds.

2. From the foregoing we can show that

$$\log(1 - z) = -\left\{ \frac{z}{1} + \frac{z^2}{2} - \frac{z^3}{3} + \cdots \right\} \tag{7}$$

is valid within the unit circle, that is, for $|z| < 1$.

For

$$\frac{1}{1-z} = 1 + z + z^2 + \cdots \qquad \text{if } |z| < 1.$$

Hence
$$\int_0^z \frac{dz}{1-z} = -\log(1-z) = \int_0^z dz + \int_0^z z dz + \cdots$$
$$= z + \tfrac{1}{2} z^2 + \tfrac{1}{3} z^3 + \cdots$$
which is 7).

3. We can show similarly that
$$\operatorname{arctg} z = z - \frac{z^3}{3} + \frac{z^5}{5} - \cdots \qquad |z| < 1. \tag{8}$$
For
$$\frac{1}{1+z^2} = 1 - z^2 + z^4 - z^6 + \cdots \qquad |z| < 1.$$
Hence
$$\int_0^z \frac{dz}{1+z^2} = \operatorname{arctg} z = \int_0^z dz - \int_0^z z^2 dz + \cdots$$
$$= z - \frac{z^3}{3} + \cdots$$
which is 8).

4. The reasoning in 1 shows that 2) holds *provided each term of* 1) *is continuous on the curve* C *and the series* 1) *converges steadily on* C.

5. Since a two-way power series
$$F = \sum_{-\infty}^{\infty} a_n (z-a)^n \tag{9}$$
converges steadily in any ring $\mathfrak{R}$ lying within its ring of convergence, we have for any curve C in $\mathfrak{R}$
$$\int_C F dz = \int_C a_0 dz + a_1 \int_C (z-a) dz + \cdots$$
$$+ a_{-1} \int_C \frac{dz}{z-a} + a_{-2} \int \frac{dz}{(z-a)^2} + \cdots$$
$$= \sum_{-\infty}^{\infty} a_n \int_C (z-a)^n dz. \tag{10}$$

Let now C be a circle $\mathfrak{K}$. Since

$$\int_{\mathfrak{K}} (z-a)^n dz = 0 \qquad n \neq -1,$$

we have

$$\int_{\mathfrak{K}} F dz = 2\pi i a_{-1}. \tag{11}$$

102. Calculation of π. Let us use the relation 8) in 101 to calculate π; it will serve as an exercise in infinite series. Putting $z = \frac{1}{5}$ in that relation we get

$$\alpha = \operatorname{arctg} \frac{1}{5} = \frac{1}{5} - \frac{1}{3} \cdot \frac{1}{5^3} + \frac{1}{5} \cdot \frac{1}{5^5} - \frac{1}{7} \cdot \frac{1}{5^7} + \cdots \tag{1}$$

The error committed in breaking off the summation of any term is less than the next term, as we saw in 15, 1.

From trigonometry we have

$$\tan 2\alpha = \frac{2 \tan \alpha}{1 - \tan^2 \alpha},$$

which gives here

$$\tan 2\alpha = \tfrac{5}{12}.$$

Similarly

$$\tan 4\alpha = \tfrac{120}{119}.$$

Let

$$\beta = 4\alpha - \frac{\pi}{4}. \tag{2}$$

Then

$$\tan \beta = \frac{\tan 4\alpha - 1}{1 + \tan 4\alpha} = \frac{1}{239}.$$

Thus 101, 8) gives

$$\beta = \frac{1}{239} - \frac{1}{3} \cdot \frac{1}{239^3} + \frac{1}{5} \cdot \frac{1}{239^5} - \cdots \tag{3}$$

and the error committed in breaking off the summation at any term is less than the next term. Thus from 1), 2), 3) we get

$$\frac{\pi}{4} = 4\left\{\frac{1}{5} - \frac{1}{3} \cdot \frac{1}{5^3} + \frac{1}{5} \cdot \frac{1}{5^5} - \cdots\right\} - \left\{\frac{1}{239} - \frac{1}{3} \cdot \frac{1}{239^3} + \cdots\right\}.$$

We have now

$$\tfrac{1}{5} = .2 \qquad \frac{1}{3} \cdot \frac{1}{5^3} = .002666667$$

$$\frac{1}{5} \cdot \frac{1}{5^5} = .000064 \qquad \frac{1}{7} \cdot \frac{1}{5^7} = .000001829$$

$$\frac{1}{9} \cdot \frac{1}{5^9} = .000000057 \qquad \frac{1}{11} \cdot \frac{1}{5^{11}} = .000000002.$$

$$\frac{1}{13} \cdot \frac{1}{5^{13}} = .0000000001$$

Thus
$$\alpha = .200064057 - .002668497$$
$$= .197395560$$
is correct to 9 places, and
$$4\,\alpha = .78958224$$
is correct to 8 places.

Also we have
$$\tfrac{1}{239} = .004184100$$
$$\frac{1}{3}\cdot\frac{1}{239^3} = .000000024.$$
Thus
$$\beta = .004184076$$
is correct to 8 places.

Thus
$$\frac{\pi}{4} = .78539816$$
or
$$\pi = 3.1415926\cdots$$
is correct in the last decimal. In fact a more elaborate calculation gives
$$\pi = 3.14159265358\cdots$$

103. Termwise Differentiation. 1. From the theorem on termwise integration of a series given in 101, 1 we can deduce a useful theorem on termwise differentiation :

In the connex $\mathfrak{A}$, *let each term of the convergent series*
$$F = f_1(z) + f_2(z) + \cdots \tag{1}$$
be one-valued and have a continuous derivative. If
$$G = f_1'(z) + f_2'(z) + \cdots \tag{2}$$
converges steadily in $\mathfrak{A}$,
$$G = \frac{dF}{dz}, \quad \text{in } \mathfrak{A}.$$

For by 101, 1
$$\int_a^z G dz = \int_a^z f_1'(z) dz + \int_a^z f_2'(z) dz + \cdots$$
$$= \{f_1(z) - f_1(a)\} + \{f_2(z) - f_2(a)\} + \cdots$$
$$= F(z) - F(a). \tag{3}$$

Thus by 95, 3 we get, on differentiating 3),
$$\frac{dF}{dz} = G.$$

2. *A power series may be differentiated termwise at any point within its circle of convergence.*

For let
$$F = a_0 + a_1 z + a_2 z^2 + \cdots \tag{4}$$
have the circle of convergence $\mathfrak{C}$. Then by 85, 2 the series
$$G = a_1 + 2\,a_2 z + 3\,a_3 z^2 + \cdots$$
obtained from F by differentiating it termwise has the same circle of convergence C. Thus if $\mathfrak{c}$ is a little circle about a point $z = a$ within C, the series F converges in $\mathfrak{c}$, and G converges steadily in $\mathfrak{c}$ by 99, 3. Thus the condition of the theorem 1 holding, we may differentiate 4) termwise, or
$$\frac{dF}{dz} = G = a_1 + 2\,a_2 z + 3\,a_3 z^2 + \cdots$$

Remark. We note this theorem was proved in 85, 1, making use of double series.

3. *A two-way power series* $F = \sum_{-\infty}^{\infty} a_n z^n$ *may be differentiated termwise at any point within its ring of convergence; that is,*
$$\frac{dF}{dz} = \sum_{-\infty}^{\infty} n a_n z^{n-1}.$$

To prove this we need to consider only the special case
$$F = \frac{b_1}{z} + \frac{b_2}{z^2} + \cdots \qquad \mathfrak{K} \text{ circle of convergence.}$$
If we set
$$z = \frac{1}{u},$$
we get
$$F = b_1 u + b_2 u^2 + \cdots$$
and
$$\frac{dF}{du} = b_1 + 2\,b_2 u + \cdots$$
If now we apply 89, 2, we get
$$\frac{dF}{dz} = \frac{dF}{du} \cdot \frac{du}{dz} \qquad \text{since } \frac{du}{dz} = -\frac{1}{z^2} \neq 0 \text{ without } \mathfrak{K}$$
$$= -\frac{1}{z^2}\{b_1 + 2\,b_2 u + \cdots\}$$
$$= -\left\{\frac{b_1}{z^2} + 2\frac{b_2}{z^3} + \cdots\right\}$$
without $\mathfrak{K}$.

4. *Differential Equation for $F(\alpha\beta\gamma z)$.* As an exercise in differentiating power series let us find the derivatives of the hypergeometric series

$$F(\alpha\beta\gamma z) = 1 + \frac{\alpha \cdot \beta}{1 \cdot \gamma} z + \frac{\alpha \cdot \alpha + 1 \cdot \beta \cdot \beta + 1}{1 \cdot 2 \cdot \gamma \cdot \gamma + 1} z^2 + \cdots \qquad (5$$

introduced in 39, 4 and show that it satisfies the differential equation

$$z(z-1)\frac{d^2F}{dz^2} + \{(\alpha + \beta + 1)z - \gamma\}\frac{dF}{dz} + \alpha\beta F = 0. \qquad (6$$

On differentiating 5) termwise we get

$$F'(\alpha\beta\gamma z) = \sum_{n=1}^{\infty} n \frac{\alpha \cdot \alpha + 1 \cdots \alpha + n - 1 \cdot \beta \cdot \beta + 1 \cdots \beta + n - 1}{1 \cdot 2 \cdots n \cdot \gamma \cdot \gamma + 1 \cdots \gamma + n - 1} z^{n-1}$$

$$= \sum_{n=0}^{\infty} \frac{\alpha \cdot \alpha + 1 \cdots \alpha + n \cdot \beta \cdot \beta + 1 \cdots \beta + n}{1 \cdot 2 \cdots n + 1 \cdot \gamma \cdot \gamma + 1 \cdots \gamma + n} z^n$$

$$= \frac{\alpha\beta}{\gamma} \sum_0^{\infty} \frac{\alpha + 1 \cdots \alpha + n \cdot \beta + 1 \cdots \beta + n}{1 \cdot 2 \cdots n + 1 \cdot \gamma + 1 \cdots \gamma + n} z^n$$

$$= \frac{\alpha\beta}{\gamma} F(\alpha + 1,\ \beta + 1,\ \gamma + 1,\ z). \qquad (7$$

Hence

$$F''(\alpha\beta\gamma z) = \frac{\alpha \cdot \beta}{\gamma} F'(\alpha + 1,\ \beta + 1,\ \gamma + 1,\ z)$$

$$= \frac{\alpha \cdot \alpha + 1 \cdot \beta \cdot \beta + 1}{\gamma \cdot \gamma + 1} F(\alpha + 2,\ \beta + 2,\ \gamma + 2,\ z); \qquad (8$$

etc.

To prove that 5) satisfies 6) let us set

$$P_n = \frac{\alpha \cdot \alpha + 1 \cdots \alpha + n - 1 \cdot \beta \cdot \beta + 1 \cdots \beta + n - 1}{1 \cdot 2 \cdots n \cdot \gamma \cdot \gamma + 1 \cdots \gamma + n - 1}.$$

Then the coefficient of z^n in z^2F'' is

$$n(n-1)P_n,$$

in $-zF''$ it is

$$-\frac{n(\alpha+n)(\beta+n)}{\gamma+n}P_n,$$

in $(\alpha+\beta+1)zF'$ it is

$$n(\alpha+\beta+1)P_n,$$

in $-\gamma F'$ it is

$$-\gamma\frac{(\alpha+n)(\beta+n)}{\gamma+n}P_n,$$

in $\alpha\beta F$ it is

$$\alpha\beta P_n.$$

Adding all these gives the coefficient of z^n in the left side of 6). We find it is 0.

CHAPTER VII

ANALYTIC FUNCTIONS

104. Definitions. 1. At this point we begin the study of the theory of functions of a complex variable. The functions considered in this theory are not the general functions considered in Chapter VI, but a subclass of these, viz. those functions which have a continuous derivative. To be more specific, let w have assigned to it a definite value for each point z of the connected region $\mathfrak{A}$ such that w has a continuous derivative in $\mathfrak{A}$. We call w a *one-valued analytic function* of z in $\mathfrak{A}$. Suppose, on the other hand, that w has in general more than one value assigned to it for the points of $\mathfrak{A}$. We will call it a many-valued analytic function if its values can be grouped in branches, each of which is a one-valued analytic function about each point of $\mathfrak{A}$.

2. From this definition it follows that

$$e^z \quad , \quad \cos z \quad , \quad \sin z \quad , \quad \cosh z \quad , \quad \sinh z$$

are one-valued analytic functions in the entire plane. For they each have a continuous derivative for any z.

Similarly

$$\frac{1}{z^2 - 1},$$

for example, is a one-valued analytic function for the region $\mathfrak{A}$ formed of the whole z-plane after deleting $z = \pm 1$, the zeros of the denominator, while

$$\tan z$$

is analytic for the region $\mathfrak{A}$ formed of the whole plane after deleting the infinite point set

$$\cdots \quad -5\frac{\pi}{2} \quad , \quad -3\frac{\pi}{2} \quad , \quad -\frac{\pi}{2} \quad , \quad \frac{\pi}{2} \quad , \quad 3\frac{\pi}{2} \quad , \quad 5\frac{\pi}{2} \quad \cdots$$

On the other hand,

$$\sqrt{1 + z^2}$$

is a two-valued function for the region $\mathfrak{A}$ formed of the whole plane after deleting the branch points $\pm i$, while

$$\log z$$

is an infinite-valued analytic function in the region $\mathfrak{A}$ formed of the whole plane after deleting the origin $z = 0$.

3. A power series

$$P(z) = a_0 + a_1(z - a) + a_2(z - a)^2 + \cdots$$

is an analytic function within its circle of convergence $\mathfrak{C}$.

For by 85, P has a derivative within $\mathfrak{C}$ which is a power series and therefore continuous within $\mathfrak{C}$.

4. The quotient of two power series

$$Q = \frac{a_0 + a_1(z - a) + \cdots}{b_0 + b_1(z - a) + \cdots} \qquad b_0 \neq 0,$$

having a common circle of convergence $\mathfrak{C}$, is an analytic function of z within some circle $\mathfrak{c}$ about the point $z = a$.

For the denominator does not vanish at $z = a$, since by hypothesis $b_0 \neq 0$. Thus by 83, it does not vanish in some $\mathfrak{c}$ lying in $\mathfrak{C}$. Hence by 84, Q has a continuous derivative within $\mathfrak{c}$ and is therefore analytic within $\mathfrak{c}$.

5. A two-way power series

$$F = \sum_{-\infty}^{\infty} a_n(z - a)^n$$

is an analytic function of z within its ring of convergence.

This follows at once from 103, 3.

6. We propose now to study the general properties of analytic functions and shall rest our treatment on two theorems of a grand importance due to Cauchy, and called his first and second integral theorems.

105. Cauchy's First Integral Theorem. 1. *Let $f(z)$ be one-valued and analytic in the simple connex $\mathfrak{A}$. Then*

$$\int_C f(z)dz = 0 \qquad (1$$

for any simple closed curve C in $\mathfrak{A}$.

For let

$$f(z) = u + iv \quad , \quad z = x + iy.$$

Then since f has a continuous derivative in $\mathfrak{A}$, the first partial derivatives of u, v are continuous functions of x, y which satisfy the Cauchy-Riemann equations

$$\frac{\partial u}{\partial x} = \frac{\partial v}{\partial y} \quad , \quad \frac{\partial u}{\partial y} = -\frac{\partial v}{\partial x}, \tag{2}$$

by 90. On the other hand, let us express 1) as line integrals, using 91, 5). Then

$$\int_C f dz = \int_C (udx - vdy) + i\int_C (udy + vdx). \tag{3}$$

We now apply Stokes' theorem 80, 1) and get

$$\int_C (udx - vdy) = -\int_{\mathfrak{C}} \left(\frac{\partial v}{\partial x} + \frac{\partial u}{\partial y}\right) dxdy = 0, \quad \text{by 2)},$$

$$\int_C (udy + vdx) = \int_{\mathfrak{C}} \left(\frac{\partial u}{\partial x} - \frac{\partial v}{\partial y}\right) dxdy = 0, \quad \text{by 2)}.$$

These in 3) give 1).

2. From this we conclude that:

$$\int_{C_1} fdz = \int_{C_2} fdz, \tag{4}$$

where C_1, C_2 are two simple curves in $\mathfrak{A}$ having the same end points but no other points in common.

For $C_1 C_2^{-1}$ is a closed curve. Hence by 1)

$$\int_{C_1 C_2^{-1}} fdz = 0$$

$$= \int_{C_1} + \int_{C_2^{-1}} = \int_{C_1} - \int_{C_2},$$

which gives 4).

3. The restriction that C_1, C_2 should have only their end points in common is obviously not necessary. For if C_1, C_2 have other points in common, we can break them up into arcs which have only their end points in common. Similarly C_1, C_2 may have multiple points.

4. *In the connex $\mathfrak{A}$ in which $f(z)$ is one-valued and analytic, let C_1, C_2 be two simple closed curves forming the complete boundary of a ring-shaped connex, as in Fig.* 1. *Then*

$$\int_{C_1} f(z)dz = \int_{C_2} f(z)dz, \tag{5}$$

the curves C_1, C_2 being passed over in the same sense.

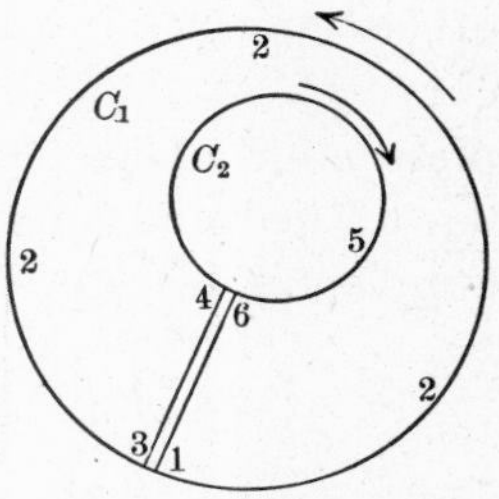

FIG. 1.

For let us join C_1, C_2 by two adjacent curves 34, 16, as in Fig. 1. Then

$$C = 123 \cdot 34 \cdot 456 \cdot 61$$

is a closed curve forming the edge of a simple connex in $\mathfrak{A}$. Thus

$$0 = \int_C fdz = \int_{123} + \int_{34} + \int_{456} + \int_{61} \cdot \tag{6}$$

Now the value of $f(z)$ at a point z on 34 does not differ by an amount greater than ϵ from a point near by on 16. Thus

$$\int_3^4 fdz \text{ and } \int_1^6$$

differ by an amount as small as we please as the curve 34 is made to approach 16.

As
$$\int_1^6 fdz = -\int_6^1 fdz,$$

we see that under these circumstances

$$\int_3^4 fdz + \int_6^1 fdz \doteq 0.$$

Similarly
$$\int_{123} fdz \doteq \int_{C_1} fdz$$

and
$$\int_{456} fdz \doteq -\int_{C_2} fdz.$$

Thus passing to the limit in 6) we get 5).

5. The little strip 1643 taken out of Fig. 1 and whose edges are then allowed to approach indefinitely near we call a *cross cut*.

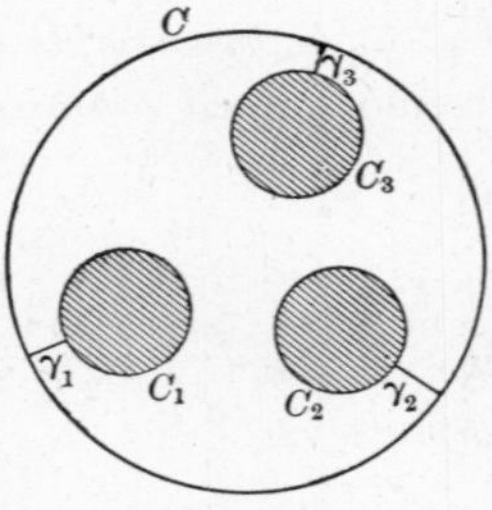

FIG. 2.

6. Let C_1, C_2, $\cdots$ C_m be simple closed curves as in Fig. 2, each exterior to the others and all interior to a simple closed curve C. Let these curves form the complete edge of a connex $\mathfrak{A}$ in which $f(z)$ is one-valued and analytic. Then if all these curves are described in the same sense,

$$\int_C f dz = \int_{C_1} f dz + \int_{C_2} f dz + \cdots + \int_{C_m} f dz.\tag{7}$$

To prove 7) we need only to put in the cross cuts $\gamma_1, \gamma_2, \cdots \gamma_m$, as in the figure. This produces a simple connex $\mathfrak{C}$ with edge $\mathfrak{E}$. As f is one-valued and analytic in $\mathfrak{C}$, we have

$$\int_{\mathfrak{E}} f dz = 0.$$

We may now reason as we did in 4.

106. Cauchy's Second Integral Theorem. 1. *Let $f(z)$ be one-valued and analytic in a simple connex whose boundary is C. Then for any point z within C*

$$f(z) = \frac{1}{2\pi i}\int_C \frac{f(u) du}{u - z}.\tag{1}$$

For by 105, 4 we can replace C by a circle $\mathfrak{K}$ of radius r and center z. Then for a point u on $\mathfrak{K}$,

$$f(u) = f(z) + \epsilon' \qquad |\epsilon'| < \epsilon$$

for all u on $\mathfrak{K}$ if the radius r is sufficiently small. Thus as $f(z)$ is constant

$$\int_{\mathfrak{K}} \frac{f(u) du}{u - z} = f(z)\int_{\mathfrak{K}} \frac{du}{u - z} + \int_{\mathfrak{K}} \frac{\epsilon'}{u - z} du = J + K.\tag{2}$$

But $J = 2\pi i f(z)$

while $|K| < 2\pi\epsilon.$

Thus $\lim_{r=0} K = 0.$

On the other hand, the left side of 2) does not depend on r. Hence letting $r \doteq 0$ in 2) we get 1) in the limit.

2. This theorem of Cauchy brings to light a tremendous difference between analytic functions of z and the general function of z. For suppose we know of a function $f(z)$ that it is one-valued in a simple connex $\mathfrak{C}$ and has a continuous derivative in $\mathfrak{C}$. Suppose also that we do not know the values of f within $\mathfrak{C}$ but only on the edge C. Then the relation 1) says that to learn the value of f at some interior point z we need only to calculate the integral in 1).

In other words the values of an analytic function $f(z)$ are completely determined when its values on the boundary C are given. This is not at all the case for the non-analytic functions of z.

3. At first it seems strange to students that the values of an analytic function $f(z)$ should be fixed for all points within C when its values are assigned on the curve C.

Here the study of nature reveals many cases of just this phenomenon. For example, the stationary flow of water, heat, or electricity in a body are all determined by the flow at the surface. In case the body assumes the form of a thin plate, it may be treated as a plane figure $\mathfrak{C}$ bounded by a curve C, provided the flow is parallel to the plane.

107. Derivatives. 1. The integrand in 106, 1)

$$\frac{f(u)}{u-z}$$

is an analytic function of z for each value of u on the curve C, provided z is restricted to lie in a connex bounded by a curve C' which lies within C. We may, therefore, apply 98 and get

$$f'(z) = \frac{1}{2\pi i}\int_C \frac{f(u)du}{(u-z)^2} \qquad (1$$

$$f''(z) = \frac{2!}{2\pi i}\int_C \frac{f(u)du}{(u-z)^3} \qquad (2$$

. . . .

$$f^{(n)}(z) = \frac{n!}{2\pi i}\int_C \frac{f(u)du}{(u-z)^{n+1}}. \qquad (3$$

From this we conclude:

An analytic function of z has derivatives of every order.

We also have the result:

If $f(z)$ is a one-valued analytic function, so is each of its derivatives.

2. From 3) we get at once an inequality called *Cauchy's Inequality*, which is of great service in theoretical work, viz.:

$$|f^{(n)}(z)| \leq \frac{n!G}{R^n}, \tag{4}$$

where $|f| \leq G$ on a circle $\mathfrak{R}$ of radius R with center z, and f is one-valued and analytic in $\mathfrak{R}$.

For we need only to replace the curve C in 3) by the circle $\mathfrak{R}$ and apply 92, 9).

108. Termwise Differentiation of Series. 1. By the aid of these integrals of Cauchy we can establish a more general theorem than that given in 103.

Let

$$F(z) = f_1(z) + f_2(z) + \cdots = \Sigma f_m(z). \tag{1}$$

We saw that if this series converges and the series

$$G(z) = f_1'(z) + f_2'(z) + \cdots = \Sigma f_m'(z) \tag{2}$$

converges steadily in the connex $\mathfrak{A}$, then G represents the derivative of F.

Let us now prove the more general theorem:

Let the terms of 1) *be one-valued analytic functions in the connex $\mathfrak{R}$. If F converges steadily in $\mathfrak{R}$, F is an analytic function within $\mathfrak{R}$ and*

$$\frac{dF}{dz} = G.$$

In other words under these conditions we may differentiate 1) termwise.

For let c be a circle of radius r and center z, lying within $\mathfrak{R}$.

From 1) we have

$$\frac{F(u)}{u-z} = \sum \frac{f_m(u)}{u-z} \tag{3}$$

and since 1) converges steadily on $\mathfrak{c}$, the series on the right converges steadily on $\mathfrak{c}$ since $|u - z| = r$ a constant on $\mathfrak{c}$. Thus by 101, 4 we may integrate 3) termwise:

$$\int_{\mathfrak{c}} \frac{F(u)du}{u - z} = \sum \int_{\mathfrak{c}} \frac{f_m(u)du}{u - z}. \tag{4}$$

Now by 106, 1)

$$\int_{\mathfrak{c}} \frac{f_m(u)du}{u - z} = 2\,\pi i f_m(z). \tag{5}$$

Hence 4), 5) give

$$\frac{1}{2\,\pi i}\int_{\mathfrak{c}} \frac{F(u)du}{u - z} = \Sigma f_m(z). \tag{6}$$

But by 1) the series on the right is $F(z)$; thus 6) gives

$$F(z) = \frac{1}{2\,\pi i}\int_{\mathfrak{c}} \frac{F(u)du}{u - z}. \tag{7}$$

Now by 98,

$$F'(z) = \frac{1}{2\,\pi i}\int_{\mathfrak{c}} \frac{F(u)du}{(u - z)^2}. \tag{8}$$

Reasoning as before, we have

$$\int_{\mathfrak{c}} \frac{F(u)du}{(u - z)^2} = \sum \int_{\mathfrak{c}} \frac{f_m(u)du}{(u - z)^2}$$

$$= 2\,\pi i \Sigma f'_m(z).$$

From this and 8) we have

$$F'(z) = \Sigma f'_m(z). \tag{9}$$

2. From 8) we get, using 98,

$$F''(z) = \frac{2\,!}{2\,\pi i}\int_{\mathfrak{c}} \frac{F(u)du}{(u - z)^3}.$$

Proceeding as in 1, we get

$$F''(z) = \Sigma f''_m(z), \tag{10}$$

and so on for higher derivatives.

109. Taylor's Development. 1. *Let $f(z)$ be a one-valued analytic function in a circle $\mathfrak{C}$ of radius R about the point $z = a$. Then at any point z within $\mathfrak{C}$*

$$f(z)=f(a)+\frac{z-a}{1!}f'(a)+\frac{(z-a)^2}{2!}f''(a)+\cdots \tag{1}$$

This theorem is a direct extension of the corresponding theorem in the calculus. It is of transcendental importance in the function theory, as we shall see at every turn. Its demonstration may be conducted very simply by resting it on the termwise integration of steadily convergent series.

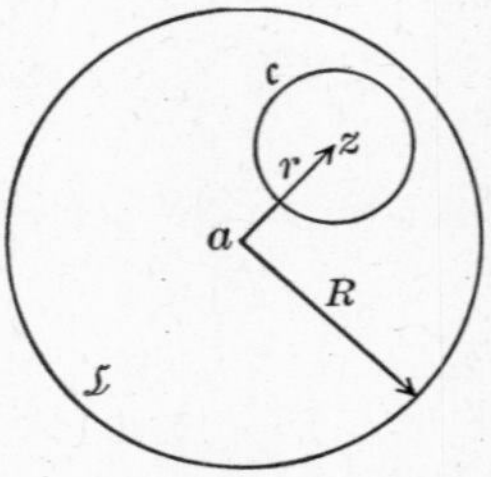

Let $\mathfrak{c}$ be a circle about z lying within $\mathfrak{C}$ as in the figure. Then by 106, 1),

$$f(z)=\frac{1}{2\pi i}\int_{\mathfrak{c}}\frac{f(u)du}{u-z}. \tag{2}$$

But $$\int_{\mathfrak{C}}\frac{f(u)du}{u-z}=\int_{\mathfrak{c}}\frac{f(u)du}{u-z}.$$

We now develop $\frac{1}{u-z}$ in a power series about the $z-a$, getting as in 39, 10),

$$\frac{1}{u-z}=\frac{1}{u-a}\left\{1+\frac{z-a}{u-a}+\left(\frac{z-a}{u-a}\right)^2+\cdots\right\}. \tag{3}$$

This series converges for any u on $\mathfrak{C}$ since

$$|z-a|=r \qquad |u-a|=R \quad \text{and} \quad r<R.$$

Hence

$$\frac{f(u)}{u-z}=\frac{f(u)}{u-a}+(z-a)\frac{f(u)}{(u-a)^2}+(z-a)^2\frac{f(u)}{(u-a)^3}+\cdots \tag{4}$$

This series converges steadily on $\mathfrak{C}$. For f being continuous,

$$|f(u)| < \text{some } M \text{ on } \mathfrak{C}.$$

Hence each term of 4) is numerically less than the corresponding term of the constant term convergent series

$$\frac{M}{r}\left(\frac{r}{R}\right)+\frac{M}{r}\left(\frac{r}{R}\right)^2+\frac{M}{r}\left(\frac{r}{R}\right)^3+\cdots$$

We may thus integrate 4) termwise and get

$$\int_{\mathfrak{C}} \frac{f(u)du}{u-z} = \int_{\mathfrak{C}} \frac{f(u)du}{u-a} + (z-a)\int_{\mathfrak{C}} \frac{f(u)du}{(u-a)^2} + \cdots$$

$$= 2\pi i \left\{ f(a) + (z-a)f'(a) + \frac{(z-a)^2}{2\,!} f''(a) + \cdots \right\}$$

on using 106, 1) and 107, 1), 2), ...

Replacing the first member of the last equation by 2) we get 1).

2. If we set $z = a + h$ in 1), it takes the form

$$f(a+h) = f(a) + hf'(a) + \frac{h^2}{2\,!} f''(a) + \cdots \tag{5}$$

This is the form of Taylor's development usually given in the calculus.

If we set $a = 0$ in 1), we get

$$f(z) = f(0) + zf'(0) + \frac{z^2}{2\,!} f''(0) + \cdots \tag{6}$$

which is often called *Maclaurin's development.*

The coefficients in 1) and 6) are constants. These series are thus power series. We say that 1) is a development of $f(z)$ about the point $z = a$. Thus Maclaurin's development 6) is merely the development of $f(z)$ about the origin. The two series on the right of 1) and 6) are called *Taylor's* and *Maclaurin's series* respectively.

3. Let $f(z)$ be one-valued and analytic in the region $\mathfrak{A}$. Let a be any point of $\mathfrak{A}$. About a as a center describe a circle $\mathfrak{K}$ which contains no point of the frontier of $\mathfrak{A}$. Then by the theorem 1, $f(z)$ can be developed in a power series valid in $\mathfrak{K}$,

$$f(z) = a_0 + a_1(z-a) + a_2(z-a)^2 + \cdots \tag{7}$$

whose coefficients are those in 1).

We may also proceed thus: With a as a center describe a circle $\mathfrak{C}$ which passes through a point of the frontier of $\mathfrak{A}$ but contains no frontier point within $\mathfrak{C}$. Then the development 7) holds for all points *within* $\mathfrak{C}$.

For let z be any given point within $\mathfrak{C}$. We can describe a circle $\mathfrak{K}$ with a as center which contains z but no point of the frontier of $\mathfrak{A}$. Thus $f(z)$ is analytic in $\mathfrak{K}$ and we can apply 1.

110. Examples of Taylor's Development. 1. *Example 1.* Let

$$f(z) = \sin z.$$

This function is analytic in any region. If we develop about the origin $z = 0$, we have, exactly as in the calculus,

$$\begin{aligned} f'(z) &= \cos z & f'(0) &= 1 \\ f''(z) &= -\sin z & f''(0) &= 0 \\ f'''(z) &= -\cos z & f'''(0) &= -1 \\ f^{\text{iv}}(z) &= \sin z = f(z) & f^{\text{iv}}(0) &= 0, \text{ etc.} \end{aligned}$$

Thus 109, 5) gives

$$\sin z = \frac{z}{1!} - \frac{z^3}{3!} + \frac{z^5}{5!} - \cdots$$

which is exactly the series we used to define $\sin z$.

Similarly we may develop

$$e^z \quad , \quad \cos z \quad , \quad \sinh z \quad , \quad \text{etc.}$$

Example 2. Let

$$f(z) = \log z.$$

This is an analytic function in the region $\mathfrak{A}$ formed of the whole plane after deleting the origin. The frontier of $\mathfrak{A}$ is thus a single point $z = 0$. It is one-valued in any connex which is acyclic relative to this point. Thus by 109, 3 we may develop $\log z$ about $z = 1$ and the development will be valid within the circle having $z = 1$ as center and passing through the frontier point $z = 0$. Proceeding as in the calculus, we have:

$$\begin{aligned} & & f(1) &= 0 \\ f'(z) &= \frac{1}{z} & f'(1) &= 1 \\ f''(z) &= -\frac{1}{z^2} & f''(1) &= -1 \\ f'''(z) &= \frac{2}{z^3} & f'''(1) &= 2, \text{ etc.} \end{aligned}$$

Thus

$$\log z = z - 1 - \frac{(z-1)^2}{2} + \frac{(z-1)^3}{3} - \cdots \qquad |z| < 1.$$

If we set

$$z = 1 + u,$$

this gives

$$\log(1 + u) = u - \frac{u^2}{2} + \frac{u^3}{3} - \cdots \qquad |u| < 1, \qquad (1$$

which is the development given in the calculus.

If the reader asks why one develops about the point $a = 1$ instead of about $a = 2$, the answer is that the values of the coefficients

$$f(a) \quad , \quad \frac{f'(a)}{1!} \quad , \quad \frac{f''(a)}{2!} \cdots$$

are simpler for $a = 1$ than for any other value of a.

Example 3. The Binomial Formula. Let

$$f(z) = (1 + z)^\mu. \tag{2}$$

From 89 we know that any branch of f is a one-valued analytic function in any connex acyclic relative to the point $z = 1$. It thus admits a development about $z = 0$ which is valid for all points within the unit circle.

Proceeding as in the calculus, we have, choosing that branch of 2) which reduces to 1) for $z = 0$,

$$f(0) = 1$$

$$f'(z) = \mu(1 + z)^{\mu-1} \qquad f'(0) = \mu$$

$$f''(z) = \mu(\mu - 1)(1 + z)^{\mu-2} \qquad f''(0) = \mu(\mu - 1), \text{etc.}$$

Thus

$$(1 + z)^\mu = 1 + \mu z + \frac{\mu(\mu - 1)}{1 \cdot 2} z^2 + \frac{\mu(\mu - 1)(\mu - 2)}{1 \cdot 2 \cdot 3} z^3 + \cdots$$
$$= 1 + \binom{\mu}{1} z + \binom{\mu}{2} z^2 + \binom{\mu}{3} z^3 + \cdots \qquad |z| < 1. \tag{3}$$

2. Let us make use of 1) to develop a formula which we shall need later. If we set

$$u = - re^{i\phi},$$

it gives for $r < 1$

$$-\log(1 - u) = -\log(1 - re^{i\phi}) = re^{i\phi} + \frac{r^2}{2} e^{2i\phi} + \frac{r^3}{3} e^{3i\phi} + \cdots$$

But

$$e^{ni\phi} = \cos n\phi + i \sin n\phi.$$

Hence

$$-\log(1 - re^{i\phi}) = \sum \frac{r^n \cos n\phi}{n} + i \sum \frac{r^n \sin n\phi}{n}. \tag{4}$$

Let us write the left side of 4) in rectangular form,

$$\log(1 - re^{i\phi}) = A + iB.$$

To determine A and B we set

$$1 - re^{i\phi} = se^{i\psi}.$$

Now

$$1 - re^{i\phi} = 1 - r(\cos\phi + i\sin\phi)$$
$$= (1 - r\cos\phi) - ir\sin\phi$$

Thus

$$s^2 = (1 - r\cos\phi)^2 + r^2\sin^2\phi = 1 - 2r\cos\phi + r^2,$$

and

$$\tan\psi = \frac{-r\sin\phi}{1 - r\cos\phi}.$$

Hence

$$A = \tfrac{1}{2}\log s^2 = \tfrac{1}{2}\log(1 - 2r\cos\phi + r^2),$$

$$B = \psi = -\operatorname{arctg}\frac{r\sin\phi}{1 - r\cos\phi}.$$

Thus, equating the real and imaginary parts in 4), we get

$$\sum_1^\infty \frac{r^n\cos n\phi}{n} = -\frac{1}{2}\log(1 - 2r\cos\phi + r^2), \tag{5}$$

$$\sum_1^\infty \frac{r^n\sin n\phi}{n} = \operatorname{arctg}\frac{r\sin\phi}{1 - r\cos\phi}. \tag{6}$$

The relations 5), 6) hold for $0 \leq r < 1$ as we have just shown; a more delicate analysis shows that they hold for $r = 1$. Without establishing this important fact we shall set $r = 1$ in these formulæ, getting, replacing ϕ by $2\pi x$,

$$\sum_1^\infty \frac{\cos 2n\pi x}{n} = -\log(2\sin\pi x), \tag{7}$$

$$\sum_1^\infty \frac{\sin 2n\pi x}{n} = \operatorname{arctg}(\cot\pi x) = \pi(\tfrac{1}{2} - x). \tag{8}$$

111. Critical Remarks on Taylor's Development. We are now in a position to point out another great advantage which we reap from the theory of functions. Let us compare Taylor's development as here presented and as given in the calculus.

To make use of the development

$$f(x + h) = f(x) + hf'(x) + \frac{h^2}{2!}f''(x) + \cdots \tag{1}$$

in the calculus we must first assure ourselves that the remainder

$$\frac{h^n}{n!} f^{(n)}(x+\theta h) \qquad 0<\theta<1,$$

or one of its equivalent forms, converges to 0 as $n \doteq \infty$. This is an easy matter for

$$e^x, \quad \sin x, \quad \cos x,$$

but it is far from easy for most functions; for example,

$$(1+x)^\mu \quad , \quad \tan x.$$

How difficult it is to show that the remainder for $(1+x)^\mu$ converges to 0, the reader may see by turning to a good work on the calculus. As to the remainder for $\tan x$, no one, as far as we know, has ever shown that it $\doteq 0$.

These considerations show that the applicability of Taylor's development in the calculus is crippled by the fact that we cannot show that the series on the right of 1) really has as sum the function of the left.

How differently we are situated in the function theory. Take, for example, $\tan z$. We know without putting pen to paper that this can be developed about $z=0$, and that the development is valid for all $|z|<\frac{\pi}{2}$, since $\tan z$ is one-valued and analytic within this circle. Thus if we wish to restrict ourselves to real values, the development holds for $-\frac{\pi}{2}<x<\frac{\pi}{2}$.

Let us look similarly at

$$(1+z)^\mu.$$

This we know is one-valued and analytic for all points within the circle of unit radius about $z=-1$. Thus the validity of the binomial formula for real values of x for which $-2<x<0$ is again established without any calculation whatever.

112. Remainder in Taylor's Development. Let us write 109, 1)

$$f(z)=f(a)+\frac{z-a}{1!}f'(a)+\frac{(z-a)^2}{2!}f''(a)+\cdots$$

$$+\frac{(z-a)^n}{n!}f^{(n)}(a)+R_n, \qquad (1$$

where

$$R_n=\sum_{s=n+1}^{\infty}\frac{(z-a)^s}{s!}f^{(s)}(a). \qquad (2$$

Let r be the radius of a circle $\mathfrak{c}$ about $z=a$, lying within the circle $\mathfrak{C}$, for which 1) holds. Let

$$|f(z)| \leq G \qquad \text{on } \mathfrak{c}.$$

Let z be any point within $\mathfrak{c}$; we set $|z-a|=\rho$. Then by Cauchy's inequalities, 107, 2,

$$|f^{(s)}(a)| \leq \frac{s!\,G}{r^s}.$$

Thus 2) becomes

$$|R_n| \leq G\left(\frac{\rho}{r}\right)^{n+1}\left\{1+\frac{\rho}{r}+\left(\frac{\rho}{r}\right)^2+\cdots\right\}$$

$$\leq G\left(\frac{\rho}{r}\right)^{n+1}\cdot\frac{1}{1-\frac{\rho}{r}}. \tag{3}$$

113. Analytic Continuation. 1. We have seen in 106, 2 that a one-valued analytic function is completely determined in a simple connex $\mathfrak{C}$ when its value is known along its edge. We now wish to generalize this result. Suppose

1° it is known that $f(z)$ is one-valued and analytic in a connected region $\mathfrak{A}$.

2° the values of $f(z)$ are given along some curve C in $\mathfrak{A}$, as, for example, a small segment of the x-axis.

We show that under these conditions the value of f may be found at any point of z in $\mathfrak{A}$; that is, the value of f at this point is determined by the above data.

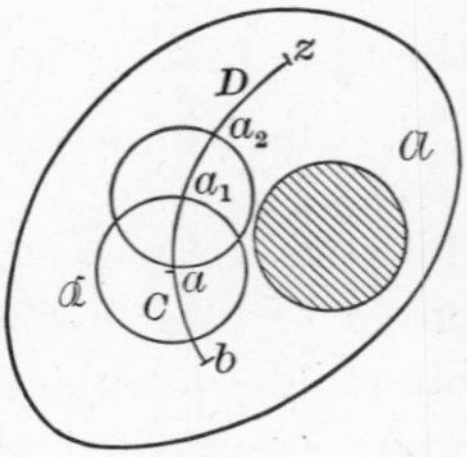

Suppose in Fig. 1 that C is the arc a, b. Join a and z by a curve D lying in $\mathfrak{A}$. Since $f(z)$ is analytic about a, it can be developed by Taylor's series

$$f(z)=f(a)+(z-a)f'(a)+\frac{(z-a)^2}{2!}f''(a)+\cdots \tag{1}$$

The value of f will be known for all values of z within a circle $\mathfrak{K}$ whose center is a and which extends as near the frontier $\mathfrak{F}$ of $\mathfrak{A}$ as we choose.

Let now u be an arbitrary but fixed point on C. Then $f'(u)$ is the limit of

$$\frac{f(z)-f(u)}{z-u} \tag{2}$$

as $z \doteq u$. Moreover $f(z)$ being analytic, this limit is the same, however z approaches u. Let us suppose that z approaches u by running along the curve C as in Fig. 2. Then for each such value of z the difference quotient 2) is known by hypothesis. Thus its limit is known, that is, $f'(z)$ is known for each z on C.

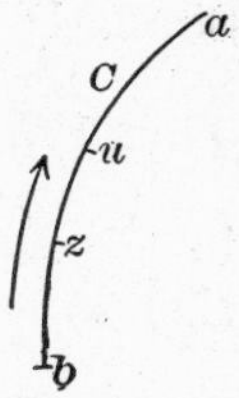

As now

$$f''(u) = \lim_{z=u} \frac{f'(z) - f'(u)}{z - u}, \tag{3}$$

we may reason on $f'(z)$ as we did on $f(z)$. Thus $f''(z)$ is known for each z on C.

In this way we see that the values of the derivatives of every order $f^{(n)}(z)$ are known for all values of z on C.

In particular they are known for $z = a$. Hence all the coefficients of 1) are known. Thus 1) gives us the values of $f(z)$ for all points in $\mathfrak{K}$.

Let $\mathfrak{K}$ cut D in a_1. About this as a center we can describe a circle $\mathfrak{K}_1$, which extends as near the frontier $\mathfrak{E}$ as we choose. Since $f(z)$ is now known on the arc $C_1 = a_1 a$, we can reason on C_1 as we did on C. If $\mathfrak{K}_1$ cuts D in a_2, these considerations show that f is now known for all z in $\mathfrak{K}_1$, and in particular on the arc $C_2 = a_1 a_2$. Continuing in this way we may finally reach z, when the value of f will be known.

2. This process of finding the value of an analytic function $f(z)$ at a point z, when its value is known at the points of some curve C, is called *analytic continuation*. It has little or no practical value as a means of actually computing f at the various points of $\mathfrak{A}$; but it has an inestimable value in many theoretic investigations.

3. In the foregoing we have supposed $f(z)$ to be one-valued in $\mathfrak{A}$. This is not necessary; we made this assumption merely for clearness. The same considerations apply if we suppose that $f(z)$ is many-valued in $\mathfrak{A}$, but such that each branch is analytic, and one-valued about each point of $\mathfrak{A}$.

4. The foregoing reasoning shows that:

If the analytic function $f(z) = \alpha$, a constant on the curve C, then $f(z) = \alpha$ everywhere in the region $\mathfrak{A}$.

For the difference quotient 2) has the value 0 and hence

$$f'(z) = 0 \qquad \text{on } C.$$

Similarly $\quad f''(z) \quad , \quad f'''(z) \quad , \quad \cdots = 0 \qquad$ on C.

Thus 1) shows that

$$f(z) = \alpha \tag{4}$$

in the circle $\mathfrak{K}$, and the remainder of the reasoning in 1 shows that 4) holds for any z in $\mathfrak{A}$.

114. Application of Analytic Continuation. 1. For the reader to realize the immense power of this process let us show how most of the analytic relations of plane trigonometry and the calculus are valid when the variable is complex. For example, suppose we wish to show that

$$\sin^2 z + \cos^2 z = 1 \tag{1}$$

holds for any complex z. This we have already proved in 58, 5 by the lengthy method of series. To this end we consider

$$f(z) = \sin^2 z + \cos^2 z.$$

As $\sin z$, $\cos z$ are one-valued analytic functions in the whole plane, so are their squares and therefore $f(z)$ is analytic. For the real axis $f(z) = 1$. Hence $f(z) = 1$ for all values of z by 113, 4. This reasoning is so simple that with a little experience the reader may do it in an instant. The same is true in the following examples.

2. Let us show by this method that

$$\frac{d \cdot \tan z}{dz} = \sec^2 z \tag{2}$$

holds for all values of z for which $\tan z$, $\sec z$ are defined, that is, for the region $\mathfrak{A}$ formed of the whole z-plane after deleting the points

$$z = \pm (2n+1)\frac{\pi}{2}.$$

Since

$$f(z) = \tan z$$

is analytic in $\mathfrak{A}$, its first derivative, call it $g(z)$, is analytic by 107, 1. Thus

$$h(z) = g(z) - \sec^2 z$$

is an analytic function in $\mathfrak{A}$. For real x in $\mathfrak{A}$, $h = 0$. Thus $h(z) = 0$ everywhere in $\mathfrak{A}$. Thus 2) holds in $\mathfrak{A}$.

3. In the calculus it is shown that

$$\int \sin^3 x dx = -\tfrac{1}{3} \cos x (\sin^2 x + 2). \qquad (3$$

From this we can show at once that

$$\int \sin^3 z dz = -\tfrac{1}{3} \cos z (\sin^2 z + 2) \qquad (4$$

for every z. For let us set

$$f(z) = \sin^3 z,$$

$$F(z) = -\tfrac{1}{3} \cos z (\sin^2 z + 2).$$

Then the relation 4) means that

$$F'(z) = f(z). \qquad (5$$

Let us set

$$G(z) = F'(z) - f(z).$$

As $F(z)$ is analytic, its derivative F' is also. Hence G is analytic. As $G = 0$ for real values of z by 3), it is 0 for all z. Thus 5) holds for all z, and hence 4).

Of course the relation 5) is easy in this case to verify by direct differentiation. But for a more complicated formula this labor of differentiation might be considerable. The method of analytic continuation enables us to avoid this operation.

4. In 61 we saw how relations in circular trigonometry go over into relations in hyperbolic trigonometry by using

$$\sin iz = i \sinh z \quad , \quad \cos iz = \cosh z \quad , \quad \text{etc.} \qquad (6$$

Let us show that relations between circular functions in the calculus give us corresponding relations between hyperbolic functions.

For example, from

$$\frac{d}{dx} \sec x = \tan x \sec x \qquad (7$$

we infer by the method of analytic continuation that

$$\frac{d}{dz} \sec z = \tan z \sec z.$$

Setting now $z = ix$, this gives

$$\frac{1}{i}\frac{d}{dx}\sec ix = \tan ix \sec ix,$$

or, using the relations 6),

$$\frac{1}{i}\frac{d}{dx}\operatorname{sech} x = i \tanh x \operatorname{sech} x,$$

or

$$\frac{d}{dx}\operatorname{sech} x = -\tanh x \operatorname{sech} x, \tag{8}$$

which is the formula in hyperbolic trigonometry corresponding to 7).

5. To illustrate integration let us start with 3). We have seen that the method of analytic continuation shows that we may replace x in 3) by ix. It becomes then

$$i\int \sin^3 ix dx = -\tfrac{1}{3}\cos ix(\sin^2 ix + 2).$$

Using the relations 6) this gives

$$\int \sinh^3 x dx = \tfrac{1}{3}\cosh x(\sinh^2 x - 2), \tag{9}$$

which is the formula corresponding to 3).

6. Let us show by the method of analytic continuation that the addition theorem

$$\sin(u + v) = \sin u \cos v + \cos u \sin v \tag{10}$$

holds for any complex u, v. This we established in 58, 1 by infinite series. We may now do it without putting pen to paper by the following simple reasoning.

Let us give to v a real value as $v = a$; we consider

$$f(u) = \sin(u + a) - \sin u \cos a - \cos u \sin a. \tag{11}$$

This is an analytic function of u which $= 0$ for real u. Hence $f = 0$ for all u.

Let us now give to u an arbitrary but fixed, real, or complex value, and consider

$$g(v) = \sin(u + v) - \sin u \cos v - \cos u \sin v. \tag{12}$$

As $g = 0$ for any real v, it $= 0$ for all v and hence 10) holds for any u and v.

115. Undetermined Coefficients. 1. A very useful method to develop a function in a power series is that of undetermined coefficients. Before explaining it let us develop a theorem on which it rests.

If
$$P = a_0 + a_1 z + a_2 z^2 + \cdots \tag{1}$$
vanishes for a set of points
$$b_1, b_2, b_3 \cdots \tag{2}$$
which are all different and $\neq 0$ *and which* $\doteq 0$, *then all the coefficients in* 1) *are* 0; *that is,* $P = 0$ *for every* z, *or as we say, it vanishes identically.*

For P being a continuous function,
$$\lim_{n=\infty} P(b_n) = P(0) \quad , \quad \text{since } b_n \doteq 0.$$
But each
$$P(b_n) = 0,$$
hence
$$P(0) = 0. \tag{3}$$
Setting $z = 0$ in 1), we see that 3) requires
$$a_0 = 0.$$
Thus
$$P = z(a_1 + a_2 z + a_3 z^2 + \cdots) = zP_1.$$
As
$$zP_1 = 0 \tag{4}$$
for the same set of points 2) and as $z \neq 0$ for these points the relation 4) requires that $P_1 = 0$ for the points 2). Thus we can reason on P_1 just as we did on P. This shows that
$$a_1 = 0.$$

Continuing in this manner we show that each
$$a_n = 0 \quad , \quad n = 0, 1, 2, \cdots$$

2. A special case of 1 is this:

If the series
$$P = a_0 + a_1 z + a_2 z^2 + \cdots$$
vanish for the points of any curve ending at the origin, it vanishes identically.

3. *If* $P = a_0 + a_1 z + a_2 z^2 + \cdots$, *and* $Q = b_0 + b_1 z + b_2 z^2 + \cdots$ *are equal for a set of different points* $c_1, c_2, c_3 \cdots$ *which* $\doteq 0$, *then the*

coefficients of like powers in P and Q are equal; that is, P and Q are the same series.

For

$$R = P - Q = (a_0 - b_0) + (a_1 - b_1)z + (a_2 - b_2)z^2 + \cdots$$

vanishes at the points c_n. Hence by 1 all the coefficients are 0. Thus

$$a_n = b_n \quad , \quad n = 0, 1, 2, \cdots$$

4. From 3 we have the important theorem:

If $f(z)$ admits a development

$$f(z) = a_0 + a_1(z - a) + a_2(z - a)^2 + \cdots$$

the series on the right must be Taylor's series, that is

$$a_n = \frac{1}{n!} f^{(n)}(a).$$

In other words, Taylor's development is *unique*.

5. The labor of calculating the coefficients of a development may be materially lessened when the following theorem applies:

Let

$$f(z) = a_0 + a_1 z + a_2 z^2 + \cdots \tag{5}$$

be the development of f about the origin. If f is an odd function, the coefficients of all the even powers are 0; if f is an even function, all the odd power coefficients are 0.

For suppose that $f(z)$ is odd. Then

$$f(-z) = -f(z) \qquad \text{by definition.}$$

But

$$f(-z) = a_0 - a_1 z + a_2 z^2 - a_3 z^3 + \cdots$$

Hence

$$0 = f(z) + f(-z) = 2(a_0 + a_2 z^2 + a_4 z^4 + \cdots).$$

As this series $= 0$ for all values of z near the origin, all its coefficients are 0, or

$$0 = a_0 = a_2 = a_4 = \cdots$$

6. The method of undetermined coefficients will be best understood if we illustrate it by two or three examples. This we now do.

116. *Example 1.* Let us develop $\tan z$ in a power series about the origin. Such a development we saw is possible and the development is valid for $|z| < \frac{\pi}{2}\cdot$ Moreover, $\tan z$ being an odd function, its development will contain only odd powers. We set therefore

$$\tan z = a_1 z + a_3 z^3 + a_5 z^5 + \cdots \tag{1}$$

where the coefficients a_1, a_3 $\cdots$ are to be determined. To do this we use the fact that

$$\tan z = \frac{\sin z}{\cos z} = \frac{z - \frac{z^3}{3!} + \frac{z^5}{5!} - \cdots}{1 - \frac{z^2}{2!} + \frac{z^4}{4!} - \cdots} \tag{2}$$

Let us equate 1), 2) and clear of fractions. We get

$$\left(1 - \frac{z^2}{2!} + \frac{z^4}{4!} - \cdots\right)(a_1 z + a_3 z^3 + \cdots) = z - \frac{z^3}{3!} + \cdots \tag{3}$$

If we multiply out the two series on the left by 33, 2 we get the series

$$a_1 z + \left(a_3 - \frac{a_1}{2!}\right) z^3 + \left(a_5 - \frac{a_3}{2!} + \frac{a_1}{4!}\right) z^5$$
$$+ \left(a_7 - \frac{a_5}{2!} + \frac{a_3}{4!} - \frac{a_1}{6!}\right) z^7 + \cdots$$

Comparing the coefficients of this series with the series on the right side of 3) gives

$$a_1 = 1$$
$$a_3 - \frac{a_1}{2!} = -\frac{1}{3!} \qquad \therefore\ a_3 = \frac{1}{3}$$
$$a_5 - \frac{a_3}{2!} + \frac{a_1}{4!} = \frac{1}{5!} \qquad a_5 = \frac{2}{15}$$
$$a_7 - \frac{a_5}{2!} + \frac{a_3}{4!} - \frac{a_1}{6!} = \frac{-1}{7!}. \qquad a_7 = \frac{17}{315}.$$
$$\cdots\cdots\cdots \qquad \cdots\cdots$$

Thus

$$\tan z = z + \frac{1}{3} z^3 + \frac{2}{15} z^5 + \frac{17}{315} z^7 + \cdots \tag{4}$$

valid for $|z| < \frac{\pi}{2}\cdot$

Example 2. Let us develop

$$\operatorname{cosec} z = \frac{1}{\sin z}$$

about the origin. At first sight it would seem that our method would not apply. For the very first thing to do is to assure ourselves that the development is possible. The conditions of Taylor's theorem, 109, are not fulfilled here, since cosec z is not even defined at $z = 0$, and for the theorem to hold it should be analytic in some circle about this point. However, a slight consideration enables us to proceed. We have

$$\sin z = z\left\{1 - \frac{z^2}{3!} + \frac{z^4}{5!} - \cdots\right\} = P = z \cdot Q.$$

Now since P converges for all values of z, so does

$$Q = 1 - \frac{z^2}{3!} + \frac{z^4}{5!} - \cdots \tag{5}$$

As $P = \sin z = 0$, for $z = \pm\pi$,

$$zQ = 0 \quad , \quad \text{for } z = \pm\pi.$$

Hence $Q = 0$ for $z = \pm\pi$. On the other hand, $Q \neq 0$, *within* the circle $\mathfrak{C}$ about the origin of radius π. For $Q \neq 0$ for $z = 0$ as 5) shows. If now $Q = 0$ for some $z \neq 0$ within $\mathfrak{C}$, $P = zQ$ would $= 0$ also. But $P = \sin z$ does not vanish at this point. Thus by 104, 4, $\frac{1}{Q}$ is an analytic function within $\mathfrak{C}$. It may therefore be developed in a power series by Taylor's theorem, about $z = 0$. Moreover Q being an even function, this development will contain only even powers of z. We may therefore set

$$\frac{1}{1 - \frac{z^2}{3!} + \frac{z^4}{5!} - \cdots} = a_0 + a_2 z^2 + a_4 z^4 + \cdots$$

or clearing of fractions,

$$1 = \left(1 - \frac{z^2}{3!} + \frac{z^4}{5!} - \cdots\right)(a_0 + a_2 z^2 + a_4 z^4 + \cdots).$$

The multiplication of the two series on the right by 33, 2 gives

$$1 = a_0 + \left(a_2 - \frac{a_0}{3!}\right)z^2 + \left(a_4 - \frac{a_2}{3!} + \frac{a_0}{5!}\right)z^4$$

$$+\left(a_6 - \frac{a_4}{3!} + \frac{a_2}{5!} - \frac{a_0}{7!}\right)z^6 + \cdots \qquad (6$$

Here the left side is to be regarded as a series $c_0 + c_1 z + c_2 z^2 + \cdots$ all of whose coefficients $= 0$ except the first. Thus equating coefficients of like powers on both sides of 6) gives

$$a_0 = 1.$$

$$a_2 - \frac{a_0}{3!} = 0. \qquad \therefore a_2 = \frac{1}{6}.$$

$$a_4 - \frac{a_2}{3!} + \frac{a_0}{5!} = 0. \qquad \therefore a_4 = \frac{7}{360}.$$

$$a_6 - \frac{a_4}{3!} + \frac{a_2}{5!} - \frac{a_0}{7!} = 0. \qquad \therefore a_6 = \frac{31}{3 \cdot 7!}.$$

. . . .

Thus

$$\frac{1}{\sin z} = \frac{1}{z} + \frac{1}{6}z + \frac{7}{360}z^3 + \frac{31}{3 \cdot 7!}z^5 + \cdots \qquad (7$$

valid for $0 < |z| < \pi$.

Example 3. Division by Power Series. In the two foregoing examples we have divided by a power series. As this operation is not infrequent, let us state the following theorem:

Let

$$P = a_0 + a_1 z + a_2 z^2 + \cdots \quad , \quad a_0 \neq 0$$

converge within a circle $\mathfrak{K}$ *about the origin and be* $\neq 0$ *within* $\mathfrak{K}$. *Then the reciprocal of P can be developed in a power series*

$$\frac{1}{P} = c_0 + c_1 z + c_2 z^2 + \cdots$$

valid within $\mathfrak{K}$ *and the first coefficient*

$$c_0 = \frac{1}{a_0}. \qquad (8$$

For P being $\neq 0$ within $\mathfrak{R}$ is analytic within $\mathfrak{R}$ and can be developed in a power series valid within $\mathfrak{R}$. The coefficients a_0, $a_1 \cdots$ are found by the method of undetermined coefficients, and this shows that c_0 has the value given in 7).

Suppose the first coefficient $a_0 = 0$. In general let us suppose

$$P = a_m z^m + a_{m+1} z^{m+1} + \cdots \qquad a_m \neq 0. \tag{9}$$

We write

$$P = z^m(a_m + a_{m+1}z + \cdots) = z^m Q.$$

Suppose now that P does not $= 0$ within $\mathfrak{R}$ except at the origin. Then $Q \neq 0$ within $\mathfrak{R}$. Therefore by what we have just seen

$$\frac{1}{Q} = \frac{1}{a_m} + c_1 z + c_2 z^2 + \cdots \qquad z \text{ within } \mathfrak{R}.$$

Hence

$$\frac{1}{P} = \frac{1}{a_m z^m} + \frac{c_1}{z^{m-1}} + \cdots + \frac{c_{m-1}}{z} + c_m + c_{m+1}z + \cdots \tag{10}$$

for any $z \neq 0$ within $\mathfrak{R}$.

This gives the theorem:

Let the series P in 8) *converge within the circle $\mathfrak{R}$ about the origin. If P does not vanish within $\mathfrak{R}$ except at $z = 0$, the reciprocal of P can be developed in a series of the form given in* 10).

117. Laurent's Development. 1. When $f(z)$ is one-valued and analytic within some circle $\mathfrak{c}$ about $z = a$, Taylor's theorem asserts that f can be developed in a power series about this point.

$$f(z) = a_0 + a_1(z-a) + a_2(z-a)^2 + \cdots \tag{1}$$

We call the point a a *regular* or *ordinary* point and we say $f(z)$ is *regular at a*. If $f(z)$ cannot be developed in a series of the form 1) about the point $z = a$, we call it a *singular point.*

Let us consider for example

$$\frac{\sqrt{z+1}}{z-1} + \log z. \tag{2}$$

Here $z = 0$, $z = 1$, $z = -1$ are singular points. For suppose 2) could be developed in a power series $P(z)$ about one of these points. Now P being a power series is defined at *every* point within its circle of convergence $\mathfrak{R}$, is one-valued, and has a continuous derivative. But the function 2) is two-valued about the point $z = -1$, and is not defined at the points $z = 0$ and $z = 1$. Thus 2) certainly cannot be developed in a power series about these points; they are therefore singular points.

When Taylor's development is not applicable at a point $z = a$, we may often use another development due to *Laurent*, as we now show.

2. *Let $f(z)$ be one-valued and analytic in the ring R determined by the circles E, F, whose centers are $z = a$. Then f can be developed in an ascending and descending integral power series*

$$f(z) = a_0 + a_1(z-a) + a_2(z-a)^2 + \cdots$$
$$+ \frac{b_1}{z-a} + \frac{b_2}{(z-a)^2} + \cdots \tag{1}$$

valid within R.

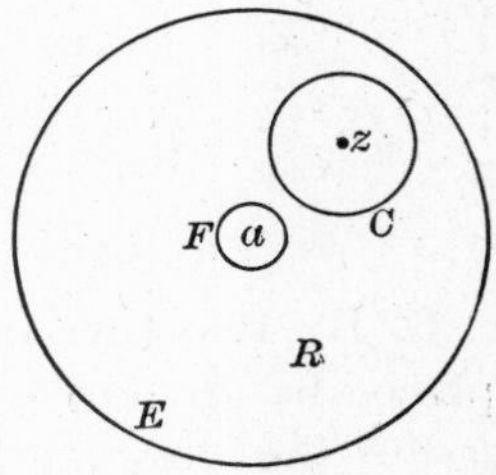

For let z be any point within R as in the figure. Then by Cauchy's integral theorem, 106,

$$f(z) = \frac{1}{2\pi i}\int_C \frac{f(u)du}{u-z}.$$

But by 105, 4,

$$\int_E = \int_C + \int_F.$$

Hence

$$f(z) = \frac{1}{2\pi i}\int_E \frac{f(u)du}{u-z} - \frac{1}{2\pi i}\int_F \frac{f(u)du}{u-z}. \tag{2}$$

We now develop $\frac{1}{u-z}$ in a power series as in 109, 3). We have for

$$u \text{ on } F \qquad \left|\frac{u-a}{z-a}\right| < 1,$$

$$u \text{ on } E \qquad \left|\frac{z-a}{u-a}\right| < 1.$$

Thus by 39, 10) we have for any u on E

$$\frac{1}{u-z} = \frac{1}{u-a}\left\{1 + \frac{z-a}{u-a} + \left(\frac{z-a}{u-a}\right)^2 + \cdots\right\},$$

while for any u on F

$$\frac{1}{u-z} = -\frac{1}{z-a}\left\{1 + \frac{u-a}{z-a} + \left(\frac{u-a}{z-a}\right)^2 + \cdots\right\}.$$

If we multiply these relations by $f(u)$, the series so obtained are steadily convergent with reference to their respective circles E, F. Thus we may integrate termwise and get

$$\int_E \frac{f(u)du}{u-z} = \int_E \frac{f(u)}{u-a}\,du + (z-a)\int_E \frac{f(u)du}{(u-a)^2}$$

$$+ (z-a)^2 \int_E \frac{f(u)du}{(u-a)^3} + \cdots$$

$$-\int_F \frac{f(u)du}{u-z} = \frac{1}{z-a}\int_F f(u)du + \frac{1}{(z-a)^2}\int_F (u-a)f(u)du + \cdots$$

Putting these values in 2), we get 1) where

$$a_n = \frac{1}{2\pi i}\int_E \frac{f(u)du}{(u-a)^{n+1}}, \tag{3}$$

$$b_n = \frac{1}{2\pi i}\int_F (u-a)^{n-1}f(u)du. \tag{4}$$

3. By 105, 4 we note that the circles E, F in 3), 4) may be replaced by any circle $\mathfrak{K}$ in the ring R.

For the integrand of 3) is analytic in the ring $E - \mathfrak{K}$, and that of 4) is analytic in $\mathfrak{K} - F$.

4. Let us now prove the important theorem :

If $f(z)$ can be developed in a two-way power series

$$f(z) = \sum_{-\infty}^{\infty} a_n(z-a)^n, \tag{5}$$

this series must be the series of Laurent.

For the function defined by the series 5) satisfies the conditions of Laurent's theorem in 2. Thus f admits the development

$$f(z) = \sum_{-\infty}^{\infty} l_n(z-a)^n \tag{6}$$

where the coefficients l_n are the coefficients of Laurent given in 3), 4). Subtracting 5) and 6) we get

$$0 = \sum_{-\infty}^{\infty} b_n(z-a)^n \quad , \quad b_n = a_n - l_n. \tag{7}$$

Let us multiply 7) by $(z-a)^{-(m+1)}$ and integrate around a circle $\mathfrak{C}$ lying within the ring of convergence of 7). Then by 101, 11)

$$0 = 2\pi i b_m. \qquad \therefore b_m = 0 \quad , \quad m = 0, \pm 1, \pm 2 \cdots$$

Thus

$$a_m = l_m$$

and the coefficients in 5) are the coefficients of Laurent.

118. Zeros and Poles. 1. Let $f(z)$ be a one-valued and analytic function within a circle $\mathfrak{K}$ about $z=a$. Then Taylor's development is valid within $\mathfrak{K}$ and we have

$$f(z) = a_0 + a_1(z-a) + a_2(z-a)^2 + \cdots \tag{1}$$

For $z=a$, this gives $f(a)=a_0$. If $a_0=0$, f vanishes at $z=a$. We say $z=a$ is a *root* or a *zero* of $f(z)$. Suppose

$$a_0 = a_1 = \cdots = a_{m-1} = 0 \quad , \quad a_m \neq 0.$$

Then 1) becomes

$$\begin{aligned} f(z) &= (z-a)^m(a_m + a_{m+1}(z-a) + a_{m+2}(z-a)^2 + \cdots) \\ &= (z-a)^m g(z). \end{aligned}$$

Here $g(z)$ is analytic within $\mathfrak{K}$ and does not vanish at $z=a$. We say $z=a$ is a root or zero of *order* m.

Since g does not vanish at a it cannot $=0$ in some circle about this point. We have thus the theorem:

Let $f(z)$ be one-valued and analytic about the point $z=a$, and vanish at this point, but not identically. Then there exists a positive integer m such that

$$f(z) = (z-a)^m g(z) \tag{2}$$

where $g(z)$ is analytic about $z=a$ and does not vanish in some domain about a.

2. Suppose now that $f(z)$ is one-valued and analytic within a circle $\mathfrak{K}$ about $z=a$ except at the center itself. Such functions are

$$\frac{1}{z^2-1} \quad , \quad \tan z.$$

In the first $a=\pm 1$, in the second $a=(2n+1)\frac{\pi}{2}$. If we describe a little circle $\mathfrak{C}$ of radius r about a, we get a ring $\mathfrak{K}-\mathfrak{C}$ and for all points within this ring Laurent's development will hold. Thus

$$f(z) = a_0 + a_1(z-a) + a_2(z-a)^2 + \cdots$$
$$+ \frac{b_1}{z-a} + \frac{b_2}{(z-a)^2} + \cdots \qquad (3$$
$$= P + Q.$$

We call

$$Q = \frac{b_1}{z-a} + \frac{b_2}{(z-a)^2} + \cdots \qquad (4$$

the *characteristic* of $f(z)$ at $z = a$ and write

$$Q = \operatorname*{Char}_{z=a} f(z).$$

The coefficient b_1 is of great importance in some investigations. It is called the *residue* of $f(z)$ at $z = a$ and we write

$$b_1 = \operatorname*{Res}_{z=a} f(z).$$

Since r may be taken just as small as we choose, the development 3) holds for all points within $\mathfrak{K}$ except its center.

Looking at the characteristic 4) all its coefficients may be zero after the mth. In this case, which is very important, we have

$$Q = \frac{b_1}{z-a} + \cdots + \frac{b_m}{(z-a)^m}$$
$$= \frac{b_m + b_{m-1}(z-a) + \cdots + b_1(z-a)^{m-1}}{(z-a)^m} \qquad (5$$
$$= \frac{p(z)}{(z-a)^m}$$

where p is a polynomial of degree $\leq m-1$. Thus Q is a *rational function* of z.

From 3), we have

$$f(z) = \frac{b_m + b_{m-1}(z-a) + \cdots + b_1(z-a)^{m-1} + a_0(z-a)^m + \cdots}{(z-a)^m}$$
$$= \frac{g(z)}{(z-a)^m}, \quad g(a) \neq 0, \qquad (6$$

where $g(z)$ is an analytic function in $\mathfrak{R}$ which does not vanish at $z=a$. Since

$$\lim_{z=a} (z-a)^m = 0 \quad , \quad \lim_{z=a} g(z) = b_m \neq 0,$$

the expression 6) shows that

$$\lim_{z=a} |f(z)| = +\infty, \tag{7}$$

that is, as z approaches a, f recedes indefinitely from the origin. This we will indicate by the symbolic equation

$$\lim_{z=a} f(z) = \infty, \tag{8}$$

so that 8) is only another way of writing 7).

On the other hand, the reciprocal of f is

$$\frac{1}{f(z)} = \frac{(z-a)^m}{g(z)}. \tag{9}$$

As g does not vanish at a, its reciprocal is an analytic function, call it $h(z)$, about this point, and h does not vanish at a, as shown in Ex. 3, 116. Thus, we may write 9)

$$\frac{1}{f(z)} = (z-a)^m h(z) \quad , \quad h(a) \neq 0. \tag{10}$$

This shows that the reciprocal of f has a zero of order m at $z=a$. The function $f(z)$ and its reciprocal behave thus in opposite manners like the poles of a magnet. As $z \doteq a$, $f \doteq \infty$ while its reciprocal $\doteq 0$. For this reason we say, that when the characteristic of a function has the form 5), that $z=a$ is a *pole* of $f(z)$, and in fact a pole of *order m*. We thus have this result:

If $f(z)$ has a pole of order m at $z=a$, it has the form

$$f(z) = \frac{g(z)}{(z-a)^m}, \tag{11}$$

where g is analytic about $z=a$ and does not vanish at this point. The reciprocal of $f(z)$ has a zero of order m. Conversely, if f has the form 11), *$z=a$ is a pole of order m.*

3. *Let $f(z)$ be one-valued about $z=a$ and analytic except at $z=a$. If the reciprocal of f has a zero of order m at a, this point is a pole of order m for $f(z)$.*

For by hypothesis, $$\frac{1}{f(z)} = (z-a)^m g(z),$$

and $g(z)$ does not vanish about $z = a$. Hence,

$$\frac{1}{g(z)} = b_0 + b_1(z-a) + b_2(z-a)^2 + \cdots$$

and thus

$$f(z) = \frac{b_0 + b_1(z-a) + \cdots}{(z-a)^m}$$

$$= \frac{b_0}{(z-a)^m} + \cdots + \frac{b_{m-1}}{z-a} + b_m + b_{m+1}(z-a) + \cdots$$

Thus the characteristic of f has the form 5).

4. *If $z = a$ is a pole of order m of $f(z)$, it is a pole of order $m+1$ of $f'(z)$.*

For about $z = a$ we have

$$f(z) = \frac{b_m}{(z-a)^m} + \cdots + \frac{b_1}{z-a} + g(z);$$

here g is analytic about $z = a$, and $b_m \neq 0$.

Hence

$$f'(z) = -\frac{mb_m}{(z-a)^{m+1}} - \cdots - \frac{b_1}{(z-a)^2} + g'(z).$$

As $b_m \neq 0$, $z = a$ is a pole of order $m+1$ for $f'(z)$.

Example 1. $$f(z) = \frac{z}{z^2-1}.$$

About any point $z = a$ for which the denominator does not $= 0$, $f(z)$ is analytic.

For $z = 1$ we have

$$f = \frac{z}{z+1} \cdot \frac{1}{z-1} = \frac{g(z)}{z-1}.$$

Now g is analytic about $z = 1$. Hence $z = 1$ is a pole of the first order.

Similarly $$f = \frac{z}{z-1} \cdot \frac{1}{z+1}$$

and this shows that $z = -1$ is a pole of order 1 also.

Example 2. $$f(z) = \tan z = \frac{\sin z}{\cos z}.$$

This is analytic except at the points

$$(2n+1)\frac{\pi}{2}.$$

Let us call one of these a. We have for $z = a + u$

$$\begin{aligned}\cos z &= \cos a \cos u - \sin a \sin u \\ &= (-1)^{n+1} \sin u \\ &= (-1)^{n+1} \left\{ u - \frac{u^3}{3\,!} + \cdots \right\} \\ &= (-1)^{n+1} (z-a) \left\{ 1 - \frac{(z-a)^2}{3\,!} + \cdots \right\}.\end{aligned}$$

Thus $$\begin{aligned}\frac{1}{\cos z} &= \frac{1}{z-a} \cdot \frac{(-1)^{n+1}}{1 - \frac{(z-a)^2}{3\,!} + \cdots} \\ &= \frac{g(z)}{z-a},\end{aligned}$$

where g is analytic about $z = a$ and $\neq 0$.
Thus
$$\tan z = \frac{\sin z \cdot g(z)}{z-a} = \frac{h(z)}{z-a}.$$

But $\sin z$ does not vanish at a. Hence $h(z)$ is analytic about $z = a$ and does not vanish at this point.
Hence
$$z = (2n+1)\frac{\pi}{2}$$
is a pole of order **1**, *for* $\tan z$.

5. Let us note that no point $z = a$ which is a pole can belong to the domain of definition of an analytic function. For by definition $f'(a)$ must exist, and this requires that $f(z)$ is continuous at a, by 84, 3. Thus by 83, 6

$$|f(z)| < \text{some } G \qquad (12$$

in $D_\delta(a)$, δ sufficiently small. On the other hand, if a is a pole of $f(z)$,
$$\lim_{z=a} |f(z)| = +\infty,$$
as we saw in 2. This contradicts 12).

6. If $z = a$ is a zero or pole of order m of $f(z)$, it is of order mn for the function

$$g = \{f(z)\}^n \quad , \quad n \text{ an integer} > 0.$$

For about $z = a$ we have

$$f(z) = (z - a)^m \phi(z),$$

where $m > 0$ for a zero and < 0 for a pole, and where $\phi(a) \neq 0$. Thus $\phi^n(z) = \psi(z)$ is an analytic function which does not vanish at $z = a$. Hence

$$g = (z - a)^{mn} \psi(z),$$

which proves the theorem.

7. *If $f(z)$ is a one-valued analytic function in the connected region $\mathfrak{A}$, the poles of its derivative are also poles of $f(z)$ and the residues of $f'(z)$ are all 0 in $\mathfrak{A}$.*

For at a pole

$$f'(z) = \frac{a_m}{(z-a)^m} + \cdots + \frac{a_1}{z-a} + g(z), \tag{13}$$

where g is regular at a. If now we integrate, we get

$$f(z) = \frac{1}{1-m} \cdot \frac{a_m}{(z-a)^{m-1}} + \cdots + a_1 \log(z-a) + h(z), \tag{14}$$

where

$$h = \int g(z) dz$$

is regular at a. As $f(z)$ is one-valued in $\mathfrak{A}$ the logarithmic term cannot appear so that

$$a_1 = \operatorname*{Res}_{z=a} f'(z) = 0.$$

8. As an *example* let us find the singular points and the residues of the function

$$h(z) = g(z) \frac{f'(z)}{f(z)}, \tag{15}$$

which we shall employ later. Here $g(z)$ is regular in the connex $\mathfrak{C}$ and has no zero in common with $f(z)$, which latter has certain poles $z = a, b, \cdots$ in $\mathfrak{C}$ but is otherwise regular.

Let $z = c$ be a regular point of f and not one of its zeros. Obviously c is a regular point of h.

Let $z = c$ be a zero or a pole of order m of $f(z)$. Then

$$f = (z - c)^m \phi(z),$$

where m is a positive integer if c is a zero, and negative if c is a pole. $\phi(z)$ is regular at c and $\neq 0$. Then

$$f' = m(z-c)^{m-1}\phi + (z-c)^m\phi'.$$

Hence

$$\frac{f'(z)}{f(z)} = \frac{m}{z-c} + \frac{\phi'}{\phi}$$

$$= \frac{m}{z-c} + \psi(z),$$

where ψ is regular at c.

On the other hand, by Taylor's theorem

$$g(z) = g(c) + c_1(z-c) + c_2(z-a)^2 + \cdots$$

Hence

$$h(z) = \frac{mg(c)}{z-c} + k(z), \tag{16}$$

where k is regular at $z = c$.

From 16) we see that $z = c$ is a pole of order 1 and that

$$\operatorname*{Res}_{z=c} h(z) = mg(c). \tag{17}$$

At a zero m is a positive integer, at a pole it is negative.

9. Before leaving this topic let us show that the relation 89, 1

or

$$\frac{dw}{dt} = \frac{dw}{dz} \cdot \frac{dz}{dt}$$

holds even when $\frac{dz}{dt} = 0$, *provided z is an analytic function of t.*

As we observed in 89, 5 we have only to show that $\Delta z \neq 0$ as $h = \Delta t \doteq 0$. But $z = \phi(t)$ being an analytic function of t,

$$\Delta z = \phi(t+h) - \phi(t)$$

considered as a function of h is regular at the point $h = 0$. It therefore does not vanish for

$$0 < |h| < \text{some } \delta$$

by 1.

10. *Let $u = a_0 + a_1 z + a_2 z^2 + \cdots$, $a_0 \neq 0$. Then $w = \log u$ considered as a function of z is regular at $z = 0$ and*

$$\frac{dw}{dz} = \frac{1}{u} \cdot \frac{du}{dz} = \frac{a_1 + 2a_2 z + \cdots}{a_0 + a_1 z + \cdots}. \tag{18}$$

For we may take δ so small that u remains in $D_\eta(a_0)$ if z remains in $D_\delta(0)$. If now $\eta < |a_0|$, the origin $u = 0$ will not lie in D_η. Thus w considered as a function of z is one-valued in D_δ and thus by 9,

$$\frac{dw}{dz} = \frac{dw}{du} \cdot \frac{du}{dz},$$

which gives 18).

Since w is regular at $z = 0$, we have, by Taylor's theorem,

$$w = w(0) + zw'(0) + \cdots$$

Here

$$w(0) = \log a_0 \quad , \quad w'(0) = \frac{a_1}{a_0} \cdots$$

Hence

$$w = \log a_0 + \frac{a_1}{a_0} z + \cdots \tag{19}$$

11. *Let*

$$u = a_0 + a_1 z + a_2 z^2 + \cdots \qquad a_0 \neq 0.$$

Then

$$w = \sqrt[n]{u}$$

is regular at $z = 0$, *and*

$$w = a_0^{\frac{1}{n}} + \frac{a_1}{a_0} \cdot \frac{a_0^{\frac{1}{n}}}{n} z + \cdots \tag{20}$$

For

$$w = e^{\frac{1}{n}\log u}.$$

As $\log u$ is regular at $z = 0$ by 10, so is w. Hence by Taylor's theorem

$$w = w(0) + w'(0)z + \cdots$$

$$w(0) = a_0^{\frac{1}{n}} \quad , \quad w'(z) = \frac{1}{n} u^{\frac{1}{n}-1} \frac{du}{dz} \quad , \quad w'(0) = \frac{1}{n} a_0^{\frac{1}{n}-1} a_1 \cdots$$

etc., which gives 20).

119. Essentially Singular Points. 1. Let $z = a$ be a singular point of $f(z)$. If f is one-valued about this point which is not a pole, we say $z = a$ is an *essentially singular point.*

It is easy to construct functions having such singular points. For example, let the infinite series,

$$a_0 + a_1 z + a_2 z^2 + \cdots \tag{1}$$

converge for all values of z. Such series we considered in 39, 4. From 1), we can form the series

$$f(z) = a_0 + \frac{a_1}{z} + \frac{a_2}{z^2} + \cdots \tag{2}$$

which converges obviously for all $z \neq 0$. Thus, the function $f(z)$ defined by 2) is an analytic function of z for all $z \neq 0$, by 104, 5.

If we develop f about the point $z = 0$ in Laurent's series, we get the series 2) again by 117, 4. Thus, by 118, 2,

$$\operatorname*{Char}_{z=0} f(z) = \frac{a_1}{z} + \frac{a_2}{z^2} + \cdots \tag{3}$$

As the a_n are not all 0 after some m, the point $z = 0$ is not a pole. It is, therefore, an essentially singular point.

From this function $f(z)$ we can form an infinity of other functions having $z = 0$ as an essentially singular point. For let $g(z)$ be regular about $z = 0$. Then

$$\phi(z) = f(z) + g(z)$$

has $z = 0$ as an essentially singular point.

2. That $z = a$ is an essentially singular point may often be seen by the aid of the following theorems. We exclude, of course, the trivial case that the functions considered are *constants*.

If $f(z)$ is regular at $z = a$, $f(z)$ cannot have the same value c at a set of distinct points $a_1, a_2, a_3 \cdots$ which $\doteq a$.

For then

$$g(z) = f(z) - c$$

is regular at $z = a$ and vanishes at each a_n.

As g is continuous at a,

$$\lim_{n=\infty} g(a_n) = g(a).$$

As each $g(a_n) = 0$, we see $g(z) = 0$ at a.

But then, by 118, 1,

$$g(z) = (z - a)^m h(z),$$

where h does not vanish in some domain about $z = a$. As $g(a_n) = 0$, it follows that $h(a_n) = 0$. Thus, $h(z)$ vanishes in any circle about $z = a$, however small.

3. *If $f(z)$ is regular at each point of a circle $\mathfrak{K}$ about $z = a$, the center a excepted, and if f has the value c at a set of distinct points, $a_1, a_2, \cdots$ which $\doteq a$, then $z = a$ is an essentially singular point.*

For we saw in 2 that a is not a regular point. If it is not an essentially singular point, it must be a pole. Then its reciprocal

$g(z)$ is regular at $z=a$, and takes on the value $\frac{1}{c}$ at the points a_n. This contradicts 2. Thus, $z=a$ is not a pole of $f(z)$.

Example.

$$w=\sin\frac{1}{z}.$$

This function is regular at each point except $z=0$. Now $w=0$ for

$$z=\frac{1}{n\pi}, \quad n=1, 2, 3 \cdots$$

and these values $\doteq 0$. Thus by 3, the origin is an essentially singular point.

4. *Let $f(z)$ be regular about $z=a$ except at a and at a set of points $a_1, a_2 \cdots$ which $\doteq a$. If each a_n is a pole, the point $z=a$ is an essentially singular point.*

The point $z=a$ cannot be regular, for $f(z)$ is infinite in any domain $D(a)$. It cannot be a pole, for the reciprocal of $f(z)$ would be regular at $z=a$ and vanish at the points a_n, which is impossible by 2.

Example.

$$f(z)=\frac{1}{\sin\frac{1}{z}}.$$

Let us set

$$g(z)=\sin\frac{1}{z}.$$

Then if we set

$$u=\frac{1}{z},$$

$$\frac{dg}{dz}=\frac{dg}{du}\cdot\frac{du}{dz}=-\frac{\cos\frac{1}{z}}{z^2}$$

about the point $a=\frac{1}{m\pi}$. Thus $g'(z)$ is continuous about $z=a$ and hence $g(z)$ is regular at a. Hence by Taylor's theorem

$$g(z)=g(a)+(z-a)g'(a)+\frac{(z-a)^2}{2!}g''(a)+\cdots$$

Here

$$g(a)=0 \quad , \quad g'(a)=(-1)^{m+1}m^2\pi^2.$$

Thus

$$g(z)=(z-a)\{(-1)^{m+1}m^2\pi^2+\cdots\}.$$

Hence

$$f(z)=\frac{(-1)^{m+1}}{m^2\pi^2}\cdot\frac{1}{z-a}+c_0+c_1(z-a)+\cdots$$

where we do not care to know the values of the coefficients c.

This shows that the points $\frac{1}{m\pi}$ are poles of order 1. Hence $z=0$ is an essentially singular point.

120. Point at Infinity. 1. In seeking to characterize an analytic function of z, it has been found extremely important to study its behavior for large values of z.

Let us change the variable by setting

$$z=\frac{1}{u}. \qquad (1$$

Then a function as

$$f(z)=\frac{1+z^2}{z^3} \qquad (2$$

goes over into a function of u,

$$g(u)=u+u^3. \qquad (3$$

To learn how f behaves for large values of z, we need only to see how g behaves about the point $u=0$. We see it has a zero of order 1.

Let us look at the geometrical side of the transformation 1).

If we set $z=re^{i\phi}$, we have

$$u=\frac{1}{r}e^{-i\phi}.$$

This shows that as z describes a unit circle U in the positive sense, u describes the unit circle $\mathfrak{U}$ in the u-plane in the negative sense. To a point $a=\rho e^{i\theta}$ within U corresponds the point $\alpha=\frac{1}{\rho}e^{-i\theta}$ without $\mathfrak{U}$. As $z\doteq 0$ along a radius as Oa, $u\doteq\infty$ along the corresponding radius $O\alpha$. To each point in the z-plane except $z=0$ corresponds a single point in the u-plane, and conversely to each point except $u=0$ in the u-plane corresponds one point in the z-plane.

To complete the correspondence, mathematicians adjoin to the plane an *ideal point* called the *point at infinity* and denoted by the symbol ∞. They say that to $z = 0$ shall correspond $u = \infty$, and to $u = 0$ shall correspond $z = \infty$.

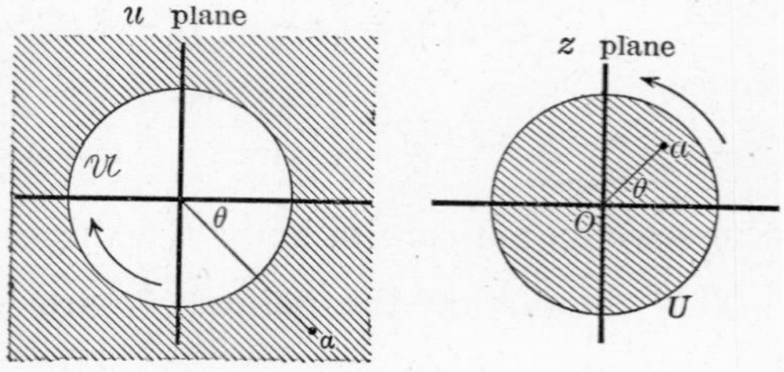

Instead then of asking how a function $f(z)$ behaves for large values of z, they ask how it behaves about the ideal point $z = \infty$. By such a question one means nothing more than this:

Change the variable from z to u as in 1). Then if f considered as a function of u is regular at $u = 0$, we say f is regular at $z = \infty$. If f considered as a function of u has a pole of order m or an essentially singular point or a branch point at $u = 0$, we say f has this same property at $z = \infty$.

2. We must caution the reader to note that we do not introduce the symbol ∞ as a number; we do not define any arithmetical operations on this symbol.

Also when we say $f(z)$ has a certain property for every z we always mean for finite z unless the contrary is stated.

3. Let us note that the theorems in 119 may at once be extended to the point $z = \infty$.

For all we have to do is to replace z by $\frac{1}{u}$, and reason on the behavior of f considered as a function of u, about $u = 0$. We may thus state:

If $f(z)$ is one-valued about $z = \infty$ and analytic for large values of z except at a set of points $a_1, a_2 \cdots$ which $\doteq \infty$; or if f is analytic also at the points a_n and has the same value at these points, then $z = \infty$ is an essentially singular point of $f(z)$.

4. It is sometimes convenient to speak of the *domain of the point* $z = \infty$. By this we mean all the points in the z-plane without some circle $\mathfrak{C}$ about the point $z = 0$. We may denote it by

$$D(\infty).$$

If we apply the substitution 1), this domain goes over into the points within some circle about the point $u = 0$ in the u-plane.

121. Integral Rational Functions. 1. Let us show how the rational and integral rational functions can be characterized from the standpoint of the function theory. We begin by proving a theorem of great value.

Let $f(z)$ be regular for every finite z. If

$$|f(z)| < \text{some } G, \tag{1}$$

however large z is taken, f is a constant.

For let us develop $f(z)$ about the origin, we have

$$f(z) = f(0) + zf'(0) + \frac{z^2}{2!}f''(0) + \cdots \tag{2}$$

Now by Cauchy's inequalities, 107, 2,

$$\left|\frac{f^{(n)}(0)}{n!}\right| \leq \frac{G}{R^n}.$$

This relation holds however large R is taken. As the right side $\doteq 0$ as $R \doteq \infty$ we see that each coefficient in 2) is 0. Thus

$$f(z) = f(0) \quad , \quad \text{a constant.}$$

2. *If $f(z)$ is regular for every z including $z = \infty$, it is a constant.* For let us describe a circle $\mathfrak{C}$ about $z = 0$. Then, f being continuous in $\mathfrak{C}$, we have

$$|f(z)| < \text{some } G_1 \text{ in } \mathfrak{C}.$$

Let us now set $u = \dfrac{1}{z}$; this converts $\mathfrak{C}$ into some circle $\mathfrak{K}$ about $u = 0$. But by hypothesis f considered as a function of u is regular at $u = 0$. Thus f is a continuous function of u in $\mathfrak{K}$, and hence

$$|f| < \text{some } G_2 \text{ in } \mathfrak{K}.$$

Thus if G is $>$ both G_1, G_2,

$$|f(z)| < G$$

for every finite z. Hence $f(z)$ is a constant by 1.

3. *Let $f(z)$ be regular for every z. If it has a pole of order m at $z=\infty$,*

$$f(z)=a_0+a_1z+a_2z^2+\cdots+a_mz^m \quad , \quad a_m\neq 0, \tag{3}$$

and conversely.

To see how f behaves for $z=\infty$ we set $z=\frac{1}{u}$ and get

$$f=\frac{a_m+a_{m-1}u+\cdots+a_0u^m}{u^m}.$$

Thus f has a pole of order m.

To prove the other part of the theorem: Since f has a pole of order m, f considered as a function of u has a pole of order m at $u=0$. Hence by 118,

$$f=\frac{c_1}{u}+\frac{c_2}{u^2}+\cdots+\frac{c_m}{u^m}+g(u) \quad , \quad c_m\neq 0, \tag{4}$$

where g is regular at $u=0$.

We show g is a constant. For f has no singular points except at $u=0$. Hence g has no singular point $u\neq 0$. But by hypothesis $u=0$ is not a singular point. Hence $g(u)$, having no singular point, is a constant c_0 by 2. Thus 4) becomes

$$f=c_0+\frac{c_1}{u}+\cdots+\frac{c_m}{u^m},$$

or going back to z, f has the form 3).

4. We now establish the fundamental theorem of algebra:

Every polynomial of degree m has m roots $\alpha_1, \alpha_2 \cdots \alpha_m$, some of which may be equal.

In other words:

If $$f=a_0+a_1z+a_2z^2+\cdots+a_mz^m \quad , \quad a_m\neq 0, \tag{5}$$

there exists m numbers $\alpha_1, \cdots \alpha_m$ such that

$$f=a_m(z-\alpha_1)\cdots(z-\alpha_m). \tag{6}$$

For since

$$\lim_{z=\infty} f(z)=\infty$$

there exists a circle C about $z=0$ such that

$$|f(x)|\geq G$$

for every z outside C.

Hence $f \neq 0$ outside C. Thus if f has any roots at all, they lie in C, that is on or within it. Suppose f were $\neq 0$ in C. Then

$$|f(z)| \geq \text{some } \eta > 0 \qquad \text{in } C,$$

since f is continuous in C, by 83, 7.

Let

$$g(z) = \frac{1}{f}.$$

Then

$$|g| \leq \frac{1}{G} \qquad \text{for } z \text{ outside } G,$$

$$\leq \frac{1}{\eta} \qquad \text{for } z \text{ in } C.$$

Thus

$$|g| < \text{some } M$$

for every z. Hence g is a constant by 1, which is absurd. Thus $f = 0$ for some z in C, say for $z = \beta_1$. Then by 118, 1,

$$f(z) = (z - \beta_1)^{m_1} f_1(z).$$

By 3, f_1 must be a polynomial. The method of undetermined coefficients, 115, shows that it is of degree $m - m_1$.

We may now reason on $f_1(z)$ as we did on $f(z)$. We thus get

$$f = a_m (z - \beta_1)^{m_1} (z - \beta_2)^{m_2} \cdots (z - \beta_s)^{m_s}, \tag{7}$$

where

$$m = m_1 + m_2 + \cdots m_s.$$

The factor a_m on the right of 7) is due to the fact that the coefficients of like powers on both sides of 7) must be equal.

122. Rational Functions. 1. These have the form

$$f(z) = \frac{a_0 + a_1 z + \cdots + a_m z^m}{b_0 + b_1 z + \cdots + b_n z^n}, \qquad a_m, b_n \neq 0 \tag{1}$$

$$= \frac{a_m (z - \alpha_1)^{m_1} \cdots (z - \alpha_r)^{m_r}}{b_n (z - \beta_1)^{n_1} \cdots (z - \beta_s)^{ns}}. \tag{2}$$

We will suppose that numerator and denominator do not have a zero in common.

Each zero of the denominator is a pole of f. For example,

$$f = \frac{1}{(z - \beta_1)^{n_1}} \cdot \frac{a_m (z - \alpha_1)^{m_1} \cdots}{b_n (z - \beta_2)^{n_2} \cdots}$$

$$= \frac{g(z)}{(z - \beta_1)^{n_1}}, \tag{3}$$

where g is regular at β_1 and does not vanish. Thus $z=\beta_1$ is a pole of $f(z)$ of order n_1.

Similarly at a zero of the numerator as α_1 we have

$$f=(z-\alpha_1)^{m_1}h(z),$$

where $h \neq 0$ at α_1. Thus $z=\alpha_1$ is a zero of order m_1.

At any point $z=c$ not a zero of the denominator, f is regular.

2. Let us now see how f behaves at $z=\infty$. Setting $z=\dfrac{1}{u}$, we have

$$f=\frac{a_0u^m+\cdots+a_m}{b_0u^n+\cdots+b_n}u^{n-m}=u^{n-m}h(u). \qquad (4$$

As $b_n \neq 0$, h is regular at $u=0$ by 1. From 4) we have:

The rational function 1) *is regular at* $z=\infty$ *if* $n \geq m$. *It has a zero of order* $n-m$ *if* $n>m$. *It has a pole of order* $m-n$ *if* $m>n$.

If we count the zeros or poles at $z=\infty$ with their proper order, we have:

The rational function 1) *has* p *zeros and* p *poles, where* p *is the degree of* 1), *that is,* p *is the greater of the two integers* m, n.

3. Let us now establish the converse theorem:

If a one-valued analytic function has only a finite number of poles, taking into account $z=\infty$, *it is a rational function of* z.

For let $z=a, b, \cdots$ be these poles. About $z=a$ we have

$$f(z)=\frac{a_m}{(z-a)^m}+\cdots+\frac{a_1}{z-a}+f_1(z)=k_1(z)+f_1(z),$$

where f_1 is regular at $z=a$.

As f has a pole at $z=b$ and as $k_1(z)$ is regular at this point, f_1 must have a pole at b. Thus

$$f_1(z)=\frac{b_n}{(z-b)^n}+\cdots+\frac{b_1}{z-b}+f_2(z)=k_2(z)+f_2(z).$$

Here f_2 is regular at $z=a$, and at $z=b$. Thus we may continue for all the poles of f in the finite part of the plane, getting, say,

$$f(z)=k_1(z)+k_2(z)+\cdots+k_s(z)+f_s(z), \qquad (5$$

where the last term has no pole at $z = a, b, \cdots$ that is, has no pole in the finite part of the plane.

We now consider the point $z = \infty$. Let us first suppose this is not a pole of the original function $f(z)$. Then 5) shows it is not a pole of $f_s(z)$. Thus f_s, having no pole even at infinity, is a constant by 121, 2.

Suppose now $z = \infty$ is a pole of $f(z)$, then 5) shows it is a pole of f_s. Thus f_s is an analytic function whose only pole is $z = \infty$; hence by 121, 3 it is a polynomial:

$$f_s = p_0 + p_1 z + \cdots + p_l z^l. \tag{6}$$

4. The foregoing section shows that we can write the fraction 1) or 2) as follows:

$$\begin{aligned} f = {} & p_0 + p_1 z + \cdots + p_l z^l \\ & + \frac{b_{11}}{z-\beta_1} + \cdots + \frac{b_{1n_1}}{(z-\beta_1)^{n_1}} \\ & + \frac{b_{21}}{z-\beta_2} + \cdots + \frac{b_{2n_2}}{(z-\beta)_2{}^{n_2}} \\ & + \cdots\cdots\cdots \\ & + \frac{b_{s1}}{z-\beta_s} + \cdots + \frac{b_{sn_s}}{(z-\beta_s)^{n_s}}, \end{aligned} \tag{7}$$

where $l = m - n$. When f is written as in 8), we say it is decomposed into *partial fractions*. Knowing that f can be written as in 8), the coefficients which enter in this expression can be determined by the method of undetermined coefficients.

123. Transcendental Functions. 1. The foregoing articles show us how the rational and integral rational functions are completely characterized by the nature of their singular points.

All one-valued analytic functions which are not rational functions are called *transcendental*. Every transcendental function must have one essentially singular point by definition. The simplest transcendental functions are those which have only one singular point, and that an essentially singular point at ∞. Such one-valued functions are called *integral transcendental* functions.

2. It is easy to show that

$$e^z \quad , \quad \sin z \quad , \quad \cos z \quad , \quad \sinh z \quad , \quad \cosh z$$

are integral transcendental functions. For being defined by power series which converge for every z, they have no singular points in the finite part of the plane.

On the other hand, if $\sin z = c$ for $z = a$, it $= c$ for

$$a + 2\pi \quad , \quad a + 4\pi \quad , \quad a + 6\pi \quad \cdots$$

But these values $\doteq \infty$. Thus $z = \infty$ is an essentially singular point by 120, 3.

3. The same reasoning shows that any one-valued periodic analytic function which has no poles in the finite part of the plane must be an integral transcendental function.

For if such a function has the period ω, it takes on the same value at

$$z \quad , \quad z + \omega \quad , \quad z + 2\omega \quad , \quad \cdots \qquad \text{which } \doteq \infty.$$

4. A one-valued transcendental function which has only poles in the finite part of the plane is called a *rational transcendental* function.

Such functions are

$$\tan z \quad , \quad \frac{1}{\sin z}.$$

5. As an example of rational transcendental functions let us consider the following, which occur in the *elliptic functions*.

Let ω_1, ω_2 be any two numbers which are not collinear with the origin $z = 0$. With these we form the series

$$F = \sum \frac{1}{(z - m_1\omega_1 - m_2\omega_2)^p} \tag{1}$$

where $m_1, m_2 = 0, \pm 1, \pm 2 \cdots$ and p is a fixed integer > 2. We show now that the function defined by 1) is a one-valued analytic function for every z except at the points

$$\omega = \omega_{m_1m_2} = m_1\omega_1 + m_2\omega_2 \tag{2}$$

which are poles of order p.

To show that F is regular at a point $z = a$ not included in 2) we describe a circle $\mathfrak{K}$ about the origin exterior to a. We now break the series 1) into two parts

$$F = F_i + F_e \tag{3}$$

where F_e contains all the terms of 1) corresponding to values of $\omega_{m_1m_2}$ which lie exterior to $\mathfrak{R}$, and F_i contains the other terms.

In 99, 5 we saw that F_e converges steadily in $\mathfrak{R}$. Hence by 108, 1, F_e is an analytic function of z in $\mathfrak{R}$. On the other hand, F_i consists of a finite number of terms of the type

$$\frac{1}{(z-\omega)^p}. \tag{4}$$

But each such term is regular except at $z=\omega$. Hence F_i is regular except at points included in 2). Thus 3) shows that F is regular at $z=a$.

To show that F has a pole of order p at the point $z=b=r\omega_1+s\omega_2$, we take $\mathfrak{R}$ so large that the point b lies within it. Then as before F_e is regular at $z=b$, while

$$F_i=\frac{1}{(z-b)^p}+G(z).$$

Now G is the sum of a finite number of terms of the type 4), each of which is regular at b. Thus F_i has a pole of order p at $z=b$, and hence F has also by 3). Thus the points 2) are poles; as these points $\doteq\infty$ the point $z=\infty$ is an essentially singular point by 120, 3.

6. Let us show that ω_1 is a period of the function defined by 1). The same reasoning will then show that ω_2 is also a period and hence the numbers 2) are also periods. We have from 1)

$$\begin{aligned}F(z+\omega_1)&=\sum\frac{1}{(z+\omega_1-m_1\omega_1-m_2\omega_2)^p}\\&=\sum\frac{1}{(z-(m_1-1)\,\omega_1-m_2\omega_2)^p}.\end{aligned} \tag{5}$$

As m_1, m_2 run over all integral values $0, \pm 1, \pm 2, \cdots$ we see that m_1-1, m_2 run over the same values. Thus the terms in 5) are identical with those in 1). As the series 1) is convergent, its sum is independent of the order of its terms and hence 5) has the same sum as 1). The points 2) are the vertices of a set of parallelograms as in the figure. Any one of them as P is called a *parallelogram of periods.* In P, the function $F(z)$ takes on every value it can take on anywhere.

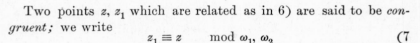

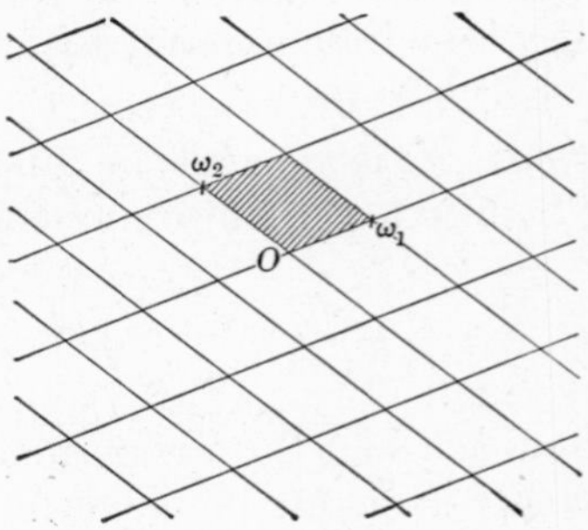

For any point z lies in one of these parallelograms as Q. Let z_1 be the point in P which is situated in P as z is in Q. Obviously,

$$z_1 = z + m_1\omega_1 + m_2\omega_2. \qquad (6$$

But then

$$F(z_1) = F(z).$$

Two points z, z_1 which are related as in 6) are said to be *congruent;* we write

$$z_1 \equiv z \qquad \text{mod } \omega_1, \omega_2 \qquad (7$$

which we read z_1 is congruent to z with respect to the periods ω_1, ω_2. When no ambiguity can result, we do not need to mention the periods and we write simply

$$z_1 \equiv z.$$

7. The series 1) define therefore an infinity of periodic functions corresponding to $p = 3, 4, \cdots$

The reader will note that they differ from the periodic functions heretofore considered as e^z, sin z in this important particular. Their periods do not all lie on one line, but are spread out over the whole plane, as in the figure.

124. Residues. 1. We saw in 117 that if f is one-valued and regular about $z = a$, but not regular at a, it can be developed in Laurent's series :

$$f(z) = a_0 + a_1(z-a) + a_2(z-a)^2 + \cdots$$

$$+ \frac{\alpha_1}{z-a} + \frac{\alpha_2}{(z-a)^2} + \cdots \qquad (1$$

The coefficient α_1 we said, in 118, 2, is the residue of f at the point a. These residues are of great importance in certain investigations, for example in the elliptic functions. A fundamental theorem is the following :

Let $f(z)$ be regular in the simple connex $\mathfrak{C}$ except at the points $z = a_1, a_2 \cdots a_m$ which we suppose do not lie on the edge $\mathfrak{E}$ of $\mathfrak{C}$. Then

$$\sum_{\mathfrak{C}} \text{Res}\, f(z) = \frac{1}{2\pi i}\int_{\mathfrak{E}} f(z)dz. \qquad (2$$

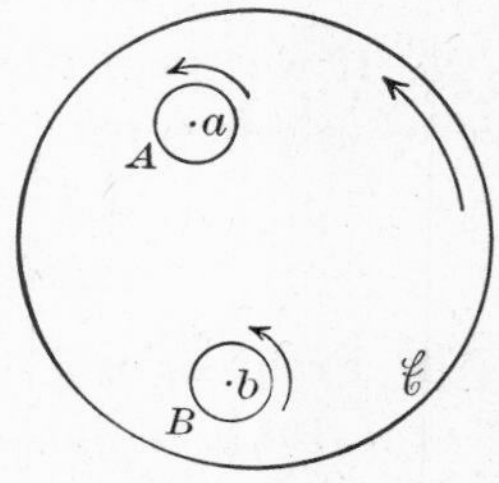

For simplicity suppose there are only two singular points a and b in $\mathfrak{C}$. Then by 105, 7)

$$\int_{\mathfrak{E}} fdz = \int_A fdz + \int_B fdz. \qquad (3$$

Let 1) be the development of f about $z = a$. Then

$$\int_A fdz = 2\pi i\alpha_1 \text{ by 101, 11)}$$
$$= 2\pi i \operatorname*{Res}_{z=a} f(z).$$

Similarly
$$\frac{1}{2\pi i}\int_B fdz = \operatorname*{Res}_{z=b} f(z).$$

These values in 3) give 2).

2. From 1 we may deduce the following general theorem from which we shall draw important conclusions, especially in the elliptic functions.

Let $f(z)$ be regular in the simple connex $\mathfrak{C}$ except for certain poles. On the edge $\mathfrak{E}$ of $\mathfrak{C}$ let f be regular and $\neq 0$. Let $g(z)$ be regular in $\mathfrak{C}$ and have no zero in common with f. Then

$$\frac{1}{2\pi i}\int_{\mathfrak{E}} g(z)d\log f(z) = \Sigma m_r g(a_r) - \Sigma n_s g(\alpha_s) \qquad (4$$

where a_r, α_s are the zeros and poles of $f(z)$ of orders m_r, n_s respectively.

The integrand in 4) is

$$h(z) = g(z)\frac{f'(z)}{f(z)}.$$

Its singular points, as we saw in 118, 8, are the zeros and poles of $f(z)$. The formula 118, 17) shows that at a zero

$$z = a_r \qquad \text{Res}\, h = m_r g(a_r), \qquad (5$$

and at a pole $z = \alpha_s$ $\quad \text{Res}\, h = -n_s g(\alpha_s).$ (6

If we now put 5), 6) in 2), we get 4).

3. If we agree to count a zero or pole of order m, as m simple zeros or poles, we can write 4) thus:

$$\frac{1}{2\pi i}\int_{\mathfrak{E}} g d \log f = \Sigma g(a_n) - \Sigma g(\alpha_n). \tag{7}$$

4. From 4) or 7) we have as corollary:

Let $f(z)$ be regular in the simple connex $\mathfrak{C}$ except for certain poles. On the edge $\mathfrak{E}$ of $\mathfrak{C}$ let f be regular and $\neq 0$. Then

$$\frac{1}{2\pi i}\int_{\mathfrak{E}} d \log f(z) = M - N, \tag{8}$$

where M, N are the number of zeros and poles of f in $\mathfrak{C}$ each counted as often as its order.

This follows from 7) on setting $g(z) = 1$.

5. As a corollary of 8) we may prove the *fundamental theorem of algebra*, viz.:

$$f(z) = a_0 z^m + a_1 z^{m-1} + \cdots + a_m \quad , \quad a_0 \neq 0$$

has just m roots, a multiple root of order s being counted as s simple roots.

For as

$$\lim_{z=\infty} f(z) = \infty$$

we can take a circle C about the the origin of radius R so large that no root of f lies on C or without it. As f has no poles in C, N in 8) is 0. Thus

$$\frac{1}{2\pi i}\int_C d \log f = M.$$

But

$$\frac{d \log f}{dz} = \frac{m a_0 z^{m-1} + (m-1) a_1 z^{m-2} + \cdots}{a_0 z^m + a_1 z^{m-1} + \cdots}$$

$$= \frac{m}{z} \cdot \frac{1 + \alpha \frac{1}{z} + \beta \frac{1}{z^2} + \cdots}{1 + \lambda \frac{1}{z} + \mu \frac{1}{z^2} + \cdots}$$

$$= \frac{m}{z}\{1 + \phi(z)\},$$

where $|\phi| < \epsilon$ on C if only R is taken $>$ some ρ. Thus

$$M = \frac{1}{2\pi i}\int_C \frac{mdz}{z} + \frac{m}{2\pi i}\int_C \frac{\phi dz}{z} = J + K. \tag{9}$$

Now by 94, 4) $J = m$, while

$$|K| \le \frac{m}{2\pi}\cdot\frac{\epsilon}{R}\cdot 2\pi R \quad , \quad \text{by 92, 2}$$
$$\le m\epsilon.$$

But this says that $$\lim_{R=\infty} K = 0.$$

Hence passing to the limit $R = \infty$ in 9), we get

$$M = m,$$

that is, f vanishes m times.

125. Inversion of a Power Series. 1. If

$$w = w(z) \tag{1}$$

is regular at $z = a$, it can be developed in a power series:

$$w = a_0 + a_1(z - a) + a_2(z - a)^2 + \cdots \tag{2}$$

It is sometimes convenient to develop the inverse function z in a series whose terms depend on w. This is called *inversion of the series* 2).

If we replace $z - a$ by z and $w - a_0$ by w, the series 2) may be written

$$w = a_1 z + a_2 z^2 + a_3 z^3 + \cdots \tag{3}$$

and without loss of generality we may suppose this is the development of 1) instead of 2).

In inverting the series 3) there are two cases which must be distinguished.

Case 1. $a_1 \neq 0$. This condition expresses the fact that $w'(z) \neq 0$ for $z = 0$. Let z range over some circle $\mathfrak{C}$ about $z = 0$; then w as given by 3) ranges over some connex $\mathfrak{K}$ whose edge does not pass through $w = 0$ if $\mathfrak{C}$ is sufficiently small by 118, 1. Also, if $\mathfrak{C}$ is sufficiently small, w will not take on the same value twice in $\mathfrak{C}$ by 119, 2.

Thus it follows by 88, 2 that the inverse function z is regular at $w=0$ and hence can be developed in the power series

$$z=b_1w+b_2w^2+b_3w^3+\cdots \tag{4}$$

valid in some $\mathfrak{D}$ about $w=0$.

As

$$\frac{dz}{dw}=\frac{1}{\frac{dw}{dz}},$$

we have for

$$w=0$$

$$b_1=\frac{1}{a_1}. \tag{5}$$

2. *Case* 2. $a_1=0$. In the series 3) suppose that a_m is the first coefficient $\neq 0$. Then

$$w=z^m(a_m+a_{m+1}z+\cdots)\quad,\quad a_m\neq 0. \tag{6}$$

Let us set

$$w=u^m. \tag{7}$$

Then

$$u=z(a_m+a_{m+1}z+\cdots)^{\frac{1}{m}}$$

$$=z(c_0+c_1z+c_2z^2+\cdots)\quad,\quad c_0=a_m^{\frac{1}{m}}$$

by 118, 11. We are thus led back to case 1.

Inverting, we get

$$z=\frac{1}{a_m^{\frac{1}{m}}}\cdot u+d_2u^2+\cdots$$

Putting in the value of u in 7), we get finally

$$z=w^{\frac{1}{m}}\left\{\frac{1}{a_m^{\frac{1}{m}}}+d_2w^{\frac{1}{m}}+\cdots\right\}. \tag{8}$$

3. Let us show how to get the coefficients of the inverse series using the method of undetermined coefficients. Let us suppose that the original series is

$$v=b_0+b_1(t-b)+b_2(t-b)^2+\cdots\qquad b_1\neq 0. \tag{9}$$

Let us set

$$w=v-b_0\qquad z=b_1(t-b).$$

Then 9) takes the form

$$w=z-a_2z^2-a_3z^3-\cdots \tag{10}$$

where we have introduced the minus signs for convenience later. Then the inverse series has the form

$$z = w + c_2 w^2 + c_3 w^3 + \cdots \tag{11}$$

Raising 11) to successive powers gives

$$\begin{aligned} z^2 &= w^2 + 2\, c_2 w^3 + (c_2^2 + 2\, c_3)\, w^4 + (2\, c_4 + 2\, c_2 c_3) w^5 + \cdots \\ z^3 &= w^3 + 3\, c_2 w^4 + (3\, c_2^2 + 3\, c_3) w^5 + \cdots \\ z^4 &= w^4 + 4\, c_2 w^5 + \cdots \\ &\cdots\cdots\cdots\cdots\cdots \end{aligned} \tag{12}$$

All these series may be denoted by

$$z^m = c_{m1} w + c_{m2} w^2 + \cdots \tag{13}$$

Putting these series for z, z^2, $z^3 \cdots$ in 10) gives rise to a double series

$$\begin{aligned} D = \quad & w + \quad c_2 w^2 + \quad c_3 w^3 + \cdots \\ & - a_2 c_{21} w - a_2 c_{22} w^2 - a_2 c_{23} w^3 - \cdots \\ & - a_3 c_{31} w - a_3 c_{32} w^2 - a_3 c_{33} w^3 - \cdots \\ & \cdots\cdots\cdots\cdots \end{aligned} \tag{14}$$

If we sum this series by rows, we fall back on 10). The sum of D by rows is thus w. If the series 14) be summed by columns, we get a power series in w, and this is what we want. Now by 42, 2 if 14) is convergent, its sum is the same whether summed by rows or by columns. To show that 14) is convergent we shall show that its adjoint is convergent. Let us denote this adjoint series by

$$\begin{aligned} & W + \quad \gamma_2 W^2 + \quad \gamma_3 W^3 + \cdots \\ & + \alpha_2 \gamma_{21} W + \alpha_2 \gamma_{22} W^2 + \alpha_2 \gamma_{23} W^3 + \cdots \\ & + \cdots \qquad \cdots \qquad \cdots \end{aligned} \tag{15}$$

Now 11) is valid in some circle $\mathfrak{k}$, it thus converges absolutely for all $W \leq$ some W_0. Then

$$Z = W + \gamma_2 W^2 + \gamma_3 W^3 + \cdots$$

converges for $W \leq W_0$.

The series 10) converges absolutely for all $Z \leq$ some Z_0. Thus the adjoint of 10)

$$Z + \alpha_2 Z^2 + \alpha_3 Z^3 + \cdots \tag{16}$$

converges for all $Z \leq Z_0$.

Returning to the adjoint series 15), we see that if we sum this by rows we get 16). As this converges, D is convergent for all $|w| \leq W_0$ by 42, 3. We may thus sum D by columns, getting a power series. As the sum of D by rows is w as we saw, the sum of this power series is also w by 42, 2.

Thus we get, replacing the c_{mn} by their values in 12), the identity

$$w = w + (c_2 - a_2)w^2 + (c_3 - 2\,a_2c_2 - a_3)w^3 + \cdots$$

Hence all the coefficients on the right are 0, except the first. The resulting equations give

$$\begin{aligned} c_2 &= a_2, \\ c_3 &= 2\,a_2c_2 + a_3, \\ c_4 &= a_2(c_2^2 + 2\,c_3) + 3\,a_3c_2 + a_4, \\ c_5 &= 2\,a_2(c_4 + c_2c_3) + 3\,a_3(c_2^2 + c_3) + 4\,a_4c_2 + a_5, \\ &\text{etc.} \end{aligned} \tag{17}$$

4. *Example.* We saw that

$$w = \log(1 + z) = z - \frac{z^2}{2} + \frac{z^3}{3} - \frac{z^4}{4} + \cdots \qquad |z| < 1. \tag{18}$$

Here

$$a_2 = \tfrac{1}{2} \;,\quad a_3 = -\tfrac{1}{3} \;,\quad a_4 = \tfrac{1}{4} \;\cdots$$

These values in 17) give

$$c_2 = \tfrac{1}{2} \;,\quad c_3 = \tfrac{1}{6} \;,\quad c_4 = \tfrac{1}{24} \;\cdots$$

Hence, inverting the series 18), we get

$$z = w + \frac{w^2}{2!} + \frac{w^3}{3!} + \frac{w^4}{4!} + \cdots \tag{19}$$

Now from 18) we have

$$1 + z = e^w = 1 + w + \frac{w^2}{2!} + \frac{w^3}{3!} + \cdots$$

which agrees with 19).

126. Fourier's Development. 1. When the real function $f(x)$ has the period $2\,\pi$, Fourier showed that in many cases it can be developed in a trigonometric series

$$\begin{aligned} f(x) = a_0 + a_1 \cos x + a_2 \cos 2\,x + \cdots \\ + b_1 \sin x + b_2 \sin 2\,x + \cdots \end{aligned} \tag{1}$$

This development is of extraordinary importance in mathematical physics and in some branches of pure mathematics. Let us show how this development appears in the function theory.

We begin by proving the theorem :

Let $f(z)$ be a one-valued function having the period ω. If it is analytic in a band B whose sides are parallel to $O\omega$, we have

$$f(z) = \sum_{-\infty}^{\infty} a_m e^{m \cdot \frac{2\pi i z}{\omega}} \tag{2}$$

where

$$a_m = \frac{1}{\omega} \int_b^{b+\omega} f(v) e^{-m\frac{2\pi i v}{\omega}} dv \tag{3}$$

and b is any point in B.

For let us set

$$u = e^{\frac{2\pi i z}{\omega}}, \tag{4}$$

then u has ω as period.

To find the image of the band B in Fig. 1, let us begin by finding the image of a line l_α parallel to $O\omega$ and cutting the real axis at $z = \alpha$. When z lies on such a line, we have

$$z = \alpha + r\omega,$$

where r ranges over all real values.

Let us set

$$\frac{i\alpha}{\omega} = \alpha' + i\alpha''.$$

Then 4) gives

$$u = e^{\frac{2\pi i}{\omega}(\alpha + r\omega)} = e^{2\pi(\alpha' + \alpha'' i)} e^{2\pi i r} = e^{2\pi\alpha'} e^{2\pi i (r + \alpha'')}.$$

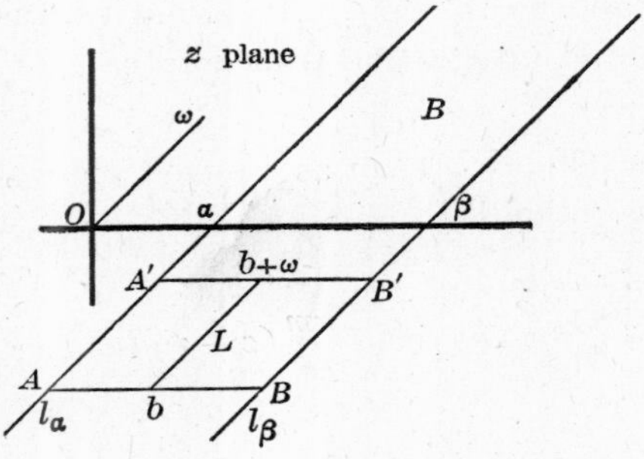

FIG. 1.

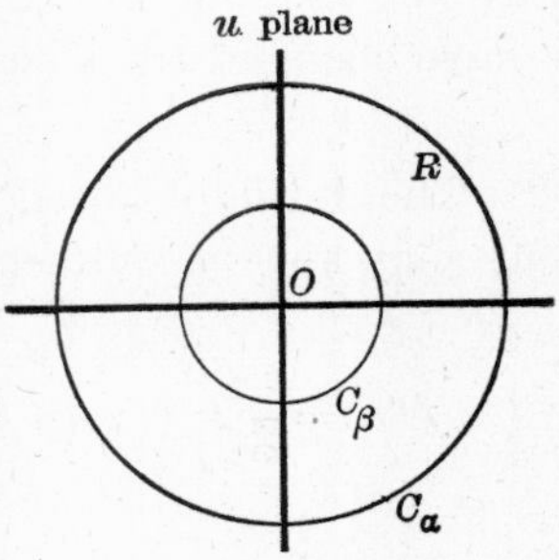

FIG. 2.

Thus when z ranges over l_α, u moves over the circle C_α in Fig. 2 of radius $e^{2\pi\alpha'}$. When r increases from $r = 0$ to $r = 1$, u has moved once around this circle. Hence when z moves on l_α over a segment of length $= |\omega|$, u has moved once around C_α. Similarly when z ranges over l_β in Fig. 1, u moves over the circle C_β in Fig. 2. Thus the image of a line L going from b to $b+\omega$ is a circle lying between C_α and C_β.

The image of the parallelogram $\mathfrak{P} = (ABA'B')$ is the ring R. To a point within $\mathfrak{P}$ corresponds a single point within R, and conversely. As $f(z)$ has the period ω, f takes on every value in $\mathfrak{P}$ that it can take on anywhere in B. Since $f(z)$ is a one-valued analytic function in $\mathfrak{P}$, it is considered as a function of u, a one-valued analytic function of u in R. Hence, by Laurent's theorem, 117

$$f = \sum_{-\infty}^{\infty} a_m u^m \tag{5}$$

where

$$a_m = \frac{1}{2\pi i}\int_C \frac{f du}{u^{m+1}} \tag{6}$$

and C is any circle in R whose center is $u = 0$.

Now from 4)

$$du = \frac{2\pi i}{\omega} u dz.$$

Hence

$$\frac{du}{u^{m+1}} = \frac{2\pi i}{\omega}\frac{dz}{u^m} = \frac{2\pi i}{\omega} e^{-m\frac{2\pi i z}{\omega}} dz.$$

Thus 5) goes over into 2), and 6) into 3). To avoid confusion we have changed the variable of integration from z to v.

2. The development 2), which is known as Fourier's development, may also be written as follows:

$$f(z) = \frac{1}{\omega}\int_L f(v)dv + \frac{2}{\omega}\sum_1^\infty \int_L f(v)\cos\frac{2\pi m}{\omega}(z-v)dv. \tag{7}$$

For we may write 2)

$$f(z) = a_0 + \left(a_1 e^{\frac{2\pi i z}{\omega}} + a_{-1} e^{-\frac{2\pi i z}{\omega}}\right) + \left(a_2 e^{2\cdot\frac{2\pi i z}{\omega}} + a_{-2} e^{-2\cdot\frac{2\pi i z}{\omega}}\right) + \cdots \tag{8}$$

Now from 3)

$$a_m e^{m\cdot\frac{2\pi i z}{\omega}} = \frac{1}{\omega}\int_L f(v) e^{-m\cdot\frac{2\pi i v}{\omega}} e^{m\cdot\frac{2\pi i z}{\omega}} dv$$

$$= \frac{1}{\omega}\int_L f(v) e^{m\cdot\frac{2\pi i}{\omega}(z-v)} dv.$$

Similarly

$$a_{-m} e^{m\cdot -\frac{2\pi i z}{\omega}} = \frac{1}{\omega}\int_L f(v) e^{-m\cdot\frac{2\pi i}{\omega}(z-v)} dv.$$

Their sum is

$$\frac{1}{\omega}\int_L f(v)\left\{e^{m\frac{2\pi i}{\omega}(z-v)} + e^{-m\frac{2\pi i}{\omega}(z-v)}\right\} dv$$

or using Euler's formula, 55, 11)

$$= \frac{2}{\omega}\int_L f(v) \cos m \cdot \frac{2\pi}{\omega}(z-v)\, dv.$$

This in 8) gives 7).

CHAPTER VIII

INFINITE PRODUCTS

127. Introduction. In the theory of the gamma function and especially in the theory of the elliptic functions, both of which will be treated later, infinite products play an important part. They are also useful in other parts of analysis. We therefore propose to give a brief account of them here.

It is easy to see how mathematicians were led to consider them. Every polynomial,

$$a_0 + a_1 z + \cdots + a_n z^n = \sum_1^n a_m z^m, \tag{1}$$

can be written in the form

$$a_n(z - \alpha_1)(z - \alpha_2) \cdots (z - \alpha_n) = a_n \prod_1^n (z - \alpha_m), \tag{2}$$

where $\alpha_1, \alpha_2 \cdots \alpha_n$ are the zeros of 1).

Since a power series,

$$f(z) = a_0 + a_1 z + a_2 z^2 + \cdots = \sum_1^\infty a_m z^m, \tag{3}$$

is the limit of a polynomial of the type 1), it is natural to expect that the function $f(z)$ defined by the series 3) can be expressed as the limit of the product of type 2), that is, as an infinite product

$$C(z - \alpha_1)(z - \alpha_2) \cdots = C \prod_1^\infty (z - \alpha_m),$$

where the $\alpha_1, \alpha_2 \cdots$ are the zeros of $f(z)$.

As an illustration let us take

$$f(z) = \sin z = \frac{z}{1!} - \frac{z^3}{3!} + \frac{z^5}{5!} - \cdots$$

whose zeros are $0, \pm\pi, \pm 2\pi, \cdots$. We shall show directly that

$$\sin z = z\left(1 - \frac{z^2}{\pi^2}\right)\left(1 - \frac{z^2}{2^2\pi^2}\right) \cdots = z \prod_1^\infty \left(1 - \frac{z^2}{n^2\pi^2}\right). \tag{4}$$

We notice that each factor

$$1-\frac{z^2}{n^2\pi^2}=\frac{1}{n^2\pi^2}(z-n\pi)(z+n\pi),$$

vanishes at two of the zeros of $\sin z$, viz. at $\pm n\pi$. If we set $z=\frac{\pi}{2}$ in 4) we get

$$\frac{\pi}{2}=\frac{2}{1}\cdot\frac{2}{3}\cdot\frac{4}{3}\cdot\frac{4}{5}\cdot\frac{6}{5}\cdot\frac{6}{7}\cdots \tag{5}$$

one of the earliest infinite products considered, due to ***Wallis***.

As examples of other infinite products we notice

$$Q=\Pi(1+q^{2n}), \qquad n=1, 2, 3 \cdots \tag{6}$$

$$\Gamma(z)=\frac{e^{-Cz}}{z\Pi\left(1+\frac{z}{n}\right)e^{-\frac{z}{n}}}. \tag{7}$$

$$\theta(z)=2\,q^{\frac{1}{4}}Q\sin\pi z\Pi(1-2\,q^{2n}\cos 2\,\pi z+q^{4n}). \tag{8}$$

Here Q is an elliptic modular function, Γ is the celebrated gamma function, and θ one of the theta functions which are so fundamental in the elliptic functions. All these we shall consider in the course of this book.

128. Definitions. 1. Let us now define infinite products more precisely. Let $a_1, a_2, a_3 \cdots$ be a sequence of complex numbers. The symbol

$$A=a_1\cdot a_2\cdot a_3\cdots=\prod_{n=1}^{\infty}a_n \tag{1}$$

is called an infinite product. As in infinite series we set

$$A_n=a_1\cdot a_2\cdots a_n \quad , \quad \overline{A}_n=a_{n+1}\cdot a_{n+2}\cdots \tag{2}$$

If

$$\lim_{n=\infty}A_n \tag{3}$$

is finite or definitely infinite, we call it the value of the product 1). As no ambiguity need be feared, we denote an infinite product and its value, when it has one, by the same letter. When 3) is finite and $\neq 0$, or when one of its factors $a_m=0$, we say A is *convergent*, otherwise *divergent*.

Let us consider
$$A = \frac{1}{1} \cdot \frac{1}{2} \cdot \frac{2}{3} \cdot \frac{3}{4} \cdot \frac{4}{5} \cdots \tag{4}$$

Here
$$A_n = \frac{1}{n},$$

and hence
$$\lim_{n=\infty} A_n = 0.$$

Thus according to our definition the value of 4) is 0, although no factor of this product is 0. For this reason we do not care in this book to consider infinite products which $=0$ although no factor is 0. We have therefore put them in the class of divergent products.

The infinite product $\overline{A}_n$ in 2) is called the co-product. Obviously if $\overline{A}_n$ is convergent, so is A, and conversely, when zero factors are not present.

In a similar manner we define infinite products whose factors are functions of z. Thus if $f_1(z), f_2(z) \cdots$ are functions of z defined over some point set $\mathfrak{A}$,
$$F = f_1(z) f_2(z) \cdots = \prod_{n=1}^{\infty} f_n(z) \tag{5}$$

is such a product. Giving z a value in $\mathfrak{A}$ as $z = a$ reduces 5) to a product of the type 1), the factors being now constants. If 5) converges for this value of z, we say it converges for $z = a$, etc.

2. Just as we have double series
$$\Sigma a_{mn}, \tag{1}$$

so we can have *double products*
$$\Pi a_{mn}. \tag{2}$$

With 2) we associate a simple product
$$\Pi a_s, \tag{3}$$

where each factor a_{mn} of 2) is some factor a_s of 3), and conversely.

Analogous to double series we will say 2) is convergent when 3) converges absolutely, otherwise 2) is divergent. When 2) is convergent, its value shall be that of 3). From these definitions we may build up a theory of double products in much the same way as we have developed the theory of double series in Chapter III.

129. Fundamental Theorem. In the infinite product

$$A = a_1 \cdot a_2 \cdot a_3 \cdots \quad , \quad a_n \neq 0 \tag{1}$$

let us set

$$a_m = \rho_m e^{i\theta_m} \tag{2}$$

where we will agree to choose θ_m so that

$$-\pi < \theta_m \leq \pi. \tag{3}$$

We now introduce the real series

$$\Theta = \theta_1 + \theta_2 + \theta_3 + \cdots \tag{4}$$

and the real product

$$R = \rho_1 \cdot \rho_2 \cdot \rho_3 \cdots \tag{5}$$

and prove a theorem on which our treatment of infinite products will rest:

For A to converge it is necessary and sufficient that Θ and R are convergent. When A is convergent,

$$A = Re^{i\Theta}. \tag{6}$$

For

$$A_n = a_1 a_2 \cdots a_n$$

$$= \rho_1 \cdots \rho_n e^{i(\theta_1 + \cdots + \theta_n)}$$

or

$$A_n = R_n e^{i\Theta_n}. \tag{7}$$

If now R and Θ are convergent,

$$\lim A_n = \lim R_n \cdot \lim e^{i\Theta_n}$$

or

$$A = Re^{i\Theta}.$$

Hence A is convergent and its value is given by 6).

Conversely, if A converges,

$$R_n \text{ and } e^{i\Theta_n}$$

must obviously converge to finite values $\neq 0$. Thus in the first place R is a convergent product.

As $e^{i\Theta_n}$ converges to some number $\neq 0$, we can denote it by e^{iT}; we have therefore

$$\lim e^{i\Theta_n} = e^{iT}. \tag{8}$$

Now from this we cannot say at once that

$$\lim \Theta_n \doteq T$$

since

$$e^{i(u+2\pi)} = e^{iu}.$$

The relation 8) however shows that

$$|e^{iT} - e^{i\Theta_n}| < \epsilon \qquad \text{for all } n > \text{some } m,$$

or that

$$e^{iT}|1 - e^{i(\Theta_n - T)}| < \epsilon.$$

This requires that aside from multiples of 2π, Θ_n shall $\doteq T$, that is

$$\lim_{n=\infty} (\Theta_n - 2k_n\pi) = T \qquad k_n \text{ an integer.}$$

Thus

$$\Theta_n = T + 2k_n\pi + \eta_n, \tag{9}$$

and however small $\eta > 0$ is taken,

$$|\eta_n| < \eta \qquad \text{for all } n > \text{some } m. \tag{10}$$

From 9) we have

$$\theta_n = \Theta_n - \Theta_{n-1}$$
$$= 2\pi(k_n - k_{n-1}) + (\eta_n - \eta_{n-1}). \tag{11}$$

Now

$$k = k_n - k_{n-1}$$

is some integer or 0, while

$$\eta' = \eta_n - \eta_{n-1}$$

is as small as we choose. Thus 11) shows that

$$\theta_n = k2\pi + \eta'.$$

Hence the value of $|\theta_n|$ is not far from $|k| \cdot 2\pi$. But from 3)

$$|\theta_n| \leq \pi.$$

To reconcile these two facts we must take $k = 0$, since $|k|$ is 0 or a positive integer. From this it follows that all the k_n in 9) after some k_s are equal. Hence denoting the constant k_s by κ we have

$$\Theta_n = T + 2\kappa\pi + \eta_n \qquad n > s.$$

As $\eta_n \doteq 0$ by 10) we have, passing to the limit $n = \infty$ in 9),

$$\lim_{n=\infty} \Theta_n = T + 2\kappa\pi.$$

This shows that Θ is convergent. We have thus shown that when A is convergent, so are R and Θ.

130. The Associate Logarithmic Series. To study the convergence of the infinite product

$$A = a_1 \cdot a_2 \cdot a_3 \cdots \quad , \quad a_n \neq 0 \tag{1}$$

we introduce the series

$$L = \log a_1 + \log a_2 + \cdots \tag{2}$$

where using the notation of 129 we take

$$\log a_n = \log \rho_n + i\theta_n, \tag{3}$$

that is, the principal branch of $\log a_n$. We call L the *associate logarithmic series.* Let us prove the theorem:

For A to converge it is necessary and sufficient that L converges. When A is convergent,

$$A = e^L. \tag{4}$$

In fact

$$L_n = \log \rho_1 + \cdots + \log \rho_n + i(\theta_1 + \cdots + \theta_n)$$

$$= \log R_n + i\Theta_n \tag{5}$$

$$= \log A_n + 2\, s_n \pi i \tag{6}$$

where s_n is some undetermined integer.

From 6) we have

$$A_n = e^{L_n}.$$

Thus, when L is convergent, A is convergent and its value is given by 4).

Conversely, suppose that A converges. Then by 129 we know that R and Θ converge. Hence passing to the limit in 5) we have

$$L = \log R + i\Theta \tag{7}$$

and L is convergent.

131. Absolute and Steady Convergence. 1. In analogy to series one would be tempted to say that A is absolutely convergent, if the product

$$R = \rho_1 \rho_2 \rho_3 \cdots$$

formed of the absolute values of the factors of

$$A = a_1 a_2 a_3 \cdots \quad , \quad a_n \neq 0 \tag{1}$$

is convergent. This is not admissible, as the following example shows. Let

$$A = \prod_1^\infty (-1)^n. \tag{2}$$

The product formed of the absolute values of the factors is

$$R = 1 \cdot 1 \cdot 1 \cdot \cdots$$

As $R_n = 1$, we see that R converges and has the value 1. On the other hand, the product of the first n factors of 2) is

$$A_n = (-1)^n$$

which has no limit as $n \doteq \infty$. Thus 2) is divergent. We could thus have divergent products which converge absolutely. Such a definition is therefore useless.

We shall therefore say:

The product 1) converges absolutely when the associate logarithmic series

$$L = \Sigma \log a_n \tag{3}$$

is absolutely convergent. Hence if L converges absolutely, L is *a fortiori* convergent and thus A converges by 130.

From this it follows that when an infinite product converges absolutely, its convergence may be determined by considering the convergence of a positive term series, viz. the adjoint series of 3).

For L to converge, it is necessary that

$$\log a_n \doteq 0.$$

As

$$a_n = \rho_n e^{i\theta_n}$$

this requires that

$$\rho_n \doteq 1. \tag{4}$$

We have already seen in 129 that

$$\theta_n \doteq 0. \tag{5}$$

2. If the factors of an infinite product

$$F = f_1(z) \cdot f_y(z) \cdots \tag{6}$$

are functions of z defined over a point set $\mathfrak{A}$, we shall say that F converges *steadily in* $\mathfrak{A}$ when the associate logarithmic series

$$L = \Sigma \log f_n(z) \tag{7}$$

converges steadily in $\mathfrak{A}$.

Thus when L converges steadily, the factors $f_n(z)$ all differ from 1 by an amount $< \epsilon$ for $n >$ some m. Thus if each $f_n(z)$ is one-valued and analytic in some circle $\mathfrak{K}$ about the point z, $\overline{L}_m(z)$ will be one-valued and analytic when L converges steadily in $\mathfrak{R}$. Hence:

$$F(z) = e^{L(z)} = f_1(z) f_2(z) \cdots \tag{8}$$

is a one-valued analytic function in $\mathfrak{R}$, *whose logarithmic derivative is*

$$\frac{F'(z)}{F(z)} = L'(z). \tag{9}$$

132. 1. *Example 1.* Let us consider the analytic character of

$$F = z \prod_1^\infty \left(1 - \frac{z^2}{n^2\pi^2}\right). \tag{1}$$

We shall prove in 136 that $F = \sin z$.

Let $\mathfrak{R}$ be a circle of radius R described about $z = 0$. We take the integer m so large that

$$m\pi > R.$$

Then for any z in $\mathfrak{R}$

$$q_n = \left|\frac{z^2}{n^2\pi^2}\right| < 1 \qquad \text{if } n > m. \tag{2}$$

We consider now the co-product

$$\bar{F}_m = \prod_{n=m+1}^\infty \left(1 - \frac{z^2}{n^2\pi^2}\right) \tag{3}$$

where m is now fixed. Obviously if $\bar{F}_m$ converges absolutely in $\mathfrak{R}$, so does F.

The associate logarithmic series of 3) is

$$\bar{L}_m = \sum_{m+1}^\infty \log\left(1 - \frac{z^2}{n^2\pi^2}\right) = \Sigma l_n. \tag{4}$$

As

$$-\log\left(1 - \frac{z^2}{n^2\pi^2}\right) = \frac{z^2}{n^2\pi^2} + \frac{1}{2}\left(\frac{z^2}{n^2\pi^2}\right)^2 + \cdots$$

we have

$$|l_n| \leq q_n + q_n^2 + q_n^3 + \cdots$$

$$\leq \frac{q_n}{1 - q_n}.$$

Now $q_n < q_m$ since $n > m$. Hence

$$|l_n| < \frac{q_n}{1 - q_m},$$

or as m is fixed

$$c = \frac{1}{1 - q_m}$$

is a constant, and thus

$$|l_n| < cq_n \leq \frac{cR^2}{\pi^2} \cdot \frac{1}{n^2} = C\frac{1}{n^2}.$$

Thus each term of the adjoint of 4) is < the corresponding term of the convergent series

$$C\sum\frac{1}{n^2}.$$

Thus $\overline{L}_m$ is absolutely and steadily convergent in $\mathfrak{R}$. Hence by 131, 2 *the product* 1) *defines a one-valued analytic function of* z *for any* z.

This function vanishes for

$$z = 0, \ \pm\pi, \ \pm 2\pi, \cdots \tag{5}$$

and for no other z. For being convergent, the product 1) cannot vanish unless one of its factors vanishes.

Each of the zeros 5) are simple. For we have

$$F = (z - m\pi)\,G,$$

where

$$G = -\frac{z}{m^2\pi^2}(z + m\pi)\Pi'\left(1 - \frac{z^2}{n^2\pi^2}\right),$$

where the dash indicates that the index n does not take on the value $n = m$. Now G, being a convergent product, does not vanish for $z = m\pi$, since none of its factors vanishes at this point.

2. Let us note that the foregoing reasoning establishes the theorem :

The series

$$L = \sum_{n=1}^{\infty}\log\left(1 - \frac{z^2}{n^2\pi^2}\right)$$

converges absolutely for all values of $z \neq n\pi$. *It converges steadily in any connex not containing any of the points* $n\pi$.

133. *Example 2.* The Γ function is defined, as we shall see, by

$$\Gamma(z) = \frac{e^{-Cz}}{z\Pi\left(1+\frac{z}{n}\right)e^{-\frac{z}{n}}} \qquad n = 1, 2, \cdots \tag{1}$$

where

$$C = \sum_1^\infty \left\{\frac{1}{n} - \log\left(1+\frac{1}{n}\right)\right\} = .577215 \cdots \tag{2}$$

is the Eulerian constant considered in 20, Ex. 4.

We show that the infinite product in the denominator

$$F = \Pi\left(1+\frac{z}{n}\right)e^{-\frac{z}{n}} \tag{3}$$

is an analytic function of z which has

$$z = -1, -2, -3, \cdots \tag{4}$$

as zeros of order 1.

To this end we describe a circle $\mathfrak{K}$ of radius R about $z = 0$. We take the integer m so great that $m > R$. Then

$$q_n = \left|\frac{z}{n}\right| < 1 \qquad n > m$$

for any z in $\mathfrak{K}$. We now consider

$$\overline{L}_m = \sum_{m+1}^\infty \left\{\log\left(1+\frac{z}{n}\right) - \frac{z}{n}\right\} = \Sigma l_n \tag{5}$$

which is the associated logarithmic series of the co-product $\overline{F}_m$ of 3).

Now

$$l_n = -\frac{1}{2}\frac{z^2}{n^2} + \frac{1}{3}\frac{z^3}{n^3} - \cdots$$

Hence

$$|l_n| < q_n^2 + q_n^3 + \cdots$$

$$< \frac{q_n^2}{1-q_n} < \frac{q_n^2}{1-q_m}.$$

Hence

$$|l_n| < \frac{M}{n^2}.$$

This shows, as in Ex. 1, that the series 5) converges steadily in $\mathfrak{K}$. Hence, as before, F is an analytic function which has 4) as simple zeros.   Thus the function Γ defined by 1) is a one-valued analytic function having $z = 0, -1, -2, \cdots$ as simple poles.   By 120, 3 $z = \infty$ is an essentially singular point.

134. Normal Form. 1. We have seen that if the infinite product

$$A = a_1 \cdot a_2 \cdot a_3 \cdots$$

is convergent, then

$$a_n \doteq 1.$$

It is natural, therefore, that many infinite products present themselves in the form

$$A = (1 + b_1)(1 + b_2) \cdots = \Pi(1 + b_n). \tag{1}$$

We call this the *normal form* of an infinite product. Since we can always set

$$a_n = 1 + (a_n - 1) = 1 + b_n,$$

we can always reduce an infinite product to the normal form.

We prove now :

For the product 1) *to converge absolutely, it is necessary and sufficient that the series*

$$B = b_1 + b_2 + \cdots \tag{2}$$

is absolutely convergent.

Suppose that A is absolutely convergent.   Then the associate logarithmic series of 1) is absolutely convergent, that is,

$$\mathfrak{L} = \Sigma \mid \log (1 + b_n) \mid = \Sigma \lambda_n$$

is convergent.   Thus $\lambda_n \doteq 0$ and hence $b_n \doteq 0$.   Thus

$$\mid b_n \mid < 1 \qquad \text{for } n > \text{some } m.$$

Thus

$$\log (1 + b_n) = b_n - \frac{b_n^2}{2} + \frac{b_n^3}{3} - \cdots \qquad n > m.$$

Hence

$$\frac{\log(1 + b_n)}{b_n} = 1 - b_n \left\{ \frac{1}{2} - \frac{b_n}{3} + \cdots \right\}.$$

Thus

$$\lim_{n = \infty} \frac{\lambda_n}{\beta_n} = \lim_{n = \infty} \left| \frac{\log (1 + b_n)}{b_n} \right| = 1. \tag{3}$$

Hence by 20, 2

$$\beta_1 + \beta_2 + \cdots \tag{4}$$

is convergent, that is, 2) is absolutely convergent.

Conversely, suppose B converges absolutely ; then 4) is convergent. Then 3) holds once more and hence by 20, 2, $\mathfrak{L}$ is convergent. But then by definition the product 1) is absolutely convergent.

Definition. The series 2) is called the *normal series* of the product 1).

2. From 1 we conclude that *if* 1) *is absolutely convergent, the series*

$$\Sigma \log (1 + \beta_n) \quad , \quad \beta_n = | b_n | \tag{5}$$

is also absolutely convergent, and conversely.

For when the product A converges absolutely, the series $\Sigma\beta_n$ converges. But this series and 5) converge simultaneously as

$$\lim_{n=\infty} \frac{\log(1 + \beta_n)}{\beta_n} = 1.$$

3. In 131, 2 we have seen how the analytic nature of

$$F(z) = \Pi f_n(z)$$

may be determined from that of the associate logarithmic series. Let us now show how it may be inferred from the analyticity of the normal series. We prove in fact :

The product

$$P = \Pi(1 + f_n(z)) \tag{6}$$

is a one-valued analytic function of z within a circle $\mathfrak{K}$ about $z = a$, if the corresponding normal series

$$F = \Sigma f_n(z) \tag{7}$$

is steadily convergent in $\mathfrak{K}$ and each $f_n(z)$ is one-valued and analytic in $\mathfrak{K}$.

For 7) being steadily convergent in $\mathfrak{K}$, each term f_n is numerically $<$ some c_n for any z in $\mathfrak{K}$, and the series Σc_n is convergent. Thus $c_n \doteq 0$, or $c_n < \epsilon$ for $n >$ some m. Hence

$$|f_n(z)| < \epsilon \qquad n > m$$

for any z in $\mathfrak{K}$.

We show now that the logarithmic series

$$L = \sum_{m+1}^{\infty} \log (1 + f_n(z)) = \Sigma l_n \tag{8}$$

converges steadily in $\mathfrak{R}$. For

$$l_n = \frac{f_n}{1} - \frac{f_n^2}{2} + \frac{f_n^3}{3} - \cdots$$

Hence

$$|l_n| \leq |f_n| + |f_n|^2 + |f_n|^3 + \cdots$$
$$\leq |f_n| \{1 + \epsilon + \epsilon^2 + \cdots\}$$
$$< \frac{c_n}{1-\epsilon} = \gamma c_n.$$

Thus each term of 8) is numerically < the corresponding term of the convergent series

$$\gamma \Sigma c_n.$$

Example 1. The product

$$A = \tfrac{1}{2} \cdot \tfrac{3}{2} \cdot \tfrac{3}{4} \cdot \tfrac{5}{4} \cdot \tfrac{5}{6} \cdots = a_1 a_2 a_3 \cdots \qquad (9$$

is convergent. For consider the product

$$P = \Pi\left(1 - \frac{1}{n^2}\right) = \frac{2^2-1}{2^2} \cdot \frac{4^2-1}{4^2} \cdot \frac{6^2-1}{6^2} \cdots$$
$$= (\tfrac{1}{2} \cdot \tfrac{3}{2})(\tfrac{3}{4} \cdot \tfrac{5}{6})(\tfrac{5}{6} \cdot \tfrac{7}{6}) \cdots$$

The normal series belonging to P is

$$-\Sigma \frac{1}{n^2}.$$

As this converges, P is convergent.

Now

$$A_{2m} = P_m \doteq P,$$
$$A_{2m+1} = a_{2m+1} \cdot P_m = \frac{2m+1}{2m+2} \cdot P_m \doteq P.$$

Thus

$$\lim_{n=\infty} A_n = P,$$

and A is convergent.

Example 2.

$$Q(z) = \Pi(1 + z^{2n}) \qquad (10$$

converges steadily in any circle $\mathfrak{R}$ about $z = 0$ of radius $R < 1$. For the normal series corresponding to 10) is

$$\Sigma z^{2n}. \qquad (11$$

But each term of 11) is $\leq$ the corresponding term of

$$\Sigma R^{2n},$$

which converges since $R < 1$. Thus Q converges steadily in $\mathfrak{R}$. The proof also shows that 10) converges absolutely for any $|z| < 1$.

The product 10) is the product 6) in 127, q being replaced by z. The function $Q(z)$ is thus an elliptic modular function. It is a most extraordinary function, since every point on a unit circle $\mathfrak{C}$ about $z = 0$ is an essentially singular point. It admits therefore no analytic continuation outside $\mathfrak{C}$. Here then is an analytic function whose domain of definition, instead of being the whole z-plane, certain isolated points excepted, as is the case with all the elementary functions, is the interior of $\mathfrak{C}$.

135. Arithmetic Operations. 1. Let us now see whether the usual transformations of finite products hold for infinite products. We have in the first place:

Let

$$A = \Pi a_n \quad , \quad B = \Pi b_n$$

be convergent. Then the products

$$C = \Pi a_n b_n \quad , \quad D = \Pi \frac{a_n}{b_n} \qquad (\text{no } b_n = 0 \text{ in } D)$$

are convergent and

$$C = A \cdot B \quad , \quad D = \frac{A}{B}.$$

Moreover if A, B converge absolutely, so do C and D.

For

$$C_n = A_n B_n.$$

Hence letting $n \doteq \infty$ we have

$$\lim C_n = \lim A_n \cdot \lim B_n = AB, \text{ etc.}$$

To show that C is absolutely convergent when A and B are, we set

$$a_n = 1 + a_n' \quad , \quad b_n = 1 + b_n' \qquad |a_n'| = \alpha_n \quad , \quad |b_n'| = \beta_n.$$

Since A and B converge absolutely,

$$\Sigma \log (1 + \alpha_n) \quad , \quad \Sigma \log (1 + \beta_n)$$

converge absolutely by 134, 2. Hence

$$\Sigma\{\log(1+\alpha_n)+\log(1+\beta_n)\}=\Sigma\log(1+\alpha_n)(1+\beta_n)$$

is convergent. Hence C is absolutely convergent.

In the same way we may reason on D.

2. *An absolutely convergent product is commutative.*

For let

$$A = \Pi a_n$$

be absolutely convergent. Then

$$L = \Sigma \log a_n$$

is absolutely convergent. As by 130,

$$A = e^L,$$

and as we may permute the terms of L without changing its value, we may do the same with the factors of A.

3. *A convergent infinite product is associative, that is, we may insert parentheses at pleasure.*

For let

$$A = a_1 a_2 a_3 \cdots$$

be convergent. Let us consider

$$B = (a_1 \cdots a_{m_1})(a_{m_1+1} \cdots a_{m_2}) \cdots$$
$$= b_1 \cdot b_2 \cdots$$

Now $\qquad B_n = b_1 \cdots b_n = a_1 \cdot a_2 \cdots a_{m_n} = A_{m_n}.$

As $\qquad n \doteq \infty \quad , \quad A_{m_n} \doteq A,$

hence $\qquad \lim_{n=\infty} B_n = A.$

Example. The following infinite products occur in the elliptic functions

$$Q_1 = \Pi(1 + q^{2n})$$
$$Q_2 = \Pi(1 + q^{2n-1}) \qquad n = 1, 2, \cdots$$
$$Q_3 = \Pi(1 - q^{2n-1}).$$

They are obviously absolutely convergent for $|q| < 1$. As an exercise, let us prove an important relation which we shall need later, viz.:

$$P = Q_1 Q_2 Q_3 = 1. \qquad (1$$

For
$$P = \Pi(1 + q^{2n})(1 + q^{2n-1})(1 - q^{2n-1})$$
$$= \Pi(1 + q^{2n})(1 - q^{4n-2}) \quad , \quad \text{by } 3.$$

Now all integers of the type $2n$ are of the form $4n - 2$ or $4n$. Hence

$$\Pi(1 - q^{2n}) = \Pi(1 - q^{4n})(1 - q^{4n-2}) = \Pi(1 - q^{4n})\Pi(1 - q^{4n-2}),$$

or
$$\Pi(1 - q^{4n-2}) = \frac{\Pi(1 - q^{2n})}{\Pi(1 - q^{4n})}.$$

Thus
$$P = \Pi\frac{(1 + q^{2n})(1 - q^{2n})}{1 - q^{4n}} = \Pi\frac{1 - q^{4n}}{1 - q^{4n}} = 1.$$

Circular Functions

136. The Sine and Cosine Products. 1. Let us show how $\sin z$ may be developed in an infinite product. This product is useful in various transformations and gives rise to many useful relations. We wish to show that

$$\sin z = z\Pi\left(1 - \frac{z^2}{n^2\pi^2}\right) \quad , \quad n = 1, 2, 3, \cdots \tag{1}$$

We begin by showing that 1) holds for real x lying in the interval

$$\mathfrak{A} = (a, b) \quad , \quad 0 < a < b < \frac{\pi}{2};$$

it will then be easy to show that it holds for complex z.

In 6 we saw that $\sin nx$ is a polynomial of degree n in $\sin x$ *when n is odd*, or

$$\sin nx = a_0 \sin^n x + a_1 \sin^{n-1} x + \cdots + a_{n-1} \sin x.$$

If we set
$$t = \sin x, \tag{2}$$

this gives
$$\sin nx = F(t) = a_0 t^n + a_1 t^{n-1} + \cdots + a_{n-1} t. \tag{3}$$

There is no constant term here, since when $t = 0$, $F = 0$ also. Now F, considered as a function of t, has n roots. On the other hand, considered as a function of x, it vanishes when

$$\sin nx = 0,$$

that is, when

$$x = 0 \quad , \quad \pm\frac{\pi}{n} \quad , \quad \pm 2 \cdot \frac{\pi}{n} \quad , \quad \cdots \pm \frac{n-1}{2} \cdot \frac{\pi}{n}.$$

Putting these values in 2), we see that $F = 0$ when

$$t = 0 \quad , \quad \pm \sin\frac{\pi}{n} \quad , \quad \pm \sin 2 \cdot \frac{\pi}{n} \quad , \quad \cdots \pm \sin\frac{n-1}{2} \cdot \frac{\pi}{n}.$$

Thus

$$F(t) = a_0 t\left(t - \sin\frac{\pi}{n}\right)\left(t + \sin\frac{\pi}{n}\right)\cdots$$

$$= a_0 t\left(t^2 - \sin^2\frac{\pi}{n}\right)\cdots\left(t^2 - \sin^2\frac{n-1}{2}\cdot\frac{\pi}{n}\right). \qquad (4$$

Dividing through by

$$\sin^2\frac{\pi}{n} \cdot \sin^2 2 \cdot \frac{\pi}{n} \cdots \sin^2\frac{n-1}{n} \cdot \frac{\pi}{n}$$

and denoting the new constant by C, we get

$$\sin nx = C \sin x \left\{1 - \frac{\sin^2 x}{\sin^2\frac{\pi}{n}}\right\} \cdots \left\{1 - \frac{\sin^2 x}{\sin^2\frac{n-1}{2}\cdot\frac{\pi}{n}}\right\}. \qquad (5$$

To find C we have from 5)

$$\frac{\sin nx}{\sin x} = C\left\{1 - \frac{\sin^2 x}{\sin^2\frac{\pi}{n}}\right\}.$$

Let now $x \doteq 0$, the last relation gives $n = C$ which in 5) gives, on replacing x by $\frac{x}{n}$,

$$\sin x = n \sin\frac{x}{n} P(x, n) \qquad (6$$

where

$$P(x, n) = \Pi\left\{1 - \frac{\sin^2\frac{x}{n}}{\sin^2\frac{r\pi}{n}}\right\} \quad , \quad r = 1, 2, \ldots\frac{n-1}{2}. \qquad (7$$

As $n \doteq \infty$ we have

$$n \sin\frac{x}{n} = \frac{\sin\frac{x}{n}}{\frac{1}{n}} \doteq x.$$

Also

$$\frac{\sin^2\frac{x}{n}}{\sin^2\frac{r\pi}{n}} \doteq \frac{x^2}{r^2\pi^2}.$$

It seems likely, therefore, that on letting $n \doteq \infty$ in 6) and 7) we shall get 1) for values of x lying in $\mathfrak{A}$. To prove this let us set

$$P(x) = \prod_{r=1}^{\infty}\left(1 - \frac{x^2}{r^2\pi^2}\right), \tag{8}$$

$$L(x, n) = \log P(x, n) = \sum_{r=1}^{s} \log \left\{1 - \frac{\sin^2\frac{x}{n}}{\sin^2\frac{r\pi}{n}}\right\}, \quad s = \frac{n-1}{2}, \tag{9}$$

$$L(x) = \log P(x) = \sum_{1}^{\infty} \log\left(1 - \frac{x^2}{r^2\pi^2}\right). \tag{10}$$

We then have

$$\lim_{n=\infty} P(x, n) = \lim_{n=\infty} e^{L(x,n)} = e^{L(x)} = P,$$

provided

$$\lim_{n=\infty} L(x, n) = L(x). \tag{11}$$

Thus we need only to prove 11), which we easily do as follows. Let us denote the sum of the first m terms of 9) by $L_m(x, n)$ and the rest of the sum by $\bar{L}_m(x, n)$. Then from

$$L(x, n) = L_m(x, n) + \bar{L}_m(x, n),$$

$$L(x) = L_m(x) + \bar{L}_m(x),$$

we have

$$|L(x, n) - L(x)| \le |L_m(x, n) - L_m(x)| + |\bar{L}_m(x, n)| + |\bar{L}_m(x)|. \tag{12}$$

Now for

$$0 < x < \frac{\pi}{2},$$

we have

$$\frac{x}{2} < \sin x < x.$$

Thus for all $r >$ some m, and for any x in $\mathfrak{A}$,

$$0 < \frac{\sin^2 \frac{x}{n}}{\sin^2 \frac{r\pi}{n}} < \frac{4x^2}{\pi^2 r^2} < 1. \tag{13}$$

Also for

$$0 < \alpha < \beta < 1$$

we have, by the law of the mean,

$$0 < -\log(1-\alpha) < -\log(1-\beta) < \beta + G\beta^2, \quad G \text{ some constant.} \tag{14}$$

Thus 13), 14) give for any value of n

$$0 < |\overline{L}_m(x, n)| < \sum_{m+1}^{\infty} \frac{1}{r^2} + G\sum_{m+1}^{\infty} \frac{1}{r^4} < \frac{\epsilon}{3},$$

if m is taken sufficiently large.

Also by 132 on taking m still larger if necessary,

$$|\overline{L}_m(x)| < \frac{\epsilon}{3}.$$

Finally if n is $>$ some ν

$$|L_m(x, n) - L_m(x)| < \frac{\epsilon}{3}.$$

Thus 12) gives

$$|L(x, n) - L(x)| < \frac{\epsilon}{3} + \frac{\epsilon}{3} + \frac{\epsilon}{3} = \epsilon \quad , \quad n > \nu,$$

which establishes 11).

Thus 1) holds for z in $\mathfrak{A}$. To extend it to all values of z we need only to observe that the right side of 1) is an analytic function of z, as we saw in 132. Thus by the principle of analytic continuation 1) holds for any complex z.

2. Let us show that $\sin z$ has the period 2π by using the product 1). From 1) we have

$$\sin z = \lim_{n=\infty} Q_n(z) \tag{15}$$

where

$$Q_n(z) = z \prod_{m=-n}^{n} \frac{z + m\pi}{m\pi} \quad , \quad m = 0 \text{ excluded.}$$

Thus

$$\frac{Q_n(z+\pi)}{Q_n(z)} = \frac{z + (n+1)\pi}{z - n\pi} \doteq -1 \quad , \quad \text{as } n \doteq \infty.$$

Hence

$$\lim Q_n(z+\pi) = -\lim Q_n(z).$$

Thus 15) gives

$$\sin(z+\pi) = -\sin z.$$

Thus 2π is a period of $\sin z$.

3. From the product expression 1) we may derive

$$\cos z = \prod_1^\infty \left(1 - \frac{4z^2}{(2n-1)^2\pi^2}\right). \tag{16}$$

For from

$$\sin 2z = 2 \sin z \cos z$$

we have

$$\cos z = \frac{1}{2} \cdot \frac{2z}{z} \frac{\Pi\left(1 - \frac{4z^2}{n^2\pi^2}\right)}{\Pi\left(1 - \frac{z^2}{n^2\pi^2}\right)}$$

$$= \frac{\Pi\left(1 - \frac{4z^2}{(2m)^2\pi^2}\right)\left(1 - \frac{4z^2}{(2m-1)^2\pi^2}\right)}{\Pi\left(1 - \frac{z^2}{n^2\pi^2}\right)}$$

$$= \frac{\Pi\left(1 - \frac{z^2}{m^2\pi^2}\right)}{\Pi\left(1 - \frac{z^2}{n^2\pi^2}\right)} \Pi\left(1 - \frac{4z^2}{(2m-1)^2\pi^2}\right),$$

which gives 16) at once.

137. Infinite Series for tan *z*, cosec *z*, etc. 1. From 136, 1), 16) we have

$$\log \sin z = \log z + \sum_1^\infty \log\left(1 - \frac{z^2}{n^2\pi^2}\right), \tag{1}$$

$$\log \cos z = \sum_1^\infty \log\left(1 - \frac{4z^2}{(2n-1)^2\pi^2}\right). \tag{2}$$

Differentiating these, we get

$$\cot z = \frac{1}{z} + 2\sum_1^\infty \frac{z}{z^2 - n^2\pi^2}, \tag{3}$$

$$\tan z = 2\sum_1^\infty \frac{z}{\left(\frac{2n-1}{2}\right)^2 \pi^2 - z^2}, \tag{4}$$

valid for all z for which $\tan z$, $\cot z$ are defined, that is for all z which do not cause a denominator to vanish.

The relations 3), 4) exhibit $\cot z$, $\tan z$ as a series of rational functions whose poles are precisely the poles of the given functions. They are analogous to the representation of a rational function as the sum of partial fractions as shown in 122, 4.

2. As an exercise let us show the periodicity of $\cot z$ from 3). We have

$$\cot z = \lim_{n=\infty} F_n(z) = \lim_{n=\infty} \sum_{m=-n}^{n} \frac{1}{z+n\pi} \quad , \quad z \neq m\pi.$$

Now

$$F_n(z+\pi) = F_n(z) + \frac{1}{z+(n+1)\pi} - \frac{1}{z-n\pi}.$$

Letting $n \doteq \infty$ we get

$$\lim F_n(z+\pi) = \lim F_n(z),$$

or

$$\cot(z+\pi) = \cot z,$$

and thus $\cot z$ admits the period π.

138. Infinite Series for sec *z*, cosec *z*. 1. From the relation

$$\operatorname{cosec} z = \tan \tfrac{1}{2} z + \cot z$$

we have, using 3), 4) of 137

$$\operatorname{cosec} z = 2\sum_1^\infty \frac{\frac{1}{2} z}{\left(\frac{2n-1}{2}\right)^2 \pi^2 - \frac{z^2}{4}} + \frac{1}{z} - 2\sum_1^\infty \frac{z}{n^2\pi^2 - z^2},$$

$$= \frac{1}{z} + \sum \frac{4z}{(2n-1)^2\pi^2 - z^2} - 2\sum \frac{z}{n^2\pi^2 - z^2}$$

$$= \frac{1}{z} + \sum_1^\infty \frac{(-1)^{n+1} 2z}{n^2\pi^2 - z^2} \quad , \quad z \neq n\pi. \tag{1}$$

2. To get $\sec z$ we use the relation

$$\operatorname{cosec}\left(\frac{\pi}{2} - z\right) = \sec z.$$

From 1) we have

$$\operatorname{cosec} z = \frac{1}{z} + \sum_1^\infty (-1)^{n+1} \left\{ \frac{1}{n\pi - z} - \frac{1}{n\pi + z} \right\}.$$

Hence

$$\operatorname{cosec}\left(\frac{\pi}{2}-z\right)=\frac{1}{\frac{\pi}{2}-z}+\sum_{1}^{\infty}(-1)^{n+1}\left\{\frac{1}{n\pi-\frac{\pi}{2}+z}-\frac{1}{n\pi+\frac{\pi}{2}-z}\right\}=S$$

Let us regroup the terms of S, forming the series

$$T=\left\{\frac{1}{\frac{\pi}{2}-z}+\frac{1}{\frac{\pi}{2}+z}\right\}-\left\{\frac{1}{\frac{3\pi}{2}-z}+\frac{1}{\frac{3\pi}{2}+z}\right\}+\cdots$$

As

$$|S_n-T_n|=\frac{1}{\left|\frac{2n-1}{2}\pi+z\right|}\doteq 0 \text{ as } n\doteq\infty,$$

we see that T is convergent and $=S$. Thus

$$\sec z=\sum_{1}^{\infty}(-1)^{n+1}\frac{(2n-1)\pi}{\left(\frac{2n-1}{2}\right)^2\pi^2-z^2}, \tag{2}$$

valid for all z for which $\sec z$ is defined.

139. Development of log sin *z*, tan *z*, etc., in Power Series. 1. From 137, 1) we have

$$\log\frac{\sin z}{z}=\sum_{1}^{\infty}\log\left(1-\frac{z^2}{n^2\pi^2}\right). \tag{1}$$

If we agree to give $\frac{\sin z}{z}$ its limiting value 1 as $z\doteq 0$, the relation 1) holds for $|z|<\pi$. For such z

$$-\log\left(1-\frac{z^2}{n^2\pi^2}\right)=\frac{z^2}{n^2\pi^2}+\frac{1}{2}\frac{z^4}{n^4\pi^4}+\cdots$$

Hence

$$\begin{aligned}-\log\frac{\sin z}{z}=&\frac{z^2}{\pi^2}+\frac{1}{2}\frac{z^4}{\pi^4}+\frac{1}{3}\frac{z^6}{\pi^6}+\cdots\\&+\frac{z^2}{2^2\pi^2}+\frac{1}{2}\frac{z^4}{2^4\pi^4}+\frac{1}{3}\frac{z^6}{2^6\pi^6}+\cdots\\&+\frac{z^2}{3^2\pi^2}+\frac{1}{2}\frac{z^4}{3^4\pi^4}+\frac{1}{3}\frac{z^6}{3^6\pi^6}+\cdots\\&+\cdots\cdots\cdots\end{aligned} \tag{2}$$

provided we sum this double series by rows. As this series has all its terms positive for a real positive value of $z < \pi$, say for $z = r$, and as this series summed by rows is convergent, since the relation 2) holds for this r, we may sum 2) by columns for all $|z| < \pi$, by 42, 2, 3.

Doing this, we get

$$-\log \frac{\sin z}{z} = H_2 \frac{z^2}{\pi^2} + \frac{1}{2} H_4 \frac{z^4}{\pi^4} + \frac{1}{3} H_6 \frac{z^6}{\pi^6} + \cdots \qquad |z| < \pi, \tag{3}$$

where as usual

$$H_n = \frac{1}{1^n} + \frac{1}{2^n} + \frac{1}{3^n} + \cdots \tag{4}$$

2. In a similar manner we find

$$-\log \cos z = G_2 \frac{2^2 z^2}{\pi^2} + \frac{1}{2} G_4 \frac{2^4 z^4}{\pi^4} + \frac{1}{3} G_6 \frac{2^6 z^6}{\pi^6} + \cdots \qquad |z| < \frac{\pi}{2} \tag{5}$$

where

$$G_n = \frac{1}{1^n} + \frac{1}{3^n} + \frac{1}{5^n} + \cdots$$

We observe that

$$G_n = \frac{2^n - 1}{2^n} H_n.$$

This in 5) gives

$$-\log \cos z = (2^2 - 1) H_2 \frac{z^2}{\pi^2} + \frac{1}{2}(2^4 - 1) H_4 \frac{z^4}{\pi^4} + \frac{1}{3}(2^6 - 1) H_6 \frac{z^6}{\pi^6} + \cdots \tag{6}$$

valid for $|z| < \frac{\pi}{2}$.

If we differentiate 3) and 6), we get

$$\tan z = 2(2^2 - 1) H_2 \frac{z}{\pi^2} + 2(2^4 - 1) H_4 \frac{z^3}{\pi^4} + 2(2^6 - 1) H_6 \frac{z^5}{\pi^6} + \cdots \tag{7}$$

valid for $|z| < \frac{\pi}{2}$.

$$\cot z = \frac{1}{z} - 2 H_2 \frac{z}{\pi^2} - 2 H_4 \frac{z^3}{\pi^4} - 2 H_6 \frac{z^5}{\pi^6} - \cdots \tag{8}$$

valid for $0 < |z| < \pi$.

3. Comparing 7) with the development of tan z given in **116**, 4), we get

$$H_2 = 1 + \frac{1}{2^2} + \frac{1}{3^2} + \cdots = \frac{\pi^2}{6} = \frac{1}{6} \cdot \frac{2\,\pi^2}{2\,!} = T_1 \cdot \frac{2\,\pi^2}{2\,!}$$

$$H_4 = 1 + \frac{1}{2^4} + \frac{1}{3^4} + \cdots = \frac{\pi^4}{90} = \frac{1}{30} \cdot \frac{2^3\,\pi^4}{4\,!} = T_3 \cdot \frac{2^3\,\pi^4}{4\,!} \tag{9}$$

$$H_6 = 1 + \frac{1}{2^6} + \frac{1}{3^6} + \cdots = \frac{\pi^6}{945} = \frac{1}{42} \cdot \frac{2^5\,\pi^6}{6\,!} = T_5 \cdot \frac{2^5\,\pi^6}{6\,!}$$

etc. Here

$$T_1 = \tfrac{1}{6}\;,\quad T_3 = \tfrac{1}{30}\;,\quad T_5 = \tfrac{1}{42}\;,\quad T_7 = \tfrac{1}{30}\;,\quad T_9 = \tfrac{5}{66}\quad \cdots$$

In general we may set

$$H_{2n} = \frac{2^{2n-1}\,\pi^{2n}}{(2\,n)\,!}\,T_{2n-1}. \tag{10}$$

Then 7) gives

$$\tan z = \frac{2^2(2^2-1)}{2\,!}\,T_1 z + \frac{2^4(2^4-1)}{4\,!}\,T_3 z^3 + \frac{2^6(2^6-1)}{6\,!}\,T_5 z^5 + \cdots \tag{11}$$

valid for $|z| < \frac{\pi}{2}$.

From 8) and 10) we get

$$\cot z = \frac{1}{z} - \sum_1^\infty \frac{2^{2n}}{(2\,n)\,!}\,T_{2n-1} z^{2n-1}. \tag{12}$$

The numbers T_1, T_2 ⋯ are called the *Bernoullian numbers.*

140. Weierstrass' Factor Theorem. 1. We have seen in **136** how the integral transcendental functions sin z, cos z may be developed as infinite products whose factors vanish at the zeros of these functions. Weierstrass by generalizing these developments arrived at the following theorem of great theoretical value:

Let the one-valued integral transcendental function $F(z)$ *have* a_1, a_2, ⋯ *as zeros which we suppose arranged so that* $|a_{n+1}| \geq |a_n| \doteq \infty$ *as* $n \doteq \infty$, *an m-tuple zero being repeated m times, and the a's being* $\neq 0$. *Then*

$$F(z) = e^{T(z)} \prod_1^\infty \left(1 - \frac{z}{a_n}\right) e^{\frac{z}{a_n} + \frac{1}{2}\left(\frac{z}{a_n}\right)^2 + \cdots + \frac{1}{n}\left(\frac{z}{a_n}\right)^n}, \tag{1}$$

where T is an undetermined integral function.

Before proving this theorem we wish to make a few explanatory remarks. We note that corresponding to each zero a_n there is a factor $1-\frac{z}{a_n}$ in 1) which vanishes at this point. Since the exponential function never vanishes, the right side of 1) will not vanish except one of the factors vanishes, provided the product on the right of 1) is convergent.

The infinite product

$$\Pi\left(1-\frac{z}{a_n}\right) \tag{2}$$

will not converge in general. For example, the zeros of $\frac{1}{\Gamma(z)}$, as we saw in 133, are $0, -1, -2, \cdots$. The product corresponding to 2) is here

$$z\Pi\left(1+\frac{z}{n}\right).$$

This does not converge, since

$$\Sigma \log\left(1+\frac{z}{n}\right)$$

is divergent.

To make the product 2) converge, Weierstrass has added the factor

$$e^{\frac{z}{a_n}+\cdots+\frac{1}{n}\left(\frac{z}{a_n}\right)^n}.$$

This introduces no zero into the product, but does make it converge, as we shall see.

Finally the factor

$$e^{T(z)}$$

has to be added, since, however the integral function T is chosen, the resulting function 1) has the assigned zeros a_n.

2. To prove 1) we begin by showing that

$$G(z)=\prod_{n=1}^{\infty}\left(1-\frac{z}{a_n}\right)e^{\frac{z}{a_n}+\cdots+\frac{1}{n}\left(\frac{z}{a_n}\right)^n} \tag{3}$$

is an integral transcendental function which vanishes only at the a_n.

For take z large at pleasure and fix it. About the origin we describe a circle $\mathfrak{K}$ of radius R including z. We next take m so large that

$$\alpha_m=|a_m|>R.$$

Let $H(z)$ denote the product 3) after deleting the first m factors, that is, the product 3) when n takes on the values

$$n = m + 1,\ m + 2, \cdots$$

We now show that the corresponding logarithmic series

$$L(z) = \sum_{n=m+1}^{\infty} \left\{ \log\left(1 - \frac{z}{a_n}\right) + \frac{z}{a_n} + \cdots + \frac{1}{n}\left(\frac{z}{a_n}\right)^n \right\} = \Sigma l_n \qquad (4$$

converges steadily in $\mathfrak{R}$. For

$$\log\left(1 - \frac{z}{a_n}\right) = -\left\{ \frac{z}{a_n} + \frac{1}{2}\left(\frac{z}{a_n}\right)^2 + \frac{1}{3}\left(\frac{z}{a_n}\right)^3 + \cdots \right\}.$$

If we set

$$|z| = \zeta \quad , \quad |l_n| = \lambda_n \quad , \quad \frac{R}{\alpha_m} = \rho < 1,$$

we have

$$\lambda_n \leq \frac{1}{n+1}\left(\frac{\zeta}{\alpha_n}\right)^{n+1} + \frac{1}{n+2}\left(\frac{\zeta}{\alpha_n}\right)^{n+2} + \cdots$$

$$< \left(\frac{R}{\alpha_m}\right)^{n+1} \left\{ 1 + \frac{R}{\alpha_m} + \left(\frac{R}{\alpha_m}\right)^2 + \cdots \right\}$$

$$< \rho^n (1 + \rho + \rho^2 + \cdots)$$

or

$$\lambda_n < \frac{\rho^n}{1-\rho}.$$

Thus each term of the adjoint of 4) is < the corresponding term of the geometric series

$$\frac{1}{1-\rho} \sum_{m+1}^{\infty} \rho^n$$

for any z in $\mathfrak{R}$. Thus H converges steadily in $\mathfrak{R}$ and is, by 131, 2, an analytic function of z which vanishes only when one of its factors vanishes.

Returning now to 3), we see this differs from H only by m factors which are analytic and vanish only at $a_1, a_2 \cdots a_m$ respectively.

3. The function $G(z)$ defined by 3) is an integral function which has the same zeros as $F(z)$. Let us find the most general

integral function $\phi(z)$ which has these zeros; we shall see that it will have the form given in 1). For the quotient

$$\frac{\phi(z)}{G(z)} = Q \tag{5}$$

has no singular points in the finite part of the plane and does not vanish for any z. Thus by 118, 10, $\log Q$ is one-valued and has no singular points in the finite part of the plane. Hence

$$T(z) = \log Q$$

is an integral function of z. This with 5) gives

$$\phi(z) = e^{T(z)} G(z),$$

which is therefore the most general expression of a one-valued integral function having the assigned zeros a_n.

4. The exponent in the nth factor in 1) is a polynomial of degree n, and this n increases indefinitely. Weierstrass has shown that:

When the zeros a_n are such that

$$\sum \frac{1}{\alpha_n^p} \quad , \quad \alpha_n = |a_n| \tag{6}$$

converges, we may replace the exponential factor in 1) *by*

$$e^{\frac{z}{a_n} + \frac{1}{2}\left(\frac{z}{a_n}\right)^2 + \cdots + \frac{1}{p-1}\left(\frac{z}{a_n}\right)^{p-1}}$$

where the polynomial is of fixed degree $p - 1$.

To establish this we need only to show that the corresponding logarithmic series

$$L(z) = \sum_{n=m+1}^{\infty} \left\{ \log\left(1 - \frac{z}{a_n}\right) + \frac{z}{a_n} + \cdots + \frac{1}{p-1}\left(\frac{z}{a_n}\right)^{p-1} \right\} = \Sigma l_n \tag{7}$$

converges steadily in $\mathfrak{R}$.

This is indeed so, for here

$$\lambda_n \leq \frac{1}{p}\left(\frac{\zeta}{\alpha_n}\right)^p + \frac{1}{p+1}\left(\frac{\zeta}{\alpha_n}\right)^{p+1} + \cdots$$

$$< \frac{R^p}{\alpha_n^p}\left\{1 + \frac{R}{\alpha_m} + \left(\frac{R}{\alpha_m}\right)^2 + \cdots\right\}.$$

Hence

$$\lambda_n < \frac{1}{\alpha_n^p} \cdot \frac{R^p}{1 - \dfrac{R}{\alpha_m}} = \frac{C}{\alpha_n^p}.$$

Each term of the adjoint of 7) is thus < the corresponding term of the convergent series

$$C \sum \frac{1}{\alpha_n^p}$$

for any z in $\mathfrak{R}$. Thus 7) converges steadily in $\mathfrak{R}$.

5. Let us apply Weierstrass' theorem to the sine function. Here we set

$$a_1 = \pi \quad , \quad a_2 = -\pi \quad , \quad a_3 = 2\pi \quad , \quad a_4 = -2\pi \quad \cdots$$

The series 6) becomes here

$$\frac{2}{\pi^p} \sum_1^\infty \frac{1}{n^p},$$

which converges for $p > 1$. Thus

$$\sin z = z e^{T(z)} \Pi \left(1 - \frac{z}{n\pi}\right) e^{\frac{z}{n\pi}} \qquad n = \pm 1, \pm 2, \cdots \tag{8}$$

$$= z e^{T(z)} \Pi \left(1 - \frac{z^2}{n^2\pi^2}\right). \tag{9}$$

Thus Weierstrass' theorem enables us to write down the product expression at once aside from the unknown exponential T. The determination of T is attended with grave difficulties. To avoid this, we have developed $\sin z$ in 136 by another method.

6. From Weierstrass' theorem 1 we may write down the most general rational transcendental function with assigned zeros

$$a_1 \ , \ a_2 \ , \ \cdots \tag{10}$$

and assigned poles

$$b_1 \ , \ b_2 \ , \ \cdots \tag{11}$$

where a zero (pole) of order m is repeated m times.

Let us suppose that the points 10), 11) are arranged as the a_n in 1. Then

$$F(z) = \Pi\left(1 - \frac{z}{a_n}\right)e^{\frac{z}{a} + \cdots + \frac{1}{n}\left(\frac{z}{a_n}\right)} \tag{12}$$

and

$$G(z) = \Pi\left(1 - \frac{z}{b_n}\right)e^{\frac{z}{b_n} + \cdots + \frac{1}{n}\left(\frac{z}{b_n}\right)^n} \tag{13}$$

will vanish at the points 10), 11), respectively, and nowhere else. Their quotient

$$H = \frac{F(z)}{G(z)}$$

will thus have the assigned zeros and poles. Let $K(z)$ be the most general one-valued analytic function having these zeros and poles. Then

$$Q = \frac{K(z)}{H(z)}$$

behaves as the quotient in 5). We have therefore as before

$$Q = e^T.$$

Hence the most general function of the kind sought is

$$e^{T(z)}\frac{F(z)}{G(z)} \tag{14}$$

where T is an integral function.

7. Let us note that the zeros 10) and the poles 11) of a rational transcendental function considered in 6 must both $\doteq \infty$, on being properly arranged.

For if in 10), for example, we could pick out a sequence

$$a_1', \quad a_2', \quad a_3' \quad \cdots \quad \text{which} \doteq \text{some point } a',$$

this point would be an essentially singular point of our function K. Thus K having an essentially singular point in the finite part of the plane is not a rational transcendental function by the definition in 123, 4.

CHAPTER IX

THE B AND Γ FUNCTIONS. ASYMPTOTIC EXPANSIONS

141. Introduction. 1. In advanced integral calculus one treats of two functions called the *Beta* and *Gamma* functions which are defined by the definite integrals

$$B(x, y) = \int_0^1 u^{x-1}(1-u)^{y-1}du = \int_0^\infty \frac{u^{x-1}du}{(1+u)^{x+y}} \quad , \quad x, y > 0 \quad (1$$

$$\Gamma(x) = \int_0^\infty e^{-u}u^{x-1}du \quad , \quad x > 0. \quad (2$$

These functions enter many parts of mathematics and on account of their great importance we shall devote a short chapter to their more important properties. The B and Γ functions are not independent functions; in fact, as is shown in the calculus, and as we shall see in the next §,

$$B(x, y) = \frac{\Gamma(x)\Gamma(y)}{\Gamma(x+y)} \quad , \quad x, y > 0. \quad (3$$

Thus of the two functions we shall devote most of our attention to the Γ function, which is a function of a single variable, whereas B is a function of two variables.

Instead of employing the definition of the B and Γ function as a definite integral, we can define the Γ function as an infinite product

$$\Gamma(x) = \frac{1}{x} \frac{e^{-Cx}}{\Pi\left(1+\frac{x}{n}\right)e^{-\frac{x}{n}}} \quad n = 1, 2, \cdots \quad (4$$

where $C = .5772157 \cdots$ is Euler's constant. We shall see directly that the integral 2) and the product 4) have the same values for $x > 0$. For the function theory, however, the product definition

4) is vastly to be preferred. In fact, if we allow the variable x to take on complex values, the right side of 4) defines, as we saw in 133, an analytic function of z for the whole z-plane except at the points $z = 0, -1, -2 \cdots$ where it has poles of the first order. We may thus regard this function as giving the analytic continuation of an analytic function which for real $x > 0$ has values given by the integral 2).

Instead of the integral definition 1) of the B function we may now take 3) as a definition where Γ is now defined by 4), the variables x, y being now of course complex.

From these product definitions of the B and Γ functions many of their properties follow very simply, as we shall show. If we prefer, however, to start with the definitions 1), 2) it is merely to preserve the continuity of the reader's knowledge. The justification of the steps we shall take in dealing with the integrals 1), 2) in the next two articles we must leave to the reader for lack of space.

2. The integrals 1), 2) may be given other forms on changing the variable. Thus in 1) let us set

$$u = \frac{v}{1 - v}.$$

We get

$$B(x, y) = \int_0^1 v^{x-1}(1 - v)^{y-1} dv. \tag{5}$$

If we set here

$$v = 1 - w,$$

we get

$$B(x, y) = \int_0^1 w^{y-1}(1 - w)^{x-1} dw. \tag{6}$$

In 5) let us set

$$v = \sin^2 \theta,$$

we get

$$B(x, y) = 2\int_0^{\frac{\pi}{2}} \sin^{2x-1}\theta \cos^{2y-1}\theta d\theta. \tag{7}$$

Finally, if we set

$$u = \log \frac{1}{v}$$

in 2), we get

$$\Gamma(x) = \int_0^1 \log^{x-1}\left(\frac{1}{v}\right) dv. \tag{8}$$

142. B(*x*, *y*) expressed in Γ Functions. We wish to establish the relation 3) of the last §, the variables being real. If in **141**, 2 we replace u by au, we get

$$\frac{1}{a^x} = \frac{1}{\Gamma(x)}\int_0^\infty e^{-au}u^{x-1}du \quad , \quad x > 0. \tag{1}$$

From this follows that

$$\frac{1}{(1+v)^{x+y}} = \frac{1}{\Gamma(x+y)}\int_0^\infty e^{-(1+v)u}u^{x+y-1}du.$$

Hence by **141**, 1

$$B(x, y) = \int_0^\infty \frac{v^{x-1}dv}{(1+v)^{x+y}} = \frac{1}{\Gamma(x+y)}\int_0^\infty dv\int_0^\infty u^{x+y-1}v^{x-1}e^{-(1+v)u}du,$$

or inverting the order of integration,

$$= \frac{1}{\Gamma(x+y)}\int_0^\infty u^{x+y-1}e^{-u}du\int_0^\infty v^{x-1}e^{-uv}dv. \tag{2}$$

In the v integral let us set $uv = w$; it becomes

$$u^{-x}\int_0^\infty w^{x-1}e^{-w}dw = u^{-x}\Gamma(x).$$

Thus 2) becomes

$$B(x, y) = \frac{\Gamma(x)}{\Gamma(x+y)}\int_0^\infty u^{y-1}e^{-u}du$$

$$= \frac{\Gamma(x)\Gamma(y)}{\Gamma(x+y)} \quad , \quad x, y > 0 \tag{3}$$

which establishes **141**, 3.

143. Γ(*x*) expressed as a Product. From the calculus we know that

$$e^{-u} = \lim_{n=\infty}\left(1 - \frac{u}{n}\right)^n.$$

Putting this in **141**, 2) gives

$$\Gamma(x) = \lim_{n=\infty}\int_0^n u^{x-1}\left(1 - \frac{u}{n}\right)^n du.$$

Setting $u = nv$, this gives

$$\Gamma(x) = \lim_{n=\infty} n^x \int_0^1 (1-v)^n v^{x-1} dv. \tag{1}$$

Integrating by parts, we get

$$\int_0^1 (1-v)^n v^{x-1} dv = \frac{n}{x+n} \int_0^1 (1-v)^{n-1} v^{x-1} dv$$

$$= \frac{n}{x+n} \cdot \frac{n-1}{x+n-1} \int_0^1 (1-v)^{n-2} v^{x-1} dv$$

$$\cdot \quad \cdot \quad \cdot \quad \cdot \quad \cdot \quad \cdot \quad \cdot \quad \cdot$$

$$= \frac{n}{x+n} \cdot \frac{n-1}{x+n-1} \cdots \frac{1}{x+1} \int_0^1 v^{x-1} dv$$

$$= \frac{n}{x+n} \cdots \frac{1}{x+1} \cdot \frac{1}{x}.$$

We may thus write 1)

$$\Gamma(x) = \lim_{n=\infty} \frac{1}{x} \cdot \frac{1 \cdot 2 \cdots (n-1)}{(x+1)(x+2) \cdots (x+n-1)} \cdot n^x. \tag{2}$$

Now

$$n^x = \left(\frac{2}{1} \cdot \frac{3}{2} \cdot \frac{4}{3} \cdots \frac{n}{n-1}\right)^x = \left(1 + \frac{1}{1}\right)^x \left(1 + \frac{1}{2}\right)^x \cdots \left(1 + \frac{1}{n-1}\right)^x.$$

Also

$$(x+1) \cdots (x+n-1) = (n-1)! \left(1 + \frac{x}{1}\right)\left(1 + \frac{x}{2}\right) \cdots \left(1 + \frac{x}{n-1}\right).$$

Putting these in 2) gives

$$\Gamma(x) = \frac{1}{x} \prod_1 \frac{\left(1 + \frac{1}{n}\right)^x}{1 + \frac{x}{n}} \tag{3}$$

$$= \frac{1}{x} \prod \frac{e^{x \log\left(1 + \frac{1}{n}\right)}}{1 + \frac{x}{n}}$$

$$= \frac{1}{x} \prod \frac{e^{x \log\left(1 + \frac{1}{n}\right)} e^{-\frac{x}{n}}}{\left(1 + \frac{x}{n}\right) e^{-\frac{x}{n}}}$$

$$= \frac{1}{x} \cdot \frac{\prod e^{x\left\{\log\left(1 + \frac{1}{n}\right) - \frac{1}{n}\right\}}}{\prod \left(1 + \frac{x}{n}\right) e^{-\frac{x}{n}}}.$$

Thus

$$\Gamma(x) = \frac{1}{x} \cdot \frac{e^{-Cx}}{\Pi\left(1 + \frac{x}{n}\right)e^{-\frac{x}{n}}} \tag{4}$$

where

$$C = \sum_1^\infty \left\{\frac{1}{n} - \log\left(1 + \frac{1}{n}\right)\right\} \tag{5}$$

is Euler's constant.

144. Properties of $\Gamma(z)$. In the foregoing articles we have seen that the B and Γ functions may be expressed as infinite products, the variables being real and positive. We propose now to start afresh and *define* these functions for complex values by these same products. Thus we say

$$\Gamma(z) = \frac{e^{-Cz}}{z\Pi\left(1 + \frac{z}{n}\right)e^{-\frac{z}{n}}} \qquad n = 1, 2, \cdots \tag{1}$$

where C is Euler's constant

$$C = \sum_1^\infty \left\{\frac{1}{n} - \log\left(1 + \frac{1}{n}\right)\right\} = .5772157 \cdots \tag{2}$$

and

$$B(u, v) = \frac{\Gamma(u)\Gamma(v)}{\Gamma(u+v)}. \tag{3}$$

Then the foregoing shows that these functions reduce to the B and Γ functions of the calculus when the variables are real and > 0.

From the definition 1) we may obtain two other expressions on using the transformations employed in 143, viz.:

$$\Gamma(z) = \lim G_n(z) = \lim_{n=\infty} \frac{1}{z} \cdot \frac{1 \cdot 2 \cdots (n-1)}{(z+1)(z+2) \cdots (z+n-1)} \cdot n^z \tag{4}$$

due to Gauss, and

$$\Gamma(z) = \frac{1}{z}\Pi \frac{\left(1 + \frac{1}{n}\right)^z}{1 + \frac{z}{n}} \qquad n = 1, 2, \cdots \tag{5}$$

where in 4), 5) we take that determination of n^z and $\left(1 + \frac{1}{n}\right)^z$ which is real and positive for $z = 1$.

The expression 1) shows, as already seen in 133, that:

1° $\Gamma(z)$ *is a one-valued analytic function of* z *whose domain of definition is the whole z-plane except the points* $z = 0, -1, -2, \cdots$ *which are poles of the first order. The point* $z = \infty$ *is an essentially singular point.*

Since the factors in 4) are positive for z real and positive, we have:

2° $\Gamma(z)$ *is real and positive for* z *real and positive.*

A very characteristic property of Γ is:

3° $$\Gamma(z+1) = z\Gamma(z). \tag{6}$$

For using the product $G_n(z)$ in 4) we have

$$G_n(z+1) = \frac{nzG_n(z)}{z+n}. \tag{7}$$

As

$$\lim_{n=\infty} \frac{nz}{n+z} = z,$$

we get 6) on letting $n \doteq \infty$.

By repeated applications of 6) we get

$$\Gamma(z+n) = z(z+1) \cdots (z+n-1)\Gamma(z). \tag{8}$$

From 5) we have

$$\Gamma(1) = 1. \tag{9}$$

Let us set $z = 1$ in 8), we get

$$\Gamma(n+1) = 1 \cdot 2 \cdot 3 \cdots n = n! \tag{10}$$

This relation gave rise to the Γ function. In fact Euler proposed to himself the problem:

Determine a continuous function which when x is an integer $x = n$ shall have the value $1 \cdot 2 \cdot 3 \cdots n = n!$ The relation 141, 2) shows that such a function is

$$\Pi(x) = \int_0^\infty e^{-u}u^x du = \Gamma(x+1). \tag{11}$$

The relation between Γ and Π may be extended to complex values by defining $\Pi(z)$ by

$$\Pi(z) = \Gamma(z+1). \tag{12}$$

The functions Π and Γ are of course essentially the same function. The Π notation was used by Gauss, the Γ notation by Legendre. Both notations are currently used to-day. The fact that $\Pi(n) = n!$ instead of $\Gamma(1+n)$ will often make it convenient to use Π instead of Γ.

Another important relation is:

4°
$$\Gamma(z)\Gamma(1-z) = \frac{\pi}{\sin \pi z}. \tag{13}$$

For

$$G_n(z)\, G_n(1-z) = \frac{1}{z} \frac{1}{\left(1-\frac{z^2}{1^2}\right)\left(1-\frac{z^2}{2^2}\right)\cdots\left(1-\frac{z^2}{(n-1)^2}\right)} \cdot \frac{n}{n-z}.$$

As

$$\lim_{n=\infty} \frac{n}{n-z} = 1,$$

we have, letting $n \doteq \infty$,

$$\Gamma(z)\Gamma(1-z) = \frac{1}{z\Pi\left(1-\frac{z^2}{n^2}\right)} = \frac{\pi}{\sin \pi z}$$

by 136, 1).

In the calculus the relation 13) is established by using the formula

$$\int_0^\infty \frac{u^{x-1}du}{1+u} = \frac{\pi}{\sin \pi x}, \tag{14}$$

whose proof is not simple.

If we set $z = \frac{1}{2}$ in 13), we get

$$\Gamma^2(\tfrac{1}{2}) = \pi$$

or

$$\Gamma(\tfrac{1}{2}) = +\sqrt{\pi}. \tag{15}$$

The + sign of the radical must be taken by 2°.

From 8) and 15) we get

5°
$$\Gamma(n+\tfrac{1}{2}) \frac{1 \cdot 3 \cdot 5 \cdots (2n-1)}{2^n} \sqrt{\pi}. \tag{16}$$

Since the exponential function vanishes for no value of z, the expression 1) enables us to state:

6° *The Γ function vanishes for no value of z.*

145. Expression for log $\Gamma(z)$ and its Derivatives. From 144, 1) we have

$$L(z) = \log \Gamma(z) = -Cz - \log z + \sum_1^\infty \left\{ \frac{z}{n} - \log\left(1 + \frac{z}{n}\right)\right\}. \qquad (1$$

Differentiating, we get

$$L'(z) = \frac{\Gamma'(z)}{\Gamma(z)} = -C - \frac{1}{z} + \sum_1^\infty \left\{ \frac{1}{n} - \frac{1}{z+n} \right\} \qquad (2$$

$$= -C + \sum_1^\infty \left\{ \frac{1}{n} - \frac{1}{z+n-1} \right\}. \qquad (3$$

In general we find

$$L^{(m)}(z) = (-1)^m (m-1)! \sum_1^\infty \frac{1}{(z+n-1)^m}, \quad m > 1. \qquad (4$$

Thus

$$L'(1) = -C. \qquad (5$$

$$L^{(m)}(1) = (-1)^m (m-1)! \sum \frac{1}{n^m} = (-1)^m (m-1)! \, H_m \qquad (6$$

146. Development of log $\Gamma(z)$ in a Power Series. We saw in 144, 6° that $\Gamma(z)$ has no zeros, thus $\log \Gamma(z)$ is a one-valued analytic function about $z=1$, whose nearest singular point is $z=0$. Thus Taylor's development is valid, and we have

$$\log \Gamma(z) = L(z) = L(1) + \frac{z-1}{1!} L'(1) + \frac{(z-1)^2}{2!} L''(1) + \cdots$$

Replacing $z-1$ by z and using 145, this gives

$$\log \Gamma(1+z) = -Cz + \sum_{n=2}^\infty \frac{(-1)^n}{n} H_n z^n, \quad |z| < 1. \qquad (1$$

Legendre has shown how we can make the series 1) converge more rapidly. We have

$$\log(1+z) = z - \sum_2^\infty (-1)^n \frac{z^n}{n}, \quad |z| < 1.$$

This when added to and subtracted from 1) gives

$$\log \Gamma(1+z) = -\log(1+z) + (1-C)z + \sum_2^\infty (-1)^n (H_n - 1) \frac{z^n}{n}.$$

Changing here z into $-z$ gives

$$\log\Gamma(1-z) = -\log(1-z) - (1-C)z + \sum_2^\infty (H_n - 1)\frac{z^n}{n}.$$

Subtracting this from the foregoing gives

$$\log\Gamma(1+z) - \log\Gamma(1-z) = -\log\frac{1+z}{1-z} + 2(1-C)z$$

$$- 2\sum_1^\infty \frac{z^{2n+1}}{2n+1}(H_{2n+1} - 1).$$

From 144, 13) we have

$$\log\Gamma(1+z) + \log\Gamma(1-z) = \log\frac{\pi z}{\sin\pi z}.$$

This in the preceding relation gives

$$\log\Gamma(1+z) = (1-C)z - \frac{1}{2}\log\frac{1+z}{1-z} + \frac{1}{2}\log\frac{\pi z}{\sin\pi z}$$

$$- \sum_1^\infty (H_{2n+1} - 1)\frac{z^{2n+1}}{2n+1} \qquad (2$$

valid for $|z| < 1$.

This series converges rapidly for $0 \leq x \leq \frac{1}{2}$ and thus enables us to compute $\log\Gamma(x)$ in the interval $1 \leq x \leq \frac{3}{2}$.

147. Graph of (Γ)*x* for Real *x*. By virtue of 144, 8) the value of $\Gamma(x)$ for any positive x is known when its value is known for values of x in the interval $(0, 1)$. By virtue of 144, 13) the value of Γ is known for $x < 0$ when it is known for $x > 0$. This relation also shows that the value of Γ is known in $(0, 1)$ if it is known either in $(0, \frac{1}{2})$ or indeed in any interval of length $\frac{1}{2}$. Gauss has given a table of $\log\Pi(x)$ for $0 \leq x \leq 1$ calculated to 20 decimals. This gives us the value of $\log\Gamma(x)$ for $1 \leq x \leq 2$. A four-place table is given in the Tables of B. O. Peirce * for $1 \leq x \leq 2$.

Since $\Gamma(1) = \Gamma(2)$, the curve has a minimum between $x = 1$ and $x = 2$. This point is found to be

$$x = 1.46163 \cdots$$

* See reference, p. 91.

From 145, 4) we see that

$$L''(x) > 0 \quad , \quad \text{for } x > 0.$$

Hence the graph of $\Gamma(x)$ is concave for $x > 0$.

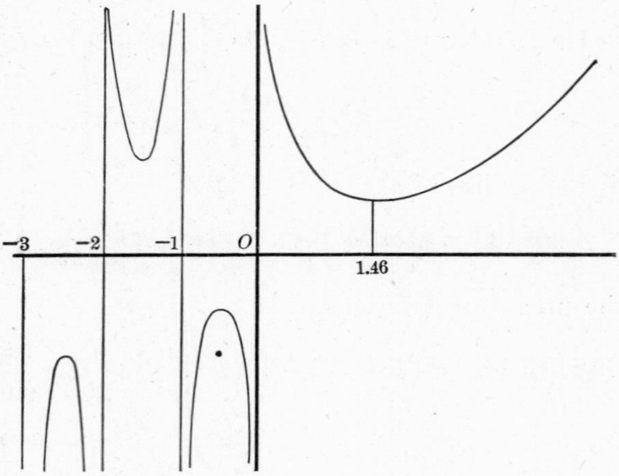

The adjoining figure will give the reader an idea of the graph for real x. The vertical lines $x = n$, $n = 0, -1, -2 \cdots$ are asymptotes to the curve, and the maxima and minima of the curve lie on opposite sides of the x-axis. The distance of the elbows from the x-axis increases as we go to the left.

148. The Γ Integral for Complex *z*. 1. For real $x > 0$, we have

$$\Gamma(x) = \int_0^\infty e^{-u} u^{x-1} du \tag{1}$$

as stated in 141, 2). Let us consider the integral

$$G(z) = \int_0^\infty e^{-u} u^{z-1} du, \tag{2}$$

where
$$z = x + iy \quad , \quad x > 0.$$

We have
$$u^{z-1} = u^{x-1} u^{iy} = u^{x-1} e^{iy \log u}$$
$$= u^{x-1} \{ \cos(y \log u) + i \sin(y \log u) \}.$$

Thus

$$G = \int_0^\infty e^{-u}u^{x-1}\cos(y\log u)du + i\int_0^\infty e^{-u}u^{x-1}\sin(y\log u)du$$
$$= H + iK.$$

Now H and K are convergent since $x > 0$, hence the integral 2) is convergent for all z for which $x > 0$.

2. Let us show that $G(z)$ is an analytic function of z. To this end we use 86, 1). Now

$$\frac{\partial H}{\partial x} = \int_0^\infty e^{-u}u^{-1}u^x \log u \cos(y\log u)du = \frac{\partial K}{\partial y}$$

$$\frac{\partial H}{\partial y} = -\int_0^\infty e^{-u}u^{x-1}\sin(y\log u)\cdot\log u du = -\frac{\partial K}{\partial x}.$$

As these derivatives are also continuous functions of x, y for $x > 0$, we see that G is an analytic function of z for all z lying to the right of the imaginary axis.

Since $G(z)$ as defined by the integral 2) and $\Gamma(z)$ as defined by an infinite product 144, 1), are analytic functions which have the same values along the positive half of the real axis, they also have the same values for any $z = x + iy$ for which $x > 0$.

149. Γ(*z*) expressed as a Loop Integral. 1. In the foregoing article we have expressed the Γ function as an integral which converges for all $z = x + iy$ for which $x > 0$. Let us now show that it may be defined as a *loop integral* which is valid for all values of z for which $\Gamma(z)$ is defined, that is, for all $z \neq 0, -1, -2, \cdots$.

To this end let us consider the integral

$$G(z) = \int_L e^{-u}u^{z-1}du, \tag{1}$$

the path of integration being the loop L extending to ∞ as in Fig. 1. Let

$$u = re^{i\phi}\ ,\quad 0 \leq \phi \lesseqgtr 2\pi.$$

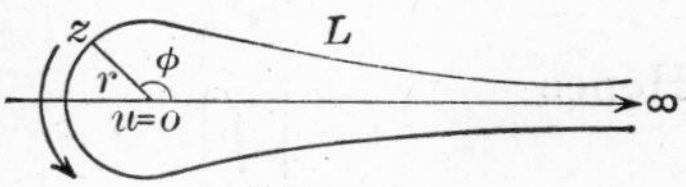

FIG. 1.

As value of u^{z-1}, we take

$$u^{z-1} = e^{(z-1)\log u} = e^{(z-1)\{\log r + i\phi\}}.$$

The integral 1) is thus defined for all values of z and is a one-valued analytic function of z by 104, since its derivative

$$\frac{dG}{dz} = \int_L e^{-u} u^{z-1} \log u du$$

is a continuous function of z.

2. We now show that

$$G(z) = (e^{2\pi i z} - 1)\Gamma(z). \tag{2}$$

To this end we need only prove 2) for $z = x > 0$, by virtue of the principle of analytic continuation, 113. Let us replace the loop L by the loop $\mathfrak{L}$ as in Fig. 2. The radius r of the circle $\alpha\beta\gamma$ converges to 0. Thus

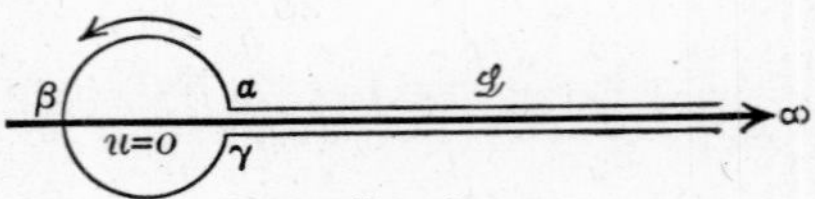

FIG. 2.

$$G(x) = \int_{\mathfrak{L}} = \int_{\infty}^{\alpha} + \int_{\alpha\beta\gamma} + \int_{\gamma}^{\infty}. \tag{3}$$

Now on the segment (∞, α), $\phi = 0$, hence

$$\int_{\infty}^{\alpha} e^{-u} u^{x-1} du \doteq -\Gamma(x) \qquad \text{as } r \doteq 0.$$

On the segment (γ, ∞), $\phi = 2\pi$. For when u passes over the circle $\alpha\beta\gamma$, ϕ increases from 0 to 2π. Thus u^{z-1} has on the segment (γ, ∞) the value

$$e^{(x-1)\{\log r + 2\pi i\}} = u^{x-1} \cdot e^{2\pi i (x-1)}.$$

Thus

$$\int_{\gamma}^{\infty} e^{-u} u^{x-1} du = e^{2\pi i x} \int_{\gamma}^{\infty} e^{-u} u^{x-1} du \doteq e^{2\pi i x}\Gamma(x)$$

as $r \doteq 0$.

Finally

$$\int_{\alpha\beta\gamma} = i r e^{(x-1)\log r} \int_{\alpha\beta\gamma} e^{-u} e^{ix\phi} d\phi.$$

Hence

$$\left| \int_{\alpha\beta\gamma} \right| = r^x \left| \int_0^{2\pi} e^{-u} e^{ix\phi} d\phi \right|$$

$$\leq 2\pi r^x \, |e^{-u}|$$

$$\doteq 0, \text{ as } r \doteq 0.$$

Thus passing to the limit $r = 0$ in 3) we get 2) for real $x > 0$. But as the two sides of 2) are analytic functions of z and as the relation 2) holds for real $x > 0$, it holds for every z.

3. Let us show that

$$G(z) = \int_L e^{-u} u^{z-1} du = \frac{2\pi i e^{\pi i z}}{\Gamma(1-z)}. \qquad (4$$

For 2) may be written

$$G = \frac{e^{\pi i z} - e^{-\pi i z}}{2i} \cdot 2 i e^{\pi i z} \cdot \Gamma(z)$$

$$= 2 i e^{\pi i z} \sin \pi z \cdot \Gamma(z), \text{ by 58, 8)}. \qquad (5$$

But by 144, 13)

$$\sin \pi z \cdot \Gamma(z) = \frac{\pi}{\Gamma(1-z)}.$$

This in 5) gives 4).

Since $e^{\pi i z}$ is an integral transcendental function having no zeros, and since $\Gamma(1-z)$ has poles of the first order at $z = 1, 2, 3, \cdots$ and no other singular points, we see that the function $G(z)$ defined by 2) is an integral transcendental function whose zeros are $z = 1, 2, 3, \cdots$ each of order 1. From the standpoint of the function theory, the G function is simpler than the Γ function.

150. The B Function as a Double Loop Integral. 1. In a similar manner we can show that

$$\int_L z^{u-1}(1-z)^{v-1} dz = -(1 - e^{2\pi i u})(1 - e^{2\pi i v}) \mathrm{B}(u, v), \qquad (1$$

where

$$\mathrm{B}(u, v) = \frac{\Gamma(u)\Gamma(v)}{\Gamma(u+v)}, \qquad (2$$

u, v being any complex numbers for which the quotient on the right of 2) is defined. The path of integration L is so chosen that the many-valued integrand in 1) returns at the end of the circuit to its original value. Such a path is

$$L = l_0 l_1 l_0^{-1} l_1^{-1},$$

where l_0, l_1 are loops about $z = 0$, $z = 1$ in the positive direction as in Fig. 1. It is easy to see that L may be replaced

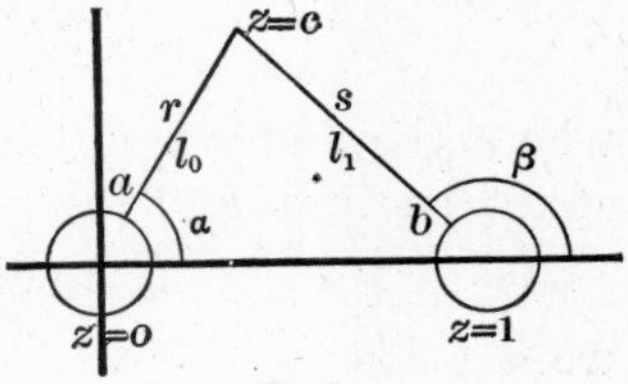

FIG. 1.

by the loop $\mathfrak{L}$ in Fig. 2, without changing the value of the integral 1). The loop $\mathfrak{L}$ is a *double loop*.

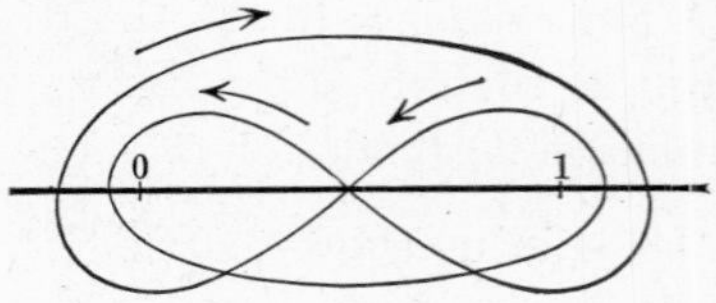

FIG. 2.

Finally we must specify which of the many values of

$$z^{u-} = e^{(u-1)\log z} \quad , \quad (1-z)^{v-1} = e^{(v-1)\log(1-z)},$$

we start with at the point $z = c$. We take

$$\log c = \log r + i\alpha \quad , \quad \log(1-c) = \log s + i\beta,$$

as indicated in Fig. 1. The values of

$$\log z = \log \rho + i\theta \quad , \quad \log(1-z) = \log \sigma + i\phi,$$

at any point of L depend only on θ and ϕ, since $\log \rho$, $\log \sigma$ are the *arithmetical* logarithms of the positive real numbers ρ, σ.

To prove 1) we shall first show that 1) is true when $u = x$, $v = y$ are real and positive. Then reasoning as in 114, 6 we see that 1) holds for complex values of u and v.

2. Let now z run over the loop l_0. When z first reaches a, $\theta = \alpha$; on reaching a after the circuit about $z = 0$, the value of θ is $\alpha + 2\pi$. Thus when z returns to $z = c$, the value of θ is $\alpha + 2\pi$. On the other hand, the value of ϕ is unchanged.

Similarly when z passes over the loop l_1, the value of θ is unchanged, while ϕ goes over into $\beta + 2\pi$, etc.

We may thus write

$$\int_L = \int_{l_0}(\alpha, \beta) + \int_{l_1}(\alpha + 2\pi, \beta) + \int_{l_0^{-1}}(\alpha + 2\pi, \beta + 2\pi)$$
$$+ \int_{l_1^{-1}}(\alpha, \beta + 2\pi) \qquad (3$$

where the numbers in the parentheses indicate the values of θ, ϕ at the beginning of the corresponding circuit.

As

$$e^{(x-1)\{\log \rho + i\alpha + 2\pi i\}} = e^{(x-1)\{\log \rho + i\alpha\}} e^{2\pi i x},$$

we see that

$$\int_{l_1}(\alpha + 2\pi, \beta) = e^{2\pi i x} \int_{l_1}(\alpha, \beta).$$

Similarly
$$\int_{l_0^{-1}}(\alpha+2\pi,\ \beta+2\pi)=e^{2\pi i x}e^{2\pi i y}\int_{l_0^{-1}}(\alpha,\ \beta),$$

$$\int_{l_1^{-1}}(\alpha,\ \beta+2\pi)=e^{2\pi i y}\int_{l_1^{-1}}(\alpha,\ \beta).$$

Now
$$\int_{l_0}(\alpha,\ \beta)=\int_c^0+e^{2\pi i x}\int_0^c=(e^{2\pi i x}-1)\int_0^c,$$

since the integral over the little circle about $z=0$ is 0.

Similarly,
$$\int_{l_1}(\alpha,\ \beta)=(1-e^{2\pi i y})\int_0^1,$$

$$\int_{l_0^{-1}}(\alpha,\ \beta)=(e^{-2\pi i x}-1)\int_0^c,$$

$$\int_{l_1^{-1}}(\alpha,\ \beta)=(1-e^{-2\pi i y})\int_c^1.$$

Putting these values in 3) we get 1) for real positive u, v.

Asymptotic Expansions

151. Introduction. In various parts of mathematics it is important to have the approximate value of a function for large values of the argument. For example, when x is a large positive integer n, we shall see in 157, 9 that $\Gamma(1+x)$ or $n!$ is nearly equal to

$$\sqrt{2n\pi}e^{-n}n^n, \tag{1}$$

a result of great value in the theory of probabilities and the kinetic theory of gases.

Another approximate expression of this type is the following. Letting $J_n(x)$ denote the Bessel function of order n, its value for large positive values of x is approximately, as we shall see in 253, 2,

$$\sqrt{\frac{2}{\pi}}\cdot\frac{1}{\sqrt{x}}\cos\left(x-\frac{(2n+1)\pi}{4}\right). \tag{2}$$

This asymptotic expression shows at once that $J_n(x)$ has an infinity of real roots, a result of utmost importance in the mathematical theory of heat, etc.

Connected with these approximate values of a function for large values of the argument is a class of divergent series

$$U = u_1 + u_2 + u_3 + \cdots \tag{3}$$

which have this remarkable property:—

The sum of the first n terms U_n gives the value of $f(x)$ with great accuracy for values of n not too large, although the series U itself is divergent.

For example, we shall see in 156, 6) that Euler's constant

$$C = \lim_{n=\infty}\left\{1 + \frac{1}{2} + \frac{1}{3} + \cdots + \frac{1}{n} - \log n\right\} = .57721566 \cdots$$

is given rapidly and with great accuracy by using the divergent series

$$\frac{1}{2n} - T_2\frac{1}{2n^2} + T_4\frac{1}{4n^4} - T_6\frac{1}{6n^6} + \cdots \tag{4}$$

where

$$T_2 = \tfrac{1}{6} \quad T_4 = \tfrac{1}{30} \quad T_6 = \tfrac{1}{42} \cdots$$

are the Bernoullian numbers introduced in 139, 3.

Divergent expansions of this type have long been used with utmost advantage in astronomy. On account of their growing importance even in pure mathematics we shall give a brief sketch of them as far as they relate to the Γ and Bessel functions.

We begin by developing a few properties of the Bernoullian numbers and a class of polynomials also named after Bernoulli.

152. Bernoullian Numbers. 1. In 139, 12) we saw that

$$\cot z = \frac{1}{z} - \sum_1^\infty \frac{2^{2n}}{(2n)!} T_{2n-1} z^{2n-1}$$

where

$$T_1 = \tfrac{1}{6} \quad , \quad T_3 = \tfrac{1}{30} \quad , \quad T_5 = \tfrac{1}{42} \cdots$$

are the Bernoullian numbers. Now

$$\cot z = \frac{\cos z}{\sin z} = i\frac{e^{iz} + e^{-iz}}{e^{iz} - e^{-iz}}$$

and

$$\coth z = i \cot iz.$$

Thus

$$\coth z = \frac{1}{z} - \sum_{1}^{\infty} (-1)^n \frac{2^{2n}}{(2n)!} T_{2n-1} z^{2n-1}$$

$$= \frac{e^z + e^{-z}}{e^z - e^{-z}} = 1 + \frac{2}{e^{2z} - 1}. \tag{1}$$

If we set $2z = u$, this gives for $|u| < 2\pi$

$$\frac{u}{e^u - 1} = 1 + B_1 u + B_2 \frac{u^2}{2!} + B_3 \frac{u^3}{3!} + \cdots \tag{2}$$

where

$$B_1 = -\tfrac{1}{2} \quad , \quad B_3 = B_5 = B_7 = \cdots = 0 \tag{3}$$

and

$$B_{2n} = (-1)^{n+1} T_{2n-1} \qquad n > 0. \tag{4}$$

Thus

$$B_{2n} = (-1)^{n+1} \frac{2(2n)!}{(2\pi)^{2n}} H_{2n} \tag{5}$$

where as usual

$$H_{2n} = 1 + \frac{1}{2^{2n}} + \frac{1}{3^{2n}} + \frac{1}{4^{2n}} + \cdots \tag{6}$$

Instead of T_n we may with *Lucas* regard the B_n as Bernoullian numbers. They may be defined therefore as the successive derivatives of

$$\frac{u}{e^u - 1}$$

at $u = 0$.

2. Let us introduce with de la Vallée-Poussin the symbol $\{e\}^{Bu}$ by the relation

$$\{e\}^{Bu} = 1 + B_1 \frac{u}{1!} + B_2 \frac{u^2}{2!} + B_3 \frac{u^3}{3!} + \cdots = \frac{u}{e^u - 1}. \tag{7}$$

We observe that the series in the middle is obtained from

$$e^{Bu} = 1 + B \frac{u}{1!} + B^2 \frac{u^2}{2!} + B^3 \frac{u^3}{3!} + \cdots$$

by replacing in it, B^n by B_n.

This new symbol has an *addition theorem* analogous to the exponential function. It is expressed by the relation

$$e^{tu} \{e\}^{Bu} = \{e\}^{(B+t)u}$$

$$= 1 + (B+t) \frac{u}{1!} + (B+t)^2 \frac{u^2}{2!} + \cdots \tag{8}$$

From 7) we have

$$u = (e^u - 1)\{e\}^{Bu} = e^u\{e\}^{Bu} - \{e\}^{Bu},$$

or using 8)

$$u = \{e\}^{(B+1)u} - \{e\}^{Bu}. \tag{9}$$

Expanding and equating coefficients of the different powers of u on both sides, we get the *symbolic relations:*

$$\begin{aligned}(B+1) - B &= 1\\ (B+1)^2 - B^2 &= 0\\ (B+1)^3 - B^3 &= 0, \text{ etc.,}\end{aligned} \tag{10}$$

where $(B+1)^n$ stands for the expression obtained by replacing B^m by B_m in the development of $(B+1)^n$ by the Binomial formula. Thus:

$$\begin{aligned}1 &= 1\\ 2B_1 + 1 &= 0\\ 3B_2 + 3B_1 + 1 &= 0, \text{ etc.}\end{aligned} \tag{11}$$

From these recursion relations we find readily the values of the T_{2n-1} given in 139.

The relations 11) show that: *The Bernoullian numbers are all rational.*

153. Polynomials of Bernoulli. 1. Instead of the function on the left of 152, 2) let us develop

$$F = \frac{e^{uz} - 1}{e^u - 1} = \frac{1}{u}(e^{uz} - 1)\{e\}^{Bu} \tag{1}$$

in a power series about $u = 0$. Since

$$e^{uz} = 1 + \frac{uz}{1!} + \frac{(uz)^2}{2!} + \cdots$$

we have

$$F = \frac{1}{u}\left\{1 + B_1\frac{u}{1!} + B_2\frac{u^2}{2!} + \cdots\right\}\left\{\frac{uz}{1!} + \frac{u^2z^2}{2!} + \frac{u^3z^3}{3!} + \cdots\right\}$$

$$= z + \beta_1(z)\frac{u}{1!} + \beta_2(z)\frac{u^2}{2!} + \cdots \tag{2}$$

On the other hand 1) gives

$$F = \frac{\{e\}^{(B+z)u} - \{e\}^{Bu}}{u}$$

$$= (B+z) - B + \frac{(B+z)^2 - B^2}{2!}u + \frac{(B+z)^3 - B^3}{3!}u^2 + \cdots$$

Comparing this with 2) gives the *symbolic equation*

$$\beta_n(z) = \frac{(B+z)^{n+1} - B^{n+1}}{n+1} \tag{3}$$

These β_n which enter as coefficients in power series 2) are the *polynomials of Bernouilli.*

From 3) we find

$$\beta_1(z) = \tfrac{1}{2}z(z-1),$$
$$\beta_2(z) = \tfrac{1}{3}z(z-\tfrac{1}{2})(z-1),$$
$$\beta_3(z) = \tfrac{1}{4}z^2(z-1)^2,$$
$$\beta_4(z) = \tfrac{1}{5}z(z-\tfrac{1}{2})(z-1)(z^2-z-\tfrac{1}{3}),$$
$$\beta_5(z) = \tfrac{1}{6}z^2(z-1)^2(z^2-z-\tfrac{1}{2}),$$

etc.

2. Let us set $z = m$ a positive integer in 1). We get on performing the division indicated in the middle member

$$F = 1 + e^u + e^{2u} + \cdots + e^{(m-1)u}$$

$$= 1 + \left(1 + u + \frac{u^2}{2!} + \frac{u^3}{3!} + \cdots\right)$$

$$+ \left(1 + 2u + \frac{(2u)^2}{2!} + \frac{(2u)^3}{3!} + \cdots\right)$$

$$+ \left(1 + 3u + \frac{(3u)^2}{2!} + \frac{(3u)^3}{3!} + \cdots\right)$$

$$+ \cdot \quad \cdot \quad \cdot \quad \cdot \quad \cdot \quad \cdot \quad \cdot \quad \cdot \quad \cdot \quad \cdot \quad \cdot$$

$$+ \left(1 + (m-1)u + \frac{(m-1)^2u^2}{2!} + \frac{(m-1)^3u^3}{3!} + \cdots\right).$$

Comparing the coefficients of u^n in this expansion and 2) gives

$$1 + 2^n + 3^n + \cdots + (m-1)^n = \beta_n(m), \tag{4}$$

which connects β_n with the sum of the nth powers of the integers 1, 2, 3, ….

3. *The polynomials $\beta_n(z)$ have $z=0$ and $z=1$ as roots.*

That $\beta_n(0)=0$ follows at once from 3). To show that $\beta_n(1)=0$ we set $z=1$ in 3) and get

$$(n+1)\,\beta_n(1)=(B+1)^{n+1}-B_{n+1}$$
$$=0 \text{ by 152, 10)}.$$

4. If we differentiate 3), we get the *derivative of β_n*:

$$\beta_n'(z)=(B+z)^n=n\beta_{n-1}(z)+B_n. \tag{5}$$

We recall that $B_{2n+1}=0$ when $n>0$.

5. We now show that:

$$\beta_n\left(\frac{1}{2}\right)=-\frac{2}{n+1}\left(1-\frac{1}{2^{n+1}}\right)B_{n+1} \tag{6}$$

For

$$\{e\}^{\left(B+\frac{1}{2}\right)z}+\{e\}^{Bz}=\left(1+e^{\frac{z}{2}}\right)\{e\}^{Bz}$$
$$=\frac{z}{e^{\frac{z}{2}}-1}=2\{e\}^{\frac{1}{2}Bz}.$$

Now the coefficient of z^{n+1} in the development of the first member is in symbolic notation

$$(B+\tfrac{1}{2})^{n+1}+B^{n+1}=(n+1)\,\beta_n(\tfrac{1}{2})+2\,B_{n+1}, \tag{7}$$

using 3), while that in the development of the last member is

$$2\left(\frac{B}{2}\right)^{n+1}=2\cdot\frac{B_{n+1}}{2^{n+1}}. \tag{8}$$

Equating 7), 8) gives 6).

Since $B_{2m+1}=0$ for $m>0$, we have from 6) that

$$\beta_{2n}(\tfrac{1}{2})=0. \tag{9}$$

6. *The polynomial β_{2s+1}, does not take on the same value at more than two different points in $\mathfrak{A}=(0, 1)$.*

For then its derivative would vanish at least at two different points within $\mathfrak{A}$. But by 5)

$$\beta'_{2s+1}(x)=(2\,s+1)\beta_{2s}(x).$$

Thus $\beta_{2s}(x)$ vanishes at least at two points within $\mathfrak{A}$; hence by 3, β_{2s} vanishes at least at three points within $\mathfrak{A}$. But by 5)

$$\beta_{2s}(x) = 2s\beta_{2s-1}(x) + B_{2s}. \tag{10}$$

Hence β_{2s-1} takes on the same value at least three times in $\mathfrak{A}$; hence

$$\beta_{2s-1} \quad , \quad \beta_{2s-3} \quad , \quad \cdots \beta_3 \quad , \quad \beta_1$$

each take on some value at least three times in $\mathfrak{A}$. But

$$\beta_1(x) = \tfrac{1}{2}(x^2 - x)$$

is of the second degree, and can take on the same value but twice.

7. *No Bernoullian number with even index B_{2s} can equal* 0.

For by 6) $\beta_{2s-1}(x)$ would vanish at $x = \frac{1}{2}$. This is impossible by 6.

8. *The polynomial $\beta_{2s+1}(x)$ does not change its sign in $\mathfrak{A} = (0, 1)$.*

For then it would $= 0$, at three different points in $\mathfrak{A}$, which contradicts 6.

9. *The polynomial $\beta_{2s}(x)$ vanishes at $x = 0, \frac{1}{2}, 1$ and at no other point in $\mathfrak{A} = (0, 1)$.*

For suppose $\beta_{2s} = 0$ at two points within $\mathfrak{A}$. Then $\beta'_{2s}(x) = 0$ at least at three points within $\mathfrak{A}$. Then 10) shows that β_{2s-1} takes on the same value at least three times in $\mathfrak{A}$ and this is impossible by 6.

154. Development of $\beta_n(x)$ in Fourier Series. 1. Let us develop the polynomials $\beta_n(x)$ in a Fourier series, valid in the interval $\mathfrak{A} = (0, 1)$. We begin by showing that

$$\beta_1(x) = \frac{x}{2}(x-1) = -\frac{1}{2\pi^2}\sum_1^\infty \frac{1}{n^2}(1 - \cos 2n\pi x)$$

$$= -\frac{1}{2\pi^2}\left\{ H_2 - \sum_1^\infty \frac{\cos 2n\pi x}{n^2} \right\} \tag{1}$$

where $H_2 = 1 + \dfrac{1}{2^2} + \dfrac{1}{3^2} + \cdots$

as usual.

Let us denote the right side of 1) by $F(x)$. Since $\beta_1(0)=F(0)$, we need only show that β_1 and F have the same derivative in $\mathfrak{A}$. The left side of 1) gives at once

$$\beta_1'(x)=x-\tfrac{1}{2}.$$

On the other hand, from 110, 8) we have

$$x-\tfrac{1}{2}=-\frac{1}{\pi}\sum_1^\infty\frac{\sin 2\,n\pi x}{n}. \tag{2}$$

But differentiating the series F, that is the last member of 1), we get precisely the series on the right of 2). This establishes 1).

2. From 1) we can express all the other β's as Fourier series by using the relations 153, 5). Thus for $n=2$, we have

$$\beta_2'(x)=2\,\beta_1(x)+B_2.$$

Integrating, we get, using 1),

$$\beta_2(x)=-\frac{H_2}{\pi^2}x+\frac{1}{2\,\pi^3}\sum_1^\infty\frac{\sin 2\,n\pi x}{n^3}+B_2x.$$

The constant of integration is 0 as $\beta_2(0)=0$. Using 152, 5), the last relation becomes

$$\beta_2(x)=\frac{1}{2\,\pi^3}\sum_1^\infty\frac{\sin 2\,n\pi x}{n^3}. \tag{3}$$

3. Let us now set

$$G_s(x)=\sum_{n=1}^\infty\frac{\cos n\,2\,\pi x}{n^s},\qquad s \text{ an even integer},$$

$$=\sum_{n=1}^\infty\frac{\sin n\,2\,\pi x}{n^s},\qquad s \text{ an odd integer}. \tag{4}$$

Also as before let

$$H_s=1+\frac{1}{2^s}+\frac{1}{3^s}+\cdots$$

Then, by using 153, 5) and reasoning from n to $n+1$, we have for any integer $s > 0$

$$\beta_{2s}(x) = (-1)^{s+1}\frac{(2s)!}{2^{2s}\pi^{2s+1}}G_{2s+1}(x),$$
$$\beta_{2s-1}(x) = (-1)^{s+1}\frac{(2s-1)!}{2^{2s-1}\pi^{2s}}\{G_{2s}(x) - H_{2s}\} \quad (5$$

valid for $0 \leq x \leq 1$.

We notice that for m an integer or 0,

$$G_{2s}(m) = H_{2s} = (-1)^{s+1}\frac{2^{2s-1}\pi^{2s}}{(2s)!}B_{2s} \qquad s = 1, 2, \cdots \quad (6$$

$$\frac{d}{dx}G_s(x) = (-1)^{s+1}\cdot 2\pi G_{s-1}(x) \quad (7$$

and
$$\int_0^x G_s(x)dx = \frac{(-1)^s}{2\pi}G_{s+1}(x) + \text{const.}$$

4. From 5) we see that in the interval $\mathfrak{A} = (0, 1)$ the signs of

$$\begin{matrix} \beta_1 & , & \beta_3 & , & \beta_5 & \cdots \\ - & & + & & - & \cdots \end{matrix}$$

are respectively.

5. Also we see from 5) that at any point x in $\mathfrak{A}$, the sign of β_{2s} is the opposite of that of β_{2s+2}.

6. In passing let us prove a formula we shall need later. Let $m < n$ be positive integers. Then by partial integration we have, using 7),

$$\int_m^n \frac{G_1(x)dx}{1+x} = \frac{1}{2\pi}\left[\frac{G_2(x)}{1+x}\right]_n^m - \frac{1}{2\pi}\int_m^n \frac{G_2(x)dx}{(1+x)^2}.$$

Now
$$G_2(m) = G_2(n) = H_2 = \frac{\pi^2}{6}$$

by 6) and 139, 9). Thus

$$\left|\int_m^n \frac{G_1 dx}{1+x}\right| < \frac{\pi}{12}\cdot\frac{1}{m}. \quad (8$$

As this $\doteq 0$ as $m \doteq \infty$ we see that

$$\int_0^\infty \frac{G_1(x)dx}{1+x} \quad (9$$

is convergent.

155. Euler's Summation Formula. 1. To derive this important formula we employ an elegant method due to Wirtinger.* Let $f(x)$ be a real or a complex function of the real variable x, having a continuous derivative in the interval $\mathfrak{A} = (a, a + nb)$, where $b > 0$ and n is a positive integer. Let m be a positive integer $< n$. Then as in 93, 1 we have

$$f(a+nb) - f(a) \qquad = b\int_0^n f'(a+bx)dx$$

$$f(a+nb) - f(a+b) \;= b\int_1^n f'(a+bx)dx$$

$$f(a+nb) - f(a+2b) = b\int_2^n f'(a+bx)dx$$

$$\cdots\cdots\cdots\cdots\cdots\cdots$$

$$f(a+nb) - f(a+nb) = b\int_n^n f'(a+bx)dx$$

where the last equation is added for symmetry. Adding these $n+1$ equations gives

$$(n+1)f(a+nb) - \sum_{s=0}^{n} f(a+sb) = b\sum_{s=0}^{n}\int_s^n f'(a+bx)dx. \qquad (1$$

Now

$$\int_s^n = \int_s^{s+1} + \int_{s+1}^{s+2} + \cdots + \int_{n-1}^{n}.$$

If this is put in 1), we see that every integral of the type

$$\int_s^{s+1}$$

occurs just $s + 1$ times. Thus the sum on the right of 1) may be written

$$\sum_{s=0}^{n-1}\int_s^{s+1}(s+1)f'(a+bx)dx \qquad (2$$

Now within the interval $(s, s+1)$

$$s + 1 = E(x) + 1$$

---

* *Acta Matematica*, vol. 26, p. 255.

where $E(x)$ is the greatest integer contained in x. Thus the sum 2) equals

$$\sum_{s=0}^{n-1}\int_s^{s+1}\{E(x)+1\}f'(a+bx)dx=\int_0^n\{E(x)+1\}f'(a+bx)dx. \quad (3$$

Now

$$E(x)=G(x)+x-\frac{1}{2},$$

where

$$G(x)=\sum_{n=1}^{\infty}\frac{\sin 2n\pi x}{n\pi}=\frac{1}{\pi}G_1(x),$$

G_1 being given in 154, 4). Thus the right side of 3) equals

$$\int_0^n\{G(x)+x+\tfrac{1}{2}\}f'(a+bx)dx$$

$$=\int_0^n G(x)f'(a+bx)dx+\int_0^n xf'(a+bx)dx+\frac{1}{2}\int_0^n f'(a+bx)dx. \quad (4$$

But by partial integration

$$b\int_0^n xf'(a+bx)dx=nf(a+nb)-\int_0^n f(a+bx)dx,$$

$$\tfrac{1}{2}b\int_0^n f'(a+bx)dx=\tfrac{1}{2}\{f(a+bn)-f(a)\}.$$

Thus 1) and 4) give

$$(n+1)f(a+nb)-\sum_{s=0}^{n}f(a+sb)=b\int_0^n G(x)f'(a+bx)dx$$

$$+nf(a+nb)-\int_0^n f(a+bx)dx+\tfrac{1}{2}\{f(a+bn)-f(a)\}.$$

Hence

$$\sum_{s=0}^{n}f(a+sb)=\tfrac{1}{2}\{f(a+bn)+f(a)\}+\int_0^n f(a+bx)dx-R \quad (5$$

where

$$R=b\int_0^n G(x)f'(a+bx)dx. \quad (6$$

2. The remainder R may be transformed by partial integration. Thus

$$\int_0^n Gf'(a+bx)\,dx = \frac{1}{\pi}\int_0^n G_1(x)f'(a+bx)\,dx$$

$$= -\frac{1}{2\pi^2}\Big[G_2(x)f'(a+bx)\Big]_0^n + \frac{b}{2\pi^2}\int_0^n G_2(x)f''(a+bx)\,dx.$$

Now

$$G_2(0) = G_2(n) = \sum_{m=1}^{\infty}\frac{1}{m^2} = H_2 = \pi^2 B_2.$$

Thus

$$R = -\frac{b}{2}B_2\{f'(a+bn) - f'(a)\} + R_1, \tag{7}$$

where

$$R_1 = \frac{b^2}{2\pi^2}\int_0^n G_2(x)f''(a+bx)\,dx. \tag{8}$$

3. Thus by repeated partial integration we get *Euler's formula of Summation:*

$$f(a) + f(a+b) + f(a+2b) + \cdots + f(a+nb)$$

$$= \int_0^n f(a+bx)\,dx + \tfrac{1}{2}\{f(a+bn) + f(a)\} + b\frac{B_2}{2!}\{f'(a+bn) - f'(a)\}$$

$$+ b^3\frac{B_4}{4!}\{f'''(a+bn) - f'''(a)\} + \cdots$$

$$+ b^{2s+1}\frac{B_{2s+2}}{(2s+2)!}\{f^{(2s+1)}(a+bn) - f^{(2s+1)}(a)\} + R_{s+1}, \tag{9}$$

where

$$R_{s+1} = (-1)^{s+1}\frac{b^{2s+2}}{2^{2s+1}\pi^{2s+2}}\int_0^n G_{2s+2}(x)f^{(2s+2)}(a+bx)\,dx. \tag{10}$$

If we integrate partially in 10) we get, since

$$G_{2s+3}(x) = 0, \text{ for } x = 0,\ x = n,$$

$$R_{s+1} = \frac{(-1)^s b^{2s+3}}{2^{2s+2}\pi^{2s+3}}\int_0^n G_{2s+3}(x)f^{(2s+3)}(a+bx)\,dx. \tag{11}$$

4. In 10) and 11) we have expressed the remainder R_s in terms of the functions G_{2s+2} and G_{2s+3}; let us now express it in terms of the β polynomials.

From 11) we have, setting for simplicity $b=1$,

$$R_{s-1}=\frac{(-1)^s}{2^{2s-2}\pi^{2s-1}}\left\{\int_0^1+\int_1^2+\cdots+\int_{n-1}^n\right\} \tag{12}$$

$$=\frac{(-1)^s}{2^{2s-2}\pi^{2s-1}}\int_0^1 G_{2s-1}(x)\{f^{(2s-1)}(a+x)+f^{(2s-1)}(a+x+1)+\cdots\}dx.$$

Now

$$\frac{(-1)^s}{2^{2s-2}\pi^{2s-1}}\int_0^1 G_{2s-1}(x)f^{(2s-1)}(a+x+m)dx$$

$$=\frac{(-1)^{s+1}}{2^{2s-1}\pi^{2s}}\left[G_{2s}(x)f^{(2s-1)}(a+x+m)\right]_0^1$$

$$-\frac{(-1)^{s+1}}{2^{2s-1}\pi^{2s}}\int_0^1 G_{2s}(x)f^{(2s)}(a+x+m)dx=A_m-B_m. \tag{13}$$

But by 154, 5)

$$\frac{(-1)^{s+1}}{2^{2s-1}\pi^{2s}}G_{2s}(x)=\frac{\beta_{2s-1}(x)}{(2s-1)!}+\frac{(-1)^{s+1}}{2^{2s-1}\pi^{2s}}H_{2s}.$$

Thus

$$A_m=\frac{(-1)^{s+1}}{2^{2s-1}\pi^{2s}}H_{2s}\{f^{(2s-1)}(a+m+1)-f^{(2s-1)}(a+m)\},$$

$$B_m=\frac{1}{(2s-1)!}\int_0^1 \beta_{2s-1}(x)f^{(2s)}(a+x+m)dx$$

$$+\frac{(-1)^{s+1}}{2^{2s-1}\pi^{2s}}H_{2s}\int_0^1 f^{(2s)}(a+x+m)dx.$$

Here the last integral is A_m. Thus 12), 13) give

$$R_{s-1}=\frac{-1}{(2s-1)!}\int_0^1 \beta_{2s-1}(x)\{f^{(2s)}(a+x)$$

$$+f^{(2s)}(a+x+1)+\cdots+f^{(2s)}(a+x+n-1)\}dx. \tag{14}$$

5. Let us return to Euler's formula 9). We may write it, setting $b=1$,

$$F=f(a)+f(a+1)+f(a+2)+\cdots+f(a+n)$$

$$=\tfrac{1}{2}\{f(a+n)+f(a)\}+\int_0^n f(a+x)dx+D_s+R_s, \tag{15}$$

where D_s is the sum of the first s terms of the series

$$D = \frac{B_2}{2!}\{f'(a+n) - f'(a)\} + \frac{B_4}{4!}\{f'''(a+n) - f'''(a)\} + \cdots \qquad (16$$
$$= d_1 + d_2 + d_3 + \cdots$$

As the Bernoullian numbers B_{2n} increase very rapidly as $n \doteq \infty$, the series 16) is in general divergent. Suppose, however, that $f^{(2s+2)}(x)$, $f^{(2s+4)}(x)$ have the same sign in $(a, a+n)$. As $\beta_{2s+1}(x)$, $\beta_{2s+3}(x)$ have opposite signs in $(0, 1)$, the relation 14) shows that R_s and R_{s+1} have opposite signs. Thus

$$|R_s| < |R_s - R_{s+1}| = |d_{s+1}|.$$

We have therefore *in this case* the remarkable result:

Although the series 16) *is divergent, the sum of its first s terms,* D_s, *enables us to calculate the sum* F *in* 15) *with an error numerically less than the* $(s+1)$*st term in* 16).

156. Asymptotic Expansion of $1 + \frac{1}{2} + \frac{1}{3} + \cdots + \frac{1}{n}$. In 155, 15) let us set

$$f(x) = \frac{1}{x}, \quad a = 1, \quad n = m - 1.$$

Then
$$1 + \frac{1}{2} + \frac{1}{3} + \cdots + \frac{1}{m} = \frac{1}{2m} + \frac{1}{2} + \log m + D_s - R_s, \qquad (1$$

where
$$D_s = \frac{B_2}{2}\left(1 - \frac{1}{m^2}\right) + \frac{B_4}{4}\left(1 - \frac{1}{m^4}\right) + \cdots + \frac{B_{2s}}{2s}\left(1 - \frac{1}{m^{2s}}\right), \qquad (2$$

$$R_s = (2s+2)\int_0^1 \beta_{2s+1}(x)\left\{\frac{1}{(x+1)^{2s+3}} + \frac{1}{(x+2)^{2s+3}} + \cdots + \frac{1}{(x+m-1)^{2s+3}}\right\} dx. \qquad (3$$

Now the Eulerian constant

$$C = \lim_{m=\infty}\left\{1 + \frac{1}{2} + \cdots + \frac{1}{m} - \log m\right\}.$$

Let us therefore keep s fixed and let $m \doteq \infty$ in 1); we get

$$C = \frac{1}{2} + \left\{\frac{B_2}{2} + \frac{B_4}{4} + \cdots + \frac{B_{2s}}{2s}\right\} - T_s, \qquad (4$$

where

$$T_s = (2s+2)\int_0^1 \sum_{p=1}^{\infty} \frac{\beta_{2s+1}(x)}{(x+p)^{2s+3}}\, dx. \tag{5}$$

Returning to 1) we have, using 4),

$$1 + \frac{1}{2} + \cdots + \frac{1}{m} = C + \frac{1}{2m} + \log m - \left\{ \frac{B_2}{2} \cdot \frac{1}{m^2} + \frac{B_4}{4m^4} + \cdots \frac{B_{2s}}{2s} \cdot \frac{1}{m^{2s}} \right\} + U_s, \tag{6}$$

where

$$U_s = (2s+2)\int_0^1 \sum_{p=m+1}^{\infty} \frac{\beta_{2s+1}(x)dx}{(x+p)^{2s+3}}. \tag{7}$$

Since the derivatives $f^{(2s+2)}(x)$, $f^{(2s+4)}(x)$ have the same sign, we are in the case considered in 155, 5. The formula 6) is thus an asymptotic development of $1 + \frac{1}{2} + \cdots + \frac{1}{m}$.

From 7) we see that U_s has the form

$$U_s = \frac{\epsilon_s(m)}{m^{2s}}, \tag{8}$$

where $\epsilon_s \doteq 0$ as $m \doteq \infty$. For in the interval $(0, 1)$

$$(2s+2)\frac{\beta_{2s+1}(x)}{(x+p)^{2s+3}} < \frac{G}{p^{2s+3}} \qquad G \text{ some constant.}$$

Hence

$$U_s < G \sum_{p=m+1}^{\infty} \frac{1}{p^{2s+3}}$$

$$< G\int_m^{\infty} \frac{dx}{x^{2s+3}} \qquad \text{by 22, 1)}$$

$$< \frac{G}{2s+2}\,\frac{1}{m^{2s+2}}.$$

Thus 8) holds since

$$\epsilon_s(m) < \frac{G}{2s+2} \cdot \frac{1}{m^2}. \tag{9}$$

157. Stirling's Formula for $n!$. In 155, 5), 6) let us set

$$a = b = 1 \quad , \quad f(a+x) = \log(1+x) \quad , \quad n = m-1.$$

Then

$$\sum_{s=0}^{m-1} \log(1+s) = \tfrac{1}{2}\log m + \int_0^{m-1} \log(1+x)dx - \int_0^{m-1} G(x)\frac{dx}{1+x}. \quad (1$$

By partial integration

$$\int_0^{m-1} \log(1+x)dx = m\log m - m + 1.$$

Thus 1) gives

$$\log(1\cdot 2\cdot 3 \cdots m) = \tfrac{1}{2}(2m+1)\log m - m + 1 - \int_0^{m-1} G(x)\frac{dx}{1+x}. \quad (2$$

We now transform 2) by using Wallis' formula, 127, 5)

$$\frac{\pi}{2} = \frac{2}{1}\cdot\frac{2}{3}\cdot\frac{4}{3}\cdot\frac{4}{5}\cdot\frac{6}{5}\cdot\frac{6}{7}\cdots \quad (3$$

From 2) we have

$$2\log(2\cdot 4 \cdots 2m) = \log(2^2\cdot 4^2\cdot 6^2 \cdots (2m)^2)$$

$$= (2m+1)\log m + 2m\log 2 - 2m + 2 - 2\int_0^{m-1} G(x)\frac{dx}{1+x}. \quad (4$$

Also if we replace m by $2m+1$ in 2) we get

$$\log(1\cdot 2\cdot 3 \cdots 2m+1) = (2m+1+\tfrac{1}{2})\log(2m+1)$$

$$-2m - \int_0^{2m} G(x)\frac{dx}{1+x}. \quad (5$$

From 4), 5) we get, on subtracting,

$$\log\frac{2\cdot 4\cdot 6 \cdots 2m}{1\cdot 3\cdot 5 \cdots 2m+1} = \frac{1}{2}\log\frac{2\cdot 2\cdot 4\cdot 4 \cdots 2m\cdot 2m}{1\cdot 3\cdot 3\cdot 5\cdot 5 \cdots 2m+1\cdot 2m+1}$$

$$= -(2m+1)\log\frac{2m+1}{m} - \frac{1}{2}\log(2m+1)$$

$$+ 2m\log 2 + 2 - 2\int_0^{m-1} + \int_0^{2m}$$

$$= -(2m+1)\log\left(1+\frac{1}{2m}\right) - \frac{1}{2}\log(2m+1) + 2 - \log 2 - \int_0^{m-1} + \int_{m-1}^{2m}.$$

Thus

$$\frac{1}{2}\log\frac{2\cdot 2\cdot 4\cdot 4\cdots 2m\cdot 2m}{1\cdot 3\cdot 3\cdot 5\cdots 2m-1\cdot 2m+1}=-(2m+1)\log\left(1+\frac{1}{2m}\right)$$

$$-\log 2+2-\int_0^{m-1}+\int_{m-1}^{2m}\cdot \qquad (6$$

Now

$$\lim_{m=\infty}(2m+1)\log\left(1+\frac{1}{2m}\right)=1,$$

$$\lim_{m=\infty}\int_0^{m-1}=\int_0^{\infty}\quad,\quad \lim_{m=\infty}\int_{m-1}^{2m}=0.$$

Thus letting $m \doteq \infty$ in 6) and using 3) we get

$$\log\sqrt{2\pi}=1-\int_0^{\infty}\frac{G(x)dx}{1+x}. \qquad (7$$

This in 2) gives

$$\log m!=\tfrac{1}{2}(2m+1)\log m-m+\log\sqrt{2\pi}+\int_{m-1}^{\infty}\frac{G(x)dx}{1+x}.$$

If we use this relation in 154, 8) we get *Stirling's Formula*:

$$\log m!=\tfrac{1}{2}(2m+1)\log m-m+\log\sqrt{2\pi}+\frac{\vartheta}{12m}, \qquad (8$$

where

$$0<\vartheta<\pi.$$

This may also be written

$$m!=\sqrt{2\pi m}\left(\frac{m}{e}\right)^m e^{\frac{\vartheta}{12m}}. \qquad (9$$

158. Asymptotic Development of $\Gamma(x)$. 1. In Euler's summation formula, 155, 5), 6) let us set

$$b=1\quad,\quad a=x\quad,\quad f(a+x)=\log(u+x),$$

then we get, as in 156, 1), taking the principal branch of the logarithm,

$$\sum_{s=0}^{m}\log(x+s)=(x+m+\tfrac{1}{2})\log(x+m)-(x-\tfrac{1}{2})\log x$$

$$-m-\int_0^m\frac{G(u)du}{x+u} \qquad (1$$

valid for any complex $x\neq 0,\,-1,\,-2\cdots$.

From 157, 2), we have

$$\log 1 \cdot 2 \cdot 3 \cdots m+1 = \left(m+\frac{3}{2}\right)\log(m+1) - m - \int_0^m \frac{G(u)du}{1+u}. \quad (2$$

Subtracting 1) from 2) and then adding

$$(x-1)\log(m+1)$$

to both sides, we get

$$\log \frac{1 \cdot 2 \cdot 3 \cdots m+1}{x \cdot x+1 \cdots x+m} \cdot (m+1)^{x-1} = -\left(m+x+\frac{1}{2}\right)\log\frac{m+1}{m+x}$$

$$+\left(x-\frac{1}{2}\right)\log x - \int_0^m \frac{Gdu}{1+u} + \int_0^m \frac{Gdu}{x+u}. \quad (3$$

Now
$$\lim_{m=\infty}\left(m+x+\frac{1}{2}\right)\log\frac{m+1}{m+x} = 1-x.$$

Thus letting $m \doteq \infty$ in 3) and using 144, 4) and 157, 7), we get

$$\log \Gamma(x) = -x + (x-\tfrac{1}{2})\log x + \log\sqrt{2\pi} + \gamma(x), \quad (4$$

where
$$\gamma(x) = \int_0^\infty \frac{G(u)du}{x+u}. \quad (5$$

In this relation let us set

$$x = y+n \qquad u = v-n.$$

Then since $G(u)$ admits the period 1,

$$\gamma(y+n) = \int_n^\infty \frac{G(v)dv}{y+v} \doteq 0 \text{ as } n \doteq \infty. \quad (6$$

We may thus write

$$\gamma(x) = \int_0^1 + \int_1^2 + \int_2^3 + \cdots = \sum_{s=1}^\infty \int_{s-1}^s \frac{G(u)du}{x+u}. \quad (7$$

In these integrals let us change the variable setting

$$u = v + (s-1) \quad , \quad s = 1, 2, \cdots$$

Then the limits of integration become 0, 1. But in this interval

$$G(v) = \tfrac{1}{2} - v.$$

Thus

$$\int_{s-1}^{s} \frac{G(u)du}{x+u} = \int_0^1 \frac{G(v)dv}{v+x+s-1} = \int_0^1 \frac{(\frac{1}{2}-v)dv}{v+x+s-1}$$

$$= \left(x+s-\frac{1}{2}\right)\log\left(1+\frac{1}{x+s-1}\right) - 1. \qquad (8$$

This in 7) gives a development of $\gamma(x)$ due to *Gudermann.*

2. In 5) let us integrate by parts. We get, using the functions $G_1, G_2 \cdots$ of 154, 4) and the relations 6), 7) of that article,

$$\gamma(x) = \frac{1}{\pi}\int_0^\infty \frac{G_1(u)du}{x+u} = -\frac{1}{2\pi^2}\left[\frac{G_2(u)}{x+u}\right]_{u=0}^\infty - \frac{1}{2\pi^2}\int_0^\infty \frac{G_2(u)du}{(x+u)^2}.$$

As

$$G_2(0) = H_2 = \pi^2 B_2,$$

we have

$$\gamma(x) = \frac{B_2}{2}\cdot\frac{1}{x} - \frac{1}{2\pi^2}\int_0^\infty \frac{G_2(u)du}{(x+u)^2}. \qquad (9$$

Integrating again by parts, we have

$$\int_0^\infty \frac{G_2(u)du}{(x+u)^2} = +\frac{1}{2\pi}\left[\frac{G_3(u)}{(x+u)^2}\right]_{u=0}^\infty + \frac{1}{\pi}\int_0^\infty \frac{G_3(u)du}{(x+u)^3}$$

$$= +\frac{1}{\pi}\int_0^\infty \frac{G_3(u)du}{(x+u)^3},$$

as $G_3(0) = 0$.

Integrating again by parts,

$$\int_0^\infty \frac{G_3(u)du}{(x+u)^3} = -\frac{1}{2\pi}\left[\frac{G_4(u)}{(x+u)^3}\right]_{u=0}^\infty - \frac{3}{2\pi}\int_0^\infty \frac{G_4(u)du}{(x+u)^4}. \qquad (10$$

As

$$G_4(0) = H_4 = -\frac{2^3\pi^4}{4!}B_4,$$

9) and 10) become

$$\gamma(x) = \frac{B_2}{1\cdot 2}\cdot\frac{1}{x} + \frac{B_4}{3\cdot 4}\cdot\frac{1}{x^3} + \frac{3}{4\pi^4}\int_0^\infty \frac{G_4(u)du}{(x+u)^4}. \qquad (11$$

3. If we continue integrating by parts we get *Stirling's Series:*—

$$\log\Gamma(x) = \log\sqrt{2\pi} - x + (x-\tfrac{1}{2})\log x$$

$$+\frac{B_2}{1\cdot 2}\cdot\frac{1}{x} + \frac{B_4}{3\cdot 4}\cdot\frac{1}{x^3} + \frac{B_6}{5\cdot 6}\cdot\frac{1}{x^5} + \cdots + R_{2n}\ , \qquad (12$$

where

$$R_{2n} = \frac{(-1)^n(2n-1)!}{2^{2n-1}\pi^{2n}} \int_0^\infty \frac{G_{2n}(u)du}{(x+u)^{2n}}. \tag{13}$$

Since here $f^{2n}(x+u)$, $f^{(2n+2)}(x+u)$ have the same sign, we are under the case considered in 155, 5, and the series 12) is in fact an asymptotic development of $\Gamma(x)$.

From 13) we see R_{2n} has the form

$$R_{2n} = \frac{\epsilon_n(x)}{x^{2n-1}}, \tag{14}$$

where $\epsilon_n \doteq 0$ as $x \doteq \infty$. For if we integrate by parts we have

$$\int_0^\infty \frac{G_{2n}(u)du}{(x+u)^{2n}} = \frac{1}{2\pi}\left[\frac{G_{2n+1}(u)}{(x+u)^{2n}}\right]_0^\infty + \frac{n}{\pi}\int_0^\infty \frac{G_{2n+1}(u)du}{(x+u)^{2n+1}}$$

$$= +\frac{n}{\pi}J.$$

Now

$$|J| < \int_0^\infty \sum_{p=1}^\infty \frac{1}{p^{2n+1}} \frac{du}{(x+u)^{2n+1}} = \frac{1}{2n}\frac{1}{x^{2n}}\sum_{p=1}^\infty \frac{1}{p^{2n+1}}$$

$$< \frac{G}{x^{2n}}, \text{ where } G \text{ is a constant.}$$

Hence

$$\epsilon_n(x) < \frac{M}{x}, \quad M \text{ a constant.} \tag{15}$$

159. Asymptotic Series. 1. In the foregoing articles we have been led to divergent series

$$D(z) = a_0 + \frac{a_1}{z} + \frac{a_2}{z^2} + \cdots \tag{1}$$

such that the sum of the first n terms $D_n(z)$ gives a very good approximation of some function $f(z)$ for large values of z, provided n is not taken too large. More specifically we may say that the series 1) is so related to the function $f(z)$ that

$$f(z) = D_{n+1}(z) + \frac{\epsilon_n(z)}{z^n}, \quad \epsilon_n \doteq 0, \tag{2}$$

as $z \doteq \infty$ along the positive real axis.

Such a series is called an asymptotic series, and we write

$$f(z) \sim a_0 + \frac{a_1}{z} + \frac{a_2}{z^2} + \cdots \tag{3}$$

Hereby we will not restrict z to move along the z real axis, but permit it to $\doteq \infty$ along any radius vector so that

$$z = re^{i\theta} \quad , \quad r \doteq \infty \quad , \quad \theta = \text{constant}. \tag{4}$$

This we call the *asymptotic vector*.

Asymptotic series figure quite prominently in astronomy and also in some parts of the theory of linear differential equations. We shall meet them in this latter connection when we come to study the Bessel functions.

We wish now to see how the ordinary operations on convergent series may be extended to these divergent series. We shall suppose that $z \doteq \infty$ along the *same* asymptotic vector unless the contrary is stated.

Let us first show that:

$f(z)$ does not admit two different asymptotic developments along the same vector.

For from
$$f(z) = a_0 + \frac{a_1}{z} + \cdots + \frac{a_n}{z^n} + \frac{\epsilon_n}{z^n} \quad , \quad \epsilon_n \doteq 0$$

$$= b_0 + \frac{b_1}{z} + \cdots + \frac{b_n}{z^n} + \frac{\eta_n}{z^n} \quad , \quad \eta_n \doteq 0,$$

we have
$$0 = (a_0 - b_0) + \frac{a_1 - b_1}{z} + \cdots + \frac{a_n - b_n}{z^n} + \frac{\epsilon_n - \eta_n}{z^n}.$$

Letting $z \doteq \infty$ we get $a_0 = b_0$. Thus

$$a_1 - b_1 + \frac{a_2 - b_2}{z} + \cdots + \frac{\epsilon_n - \eta_n}{z^{n-1}} = 0.$$

From this we get as before $a_1 = b_1$, etc.

2. *Addition and Subtraction.* Suppose

$$\begin{aligned} f(z) &\sim a_0 + \frac{a_1}{z} + \cdots \\ g(z) &\sim b_0 + \frac{b_1}{z} + \cdots \end{aligned} \tag{5}$$

Then
$$f \pm g \sim (a_0 \pm b_0) + \frac{a_1 \pm b_1}{z} + \cdots \tag{6}$$

For 5) stand for

$$f = a_0 + \frac{a_1}{z} + \cdots + \frac{a_n}{z^n} + \frac{\epsilon_n}{z^n} = f_n + \frac{\epsilon_n}{z^n},$$

$$g = b_0 + \frac{b_1}{z} + \cdots + \frac{b_n}{z^n} + \frac{\eta_n}{z^n} = g_n + \frac{\eta_n}{z^n}, \tag{7}$$

where

$$\epsilon_n \quad , \quad \eta_n \doteq 0 \qquad \text{as } z \doteq \infty.$$

Thus

$$f \pm g = a_0 \pm b_0 + \frac{a_1 \pm b_1}{z} + \cdots + \frac{a_n \pm b_n}{z^n} + \frac{\vartheta_n}{z^n},$$

where

$$\vartheta_n = \epsilon_n \pm \eta_n \doteq 0 \qquad \text{as } z \doteq \infty.$$

Hence 6) holds.

3. *Multiplication.* The functions $f(z)$, $g(z)$ admitting the asymptotic developments 7), let us show that

$$f \cdot g \sim c_0 + \frac{c_1}{z} + \frac{c_2}{z^2} + \cdots \tag{8}$$

where

$$c_0 = a_0 b_0 \quad , \quad c_1 = a_0 b_1 + a_1 b_0 \quad , \quad c_2 = a_0 b_2 + a_1 b_1 + a_2 b_0 \cdots \tag{9}$$

as in the multiplication of series.

For 7) gives

$$fg = f_n g_n + \frac{1}{z^n}(\epsilon_n g_n + \eta_n f_n) + \frac{\epsilon_n \eta_n}{z^{2n}}.$$

But

$$f_n g_n = c_0 + \frac{c_1}{z} + \cdots + \frac{c_n}{z^n} + \frac{\vartheta_n}{z^{2n}},$$

where ϑ_n is a polynomial of order $\leq n - 1$. Thus 8) is valid.

4. *Division.* Since

$$\frac{f}{g} = f \cdot \frac{1}{g},$$

the problem of dividing one asymptotic development by another may be reduced to finding the reciprocal of an asymptotic development.

Let us suppose in 5) that $a_0 \neq 0$. We will write

$$f = f_n + \frac{\epsilon_n}{z^n} = a_0\left(1 + \frac{a_1}{a_0} \cdot \frac{1}{z} + \cdots + \frac{a_n}{a_0}\frac{1}{z^n}\right) + \frac{\epsilon_n}{z^n}$$

$$= a_0(1 + h_n) + \frac{\epsilon_n}{z^n}.$$

Thus

$$\frac{1}{f}=\frac{1}{f_n+\frac{\epsilon_n}{z^n}}=\frac{1}{f_n}-\frac{\epsilon_n}{z^n}\frac{1}{ff_n},$$

$$\frac{1}{f_n}=\frac{1}{a_0}\cdot\frac{1}{1+h_n}=\frac{1}{a_0}\left\{1-h_n+h_n^2-\cdots+(-1)^{n+1}\frac{h_n^{n+1}}{1+h_n}\right\}.$$

Hence $$\frac{1}{f}=c_0+\frac{c_1}{z}+\frac{c_2}{z^2}+\cdots+\frac{c_n}{z^n}+\frac{\vartheta_n}{z^n}\quad,\quad c_0=\frac{1}{a_0}, \tag{10}$$

where $$\vartheta_n \doteq 0 \qquad \text{as } z\doteq\infty.$$

5. *Integration.* We show that:

An asymptotic development of $f(z)$ may be integrated termwise along the asymptotic vector when the function $f(z)$ is integrable along this vector as indicated in 12).

For from 7) we have

$$\int_z^\infty f(z)dz=\int_z^\infty f_{n+1}dz+\int_z^\infty \frac{\epsilon^{n+1}}{z^{n+1}}\,dz. \tag{11}$$

Now along the asymptotic vector

$$\left|\int_z^\infty \frac{\epsilon_{n+1}}{z^{n+1}}\,dz\right|<\frac{\vartheta_n}{r^n}\qquad \vartheta_n\doteq 0\quad,\quad \text{as } z\doteq\infty.$$

Thus 11) may be written

$$\int_z^\infty\left(f(z)-a_0-\frac{a_1}{z}\right)dz$$
$$=\int_z^\infty\frac{a_2}{z^2}\,dz+\int_z^\infty\frac{a_3}{z^3}dz+\cdots\int_z^\infty\frac{a_{n+1}}{z^{n+1}}\,dz+\frac{\theta_n(z)}{z^n},$$

where $$\theta_n\doteq 0 \qquad \text{as } z\doteq\infty.$$

Thus from $$f(z)\sim a_0+\frac{a_1}{z}+\frac{a_2}{z^2}+\cdots$$

we can infer that

$$\int_z^\infty\left(f(z)-a_0-\frac{a_1}{z}\right)dz\sim\int_z^\infty\frac{a_2}{z^2}\,dz+\int_z^\infty\frac{a_3}{z^3}\,dz+\cdots \tag{12}$$

6. *Differentiation. Suppose that we know that $f(z)$ has an asymptotic development*

$$f(z) \sim \frac{a_1}{z} + \frac{a_2}{z^2} + \cdots; \tag{13}$$

also that $f'(z)$ has an asymptotic development of the form

$$f'(z) \sim \frac{b_2}{z^2} + \frac{b_3}{z^3} + \cdots \tag{14}$$

Then the asymptotic development of $f'(z)$ may be obtained from that of $f(z)$ by termwise differentiation.

For from 14) we have, using 5,

$$\int_z^\infty f'(z)\,dz \sim \int_z^\infty \frac{b_2}{z^2}\,dz + \int_z^\infty \frac{b_3}{z^3}\,dz + \cdots \tag{15}$$

Since

$$f(\infty) = \lim_{z=\infty} f(z) = 0, \qquad \text{by 13)},$$

we have, from 15),

$$-f(z) \sim \frac{b_2}{z} + \frac{1}{2}\frac{b_3}{z^2} + \frac{1}{3}\frac{b_4}{z^3} + \cdots \tag{16}$$

Since by 1, a function admits but one asymptotic development along the same vector, the comparison of 13), 16) gives

$$b_2 = -a_1 \quad , \quad b_3 = -2a_2 \cdots$$

These in 14) establish the theorem.

CHAPTER X

THE FUNCTIONS OF WEIERSTRASS

160. Limiting Points. 1. At this point it is convenient to introduce a notion which is fundamental in many parts of mathematics, that of a limiting point.

Let $\mathfrak{A}$ be a point set. If in any domain $D(b)$ of the point b, there lie an infinite number of points of $\mathfrak{A}$, we say b is a *limiting point of* $\mathfrak{A}$. The point b may or may not lie in $\mathfrak{A}$.

Example 1. Let $\mathfrak{A} = 1, \frac{1}{2}, \frac{1}{3}, \cdots$. Then the origin 0 is a limiting point of $\mathfrak{A}$. It does not lie in $\mathfrak{A}$.

Example 2. Let $\mathfrak{A}$ denote all the points *within* a circle $\mathfrak{K}$. Then any point of $\mathfrak{A}$ is a limiting point of $\mathfrak{A}$. Also any point k of the circumference $\mathfrak{K}$ is a limiting point of $\mathfrak{A}$, although k does not lie in $\mathfrak{A}$.

2. A set of points $\mathfrak{A}$ which lie in some square $\mathfrak{S}$ is called *limited*, otherwise *unlimited*.

A set of points which embraces an infinity of points is called an *infinite* point set, otherwise a finite set.

Thus the point set formed of the points corresponding to the positive integers

$$\mathfrak{A} = 1, 2, 3, \cdots$$

is an infinite unlimited set. For obviously no square contains them all.

The set of points on an ellipse form a limited point set.

We now prove the fundamental theorem:

Every infinite limited point set $\mathfrak{A}$ has at least one limiting point.

For $\mathfrak{A}$ being limited lies in some square $\mathfrak{S}$. Let us divide $\mathfrak{S}$ into 4 equal squares. Since $\mathfrak{A}$ contains an infinite number of points, at least one of these squares contains an infinite number of points belonging to $\mathfrak{A}$. Call this square $\mathfrak{S}_1$. This we divide into 4 equal squares. At least one of these must contain an infinite number of points of $\mathfrak{A}$. Call this $\mathfrak{S}_2$. Continuing in this way we get a sequence of squares

$$\mathfrak{S}_1 \quad , \quad \mathfrak{S}_2 \quad , \quad \mathfrak{S}_3 \quad \cdots \tag{1}$$

each contained in the foregoing. As the sides of these squares $\doteq 0$, the squares 1) shut down to a point α which lies in all of them. Since each square contains an infinite number of points of $\mathfrak{A}$, any circle about α, however small, will contain an infinity of points of $\mathfrak{A}$. Thus α is a limiting point of $\mathfrak{A}$.

3. Suppose the point set $\mathfrak{A}$ is not limited. Then there are an infinite number of points of $\mathfrak{A}$ without any circle $\mathfrak{K}$ about $z = 0$; that is, there are an infinity of points of $\mathfrak{A}$ in any domain of the point $z = \infty$. It is convenient to say that $z = \infty$ is a limiting point of $\mathfrak{A}$.

We may thus say that:

Every unlimited point set admits $z = \infty$ as a limiting point.

Putting this in connection with the theorem in 2 gives:

Every infinite point set has at least one limiting point. This may be the ideal point $z = \infty$.

4. *Let the one-valued analytic function $f(z)$ take on the value c for the points of some set $\mathfrak{A}$. Any limiting point of $\mathfrak{A}$ is any essentially singular point of $f(z)$, provided f is not a constant.*

161. Periodicity. 1. Let the one-valued analytic function $f(z)$ satisfy the relation

$$f(z+\omega) = f(z) \quad , \quad \omega \text{ constant} \neq 0, \tag{1}$$

for every z for which f is defined. We call ω a *period* of f and say f *admits ω as a period.* We shall of course exclude the case that $f(z)$ is a constant. Thus

$$e^z \quad , \quad \sin z \quad , \quad \tan z \tag{2}$$

admit respectively

$$2\pi i \quad , \quad 2\pi \quad , \quad \pi \tag{3}$$

as periods.

Obviously if ω is a period of $f(z)$ so are

$$\cdots, \ -3\omega, \ -2\omega, \ -\omega, \ \omega, \ 2\omega, \ 3\omega, \ \cdots \tag{4}$$

Thus if f admits one period, it admits an infinite number of periods. Sometimes these lie on a right line as in the case of the functions 2); sometimes they are spread over the plane as we saw in the case of the functions

$$\sum \frac{1}{(z+m_1\omega_1+m_2\omega_2)^p} \qquad p=3, 4, \cdots \tag{5}$$

considered in 123, 6.

It will be convenient to say that two points a, b are *congruent* when their difference $a-b$ is any period of $f(z)$. This we write

$$a \equiv b$$

and read *a is congruent b*. If we write more specifically,

$$a \equiv b \quad , \quad \text{mod } \omega,$$

read *a is congruent b with respect to the modulus* ω, we mean that

$$a-b=m\omega \quad , \quad m \text{ some integer or } 0.$$

If we write

$$a \equiv b \quad , \quad \text{mod } \omega_1, \omega_2,$$

we mean

$$a-b=m_1\omega_1+m_2\omega_2 \quad , \quad m_1, m_2 \text{ integers or } 0.$$

If ω_1, ω_2 are any two periods of $f(z)$, so are obviously $\omega_1+\omega_2$, and $\omega_1-\omega_2$ periods and still more generally $m_1\omega_1+m_2\omega_2$ are periods, m_1, m_2 being integers or 0.

If a, b are not congruent we say *a is incongruent b* and write

$$a \not\equiv b.$$

2. Let $\mathfrak{P}$ denote the totality of all the periods of $f(z)$. The point set $\mathfrak{P}$ must have $z=\infty$ as a limiting point as it always contains a set of points as 4), and $n\omega \doteq \infty$ as $n \doteq \infty$. On the other hand, we now prove the important theorem:

The point set $\mathfrak{P}$ *has no limiting point in the finite part of the plane.*

For suppose η were a limiting point. Then within $D_\delta(\eta)$ there are an infinity of points of $\mathfrak{P}$, however small δ is taken. If α, β are two of these, $\gamma=\alpha-\beta$ is a period and $|\gamma|<2\delta$. As δ is small at pleasure, this shows that $f(z)$ has periods which are numerically $<$ any given $\epsilon>0$. But $f(z)$ is an analytic function and cannot have such periods. For if $z=a$ is a regular point and $f(a)=c$, we know that $f(z)$ cannot $= c$ in some $D_\sigma^*(a)$. But $f(z)$ having periods η numerically $< \sigma$, we have

$$f(a+\eta) = f(a) = c$$

and $a + \eta$ lies in $D_\sigma^*(a)$, which is a contradiction. This shows that every point z is a singular point of $f(z)$, and $f(z)$ is not analytic.

3. Let ω be any period of $f(z)$. On the line l passing through the origin and ω will lie an infinity of periods, for at least the periods 4) will lie on l. Since the origin is not a limiting point, there are two periods $\pm \lambda$ on l nearer $z = 0$ than the others.

All periods on l can be expressed as multiples of λ.

For let ω be any period of $f(z)$ lying on l. We can write

$$\omega = n\lambda + \eta$$

and take the integer n so large that $|\eta| < |\lambda|$. If now $\eta \neq 0$, it is a period on l which is nearer 0 than λ, which is contrary to hypothesis. We call λ a *primitive period.*

Thus the periods 3) are primitive periods of their respective functions 2).

162. Jacobi's Theorem. 1. *If the one-valued analytic function $f(z)$ has more than one primitive period ω_1, there exists a primitive period ω_2 such that every period of f has the form*

$$m_1\omega_1 + m_2\omega_2, \tag{1}$$

where m_1, m_2 are integers or 0.

For let ω be any primitive period other than ω_1. In the parallelogram Q whose sides are $O\omega_1$ and $O\omega$ there are but a finite number of periods. None of these can fall on the edge of Q. For if η were such a period $\eta_1 \equiv \eta$ would fall in (O, ω_1) and as η_1 is a period, ω_1 cannot be a primitive period.

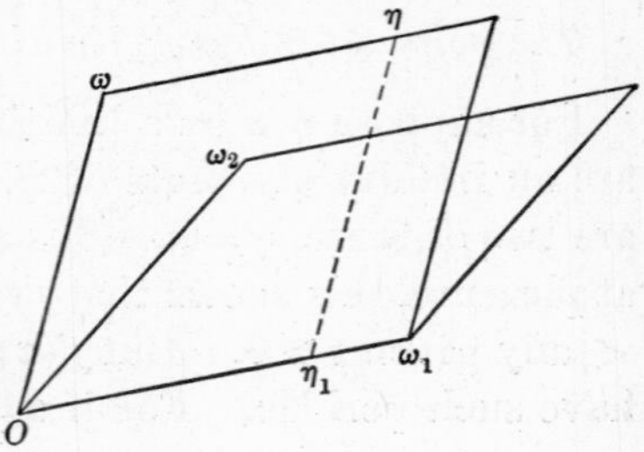

Let now ω_2 be that period in Q for which the angle $\omega_2 O \omega_1$ is least. Then every period of f has the form 1).

For let P be the parallelogram whose sides are $O\omega_1$, $O\omega_2$. If there is a period ω of f not included in 1), let ω' be that point of P which is $\equiv \omega$. Then ω' is a period and

$$\text{Angle } \omega' O\omega_1 < \text{Angle } \omega_2 O\omega_1,$$

which is contrary to hypothesis.

2. An analytic function $f(z)$ which has more than one primitive period is called a *double periodic* function.

Two primitive periods ω_1, ω_2 such that all other periods of the double periodic function $f(z)$ can be expressed linearly in terms of them, as in 1), form a *primitive pair* of periods.

The functions e^z, $\sin z$, etc., are simply periodic. All their periods are multiples of a primitive period.

As examples of double periodic functions we may take the functions

$$F(z) = \sum \frac{1}{(z + m_1\omega_1 + m_2\omega_2)^p}, \tag{2}$$

p an integer > 2 considered in 123, 6.

These functions have

$$m\omega_1 + m_2\omega_2 \tag{3}$$

as poles of order p. All other points in the finite part of the plane are regular. The point $z = \infty$ is of course an essentially singular point.

3. Let $f(z)$ be a double periodic function having ω_1, ω_2 as a pair of primitive periods. Let a be another point. The parallelogram P whose four vertices are

$$a \quad , \quad a + \omega_1 \quad , \quad a + \omega_2 \quad , \quad a + \omega_1 + \omega_2$$

is called a *primitive parallelogram of periods*. By drawing parallels to the sides of P through the points

$$a + m_1\omega_1 + m_2\omega_2$$

we may divide the whole plane into a set of parallelograms similar to P.

Any parallelogram Q built up on two periods η_1, η_2 not necessarily a pair of primitive periods will be called a *parallelogram of periods*. We shall often have occasion to integrate over the edge of such parallelograms, and in such cases we shall suppose the point a chosen so that the edge of the parallelogram does not pass through a singular point of the integrand. To indicate what periods η_1, η_2 are used we may denote Q by $Q(\eta_1, \eta_2)$.

The fact that $f(z)$ admits ω_1, ω_2 as a primitive pair of periods we may indicate by the notation

$$f(z, \omega_1, \omega_2).$$

4. From one primitive pair of periods ω_1, ω_2 it is possible to form an infinity of other pairs.

For let

$$\begin{aligned}\eta_1 &= m_1\omega_1 + m_2\omega_2, \\ \eta_2 &= n_1\omega_1 + n_2\omega_2,\end{aligned} \tag{4}$$

where the m, n are integers. Obviously η_1, η_2 are also periods. For them to form a primitive pair it is necessary that the determinant

$$D = m_1n_2 - m_2n_1$$

is ± 1. In fact, solving, we get

$$\omega_1 = \frac{n_2\eta_1 - m_2\eta_2}{D},$$

$$\omega_2 = \frac{m_1\eta_2 - n_1\eta_1}{D}.$$

Hence when $D = \pm 1$, ω_1, ω_2 are linear functions of η_1, η_2 with integral coefficients.

Let us call the set of points

$$l_1\omega_1 + l_2\omega_2 \qquad l_1, l_2 = 0, \pm 1, \pm 2 \cdots \tag{5}$$

a *network*. We may denote it by (ω_1, ω_2).

We now see that the (η_1, η_2) network is the same as (ω_1, ω_2) when and only when $D = \pm 1$.

5. Let P be a parallelogram formed by the points

$$O \quad , \quad \omega_1 \quad , \quad \omega_2 \quad , \quad \omega_1 + \omega_2.$$

If

$$\omega_1 = a_1 + ib_1 \qquad \omega_2 = a_2 + ib_2,$$

we know from analytic geometry that

$$\text{Area } P(\omega_1, \omega_2) = \begin{vmatrix} a_1 & b_1 \\ a_2 & b_2 \end{vmatrix}. \tag{6}$$

Thus the area of $P(\eta_1, \eta_2)$ is

$$\begin{vmatrix} m_1a_1 + m_2a_2 & m_1b_1 + m_2b_2 \\ n_1a_1 + n_2a_2 & n_1b_1 + n_2b_2 \end{vmatrix} = \begin{vmatrix} m_1 m_2 \\ n_1 n_2 \end{vmatrix} \begin{vmatrix} a_1 b_1 \\ a_2 b_2 \end{vmatrix}.$$

Hence

$$\text{Area } P(\eta_1, \eta_2) = \Delta \cdot \text{Area } P(\omega_1, \omega_2), \tag{7}$$

where $\Delta = |D|$.

163. Various Periodic Functions. 1. From a periodic function $f(z)$ admitting ω as period we can form an infinity of others admitting this period. For example

$$g(z) = cf^m(z) \qquad m \text{ an integer}, \tag{1}$$

admits the period ω. For

$$g(z+\omega) = cf^m(z+\omega) = cf^m(z) = g(z).$$

If ω is a primitive period of f, it does not need to be a primitive period of 1). For example 2π is a primitive period of $\sin z$, but it is not a primitive period of $\sin^2 z$, whose primitive period is π.

2. *If $f(z)$, $g(z)$ admit the period ω, their sum, difference, product and quotient will also admit this period.*

For example let

$$h(z) = f(z)g(z).$$

Then

$$h(z+\omega) = f(z+\omega)g(z+\omega) = f(z)g(z) = h(z).$$

We must, however, guard against the case that h reduces to a constant. Thus $f = \sin^2 z$, $g = \cos^2 z$ admit the period π. Their sum

$$h = \sin^2 z + \cos^2 z = 1$$

is not properly periodic at all.

From the above it follows that any rational function h of the periodic function $f(z)$ is also periodic, guarding against the case of course that h is a constant.

3. Let $f_1(z), f_2(z) \cdots f_n(z)$ *be one-valued analytic functions admitting ω as a period. Then the analytic function w satisfying the equation*

$$w^n + f_1(z)w^{n-1} + f_2(z)w^{n-2} + \cdots + f_n(z) = 0 \tag{2}$$

will admit ω as period.

For let $w(z)$ be a value of w corresponding to a value of w at z. The value of w at the point $z+\omega$ will be $w(z+\omega)$. As the coefficients of 2) have the same value at $z+\omega$ as at z, we see

$$w(z+\omega)=w(z).$$

4. *If the one-valued analytic function $f(z)$ admits ω as a period, so does its derivative $f'(z)$.*

For $f'(z)$ is the limit of

$$g(z)=\frac{f(z+h)-f(z)}{h}.$$

But
$$g(z+\omega)=\frac{f(z+\omega+h)-f(z+\omega)}{h}=g(z). \tag{3}$$

Passing to the limit $h=0$ in 3) gives

$$f'(z+\omega)=f'(z).$$

5. If $f(z)$ admits the period ω, we cannot say that the primitive function $F(z)$ admits this period, as the following example shows.

Let
$$f(z)=\cos z+2.$$

Then
$$F(z)=\int(\cos z+2)dz=\sin z+2z+C$$

is not periodic although $f(z)$ admits the period 2π.

There is, however, an important case when the primitive function $F(z)$ does admit the period ω, viz.:

Let the derivative $f(z)$ of the one-valued function $F(z)$ admit the period ω. If F is an even function, F admits the period ω.

For from
$$f(z+\omega)=f(z)$$

we have, on integrating,

$$F(z+\omega)=F(z)+C.$$

In this relation set $z=-\frac{\omega}{2}$, then

$$F\left(\frac{\omega}{2}\right)=F\left(-\frac{\omega}{2}\right)+C.$$

As $F\left(\frac{\omega}{2}\right)=F\left(-\frac{\omega}{2}\right)$, this gives $C=0$; thus

$$F(z+\omega)=F(z),$$

and F admits the period ω.

6. From a one-valued periodic function $f(z)$ having no essentially singular points in the finite part of the plane let us show how to construct a periodic function having $z=a$ as an essentially singular point.

To fix the ideas let us take

$$f(z)=\cot z.$$

This has the period π and the poles

$$p_m = m\pi \qquad m=0, \pm 1, \pm 2, \cdots$$

Let us set

$$f_n(z)=\frac{1}{n!}\cot(z-a-a_n),$$

where $a_1, a_2 \cdots$ is a properly chosen sequence which $\doteq 0$. For example we may take here

$$a_n=\frac{i}{n}.$$

Consider now

$$g(z)=\Sigma f_n(z)=\sum \frac{1}{n!}\cot\left(z-a-\frac{i}{n}\right). \qquad (4$$

The poles of $f_n(z)$ are

$$g_{n,m}=a+\frac{i}{n}+p_m \qquad m=0, \pm 1, \cdots \qquad (5$$

No two terms f_r, f_s have a pole in common. Let $\mathfrak{P}$ be the set of points formed of the sets 5) and their limiting points

$$l_m = a + p_m.$$

If $z=b$ is not in $\mathfrak{P}$, we can describe about it a circle $\mathfrak{K}$ which contains no point of $\mathfrak{P}$. Then each and every f_n in 4) is numerically $<$ some fixed G for any z in $\mathfrak{K}$. Thus each term of 4) is numerically $<$ the corresponding term in the convergent series

$$G\sum \frac{1}{n!}.$$

Hence the series 4) converges steadily in $\mathfrak{K}$ and as each term of 4) is analytic in $\mathfrak{K}$, the function $g(z)$ is regular at $z=b$.

On the other hand, each pole q of any term f_s of 4) is a pole of g. For we have

$$g(z)=f_s(z)+h(z),$$

where h is the series obtained from 4) by omitting the term f_s. From the foregoing reasoning h is regular at q. Thus g has a pole at q and of the same order as f_s.

The point $z = a$ is an essentially singular point, since it is the limiting point of the set of poles

$$q_{n,o} = a + \frac{i}{n}.$$

Finally $g(z)$ admits the period π since each term of 4) does. This shows that not only a but also $l_m = a + m\pi$ are essentially singular points. This is as it should be, since the l_m are limiting points of the poles 5), and $g(z)$ has the period π.

7. Instead of the function cot z we can take a double periodic function as

$$f(z) = \sum \frac{1}{(z + m_1\omega_1 + m_2\omega_2)^3}.$$

With this we can construct a series of the type 4) which will define a double periodic function having a given point $z = a$ as an essentially singular point. Of course all points $\equiv a$ will also be essentially singular points.

164. Elliptic Functions. 1. Having now an idea of some of the singularities a double periodic function may possess, let us pick out a class of great importance called the elliptic functions. These are defined as *one-valued analytic double periodic functions which have no essentially singular point in the finite part of the plane.* The reader will recall that, as we saw in 123, every periodic function must have $z = \infty$ as an essentially singular point. Thus the elliptic functions are the simplest double periodic functions, in that they are one-valued and the number of their essentially singular points is the least possible.

Such functions are

$$p_1(z) = -2 \sum \frac{1}{(z - 2m_1\omega_1 - 2m_2\omega_2)^3} \qquad (1$$

. . . .

$$p_n(z) = (-1)^n (n+1)! \sum \frac{1}{(z - 2m_1\omega_1 - 2m_2\omega_2)^{n+2}} \qquad (2$$

where $2\omega_1$, $2\omega_2$ are any two complex numbers not collinear with the origin and m_1, m_2 range over all positive and negative integers and 0. We notice that p_2 is the derivative of p_1, p_3 the derivative of p_2, etc. These functions are essentially the functions considered in 123, 6; we have replaced ω_1, ω_2 by $2\,\omega_1$, $2\,\omega_2$ to avoid writing the fraction $\frac{1}{2}$, as we shall see.

2. From $p_1(z)$ we can get by integration another elliptic function of fundamental importance. In fact let us write

$$p_1(z) = -\frac{2}{z^3} + g(z), \tag{3}$$

where the first term on the right corresponds to the values $m_1 = 0$, $m_2 = 0$ in 1).

The function $g(z)$ is regular in any part of the plane which does not contain one of the points

$$2\,m_1\omega_1 + 2\,m_2\omega_2 \quad , \quad m_1 = m_2 = 0 \text{ excluded.}$$

In particular it is regular about $z = 0$. Thus

$$\int_0^z g(z)dz = -2\sum{}'\int_0^z \frac{dz}{(z - 2\,m_1\omega_1 - 2\,m_2\omega_2)^3}$$

$$= \sum{}'\left\{\frac{1}{(z - 2\,m_1\omega_1 - 2\,m_2\omega_2)^2} - \frac{1}{(2\,m_1\omega_1 + 2\,m_2\omega_2)^2}\right\} = h(z), \tag{4}$$

where the dash indicates that in effecting the summation the combination $m_1 = m_2 = 0$ is excluded. This dash we shall often employ in this sense. Let us now set

$$p(z) = \frac{1}{z^2} + h(z). \tag{5}$$

Then

$$p'(z) = -\frac{2}{z^3} + g(z) = p_1(z). \tag{6}$$

Thus 5) is the primitive of 6). Let us now show that $h(z)$ is even. For to the term indicated in 4) there corresponds another term in which m_1, m_2 have the same values but with opposite signs. Thus $h(-z) = h(z)$ and h is an even function. Hence by 163, 5 the function 5) is double periodic admitting the same periods $2\,\omega_1$, $2\,\omega_2$ as $p_1(z)$.

Thus the function

$$p(z) = \frac{1}{z^2} + \sum{}' \left\{ \frac{1}{(z - 2m_1\omega_1 - 2m_2\omega_2)^2} - \frac{1}{(2m_1\omega_1 + 2m_2\omega_2)^2} \right\} \quad (7$$

is an elliptic function admitting $2\omega_1$, $2\omega_2$ as periods. It is the fundamental elliptic function in Weierstrass' theory. To denote it, he has invented a modified p, viz. the symbol $\wp$, and this has been generally adopted. We shall, however, retain the ordinary p.

By virtue of 6) we see that the functions defined in 1), 2) are the derivatives of $p(u)$.

165. General Properties of Elliptic Functions.

1. *Every elliptic function has at least one pole in any parallelogram of periods P.*

For having no singular point in P, it has no singular point anywhere in the infinite plane. It is thus a constant by 121, 2.

2. *Let $f(z)$ be an elliptic function admitting ω_1 and ω_2 as periods. Then*

$$\int_P f dz = 0, \quad (1$$

P being a parallelogram of periods not passing through a pole of f.

For

$$\int_P = \int_{12} + \int_{23} + \int_{34} + \int_{41}. \quad (2$$

Now

$$\int_{43} f dz = \int_{12} f dz$$

since f has the same value at $z' = z + \omega_2$ as it has at z, by virtue of its periodicity. Hence

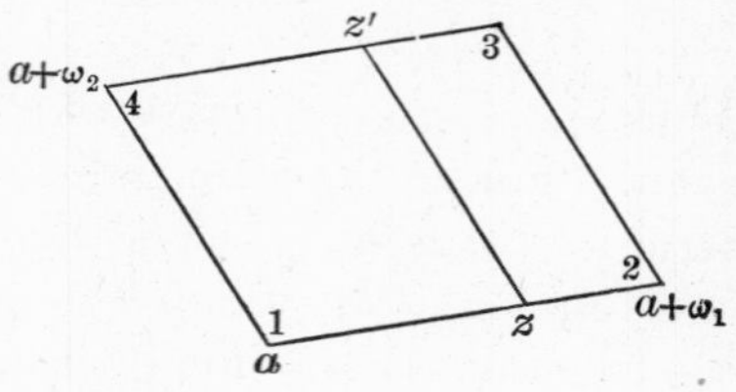

$$\int_{34} = -\int_{12}.$$

Similarly

$$\int_{41} = -\int_{23}.$$

Thus the right side of 2) vanishes.

3. *The sum of the residues of $f(z)$ in any parallelogram of periods P, not passing through a pole of f, is* 0.

For this sum is by 124, 1

$$\frac{1}{2\pi i}\int_P f(z)\,dz,$$

which $= 0$ by 2.

4. *The sum of the orders of the poles of an elliptic function in any parallelogram of periods not passing through a pole is at least* 2.

For if the sum is 1, f can have but a single pole $z = a$ in P and its development must have the form

$$f = \frac{c}{z-a} + c_0 + c_1(z-a) + \cdots \tag{3}$$

Here

$$c = \operatorname*{Res}_{z=a} f(z).$$

As the sum of all the residues in P is 0 by 3 and as there is but a single pole, we must have $c = 0$. But then 3) shows that f has no pole at a, which is contrary to hypothesis.

5. *Definition.* The sum of the orders of the poles in a *primitive* parallelogram of periods not passing through a pole is called the *order* of an elliptic function.

From 4 we have:

There is no elliptic function of order less than 2.

By means of this theorem we can often show that a pair of periods of an elliptic function form a *primitive* pair, as the following theorem shows:

6. *Let ω_1, ω_2 be a pair of periods of the elliptic function $f(z)$. This is a primitive pair if the sum of the orders of the poles of f in a parallelogram $P(\omega_1, \omega_2)$ not passing through a pole is* 2.

For if not, let η_1, η_2 be a primitive pair. Then

$$\omega_1 = m_1\eta_1 + m_2\eta_2 \quad , \quad \omega_2 = n_1\eta_1 + n_2\eta_2$$

and

$$\Delta = |m_1 n_2 - m_2 n_1|,$$

is >1 by 162, 4. Now by 162, 5 the area of $P(\omega_1, \omega_2)$ is Δ times that of $P(\eta_1, \eta_2)$. From this it follows geometrically that there are η parallelograms which either contain no pole or a pole of order 1. As $f(z)$ behaves in all parallelograms of periods just as it does in any one parallelogram, we see that f violates the theorem 4. Hence ω_1, ω_2 must form a primitive pair of periods.

7. From this we see that $2\omega_1, 2\omega_2$ form a primitive pair of periods of the function $p(u)$ defined in 164, 7.

For as we have seen, its poles are the points of the network $(2\omega_1, 2\omega_2)$ and each is of order 2.

From 118, 4 and 163, 4 we also see that $2\omega_1, 2\omega_2$ form a primitive pair for the derivatives $p'(u), p''(u) \cdots$

8. On account of periodicity an elliptic function takes on the same values at a and $b = a + \omega$ where ω is a period. Thus in counting up the points where an elliptic function takes on the same value in a primitive parallelogram of periods we agree to consider only one of the two opposite sides. Also if $f(z) = c$ at $z = a$ the function $g(z) = f(z) - c$ will have a zero at a. If this zero is of order s, we will say that $f(z)$ takes on the value c at a, s times.

This being agreed upon we now prove:

An elliptic function $f(z)$ of order n takes on any given value c just n times in a primitive parallelogram P.

For choosing P so that no zero or pole of $f(z)$ lies on its edge, we have, by 124, 4,

$$\frac{1}{2\pi i}\int_P \frac{f'(z)}{f(z)} dz = m_0 - m_\infty, \tag{4}$$

where m_0 is the sum of the orders of the zeros and m_∞ the sum of the orders of the poles of $f(z)$ in P.

Now P being a parallelogram of periods of $f(z)$, it is also for the function $\dfrac{f'(z)}{f(z)}$. Thus the integral in 4) vanishes by 2. Hence

$$m_0 = m_\infty.$$

But $m_\infty = n$ by definition. Thus f vanishes n times in P.

Consider now

$$g(z) = f(z) - c.$$

This vanishes when $f = c$. On the other hand, P is a primitive parallelogram for g as it is for f. Finally, g having the same poles as f, and to the same orders, the order of g is n. Hence g vanishes n times in P.

9. A theorem of great use in the elliptic functions is the following:

Two elliptic functions having the same periods, the same zeros, and poles to the same orders, can differ only by a constant factor.

For let $f(z)$, $g(z)$ be two such functions. In the vicinity of a zero or a pole $z = a$ we have

$$f = (z - a)^m \phi(z) \qquad g = (z - a)^m \psi(z)$$

where ϕ, ψ are regular at a and do not vanish. Hence in the vicinity of a zero or pole

$$q = \frac{f(z)}{g(z)} = \frac{\phi(z)}{\psi(z)}$$

is an analytic function. If we give to q at a the value

$$\frac{\phi(a)}{\psi(a)},$$

q is regular at a. Thus q has no singular points in the finite part of the plane. It is therefore a constant. Thus

$$f(z) = Cg(z).$$

10. A similar theorem but not so often used is the following:

If the elliptic functions $f(z)$ $g(z)$ have the same periods and at each pole the same characteristic, they differ only by an additive constant.

For at a pole $z = a$, let

$$f(z) = \phi(z) + F(z),$$
$$g(z) = \phi(z) + G(z),$$

where ϕ is the common characteristic at a. The functions F, G are regular at a by 118, 2.

Thus $f(z) - g(z) = h$ is regular at a as it is the difference of two regular functions. Thus the function is regular everywhere, and is therefore a constant. Hence

$$f(z) = g(z) + C.$$

11. *Abel's Relation. Let $f(z)$ be an elliptic function of order n. Let P be a primitive parallelogram of periods not passing through a zero or pole of f. If $a_1, a_2 \cdots a_n$ are the zeros and $p_1, p_2 \cdots p_n$ the poles which fall in P, then*

$$(a_1 + a_2 + \cdots + a_n) - (p_1 + p_2 + \cdots + p_n) = a \text{ period}. \qquad (5$$

Before proving this theorem let us see its significance in the function theory. It is often convenient to construct functions having assigned properties, and it is therefore necessary for us to know which such functions are possible.

For example we know it is possible to construct a one-valued analytic function which vanishes at $a_1, a_2 \cdots a_m$, which has poles at $p_1, p_2 \cdots p_n$ and which has no essential singularity even at ∞. Such a function is

$$\frac{(z-a_1)\cdots(z-a_m)}{(z-p_1)\cdots(z-p_n)}.$$

Now if we were asked to construct an elliptic function having these zeros and poles in a primitive parallelogram of periods P we would say at once that this is impossible unless in the first place $m = n$ by 8. This is the first restriction. Abel's relation 5) is another restriction. It says that having chosen $2n-1$ of the zeros and poles in P, the last one is no longer free to choose ; it is, in fact, completely determined by 5). Are there any other conditions to inpose? We shall see in 166, 4 that there are not.

Let us note that we may write 5)

$$\Sigma a_m \equiv \Sigma p_m \quad , \quad \text{mod } \omega_1, \omega_2. \qquad (6$$

We turn now to the proof of this relation.

From 124, 2 we have

$$\frac{1}{2\pi i}\int_P z d \log f(z) = \Sigma a_m - \Sigma p_m. \qquad (7$$

Now

$$\int_P = \int_{12} + \int_{23} + \int_{34} + \int_{41}. \qquad (8$$

Also

$$\int_{34} = \int_{c+\omega_1+\omega_2}^{c+\omega_2} = -\int_{43}.$$

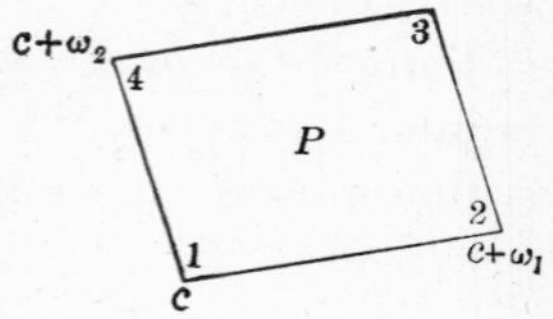

Let us change the variable setting

$$z = u + \omega_2.$$

Then
$$\int_{43} z d\log f(z) = \int_c^{c+\omega_1} (u+\omega_2) d\log f(u)$$
$$= \int_{12} u d\log f(u) + \omega_2 \Big[\log f(u)\Big]_c^{c+\omega_1}. \quad (9$$

Now if the reader will remember that an integral is the limit of a sum, he will see that the letter chosen for the variable has no influence on its value. Thus

$$\int_{12} u d\log f(u) = \int_{12} z d\log f(z) = \int_{12}.$$

Also if $\log f(u)$ has the value $\log f(c)$ at $u = c$, its value at $c + \omega_1$ is one of the many values $\log f(c+\omega_1)$ has at this point. But $f(c+\omega_1) = f(c)$; thus the value $\log f$ has at $c + \omega_1$ is

$$\log f(c) - 2\, m_2 \pi i, \qquad m_2 \text{ an integer.}$$

Thus 9) gives
$$\int_{12} + \int_{34} = 2\, m_2 \pi i \omega_2.$$

Similarly
$$\int_{23} + \int_{41} = 2\, m_1 \pi i \omega_1.$$

Thus 7) gives
$$\Sigma a_m - \Sigma p_m = \frac{1}{2\pi i} \int_P = m_1\omega_1 + m_2\omega_2$$
$$= \text{a period.}$$

12. From Abel's relation we have :

Let the elliptic function $f(z) = c$ *at the points* $z_1, z_2 \cdots z_n$ *in* P. *Then*
$$\Sigma z_m \equiv \Sigma p_m. \quad (10$$

For
$$g(z) = f(z) - c$$

has the same poles as $f(z)$, and its zeros are $z_1 \cdots z_n$. We thus need only to apply 6) to the function g.

Remark. In Abel's relation 5) the a's and p's lie in one and the same primitive parallelogram. We can give this relation a slightly more general form as follows. Let us say that any set of points form an *incongruent set* when no two of them are congruent. Let then
$$a_1' \; a_2' \cdots a_n' \quad (11$$

be any incongruent set of zeros, and

$$p_1' \, p_2' \cdots p_n' \tag{12}$$

any incongruent set of poles of $f(z)$. Then 5) may be written

$$a_1' + \cdots + a_n' \equiv p_1' + \cdots + p_n'. \tag{13}$$

For each a_r' must be congruent to some a_m, and no two of the points 11) are congruent to the same a_m, since then they would be congruent to each other, in which case 11) would not be an incongruent set. Thus

$$a_1' + \cdots + a_n' = a_1 + \cdots + a_n + \text{a period.}$$

Similarly

$$p_1' + \cdots + p_n' = p_1 + \cdots + p_2 + \text{a period.}$$

Thus 13) is a consequence of 5).

A similar remark holds for the relation 10). Here it is not necessary that the $z_1 \cdots z_n$ all lie in the same primitive parallelogram; they can be any set of incongruent points for which $f(z) = c$.

13. In case of an elliptic function $f(z)$ of order 2 Abel's relation enables us to solve the problem of finding all the values of z for which $f(z)$ takes on a given value as follows:

Let p_1, p_2 be incongruent poles of an elliptic function $f(z, \omega_1, \omega_2)$ of order 2. If f takes on the value c at $z = z_0$, then all the roots of

$$f(z) = c \tag{14}$$

are given by

$$z_0 + m_1\omega_1 + m_2\omega_2 \tag{15}$$

$$p_1 + p_2 - z_0 + m_1\omega_1 + m_2\omega_2,$$

where

$$m_1, m_2 = 0, \pm 1, \pm 2 \cdots$$

For if z_1 is the other value of z for which $f = c$ in the primitive parallelogram $P(\omega_1, \omega_2)$ in which z_0 lies, we have, by Abel's relation,

$$z_0 + z_1 - (p_1 + p_2) = \text{a period.}$$

Thus

$$z_1 \equiv p_1 + p_2 - z_0$$

as stated in 15).

Remark. In case $f(z)$ has a double pole p we replace $p_1 + p_2$ in 15) by $2p$.

14. Between the poles of an elliptic function of order 2 and the zeros of its derivative there exists a remarkable relation which is expressed in the following theorem :

If the elliptic function $f(z, \omega_1, \omega_2)$ *of order* 2 *has* p_1, p_2 *as incongruent simple poles, its derivative* $f'(z)$ *is of order* 4 *and admits the incongruent points*

$$z_1 = \frac{p_1 + p_2}{2}, \quad z_2 = z_1 + \frac{\omega_1}{2}, \quad z_3 = z_1 + \frac{\omega_2}{2}, \quad z_4 = z_1 + \frac{\omega_1 + \omega_2}{2} \tag{16}$$

as zeros.

That $f'(z)$ is of order 4 follows from 118, 4. That the points 16) are incongruent is easily seen. For suppose

$$z_2 \equiv z_3 = z_1 + \frac{\omega_2}{2}.$$

Then

$$z_2 - z_3 = \frac{\omega_1}{2} - \frac{\omega_2}{2}$$

is a period, which is not so, since ω_1, ω_2 form a primitive pair.

From 13 we have

$$f(p_1 + p_2 - z) = f(z).$$

Hence

$$f'(2z_1 - z) = -f'(z). \tag{17}$$

As z_1 is incongruent to p_1 or p_2, it is not a pole of $f'(z)$. Let us therefore set $z = z_1$ in 17). We get

$$f'(z_1) = -f'(z_1),$$

or,

$$2f'(z_1) = 0.$$

This shows that z_1 is a zero of $f'(z)$.

Again, set $z = z_2$ in 17); we get

$$f'(2z_1 - z_2) = -f'(z_2). \tag{18}$$

Now

$$2z_1 - z_2 = z_1 - \frac{\omega_1}{2} \equiv z_1 + \frac{\omega_1}{2} = z_2.$$

Thus 18) shows that $f'(z_2) = -f'(z_2)$ or

$$2f'(z_2) = 0.$$

Hence z_2 is a zero of $f'(z)$. Similarly we show the other points of 16) are zeros.

15. Similar reasoning applied to 17) gives:

If the elliptic function $f(z, \omega_1, \omega_2)$ of order 2 has the double pole p, its derivative is of order 3, and it admits the incongruent points

$$z_1 = p + \frac{\omega_1}{2} \quad , \quad z_2 = p + \frac{\omega_2}{2} \quad , \quad z_3 = p + \frac{\omega_1 + \omega_2}{2}, \tag{19}$$

as zeros.

Remark. The reader may ask: Why does not the same reasoning prove that p is also a zero of $f'(z)$? As we know that a pole of f is also a pole of $f'(z)$, our reasoning would then be quite fallacious, since p cannot be at once a zero and a pole of an analytic function.

The fault in such reasoning on p would lie in setting $z = p$ in 17). Since we know that $z = p$ is a pole of $f'(z)$, this latter is not defined at this point. The relation 17) holds for values of z near p but not at p.

16. An elliptic function of the second order having simple poles satisfies a very simple differential equation, as the following theorem shows:

If $f(z)$ is as in 14, *it satisfies*

$$\left(\frac{df}{dz}\right)^2 = C(f - e_1)(f - e_2)(f - e_3)(f - e_4), \tag{20}$$

where $f(z_m) = e_m$, $m = 1, 2, 3, 4$, and z_m are the numbers 16).

Let us first show that the e's are all different. For if $e_1 = e_2$, for example, then

$$f(z_1) = f(z_2),$$

and either

$$z_2 \equiv z_1,$$

or,

$$z_1 + z_2 \equiv p_1 + p_2, \qquad \text{by 13.}$$

Neither is true. Let us now set

$$g_m(z) = f(z) - e_m \quad , \quad m = 1, 2, 3, 4,$$

and

$$g(z) = g_1 g_2 g_3 g_4.$$

We show that g admits ω_1, ω_2 as periods and has the same zeros and poles, and to the same order as $(f'(z))^2 = h$. Thus h and g differ only by a constant factor by 9.

For in the first place f and g obviously have the same periods. Next g being the product of four factors of order 2, is of order 8.

As $g_m = 0$ for $z = z_m$, we see that g vanishes at the four points z_m. Each of these points is a zero of order 2 for $g(z)$. In fact

$$g'(z) = g_1' \cdot g_2 g_3 g_4 + g_2' \cdot g_1 g_3 g_4 + g_3' \cdot g_1 g_2 g_4 + g_4' \cdot g_1 g_2 g_3.$$

Let us set $z = z_1$ in this relation. The first term on the right vanishes, since the factor

$$g_1'(z_1) = f'(z_1) = 0 \qquad \text{by } 14.$$

The other three terms $= 0$, since each contains the factor g_1. Thus $g'(z_1) = 0$ and hence z_1 is a zero of $g(z)$ of order 2 at least. Hence $g(z)$ and $h(z)$ have the same zeros to the same order.

The poles of $g(z)$ are p_1, p_2 each of order 4. The same is true of $h(z)$. Hence by 9, $h = C \cdot g$.

17. When the elliptic function of order 2 has double poles, we have:

If $f(z)$ is as in 15, it satisfies the differential equation

$$\left(\frac{df}{dz}\right)^2 = C(f - e_1)(f - e_2)(f - e_3), \tag{21}$$

where $f(z_m) = e_m$, $m = 1, 2, 3$, and z_m are the points 19).

The proof is entirely analogous to that in 16.

18. *Application to the p function.* This function is defined by

$$p(z) = \frac{1}{z^2} + \sum \left\{ \frac{1}{(z - \bar{\omega})^2} - \frac{1}{\bar{\omega}^2} \right\}, \tag{22}$$

where

$$\bar{\omega} = 2 m_1 \omega_1 + 2 m_2 \omega_2.$$

Here $p = 0$ is a double pole, and the periods are $2\omega_1$, $2\omega_2$. Thus 19) becomes

$$z_1 = \omega_1 \quad , \quad z_2 = \omega_2 \quad , \quad z_3 = \omega_1 + \omega_2 \tag{23}$$

and

$$p(\omega_1) = e_1 \quad , \quad p(\omega_2) = e_2 \quad , \quad p(\omega_1 + \omega_2) = e_3. \tag{24}$$

Hence 21) shows that $p(z)$ satisfies the differential equation

$$\left(\frac{dp}{dz}\right)^2 = C(p - e_1)(p - e_2)(p - e_3). \tag{25}$$

From this follows that

$$z=\int\frac{dp}{\sqrt{C(p-e_1)(p-e_2)(p-e_3)}}. \tag{26}$$

Remark. The reader can now see why we have denoted the periods of $p(z)$ by $2\omega_1$, $2\omega_2$ instead of ω_1, ω_2. It is the half periods which enter in the definition of the e_1, e_2, e_3, and these quantities are of fundamental importance. Also in many other relations the half period figures. If we call the periods $2\omega_1$, $2\omega_2$, we avoid the fraction $\frac{1}{2}$ when using the half periods.

The reader will also note that the period of $\sin z$ is denoted by 2π.

19. It will greatly simplify our equations, as the reader will see later, if we introduce a half period ω_3 by means of the relation

$$\omega_1+\omega_2+\omega_3=0. \tag{27}$$

Then p being an even function we see that

$$p(\omega_1+\omega_2)=p(\omega_3)=e_3.$$

Thus the three equations 24) can be written

$$p(\omega_s)=e_s \qquad s=1,2,3. \tag{28}$$

Also the zeros of $p'(z)$ are

$$\equiv \omega_1 \quad , \quad \omega_2 \quad , \quad \omega_3. \tag{29}$$

166. Elliptic Functions expressed by $\sigma(z)$. 1. Let the elliptic function $f(z)$ of order n have $P(2\omega_1, 2\omega_2)$ as a primitive parallelogram of periods. Let its zeros be

$$a_1 \quad , \quad a_2 \quad , \quad a_3 \quad \cdots \tag{1}$$

arranged so that $|a_{n+1}|\geq|a_n|\neq 0$; let its poles be

$$b_1 \quad , \quad b_2 \quad , \quad b_3 \quad \cdots \tag{2}$$

arranged so that $|b_{n+1}|\geq|b_n|\neq 0$. Then by 140, 4, and 6,

$$f(z)=e^{T(z)}\frac{\Pi\left(1-\frac{z}{a_n}\right)e^{\frac{z}{a_n}+\frac{1}{2}\left(\frac{z}{a_n}\right)^2}}{\Pi\left(1-\frac{z}{b_n}\right)e^{\frac{z}{b_n}+\frac{1}{2}\left(\frac{z}{b_n}\right)^2}}, \tag{3}$$

since

$$\sum \frac{1}{|a_n|^3}, \quad \sum \frac{1}{|b_n|^3}$$

converge.

To determine T let us observe that

$$g(z) = \frac{d^2 \log f(z)}{dz^2} \tag{4}$$

also admits $2\omega_1$, $2\omega_2$ as periods. Thus

$$g(z) = T''(z) - \sum \left\{ \frac{1}{(z-a_n)^2} - \frac{1}{a_n^2} \right\} + \sum \left\{ \frac{1}{(z-b_n)^2} - \frac{1}{b_n^2} \right\}$$

is double periodic.

Now each Σ here admits $2\omega_1$, $2\omega_2$ as periods. Hence

$$T''(z) = g(z) + \sum_a - \sum_b$$

admits $2\omega_1$, $2\omega_2$ as periods. As T is an integral function, so is T''. But then

$$T''(z) = 2c, \quad \text{a constant.}$$

Hence

$$T = a + bz + cz^2.$$

The infinite products entering 3) can be expressed as the product of m simpler products as follows: Let

$$\begin{matrix} c_1, & c_2 & \cdots c_m \\ p_1, & p_2 & \cdots p_m \end{matrix} \tag{5}$$

be the zeros and poles which fall in the parallelogram P. Let

$$c_{11}, \quad c_{12}, \quad c_{13} \quad \cdots \tag{6}$$

be all points 1) which are $\equiv c_1$. Let

$$p_{11}, \quad p_{12}, \quad p_{13} \quad \cdots \tag{7}$$

be all the points 2) which are $\equiv p_1$. If we treat the other points in 5) in a similar manner, all the zeros 1) will be thrown into m classes, the points in each class being $\equiv$ some zero in 5). A similar remark applies to the poles 2).

Let us therefore set

$$t(z, c_1) = \Pi\left(1 - \frac{z}{c_{1n}}\right) e^{\frac{z}{c_{1n}} + \frac{1}{2}\left(\frac{z}{c_{1n}}\right)^2}. \tag{8}$$

Then the numerator and denominator in 3) are each the product of m factors of the type 8). We have, in fact,

$$f(z) = e^{a+bz+cz^2} \frac{t(z, c_1)t(z, c_2) \cdots t(z, c_m)}{t(z, p_1)t(z, p_2) \cdots t(z, p_m)}. \tag{9}$$

2. The simplest t function is obtained by taking c_1 at the origin. It is denoted by $\sigma(z)$ and is called Weierstrass' *sigma function.* Thus

$$\sigma(z) = z\Pi\left(1 - \frac{z}{\omega}\right)e^{\frac{z}{\omega}+\frac{1}{2}\left(\frac{z}{\omega}\right)^2}, \tag{10}$$

where $\omega = 2\,m_1\omega_1 + 2\,m_2\omega_2 \qquad m_1 = m_2 = 0$ excluded.

By 140, the zeros of $\sigma(z)$ are $z = 0$ and the points ω. They are of order 1. By using the σ function the formula 9) can be much simplified. To show this we make use of the fact that

$$-\frac{d^2 \log \sigma(z)}{dz^2} = \frac{1}{z^2} + \sum \left\{ \frac{1}{(z-\omega)^2} - \frac{1}{\omega^2} \right\} = p(z). \tag{11}$$

From 10) we have

$$\log \sigma(z) = \log z + \sum \left\{ \log\left(1 - \frac{z}{\omega}\right) + \frac{z}{\omega} + \frac{1}{2}\left(\frac{z}{\omega}\right)^2 \right\}. \tag{12}$$

The derivative of this function is so important that it has a special symbol; we set with Weierstrass

$$\zeta(z) = \frac{d \log \sigma(z)}{dz} = \frac{\sigma'(z)}{\sigma(z)}. \tag{13}$$

Thus

$$\zeta(z) = \frac{1}{z} + \Sigma \left\{ \frac{1}{z-\omega} + \frac{1}{\omega} + \frac{z}{\omega^2} \right\}. \tag{14}$$

Hence finally

$$\zeta'(z) = -p(z).$$

Let us note that $\sigma(z)$ is an odd function.

For replacing z by $-z$ in the Π in 10) it becomes

$$\Pi\left(1 + \frac{z}{\omega}\right)e^{-\frac{z}{\omega}+\frac{1}{2}\left(\frac{z}{\omega}\right)^2}. \tag{15}$$

As ω and $-\omega$ give the same network of points, we can replace ω by $-\omega$ in 15); but then 15) goes back to Π in 10). Thus this product Π is an even function. As $\sigma = z\Pi$ we see σ is odd.

As $\sigma'(z)$ is now seen to be even, the definition of $\zeta(z)$ given in 13) shows that ζ is also an odd function.

We have introduced these relations at this point in order to see how $\sigma(z)$ behaves when z is replaced by

$$z+2\,\omega_1 \quad \text{or} \quad z+2\,\omega_2.$$

We start with the relation

$$p(z+2\,\omega_1)=p(z).$$

Integrating gives

$$\zeta(z+2\,\omega_1)=\zeta(z)+C.$$

To determine the constant C, we set $z=-\omega_1$; we get

$$\zeta(\omega_1)=\zeta(-\omega_1)+C=-\zeta(\omega_1)+C,$$

since ζ is an odd function. Hence

$$C=2\,\zeta(\omega_1).$$

Let us set for brevity

$$\eta_1=\zeta(\omega_1) \quad , \quad \eta_2=\zeta(\omega_2). \tag{16}$$

These two constants are of constant occurrence. Then we have

$$\begin{aligned}\zeta(z+2\,\omega_1)&=\zeta(z)+2\,\eta_1,\\ \zeta(z+2\,\omega_2)&=\zeta(z)+2\,\eta_2.\end{aligned} \tag{17}$$

Integrating the first equation of 17), we get

$$\log\sigma(z+2\,\omega_1)=\log\sigma(z)+2\,\eta_1 z+C$$

or

$$\sigma(z+2\,\omega_1)=ce^{2\eta_1 z}\sigma(z).$$

To determine c we set $z=-\omega_1$, and remember that $\sigma(z)$ is an odd function; we get

$$\sigma(\omega_1)=ce^{-2\omega_1\eta_1}\,\sigma(-\omega_1)=-ce^{-2\omega_1\eta_1}\,\sigma(\omega_1).$$

Hence

$$c=-e^{2\omega_1\eta_1}.$$

Thus

$$\begin{aligned}\sigma(z+2\,\omega_1)&=-e^{2\eta_1(z+\omega_1)}\sigma(z),\\ \sigma(z+2\,\omega_2)&=-e^{2\eta_2(z+\omega_2)}\sigma(z).\end{aligned} \tag{18}$$

3. Using the relations 18), we can now simplify 9) as follows. We saw from Abel's relation that

$$c_1+c_2+\cdots+c_m-(p_1+p_2+\cdots+p_m)=\text{a period}. \tag{19}$$

Let us therefore pick out a set of incongruent zeros $a_1, a_2 \cdots a_m$ and a set of incongruent poles $b_1, \cdots b_m$ so that

$$a_1 + a_2 + \cdots + a_m = b_1 + b_2 + \cdots + b_m. \tag{20}$$

From 19) this can be done in an infinite variety of ways. Let us now form the function

$$g(z) = \frac{\sigma(z-a_1)\cdots\sigma(z-a_m)}{\sigma(z-b_1)\cdots\sigma(z-b_m)}. \tag{21}$$

We show that g admits $2\,\omega_1$, $2\,\omega_2$ as periods. For from 18)

$$g(z+2\,\omega_1) = \frac{e^{2\eta_1\Sigma(z-a_n+\omega_1)}\,\Pi\sigma(z-a_n)}{e^{2\eta_1\Sigma(z-b_n+\omega_1)}\,\Pi\sigma(z-b_n)} \qquad n = 1,\ 2\cdots m$$

$$= \frac{e^{2\eta_1\Sigma b_n}}{e^{2\eta_1\Sigma a_n}}\,g(z).$$

But by 20)

$$\Sigma a_n = \Sigma b_n.$$

Thus

$$g(z+2\,\omega_1) = g(z).$$

Similarly

$$g(z+2\,\omega_2) = g(z).$$

On the other hand, the zeros and poles of 21) are the same as those of $f(z)$, and to the same order. Thus by 165, 9 f and g differ only by a constant factor. Hence the theorem:

Let $f(z)$ be an elliptic function of order m having $2\,\omega_1$, $2\,\omega_2$ as a primitive pair of periods. Let $a_1, \cdots a_m$; $b_1, \cdots b_m$ be a set of incongruent zeros and poles such that $\Sigma a_n = \Sigma b_n$. Then

$$f(z) = C\frac{\sigma(z-a_1)\cdots\sigma(z-a_m)}{\sigma(z-b_1)\cdots\sigma(z-b_m)}. \tag{22}$$

4. From this we conclude that elliptic functions exist having assigned zeros and poles provided:

1° the sum of the orders of the zeros in any parallelogram of periods equals the sum of the orders of its poles, and

2° the zeros and poles satisfy Abel's relation.

In fact these functions are all given by 22).

5. The relation 22) shows that every elliptic function can be expressed by means of the σ function, which thus dominates the theory of elliptic functions.

It is interesting to note how naturally we have been led to consider this function. By Weierstrass' factor theorem, 140, 4, 6, every elliptic function must have the form 3). The products in 3) can be decomposed into simpler products, each vanishing for one of the m classes of zeros or poles of the given function. Of all these simple products 9) the simplest is the product 10). It is an integral transcendental function like $\sin z$, and as the circular functions can be built up on $\sin z$ as a fundamental function, so the elliptic functions can be expressed by means of this new transcendent. It is natural to denote it by $\sigma(z)$ where σ reminds one of the first letter s of sine.

The first logarithmic derivative of $\sin z$ gives $\cot z$ which has, as poles of order 1, the zeros of $\sin z$. The first logarithmic derivative of $\sigma(z)$ gives a function which Weierstrass has denoted by $\zeta(z)$. This also has, as poles of order 1, the zeros of $\sigma(z)$. It is not periodic since

$$\zeta(z + 2\,\omega_i) = \zeta(z) + 2\,\eta_i \qquad i = 1,\ 2.$$

Its first derivative is periodic, and this leads to the p-function

$$p(z) = -\frac{d\zeta}{dz}.$$

The minus sign is inserted so that the term $\frac{1}{z^2}$ in the expression 164, 7) has a positive sign. The letter p reminds one that the most essential characteristic of this function is its *double periodicity*.

6. If in 10), 11), 14), defining the functions σ, ζ, p, we replace

$$z\ ,\quad \omega_1\ ,\quad \omega_2$$

by

$$\mu z\ ,\quad \mu\omega_1\ ,\quad \mu\omega_2,$$

we see that

$$\sigma(\mu z, \mu\omega_1, \mu\omega_2) = \mu\sigma(z, \omega_1, \omega_2),$$
$$\zeta(\mu z, \mu\omega_1, \mu\omega_2) = \frac{1}{\mu}\zeta(z, \omega_1, \omega_2), \qquad (23$$
$$p(\mu z, \mu\omega_1, \mu\omega_2) = \frac{1}{\mu^2}p(z, \omega_1, \omega_2),$$

which shows that σ, ζ, p are *homogeneous* functions of z, ω_1, ω_2 of degrees 1, -1, -2 respectively. This property is useful at times.

The relations 16) show that

$$\eta_r(\mu\omega_1, \mu\omega_2) = \frac{1}{\mu}\eta_r(\omega_1, \omega_2) \qquad r = 1, 2. \tag{24}$$

Since $e_s = p(\omega_s)$ we see that

$$e_s(\mu\omega_1, \mu\omega_2) = \frac{1}{\mu^2}e_s(\omega_1, \omega_2) \qquad s = 1, 2, 3. \tag{25}$$

167. Elliptic Functions expressed by $p(z)$, $p'(z)$. 1. We suppose first that the elliptic function $f(z)$ is an even function of order $2s$. Then if $z = a$ is a zero or a pole of $f(z)$, so is $z = -a$. Let a set of incongruent zeros and poles be

$$\pm a_1, \quad \pm a_2, \quad \cdots; \quad \pm b_1, \quad \pm b_2, \quad \cdots$$

of orders

$$m_1, \quad m_2, \quad \cdots; \quad n_1, \quad n_2, \quad \cdots$$

so that

$$2m_1 + 2m_2 + \cdots = 2n_1 + 2n_2 + \cdots = 2s.$$

We consider first the case that none of these zeros and poles is $\equiv 0$. Let $p(z)$ have the same periods as $f(z)$, we consider the function

$$g(z) = \frac{(pz - pa_1)^{m_1}(pz - pa_2)^{m_2}\cdots}{(pz - pb_1)^{n_1}(pz - pb_2)^{n_2}\cdots}.$$

It has the same zeros and poles and to the same orders as $f(z)$. As g admits the same periods as f, we see that it can differ from $f(z)$ only by a constant factor.

Next let us suppose that $z = 0$ is a zero of $f(z)$. Since f is an even function by hypothesis, the order of this zero must be an even integer, say $2m$. Suppose now

$$0, \quad \pm a_1, \quad \pm a_2 \quad \cdots$$

form a set of incongruent zeros of orders

$$2m, \quad m_1, \quad m_2 \quad \cdots$$

respectively. Then as before

$$2m + 2m_1 + 2m_2 + \cdots = 2s.$$

Let us now form the same function g as before, where no factor, however, corresponds to $z = 0$. The numerator is of degree $s - 1$ in p and the denominator of degree s. As $z = 0$ is a pole of order

2 for $p(z)$, it follows that $z=0$ is a zero of order $2m$ for $g(z)$. Thus as before g has the same zeros and poles and to the same orders as $f(z)$. It can differ from f only by a constant factor. We get the same result if $z=0$ is a pole of $f(z)$. Thus in all cases when $f(z)$ is an even function,

$$f(z) = C\frac{(pz-pa_1)^{m_1}(pz-pa_2)^{m_2}\cdots}{(pz-pb_1)^{n_1}(pz-pb_2)^{n_2}\cdots}, \tag{1}$$

where we use a set of incongruent zeros and poles, always omitting that one which may be $\equiv 0$.

Case 2. *$f(z)$ is not even.* Let us form

$$g(z) = \frac{f(z)+f(-z)}{2},$$

$$h(z) = \frac{f(z)-f(-z)}{2\,p'(z)},$$

which give

$$f(z) = g(z) + h(z)\,p'(z).$$

As g and h are even functions, they may be expressed as in Case 1. We have thus proved the theorem:

Any elliptic function is a rational function of $p(z)$, $p'(z)$.

168. Elliptic Functions expressed by $\zeta(z)$. 1. In 166, 167 we have learned two ways of expressing an elliptic function. Both require a knowledge of the zeros and poles of the function $f(z)$. When these are not readily found, it is convenient to have another representation. Such is the following, which depends on the knowledge of the characteristic at each of the poles.

We will suppose, therefore, that $a, b, \cdots$ are the poles of $f(z)$ in a primitive parallelogram of periods, and that its characteristics at these points are

$$\frac{A_\lambda}{(z-a)_\lambda} + \cdots + \frac{A_1}{z-a} \qquad \text{for } z=a$$

$$\frac{B_\mu}{(z-b)^\mu} + \cdots + \frac{B_1}{z-b} \qquad \text{for } z=b \tag{1}$$

$$\cdots\cdots\cdots\cdots\cdots$$

We now construct a ζ function on the periods $2\,\omega_1$, $2\,\omega_2$ of $f(z)$ and then the function

$$g(z)=A_1\zeta(z-a)-A_2\zeta'(z-a)+\frac{A_3}{2!}\zeta''(z-a)+\cdots$$
$$+\frac{(-1)^{\lambda-1}}{(\lambda-1)!}A_\lambda\zeta^{(\lambda-1)}(z-a)+B_1\zeta(z-b)-B_2\zeta'(z-b)$$
$$+\frac{B_2}{2!}\zeta''(z-b)+\cdots+\frac{(-1)^{\mu-1}}{(\mu-1)!}B_\mu\zeta^{(\mu-1)}(z-b)+\cdots \qquad (2$$

As

$$\zeta'(z)=-p(z)\quad,\quad \zeta''(z)=-p'(z)\quad\cdots$$

all the terms in the 2d, 3d ⋯ columns on the right of 2) are periodic.

On the other hand,

$$\zeta(z+2\,\omega_1)=\zeta(z)+2\,\eta_1,\ \text{etc.}$$

Thus

$$g(z+2\,\omega_1)=2\,\eta_1(A_1+B_1+\cdots)+g(z).$$

But A_1, B_1 ⋯ are the residues of $f(z)$ in a parallelogram of periods. Their sum is 0 by 165, 3. Thus

$$g(z+2\,\omega_1)=g(z).$$

A similar relation holds for $2\,\omega_2$. Hence g also admits $2\,\omega_1$, $2\,\omega_2$ as periods.

Let us now show that g has at each pole as $z=a$ the same characteristic as f. For from 166, 14), we have obviously

$$\zeta(z-a)=\frac{1}{z-a}+h(z),$$

where h is regular at $z=a$. Hence

$$\zeta'(z-a)=-\frac{1}{(z-a)^2}+h'(z),$$

$$\zeta^{(\lambda-1)}(z-a)=\frac{(-1)^{\lambda-1}(\lambda-1)!}{(z-a)^\lambda}+h^{(\lambda-1)}(z).$$

Thus the characteristic of $g(z)$ at $z=a$ is given by the first row in 2). Thus f and g have the same characteristic at $z=a$. The same is true at the other poles. Thus by 165, 10

$$f(z)=g(z)+\text{constant}. \qquad (3$$

2. From the foregoing we have:

Any elliptic function can be expressed in terms of $\zeta(z)$ *and its derivatives.*

169. Development of σ, ζ, p in Power Series. 1. We have now seen that the three functions

$$\sigma(z)=z\Pi\left(1-\frac{z}{\omega}\right)e^{\frac{z}{\omega}+\frac{1}{2}\left(\frac{z}{\omega}\right)^2}, \tag{1}$$

$$\zeta(z)=\frac{1}{z}+\sum\left\{\frac{1}{z-\omega}+\frac{1}{\omega}+\frac{z}{\omega^2}\right\}, \tag{2}$$

$$p(z)=\frac{1}{z^2}+\sum\left\{\frac{1}{(z-\omega)^2}-\frac{1}{\omega^2}\right\}, \tag{3}$$

where $\omega=2\,m_1\omega_1+2\,m_2\omega_2 \qquad m_1=m_2=0$ excluded (4

may be taken as the basis of a theory of the elliptic functions. We propose in the articles which immediately follow to develop some of the properties of these three functions.

We begin by developing them in a power series about $z=0$. Since

$$p(z)-\frac{1}{z^2}=\phi(z)$$

is regular at $z=0$ it can be developed in Taylor's series

$$\phi(z)=\phi(0)+z\phi'(0)+\frac{z^2}{2!}\phi''(0)+\cdots$$

which is valid within a circle $\mathfrak{K}$ which passes through the nearest point ω in 4),

Now $$\phi^{(n)}(z)=(-1)^n(n+1)!\sum\frac{1}{(z-\omega)^{n+2}}.$$

Hence $$\frac{1}{n!}\phi^{(n)}(0)=(n+1)\sum\frac{1}{\omega^{n+2}}.$$

Let us therefore set $$s_n=\sum\frac{1}{\omega^{n+2}}. \tag{5}$$

We note that when n is odd, $s_n=0$.

For to each $2\,m_1\omega_1+2\,m_2\omega_2$ in s_n there corresponds a

$$-\,2\,m_1\omega_1-2\,m_2\omega_2.$$

When n is odd, the two corresponding terms in s_n will have opposite signs and cancel each other. We thus have

$$p(z)=\frac{1}{z^2}+3\,s_2z^2+5\,s_4z^4+7\,s_6z^6+\cdots \tag{6}$$

Integrating, we have

$$\zeta(z)=\frac{1}{z}-s_2z^3-s_4z^5-\cdots \tag{7}$$

Integrating again gives

$$\log\sigma(z)=\log z-\tfrac{1}{4}\,s_2z^4-\tfrac{1}{6}\,s_4z^6-\cdots \tag{8}$$

Hence

$$\sigma(z)=z-\tfrac{1}{4}\,s_2z^5-\tfrac{1}{6}\,s_4z^7-\tfrac{1}{8}\,s_6z^9-\cdots \tag{9}$$

2. *Differential Equation satisfied by $p(z)$.* Further coefficients in the developments 6), 7), 9) can be obtained by a recurrent relation which we deduce from a differential equation. In fact, we saw in 165, 25) that p satisfies a very simple differential equation which we now proceed to find.

From 6) we obtain, on differentiation and slightly changing the notation,

$$p'(z)=-\frac{2}{z^3}+6\,c_2z+20\,c_3z^3+\cdots$$

This squared gives

$$p'(z)^2=\frac{4}{z^6}-24\,c_2\frac{1}{z^2}-80\,c_3+\cdots$$

Also cubing the series 6) gives

$$p(z)^3=\frac{1}{z^6}+9\,c_2\frac{1}{z^2}+15\,c_3+\cdots$$

Let us now set

$$g_2=60\,c_2=60\sum\frac{1}{\omega^4}\quad,\quad g_3=140\,c_3=140\sum\frac{1}{\omega^6}. \tag{10}$$

These are called the *invariants.* From the foregoing equations we get on adding

$$p'(z)^2-4\,p(z)^3+g_2p(z)+g_3=z(a_1+a_2z+\cdots)$$

It thus admits $2\omega_1$, $2\omega_2$ and yet admits no pole in a parallelogram of periods. It is therefore a constant. Since it vanishes for $z = 0$, we have the desired differential equation

$$p'(z)^2 = 4\,p(z)^3 - g_2 p(z) - g_3. \qquad (11$$

From this we get on differentiating

$$p'' = 6\,p^2 - \tfrac{1}{2}\,g_2. \qquad (12$$

3. We can now get the desired *recursion formula*. Let us write

$$p(z) = \frac{1}{z^2} + a_1 z^2 + a_2 z^4 + a_3 z^6 + \cdots$$

and put this in 12). Equating the coefficients of z^{2n-2} on each side of the resulting equation gives

$$2\,n(2\,n-1)\,a_n = 6\,(a_n + a_1 a_{n-2} + \cdots + a_{n-2}a_1 + a_n).$$

Hence

$$a_n = \frac{3}{n\,(2\,n-1)-6}\{a_1 a_{n-2} + \cdots + a_{n-2}a_1\}. \qquad (13$$

This shows that a_3, a_4, $a_5 \cdots$ can be expressed as integral rational functions of a_1, a_3, that is of g_2, g_3, since

$$a_1 = \tfrac{1}{20}\,g_2 \quad , \quad a_2 = \tfrac{1}{28}\,g_3.$$

For $n = 3$ we get from 13)

$$a_3 = \tfrac{3}{9}\,a_1^2 = \tfrac{1}{1200}\,g_2^2.$$

For $n = 4$,

$$a_4 = \tfrac{3}{22}\,(a_1 a_2 + a_2 a_1) = \tfrac{3}{6160}\,g_2 g_3.$$

In this way we may continue. Thus we find

$$\sigma(z) = z + * - \frac{g_2 z^5}{2^4 \cdot 3 \cdot 5} - \frac{g_3 z^7}{2^3 \cdot 3 \cdot 5 \cdot 7} - \frac{g_2^2 z^9}{2^9 \cdot 3^2 \cdot 5 \cdot 7} - \cdots \qquad (14$$

$$\zeta(z) = \frac{1}{z} + * - \frac{g_2 z^3}{2^2 \cdot 3 \cdot 5} - \frac{g_3 z^5}{2^2 \cdot 5 \cdot 7} - \frac{g_2^2 \cdot z^7}{2^4 \cdot 3 \cdot 5^2 \cdot 7} - \cdots \qquad (15$$

$$p(z) = \frac{1}{z^2} + * + \frac{g_2 z^2}{2^2 \cdot 5} + \frac{g_3 z^4}{2^2 \cdot 7} + \frac{g_2^2 z^6}{2^4 \cdot 3 \cdot 5^2} + \cdots \qquad (16$$

$$p'(z) = -\frac{2}{z^3} + * + \frac{g_2 z}{2 \cdot 5} + \frac{g_3 z^3}{7} + \frac{g_2^2 z^5}{2^3 \cdot 5^2} + \cdots \qquad (17$$

From the definition of g_2, g_3 we see that

$$g_2(\mu\omega_1, \mu\omega_2) = \frac{1}{\mu^4} g_2(\omega_1, \omega_2),$$
$$g_3(\mu\omega_1, \mu\omega_2) = \frac{1}{\mu^6} g_3(\omega_1, \omega_2). \quad (18$$

170. Addition Formulæ. 1. We have seen how important are the addition theorems

$$e^{u+v} = e^u e^v$$
$$\sin(u+v) = \sin u \cos v + \cos u \sin v, \text{ etc.}$$

for the elementary transcendental functions. We wish to establish analogous formulæ for the new functions, viz.:

$$\frac{\sigma(u+v)\,\sigma(u-v)}{\sigma^2 u \cdot \sigma^2 v} = p(v) - p(u), \quad (1$$

$$\zeta(u+v) = \zeta(u) + \zeta(v) + \frac{1}{2}\left(\frac{p'u - p'v}{pu - pv}\right), \quad (2$$

$$p(u+v) = pu - \frac{1}{2}\frac{d}{du}\left(\frac{p'u - p'v}{pu - pv}\right). \quad (3$$

These relations are fundamental and of constant service. We begin by proving 1).

Regarding u as a constant let us look at the zeros and poles of

$$f(v) = p(v) - p(u)$$

in the parallelogram of periods $P(2\omega_1, 2\omega_2)$. Obviously, $f = 0$ for $v = u$, and hence for $v \equiv u$. As $p(-u) = p(u)$, it follows that $f = 0$ at $v = -u$, and hence at $v \equiv -u$. As f is of order 2, it can vanish only twice in P. Thus all the zeros of $f(v)$ are $\equiv \pm u$. The poles of $f(v)$ are $v \equiv 0$, and these are of order 2.

Thus the two functions of v, on the two sides of 1), have the same zeros, poles, and periods. They can only differ by a constant factor C.

To determine this we develop both sides about $v = 0$ and compare the coefficient of $\frac{1}{v^2}$. Now by 169, 14),

$$\sigma(v) = v + av^5 + \cdots$$

Hence

$$\sigma^2 v = v^2 + \cdots$$

Thus
$$\frac{1}{\sigma^2 u\, \sigma^2 v} = \frac{1}{\sigma^2 u} \cdot \frac{1}{v^2} + \cdots$$

To develop $\sigma(u+v)$, $\sigma(u-v)$ about $v=0$, we set

$$g(v) = \sigma(u+v) = g(0) + vg'(0) + \cdots$$
$$= \sigma(u) + v\sigma'(u) + \cdots$$

Similarly
$$\sigma(u-v) = \sigma(u) - v\sigma'(u) + \cdots$$

Thus
$$\sigma(u+v)\,\sigma(u-v) = \sigma^2 u + \cdots$$

Thus the left side of 1) has 1 as coefficient of $\frac{1}{v^2}$. The same is true of the right side. Hence $C=1$ and 1) is established.

2. To prove 2) we take the logarithmic derivative of 1) with respect to v, and get

$$\zeta(u+v) - \zeta(u-v) - 2\,\zeta(v) = \frac{p'v}{pv - pu}.$$

But this relation holds for u as well as for v. Thus interchanging u, v gives

$$\zeta(u+v) + \zeta(u-v) - 2\,\zeta(u) = -\frac{p'u}{pv - pu}.$$

Adding and dividing by 2 gives 2).

3. To prove 3) we need only take the derivative of 2) with respect to u.

4. Another form of the addition theorem for the p function is the following:

$$p(u+v) + p(u) + p(v) = \tfrac{1}{4}\left(\frac{p'u - p'v}{pu - pv}\right)^2. \tag{4}$$

To prove this we square 2), getting

$$\{\zeta(u+v) - \zeta(u) - \zeta(v)\}^2 = \tfrac{1}{4}\left(\frac{p'u - p'v}{pu - pv}\right). \tag{5}$$

Let us denote the left side of this relation by $g(u)$, regarding v as a constant. The right side of 5) shows that $g(u)$ is an elliptic function.

We propose now to express g by means of ζ and its derivatives, using 168. To this end we must find the characteristics of $g(u)$ about its poles. These are $\equiv 0$ and $-v$, each pole being of order **2**.

Developing about $u = 0$ we have

$$\zeta(u) = \frac{1}{u} + au^3 + \cdots$$

$$\zeta(u+v) = \zeta(v) + u\zeta'(v) + \cdots$$

Hence

$$\zeta(u+v) - \zeta(u) - \zeta(v) = \frac{-1}{u} + u\zeta'(v) + \cdots$$

and thus

$$g(u) = \frac{1}{u^2} - 2\,\zeta'(v) + \cdots \tag{6}$$

Hence in this case the coefficients A in 168, 1) are

$$A_1 = 0 \quad , \quad A_2 = 1,$$

Let us now develop about the point $u = -v$. We have

$$\zeta(u+v) = \frac{1}{u+v} + a(u+v)^3 + \cdots$$

$$\zeta(u) = \zeta\{-v + (u+v)\} = \zeta(-v) + (u+v)\zeta'(-v) + \cdots$$
$$= -\zeta(v) + (u+v)\zeta'(v) + \cdots$$

Hence

$$\zeta(u+v) - \zeta(u) - \zeta(v) = \frac{1}{u+v} - (u+v)\zeta'(v) + \cdots$$

Thus

$$g(u) = \frac{1}{(u+v)^2} - 2\,\zeta'(v) + \cdots$$

The coefficients B in 168, 1) are here

$$B_1 = 0 \quad , \quad B_2 = 1.$$

Putting these values of A_1, A_2, B_1, B_2, in 168, 2) gives

$$g(u) = -\zeta'(u) - \zeta'(u+v) + C, \text{ or}$$

$$\{\zeta(u+v) - \zeta(u) - \zeta(v)\}^2 = p(u) + p(u+v) + C. \tag{7}$$

To determine the constant C, let us equate the absolute terms of the developments of both sides about $u = 0$. From 6) this term on the left side of 7) is $2\,p(v)$.

On the right side of 7) it is $p(v) + C$. Equating these, we get

$$C = p(v).$$

This in 7) gives 4).

171. The ω_i, η_i, e_i and g_2, g_3. 1. We saw in 169, 11) that

$$p'(z)^2 = 4\,p^3(z) - g_2 p(z) - g_3. \tag{1}$$

On the other hand we saw in 165, 18, that $p'(z) = 0$ for $z = \omega_1$, ω_2, ω_3. The three roots of the cubic

$$4\,p^3 - g_2 p - g_3 = 0 \tag{2}$$

are therefore $$e_i = p(\omega_i) \qquad i = 1, 2, 3.$$

Thus we can write 1)

$$p'(z)^2 = 4(pz - e_1)(pz - e_2)(pz - e_3), \tag{3}$$

which shows that the constant $C = 4$ in 165, 25).

Since the coefficient of p^2 in 2) is 0, we have

$$e_1 + e_2 + e_3 = 0. \tag{4}$$

The other coefficients of 4) give

$$e_1e_2 + e_1e_3 + e_2e_3 = -\tfrac{1}{4}g_2 \quad , \quad e_1e_2e_3 = \tfrac{1}{4}g_3. \tag{5}$$

To complete the symmetry let us introduce η_3 defined by

$$\eta_1 + \eta_2 + \eta_3 = 0. \tag{6}$$

We show that also $$\eta_3 = \zeta(\omega_3). \tag{7}$$

Since ζ is an odd function,

$$\begin{aligned}\zeta(\omega_3) &= \zeta(-\omega_1 - \omega_2) = -\zeta(\omega_1 + \omega_2)\\ &= -\zeta(\omega_1) - \zeta(\omega_2) \quad \text{by 170, 2)}\\ &= -\eta_1 - \eta_2 = \eta_3 \quad , \quad \text{by 6)},\end{aligned}$$

and this establishes 7).

2. Between the ω_1, η_i exists a relation due to *Legendre*. Let us suppose that we pass from $a + \omega_1$ to $a + \omega_2$ by a positive rotation of angle $< \pi$ as in the figure. Then *Legendre's relation* states that

$$\eta_1\omega_2 - \eta_2\omega_1 = \frac{\pi i}{2}. \tag{8}$$

Let us take the parallelogram P so that $z = 0$ lies within it. Then

$$\frac{1}{2\,\pi i}\int_P \zeta(z)dz = \sum_P \text{Res}\,\zeta.$$

But ζ has only one pole in P, viz. $z=0$, and by 169, 2) its residue is 1. Thus

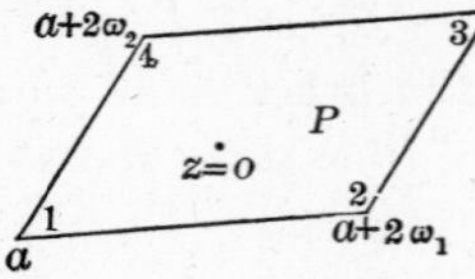

$$\int_P \zeta dz = 2\pi i. \tag{9}$$

Now

$$\int_{43} \zeta(z)dz = \int_{12} \zeta(z+2\,\omega_2)dz$$

$$= \int_{12} \{\zeta(z) + 2\,\eta_2\}dz \quad , \quad \text{by 166, 17)},$$

$$= \int_{12} \zeta dz + 4\,\eta_2\omega_1.$$

Similarly

$$\int_{23} \zeta(z)dz = \int_{14} \zeta dz + 4\,\eta_1\omega_2.$$

Hence

$$\int_P \zeta dz = \int_{12} + \int_{23} + \int_{34} + \int_{41}$$

$$= -4\,\eta_2\omega_1 + 4\,\eta_1\omega_2.$$

Putting this in 9) gives 8).

By using 6) and $\omega_1 + \omega_2 + \omega_3 = 0$ we have for any two indices

$$r,\ s = 1,\ 2,\ 3,$$

$$\eta_r\omega_s - \eta_s\omega_r = \epsilon\frac{\pi i}{2}, \tag{10}$$

where $\epsilon = 1$ when we pass from ω_r to ω_s by a positive rotation of angle $< \pi$; otherwise $\epsilon = -1$.

3. The relations 166, 17), 18) may be at once extended to ω_3 and give for $r = 1, 2, 3$,

$$\sigma(z + 2\,\omega_r) = -\,e^{2\eta_r(z+\omega_r)}\sigma(z), \tag{11}$$

$$\zeta(z + 2\,\omega_r) = \zeta(z) + 2\,\eta_r. \tag{12}$$

172. The Co-sigmas $\sigma_r(z)$. 1. We introduce now three new sigma functions

$$\sigma_r(z) = e^{-\eta_r z}\frac{\sigma(z+\omega_r)}{\sigma(\omega_r)} \quad , \quad r = 1, 2, 3. \tag{1}$$

This we can transform as follows. From

$$\sigma(u + 2\,\omega_r) = -\,e^{2\eta_r(u+\omega_r)}\sigma(u)$$

we have, setting $u = -z - \omega_r$,

$$\sigma(-z + \omega_r) = e^{-2\eta_r z}\sigma(z + \omega_r).$$

This in 1) gives

$$\sigma_r(z) = \frac{e^{\eta_r z}\sigma(\omega_r - z)}{\sigma(\omega_r)}. \tag{2}$$

Replacing z by $-z$ in 1) and using 2), we get

$$\sigma_r(-z) = \sigma_r(z) \quad , \quad \sigma_r(0) = 1. \tag{3}$$

We find without trouble

$$\sigma_r(z + 2\,\omega_r) = -\,e^{2\eta_r(z+\omega_r)}\sigma_r(z), \tag{4}$$

$$\sigma_r(z + 2\,\omega_s) = e^{2\eta_s(z+\omega_s)}\sigma_r(z), \tag{5}$$

$$\sigma(z \pm \omega_r) = \pm\, e^{\pm\eta_r z}\sigma(\omega_r)\sigma_r(z), \tag{6}$$

$$\sigma_r(z \pm \omega_r) = \mp\, e^{\eta_r(\omega_r \pm z)}\frac{\sigma(z)}{\sigma\omega_r}, \tag{7}$$

$$\sigma_r(z \pm \omega_s) = -\frac{\sigma\omega_t}{\sigma\omega_r}\, e^{\pm\eta_s z - \eta_r\omega_s}\sigma_t(z), \tag{8}$$

where r, s, t are the integers 1, 2, 3 in any order.

For example let us prove 7) for the + sign. From 1) we have

$$\sigma_r(z + \omega_r) = e^{-\eta_r(z+\omega_r)}\frac{\sigma(z + 2\,\omega_r)}{\sigma\omega_r},$$

or using 171, 11),

$$= -\,e^{-\eta_r(z+\omega_r)}\,e^{2\eta_r(z+\omega_r)}\frac{\sigma(z)}{\sigma\omega_r}$$

$$= -\,e^{\eta_r(z+\omega_r)}\frac{\sigma(z)}{\sigma\omega_r},$$

which is 7).

2. In 1) let us set $z = \omega_s$, then

$$\sigma_r\omega_s = -\,e^{-\eta_r\omega_s}\frac{\sigma\omega_t}{\sigma\omega_r}, \tag{9}$$

since $\sigma(\omega_r + \omega_s) = \sigma(-\omega_t) = -\sigma\omega_t$. Here as usual r, s, t are 1, 2, 3 in any order.

Setting $z = \omega_r$ in 2) gives

$$\sigma_r(\omega_r) = 0. \tag{10}$$

Let us put 9) in 8), we get

$$\sigma_r(z \pm \omega_s) = e^{\pm\eta_s z}\sigma_r\omega_s\sigma_t z. \tag{11}$$

In this formula with the lower sign, set $z = \omega_s$. As $\sigma_r(0) = 1$ by 3), it gives

$$e^{\eta_s \omega_s} = \sigma_r \omega_s \sigma_t \omega_s. \tag{12}$$

Let us now make use of this in 7), it gives

$$\sigma_r(z \pm \omega_r) = \mp e^{\pm \eta_r z} \frac{\sigma_s \omega_r \sigma_t \omega_r}{\sigma \omega_r} \sigma(z). \tag{13}$$

From the definition 1) we see

$$\sigma_r(\mu z, \mu\omega_1, \mu\omega_2) = \sigma_r(z, \omega_1, \omega_2). \tag{14}$$

3. In 170, 1) let us set $v = \omega_s$; we get, using 1), 2),

$$p(z) - e_s = \frac{\sigma_s^2(z)}{\sigma^2(z)}. \tag{15}$$

This shows that the square root of the left side is a one-valued function of z. We set

$$\sqrt{p(z) - e_s} = + \frac{\sigma_s(z)}{\sigma(z)}, \tag{16}$$

which determines the sign of the radical.

Let us set $z = \omega_r$ in 16), we get

$$\sqrt{e_r - e_s} = \frac{\sigma_s \omega_r}{\sigma \omega_r} \tag{17}$$

and the sign of the radical on the left is determined.

Putting 9) in 17) gives

$$\sqrt{e_r - e_s} = - e^{-\omega_r \eta_s} \frac{\sigma \omega_t}{\sigma \omega_r \sigma \omega_s}.$$

Interchanging r and s, we get, dividing,

$$\frac{\sqrt{e_r - e_s}}{\sqrt{e_s - e_r}} = e^{\eta_r \omega_s - \eta_s \omega_r}.$$

Hence using Legendre's relation 171, 10)

$$\sqrt{e_1 - e_2} = i\sqrt{e_2 - e_1}\ , \quad \sqrt{e_1 - e_3} = -i\sqrt{e_3 - e_1}\ ,$$
$$\sqrt{e_2 - e_3} = i\sqrt{e_3 - e_2}. \tag{18}$$

Here we suppose ω_1, ω_2 such that we pass from ω_1 to ω_2 by a positive rotation $< \pi$.

The relations 18) enable us to replace in our formula a radical $\sqrt{e_r - e_s}$ by $\sqrt{e_s - e_r}$, a substitution which is often useful to make reductions.

4. In 15) let us replace z by $z+\omega_s$, we get

$$p(z+\omega_s)-e_s=\frac{\sigma_s^2(z+\omega_s)}{\sigma^2(z+\omega_s)},$$

or using 6), 13),

$$=e^{2\eta_s z}\frac{\sigma_r^2\omega_s\sigma_t^2\omega_s}{\sigma^2\omega_s}\cdot\frac{1}{e^{2\eta_s z}\sigma^2\omega_s}\cdot\frac{\sigma^2(z)}{\sigma_s^2(z)}.$$

Using 15), 17) this gives

$$p(z+\omega_s)=e_s+\frac{(e_s-e_r)(e_s-e_t)}{p(z)-e_s}. \tag{19}$$

5. To find the development of $\sigma_r(z)$ in a power series about the origin we have, from 16),

$$\sigma_r(z)=\sigma(z)\sqrt{p(z)-e_r}.$$

Now from 169, 16)

$$p(z)-e_r=\frac{1}{z^2}-e_r+\frac{1}{20}g_2z^2+\cdots$$

Thus

$$\sigma_r(z)=\sigma(z)\left\{\frac{1}{z^2}-e_r+\frac{1}{20}g_2z^2+\cdots\right\}^{\frac{1}{2}}$$

$$=1-\frac{1}{2}e_rz^2-\frac{1}{48}(6\,e_r^2-g_2)z^4-\cdots \tag{20}$$

6. We have obviously

$$p'u=-2\frac{\sigma_1(u)\sigma_2(u)\sigma_3(u)}{\sigma^3u}. \tag{21}$$

173. The Inverse p Function. **Case 1.** 1. We have

$$p(z)=\frac{1}{z^2}+\frac{g_2}{20}z^2+\cdots \tag{1}$$

$$p'(z)=-\frac{2}{z^3}+\frac{g_2}{10}z+\cdots \tag{2}$$

$$g_2=60\sum\frac{1}{\omega^4}\quad,\qquad g_3=140\sum\frac{1}{\omega^6}\quad,\qquad \omega=2\,m_1\omega_1+2\,m_2\omega_2. \tag{3}$$

The relation 1) defines p as a function of z. We wish now to consider the inverse function z of p.

Case 1. ω_1 *real and positive*, $\omega_2=i\overline{\omega}_2$, $\omega_2>0$. We note first that the invariants g_2, g_3 are real. For in ω to each positive m_2 corresponds a negative value $-m_2$. Then the two values of ω,

$$2\,m_1\omega_1+2\,m_2i\overline{\omega}_2\quad,\qquad 2\,m_1\omega_1-2\,m_2i\overline{\omega}_2,$$

are conjugate imaginary. Thus the terms in g_2, g_3 enter in pairs which are conjugate imaginary numbers. As the sum of two conjugate imaginaries is real, g_2, g_3 are real.

From 1) we see that p is real for real values of z, say for $z = x$. As p has the real period $2\,\omega_1$, $p(x)$ is periodic.

The relation 1) shows that the p-axis in Fig. 1 is an asymptote.

From 2) we see that $p'(x)$ is negative for small values of x. Thus p decreases until $p'(x)$ vanishes. The roots of $p'(z) = 0$ are ω_1, ω_2, ω_3, of which only the first is real.

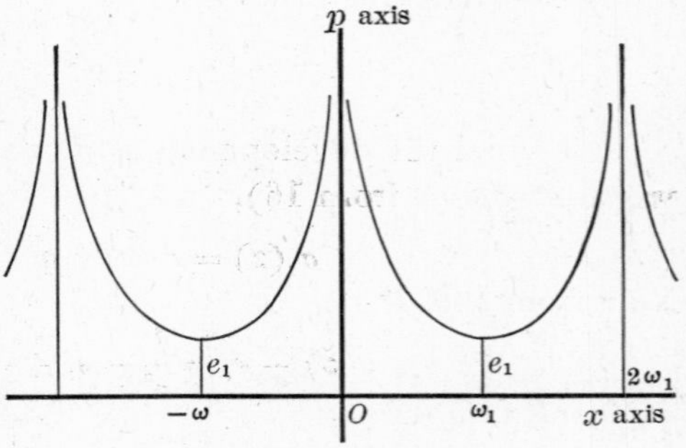

FIG. 1.

Thus p decreases from $x = 0$ to $x = \omega_1$, at which last point $p(\omega_1) = e_1$. Since $p(x)$ is an even function, p is symmetric with respect to the p-axis. Thus p decreases as x ranges from 0 to $-\omega_1$. As p has $2\,\omega_1$ as period, the graph of p in the interval $(\omega_1, 2\,\omega_1)$ is the same as in $(-\omega_1, 0)$.

2. The graph of $p = p(x)$ shows that the relation 1) defines a many-valued inverse function

$$x = \phi(p), \tag{4}$$

one of whose branches may be characterized by the conditions

1° $x \doteq 0$ as $p \doteq +\infty$, (5

2° x is positive for $p \geq e_1$.

This branch is shown in Fig. 2.

We show now how this inverse function may be represented by an integral. The derivative of $p(x)$ is

$$\frac{dp}{dx} = \pm\sqrt{4\,p^3 - g_2 p - g_3}. \tag{6}$$

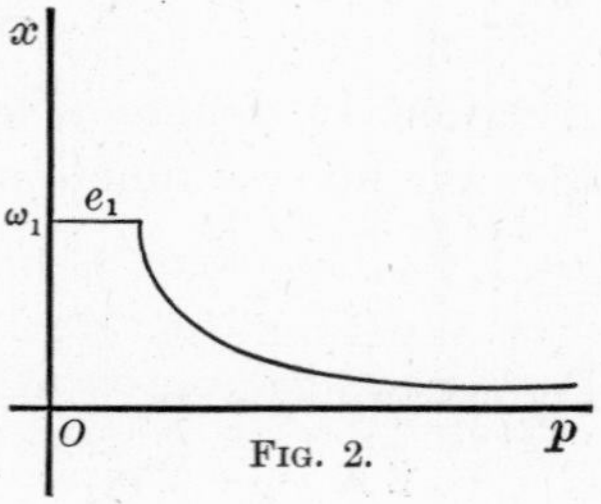

FIG. 2.

To determine the sign of the radical we observe that for $0 < x \leq \omega_1$, $\frac{dp}{dx}$

is negative, while the polynomial under the radical is large and positive. We must therefore take the minus sign in 6). Then the derivative of the branch of 4) as determined by 5) is

$$\frac{dx}{dp} = \frac{1}{\frac{dp}{dx}} = \frac{1}{-\sqrt{4p^3 - g_2 p - g_3}}. \tag{7}$$

From this follows that the inverse function x defined by 4), 5) is

$$x = \int_p^\infty \frac{dp}{\sqrt{4p^3 - g_2 p - g_3}}. \tag{8}$$

In fact the quantity under the radical is $p'(x)^2$; it is therefore positive for $p \geq e_1$. Also as $p \doteq +\infty$ the integral 8) converges to 0. Thus the conditions 5) are satisfied.

From $p(\omega_1) = e_1$ follows now that $x = \omega_1$ when $p = e_1$. Putting this in 8) gives

$$\omega_1 = \int_{e_1}^\infty \frac{dp}{+\sqrt{4p^3 - g_2 p - g_3}}. \tag{9}$$

This expresses the period $2\omega_1$ as a real integral.

3. *We show now how ω_2 can be expressed as an integral.* To this end we note that 1) shows that $p(z)$ is real and negative for small values of z of the form $z = iv$. We have in fact

$$q = p(iv) = -\frac{1}{v_2} - \frac{g_2}{20}v^2 - \cdots \tag{10}$$

By analytic continuation the series 10) will give the values of q for all values of z from 0 to ω_2, that is, for values $0 < v < \bar{\omega}_2$.

As the terms of 10) are all real, the values of q obtained by this process will be real. When

$$v = \bar{\omega}_2, \quad q = p(i\bar{\omega}_2) = p(\omega_2) = e_2,$$

which is therefore real.

As $p'(z)$ does not vanish as z moves from 0 to ω_2 until it reaches ω_2, $\frac{dq}{dv}$ does not vanish as v moves from 0 to $\bar{\omega}_2$, until it reaches $\bar{\omega}_2$.

The graph of q considered as a function of v is given in Fig. 3. It shows that 10) defines a many-valued inverse function.

$$v = \psi(q), \tag{11}$$

entirely analogous to 4). One of its branches is given in Fig. 4 and is characterized by

$$v \doteq 0 \text{ as } q \doteq -\infty; \quad v > 0 \text{ for } q \leq e_2. \tag{12}$$

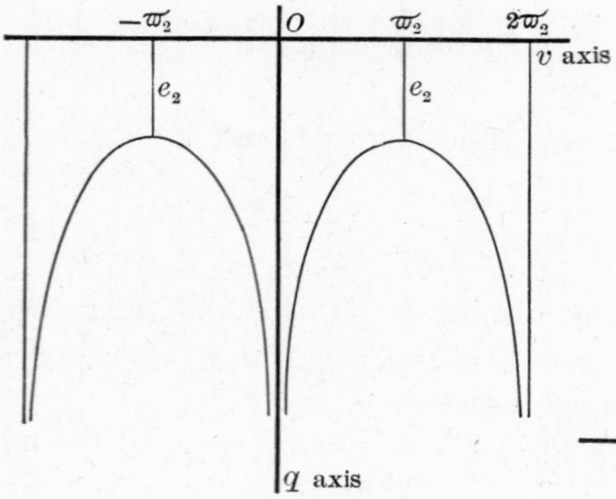

FIG. 3.

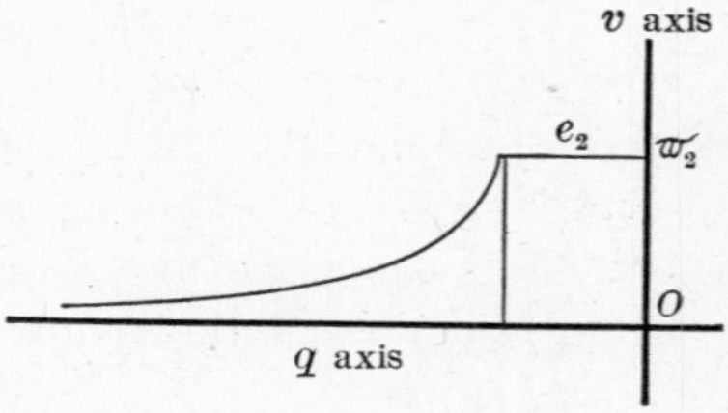

FIG. 4.

To represent this inverse function by an integral we observe that

$$\frac{dq}{dv} = \frac{dp(z)}{dz} \cdot \frac{dz}{dv} = ip'(z) = \pm i\sqrt{4\,p^3 - g_2 p - g_3}.$$

As the derivative is real and positive for this branch, and as $p(z) = p(iv) = q$, we may write this

$$\frac{dv}{dq} = \frac{1}{+\sqrt{-(4\,q^3 - g_2 q - g_3)}},$$

the radical being real and positive for $q < e_2$.

Let us now consider

$$v = \int_{-\infty}^{q} \frac{dg}{\sqrt{-(4\,q^3 - g_2 q - g_3)}}. \tag{13}$$

We see this is positive for $q < -e_2$ and that $v \doteq 0$ as $q \doteq -\infty$. It is therefore the function defined by 11), 12).

Setting $q = e_2$, we have

$$\bar{\omega}_2 = \int_{-\infty}^{e_2} \frac{dq}{\sqrt{-(4\,q^3 - g_2 q - g_3)}}. \tag{14}$$

From this, we have expressed $\omega_2 = i\bar{\omega}_2$ as an integral.

4. We have seen that e_1, e_2 are real. As g_2, g_3 are real, all the roots of

$$4\,p^3 - g_2 p - g_3 = 0 \tag{15}$$

are real. Since

$$e_1 + e_2 + e_3 = 0, \tag{16}$$

it follows that at least one root e must be negative. As the first root of 15) which we meet as p moves from $-\infty$ toward the origin is e_2, this root is certainly negative.

The sign of the root e_2 is given by 16).

174. Case 2. Periods Conjugate Imaginary. 1. Let us suppose now that

$$\omega_1 = \omega - i\omega' \quad , \quad \omega_2 = \omega + i\omega' \quad , \quad \omega' > 0. \tag{1}$$

Then

$$\begin{aligned} 2\,\omega &= \omega_1 + \omega_2 = -\,\omega_3 \equiv \omega_3, \\ 2\,i\omega' &= \omega_2 - \omega_1 \equiv -\,\omega_3 \equiv \omega_3, \\ 2\,\omega &\equiv 2\,i\omega' \quad , \quad 2\,\omega + 2\,i\omega' = 2\,\omega_2 \equiv 0. \end{aligned} \tag{2}$$

As in Case 1, the invariants g_2, g_3 are real.

For

$$2\,m_1\omega_1 + 2\,m_2\omega_2 = 2(m_1 + m_2)\omega + 2i\omega'(m_2 - m_1).$$

On interchanging m_1, m_2 this period goes over into one which is conjugate imaginary.

From the series 173, 1), 2), we see that $p(z)$, $p'(z)$ are real for real z, and that p is real for purely imaginary z.

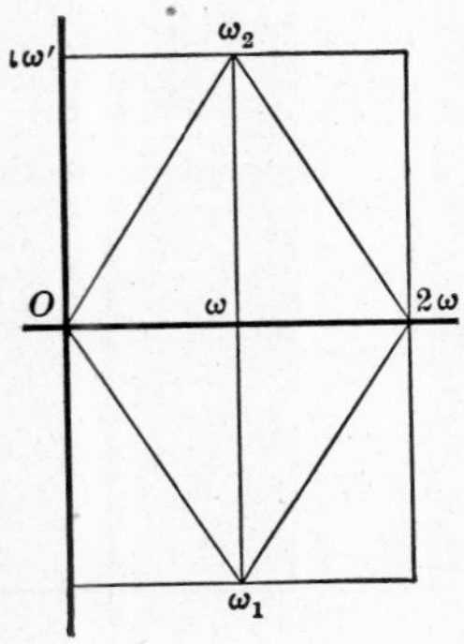

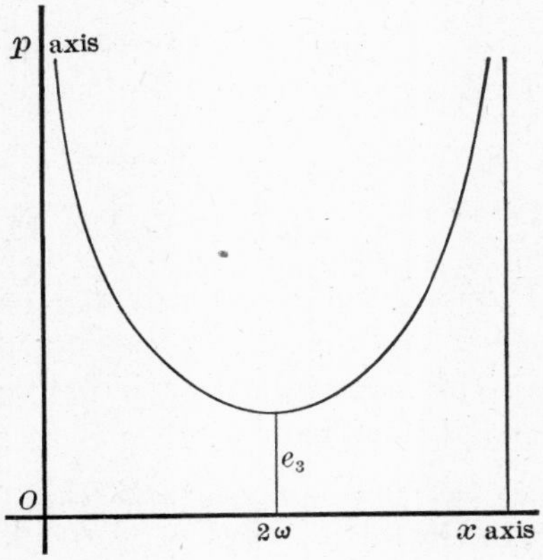

As in Case 1, we see that as x moves from 0 to 2ω, $p(x)$ decreases. At $x = 2\omega$

$$p(x) = p(\omega_3) = e_3,$$

at which point p has a minimum, and $p'(\omega_3) = 0$.

Let us note that $p'(x)$ has only one incongruent real root, as ω_1, ω_2 are complex.

The inverse function defined by

$$p = p(x)$$

is many-valued. One of its branches is given by

$$x = \int_p^\infty \frac{dp}{+\sqrt{4p^3 - g_2 p - g_3}} \qquad (3$$

which is positive for $p \geq e_3$, and which $\doteq 0$ as $p \doteq \infty$.

When $p = e_3$, $x = 2\omega$. Thus

$$2\omega = \int_{e_3}^\infty \frac{dp}{+\sqrt{4p^3 - g_2 p - g_3}}. \qquad (4$$

2. *Let us now express ω' as an integral.* Knowing ω, ω', we can express the periods $2\omega_1$, $2\omega_2$ as integrals by 1).

As $z = iv$ moves from 0 to $2i\omega'$, p is real and moves from $-\infty$ to

$$p(2i\omega') = p(\omega_3) = e_3.$$

We have

$$q = p(iv) = -\frac{1}{v^2} - \frac{g_2}{20}v^2 - \cdots \qquad (5$$

$$\frac{dq}{dv} = \frac{2}{v^3} - \cdots$$

Thus q is increasing for small values of v. As $\frac{dq}{dv}$ does not vanish unless $p'(z) = 0$, and as the first root of this on the imaginary axis is $\omega_3 = 2i\omega'$, we see that q increases steadily from $-\infty$ to e_3.

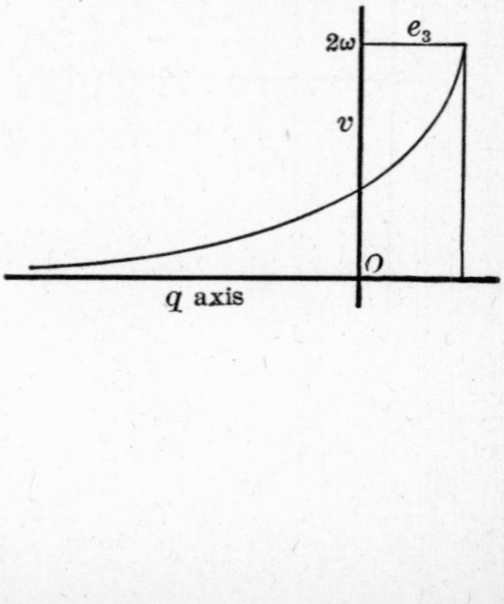

Thus the relation 5) defines an inverse function v of q, one of whose branches is characterized by the condition that

$$v \doteq 0 \quad \text{as} \quad q \doteq -\infty, \quad \text{and} \quad v > 0 \quad \text{for} \quad q \leq e_3. \qquad (6$$

Thus, as in Case 1, this branch is represented by

$$v = \int_{-\infty}^{q} \frac{dq}{\sqrt{-(4q^3 - g_2 q - g_3)}}. \qquad (7$$

As $v = 2\omega'$ for $q = e_3$, this gives

$$2\omega' = \int_{-\infty}^{e_3} \frac{dq}{+\sqrt{-(4q^3 - g_2 q - g_3)}}. \qquad (8$$

175. The p Function defined by g_2, g_3. 1. Up to the present we have considered $p(u)$ as defined by means of the periods $2\omega_1$, $2\omega_2$. These numbers being taken at pleasure but not collinear with the origin, we constructed the sum

$$p(z, 2\omega_1, 2\omega_2) = \frac{1}{z^2} + \sum \left\{ \frac{1}{(z-\omega)^2} - \frac{1}{\omega^2} \right\} \qquad (1$$

as in 169, 3), and showed that

$$p(z) = \frac{1}{z^2} + * + \frac{g_2}{20} z^2 + \frac{g_3}{28} z^4 + \cdots \qquad (2$$

all of whose coefficients are rational integral functions of the invariants

$$g_2 = 60 \sum \frac{1}{\omega^4}, \quad g_3 = 140 \sum \frac{1}{\omega^6}. \qquad (3$$

We ask now: Can we start with two numbers g_2, g_3 taken at pleasure, and find the periods $2\omega_1$, $2\omega_2$ with which to construct the p function 1)?

Let us consider the roots e_1, e_2, e_3 of the cubic

$$4t^3 - g_2 t - g_3 = 0 \text{ or } 4(t - e_1)(t - e_2)(t - e_3) = 0. \qquad (4$$

We must in the first place suppose that two of them are not equal. For we have seen, 169, 11), that $p(z)$ satisfies the equation

$$\frac{dp}{dz} = \sqrt{4p^3 - g_2 p - g_3} = \sqrt{4(p - e_1)(p - e_2)(p - e_3)}. \qquad (5$$

If now $e_1 = e_2$, this gives

$$\frac{dp}{dz} = 2(p - e_1)\sqrt{p - e_3}. \qquad (6$$

Hence

$$z = \int \frac{dp}{2(p - e_1)\sqrt{p - e_3}}. \qquad (7$$

Thus z can be expressed by means of the elementary functions, and p cannot be a double periodic function.

2. The roots e_s being unequal, let us suppose they are real. We define $2\,\omega_1$, $2\,\omega_2$ by the equations

$$2\,\omega_1 = 2\int_{e_1}^{\infty}\frac{dt}{\sqrt{4\,t^3 - g_2t - g_3}}, \tag{8}$$

$$2\,\omega_2 = 2\,i\int_{-\infty}^{e_2}\frac{dt}{\sqrt{-(4\,t^3 - g_2t - g_3)}}, \tag{9}$$

where we suppose the e's so numbered that

$$e_2 < e_3 < e_1. \tag{10}$$

Then $2\,\omega_1$ is real and $2\,\omega_2$ is purely imaginary, since the radicals in both 8) and 9) are positive. As $2\,\omega_1$, $2\,\omega_2$ are not collinear with the origin, the series 1) constructed with these two numbers defines an elliptic function $p(z, 2\,\omega_1, 2\,\omega_2)$ which we have seen satisfies 5). The reasoning of 169, 2, 3 shows that this function p will have the development 2) about $z=0$ and that g_2, g_3 will satisfy 3).

3. Let us next suppose one root e_3 of the cubic 4) is real, while the other two are conjugate imaginary. We define $2\,\omega$, $2\,\omega'$ by the equations

$$2\,\omega = \int_{e_3}^{\infty}\frac{dt}{\sqrt{4\,t^3 - g_2t - g_3}}, \tag{11}$$

$$2\,\omega' = \int_{-\infty}^{e_3}\frac{dt}{\sqrt{-(4\,t^3 - g_2t - g_3)}}. \tag{12}$$

These are real and positive, since the radicals in 11), 12) are both positive.

We now set

$$2\,\omega_1 = 2\,\omega - 2\,i\omega' \quad , \quad 2\,\omega_2 = 2\,\omega + 2\,i\omega'. \tag{13}$$

Since these are not collinear with the origin, the series 1) converges and defines an elliptic function $p(z, 2\,\omega_1, 2\,\omega_2)$. As before, we see that this function satisfies the differential equation 5); its development about $z=0$ is given by 2) and g_2, g_3 satisfy the relations 3).

4. Suppose finally that g_2, g_3 are any complex numbers, such however that the cubic 4) does not have two equal roots. From algebra we know that

$$G = (e_1 - e_2)^2(e_1 - e_3)^2(e_2 - e_3)^2 = \tfrac{1}{16}(g_2^3 - 27\, g_3^2). \qquad (14$$

Obviously 4) will have equal roots when and only when $G = 0$. For this reason G is called the *discriminant* of the cubic.

We shall not treat the *general case* but merely state that:

If we set

$$\omega_1 = \int_{e_2}^{e_3} \frac{dt}{\sqrt{4\, t^3 - g_2 t - g_3}} \quad , \quad \omega_2 = \int_{e_3}^{e_1} \frac{dt}{\sqrt{4\, t^3 - g_2 t - g_3}},$$

the series 1) *constructed on these numbers is convergent and defines an elliptic function* $p(z, 2\,\omega_1, 2\,\omega_2)$ *having* $2\,\omega_1$, $2\,\omega_2$ *as a primitive pair of periods. This function satisfies* 5), *its development about the origin is* 2), *and* g_2, g_3 *satisfy* 3).

176. The Radicals $\sqrt{p(z) - e_m}$. These are factors in

$$\frac{dp}{dz} = \sqrt{4\, p^3 - g_2 p - g_3} = 2\sqrt{p - e_1}\, \sqrt{p - e_2}\, \sqrt{p - e_3}.$$

In 172, 15 we saw that they are one-valued functions of z, viz.:

$$\sqrt{p - e_m} = \frac{\sigma_m(z)}{\sigma(z)} \qquad m = 1, 2, 3. \qquad (1$$

Let us set in general

$$\sigma_{m0} = \frac{\sigma_m(z)}{\sigma(z)} \quad , \quad \sigma_{0m} = \frac{\sigma(z)}{\sigma_m(z)} \quad , \quad \sigma_{mn} = \frac{\sigma_m(z)}{\sigma_n(z)}. \qquad (2$$

They are homogeneous functions of z, ω_1, ω_2, of orders -1, 1, 0 respectively.

Of these 12 functions, 6 are reciprocals of the other 6. Let us consider one of them as

$$q = \sigma_{02}(z) = \frac{\sigma(z)}{\sigma_2(z)} = \frac{1}{\sqrt{p(z) - e_2}}. \qquad (3$$

From 172, 1 we have

$$q(z + 2\,\omega_1) = -\,q(z) \quad , \quad q(z + 2\,\omega_2) = q(z).$$

Thus q admits $4\,\omega_1$, $2\,\omega_2$ as periods.

As $\sigma(z)=0$ for $z\equiv 0 \mod 2\,\omega_1,\ 2\,\omega_2$, we see that the zeros of q are $\equiv 0$, mod $2\,\omega_1,\ 2\,\omega_2$.

As $\sigma_2(z)=0$ for $z\equiv\omega_2$, we see that the poles of q are $\equiv\omega_2$, mod $2\,\omega_1,\ 2\,\omega_2$, and simple.

Thus q is an elliptic function of order 2 for which $4\,\omega_1,\ 2\,\omega_2$ form a primitive pair of periods.

By 165, 14 the zeros of $q'(z)$ are $\equiv$

$$\omega_1\ ,\quad 3\,\omega_1\ ,\quad \omega_3\ ,\quad \omega_3+2\,\omega_1 \qquad \mod 4\,\omega_1,\quad 2\,\omega_2.$$

At these points q has respectively the values

$$\frac{1}{\sqrt{e_1-e_2}}\ ,\quad \frac{-1}{\sqrt{e_1-e_2}}\ ,\quad \frac{1}{\sqrt{e_3-e_2}}\ ,\quad \frac{-1}{\sqrt{e_3-e_2}}.$$

Thus by 165, 16 q satisfies the differential equation

$$\left(\frac{dq}{dz}\right)^2 = C\left\{q^2-\frac{1}{e_1-e_2}\right\}\left\{q^2-\frac{1}{e_3-e_2}\right\}. \qquad (4$$

To determine the constant C we observe that

$$q=\{p(z)-e_2\}^{-\frac{1}{2}}=\left\{\frac{1}{z^2}-e_2+\cdots\right\}^{-\frac{1}{2}}$$

$$=z\{1-e_2z^2+\cdots\}^{-\frac{1}{2}}$$

$$=z\{1+az^2+\cdots\}.$$

Hence

$$\frac{dq}{dz}=1+3\,az^2+\cdots$$

Putting these developments in 4) and equating the absolute terms, we get

$$1=\frac{C}{(e_1-e_2)(e_3-e_2)}.$$

Thus 4) becomes

$$\left(\frac{dq}{dz}\right)^2=\{1-(e_1-e_2)q^2\}\{1-(e_3-e_2)q^2\}. \qquad (5$$

CHAPTER XI

THE FUNCTIONS OF LEGENDRE AND JACOBI

177. Rectification. 1. In the previous chapter we have studied the elliptic functions from the point of view of their most characteristic property, viz. as double periodic functions. Historically they presented themselves from quite another standpoint, and this we wish now to develop.

The integral calculus enables us to find the lengths of a great variety of curves found by effecting the integration in the formula

$$s = \int_\alpha^\beta \sqrt{1 + \frac{dy^2}{dx^2}} \cdot dx ; \qquad (1$$

for example, the circle, parabola, catenary, cycloid, cissoid of Diocles, the cardioid, etc. When the contemporaries of Newton and Leibnitz attempted to rectify the ellipse, hyperbola, and the lemniscate by means of 1) they met a most unexpected difficulty. In spite of every effort they could not effect the integration. Let us see how these integrals look.

2. *The Ellipse.* The equation being

$$a^2y^2 + b^2x^2 = a^2b^2, \qquad (2$$

we have

$$s = \frac{1}{a}\int \frac{a^4 - c^2x^2}{\sqrt{(a^2 - x^2)(a^4 - c^2x^4)}} dx \quad , \quad c^2 = a^2 - b^2. \qquad (3$$

Instead of the equation 2) we may use the parameter equations of the ellipse,

$$x = a \sin \phi \quad , \quad y = b \cos \phi. \qquad (4$$

Then

$$s = a \int \sqrt{a^2 \cos^2 \phi + b^2 \sin^2 \phi} \cdot d\phi, \qquad (5$$

or setting

$$k^2 = \frac{a^2 - b^2}{a^2} = \frac{c^2}{a^2} \qquad (6$$

$$s = a \int \sqrt{1 - k^2 \sin^2 \phi} \cdot d\phi. \qquad (7$$

As we now know, the integrals 3), 7) cannot be expressed in terms of the elementary functions; the efforts of the mathematicians of the seventeenth and eighteenth centuries in this direction were doomed to fail. And yet only failure in a narrow sense, for from their apparently fruitless efforts has sprung a whole new branch of mathematics, the elliptic functions.

3. *The Lemniscate.* If we take the equation in polar form, it is

$$\rho = a \cos^{\frac{1}{2}} 2\,\phi.$$

Then 1) gives

$$s = a\int \frac{d\theta}{\sqrt{1 - 2\sin^2\theta}}. \tag{8}$$

If we set $x = \sin\theta$, we get also

$$s = a\int \frac{dx}{\sqrt{(1 - x^2)(1 - 2\,x^2)}}. \tag{9}$$

178. Elliptic Integrals. 1. Many problems of pure and applied mathematics lead to integrals whose integrands are rational functions of x and the square root of a polynomial P of the third or fourth degree, that is, to integrals of the type

$$\int \phi(x, \sqrt{P})dx. \tag{1}$$

Such integrals are called *elliptic integrals;* they include the integrals 3) and 9) of 177, and cannot be expressed in general in terms of the elementary functions. They therefore define new functions in the same way that

$$\int\frac{dx}{x}\ ,\quad \int\frac{dx}{\sqrt{1-x^2}}$$

define transcendental functions although their integrands are algebraic.

The question arises, how many different types of integrals are included in 1). We propose to show that all these integrals may be reduced to three, viz.:

$$\int \frac{dx}{\sqrt{(1-x^2)(1-k^2x^2)}}, \tag{2}$$

$$\int \frac{x^2dx}{\sqrt{(1-x^2)(1-k^2x^2)}}, \tag{3}$$

$$\int \frac{dx}{(x-a)\sqrt{(1-x^2)(1-k^2x^2)}}, \tag{4}$$

which are called elliptic integrals of the 1°, 2°, and 3° species, respectively.

The number k is called the *modulus*, the number a which enters 4) is called the *parameter*.

2. To reduce the integrals 1), let us note that if the polynomial P is of the third degree,

$$ax^3 + bx^2 + cx + d, \tag{5}$$

the integral 1) may be replaced by one in which the polynomial under the radical is of the fourth degree.

For let α be a root of 5), then P has the form

$$P = (x-\alpha)(px^2 + qx + r). \tag{6}$$

Let us set

$$x - \alpha = y^2,$$

then

$$\sqrt{P} = y\sqrt{p(y^2+\alpha)^2 + q(y^2+\alpha) + r}$$

and the polynomial under the radical is of the fourth degree if $p \neq 0$.

But if $p = 0$, the polynomial P is of the second degree, as 6) shows, and this is contrary to hypothesis.

3. Let us suppose then that

$$P = p_0x^4 + p_1x^3 + p_2x^2 + p_3x + p_4 \quad , \quad p_0 \neq 0. \tag{7}$$

Since ϕ is a rational function of x and

$$y = \sqrt{P},$$

let us arrange its numerator and denominator according to y. Then

$$\phi = \frac{b_0 + b_1 y + b_2 y^2 + \cdots}{c_0 + c_1 y + c_2 y^2 + \cdots}. \tag{8}$$

As

$$y^2 = P \quad , \quad y^3 = yP \quad , \quad y^4 = P^2 \cdots$$

we see that 8) has the form

$$\phi = \frac{A + By}{C + Dy}, \tag{9}$$

where A, B, C, D are polynomials in x.

If we multiply numerator and denominator in 9) by $C - Dy$, we get

$$\phi = E + Fy = E + \frac{Fy^2}{y} = E + \frac{G}{\sqrt{P}},$$

where E, F, G are rational functions of x. Thus

$$\int \phi dx = \int E dx + \int \frac{G}{\sqrt{P}} dx. \tag{10}$$

Here the first term on the right may be integrated by means of the elementary functions as shown in the calculus. We are thus led to consider

$$\int \frac{G dx}{\sqrt{P}}. \tag{11}$$

4. As G is a rational function of x, it may be broken up into partial fractions as shown in 122, 4). Thus G is the sum of a polynomial which may reduce to a constant and a number of terms of the type

$$\frac{a_m}{(x-a)^m} + \frac{a_{m-1}}{(x-a)^{m-1}} + \cdots + \frac{a_1}{x-a}.$$

Thus the integral 11) reduces to integrals

$$\int \frac{x^m dx}{\sqrt{P}} \quad \text{and} \quad \int \frac{dx}{(x-a)^m \sqrt{P}}. \tag{12}$$

Both of these may be represented by

$$Q_m = \int (x-a)^m \frac{dx}{\sqrt{P}}, \tag{13}$$

if we let m be a positive or negative integer or 0, and a any number including 0. There are now two cases.

5. *Case* 1. *a is not a root of P.* Then we may write

$$P = A_0(x-a)^4 + 4\,A_1(x-a)^3 + 6\,A_2(x-a)^2 + 4\,A_3(x-a) + A_4 \tag{14}$$

and $A_4 \neq 0$. For setting $x = a$ in 14), it reduces to A_4, and if this were 0, P would $= 0$ for $x = a$, which is contrary to our hypothesis.

Let us note now that for any integer

$$\frac{d}{dx}\{(x-a)^n\sqrt{P}\} = \frac{n(x-a)^{n-1}P + \frac{1}{2}(x-a)^n P'}{\sqrt{P}}.$$

Hence, integrating,

$$(x-a)^n\sqrt{P} = n\int\frac{(x-a)^{n-1}P\,dx}{\sqrt{P}} + \frac{1}{2}\int\frac{(x-a)^n P'\,dx}{\sqrt{P}}.$$

If we put in the value of P and P' as given by 14), we find

$$(x-a)^n\sqrt{P} = (n+2)A_0Q_{n+3} + 2(2\,n+3)A_1Q_{n+2} + 6(n+1)A_2Q_{n+1} + 2(2\,n+1)A_3Q_n + nA_4Q_{n-1}. \tag{15}$$

If we take $n = -1$, this relation enables us to express Q_{-2} in terms of Q_{-1}, Q_1, Q_2 and an algebraic function. If we take $n = -2$, we see Q_{-3} can be expressed by means of Q_{-2}, Q_{-1}, Q_0. But we have just seen that Q_{-2} can be expressed in terms of Q_{-1}, Q_1, Q_2. Thus Q_{-2} can be expressed in terms of Q_{-1}, Q_0, Q_1, Q_2. In the same manner we may reason for higher negative values of n. This shows that the integrals 13) when m is negative may be reduced to

$$\int\frac{dx}{\sqrt{P}}\ , \quad \int\frac{dx}{(x-a)\sqrt{P}}, \tag{16}$$

and to Q_n with positive indices.

Case 2. Suppose a is a root of P. It cannot be a double root of P. For then P would have the form

$$P = (x-a)^2(px^2 + qx + r),$$

and hence

$$\sqrt{P} = (x-a)\sqrt{px^2 + qx + r},$$

that is, the polynomial P under the radical can be replaced by one of degree 2. But in this case the integral 1) leads only to the elementary functions, as is shown in the calculus.

In the present case therefore $A_4 = 0$ but $A_3 \neq 0$. Thus the last term in 14) disappears, but not the next to the last term in 15). Hence if we set $n = -1$ in 15), this relation enables us to express Q_{-1} in terms of Q_1 and Q_2.

If we set $n = -2$, it gives Q_{-2} in terms of Q_{-1} and Q_0, etc. We are thus led to the first integral in 16) and integrals of the type 13) for which $m > 0$.

6. When $m > 0$, the integrals 13) give rise to integrals of the form

$$R_m = \int \frac{x^m dx}{\sqrt{P}}. \tag{17}$$

In the relation 15) we may set $a = 0$, then the Q's will go over into the integrals 17). The relation 14) shows that the A's are the coefficients p in 7).

In 15) let us take $n = 0$; this enables us to express R_3 in terms of R_2, R_1, and R_0. If we set $n = 1$ in 15), it shows that R_4 may be expressed in terms of R_3, R_2, and R_1, and hence in terms of R_2, R_1, and R_0, as just seen.

Thus all the integrals 13) reduce to

$$\int \frac{dx}{\sqrt{P}}, \quad \int \frac{x\,dx}{\sqrt{P}}, \quad \int \frac{x^2 dx}{\sqrt{P}} \tag{18}$$

when $m > 0$.

179. Linear Transformation. 1. To complete the reduction let us show how to determine the linear transformation

$$y = \frac{a + bx}{1 + cx} \tag{1}$$

so that
$$\frac{dy}{\sqrt{Y}} = \frac{dy}{\sqrt{(y - y_1)(y - y_2)(y - y_3)(y - y_4)}}$$

$$= \frac{dx}{M\sqrt{(1 - x^2)(1 - k^2x^2)}} = \frac{dx}{M\sqrt{X}}. \tag{2}$$

Let us determine a, b, c, k so that when

$$y = y_1 \quad , \quad y_2 \quad , \quad y_3 \quad , \quad y_4$$

we have respectively

$$x = 1, \quad -1, \quad \frac{1}{k} \quad , \quad -\frac{1}{k}. \tag{3}$$

Then

$$y - y_1 = \frac{g_1(1-x)}{1+cx} \quad , \quad y - y_2 = \frac{g_2(1+x)}{1+cx},$$
$$y - y_3 = \frac{g_3(1-kx)}{1+cx} \quad , \quad y - y_4 = \frac{g_4(1+kx)}{1+cx}. \tag{4}$$

Set $x = -1$, $y = y_2$ in the first equation of 4), then

$$y_2 - y_1 = \frac{2\, g_1}{1-c}.$$

Similarly if we put the other pairs of values of 3) in the remaining equations of 4) we have

$$y_1 - y_2 = \frac{2\, g_2}{1+c} \quad , \quad y_4 - y_3 = \frac{2\, g_3}{1-\frac{c}{k}} \quad , \quad y_3 - y_4 = \frac{2\, g_4}{1+\frac{c}{k}}.$$

These relations give

$$g_1 = \frac{(1-c)(y_2 - y_1)}{2} \quad , \quad g_2 = \frac{(y_1 - y_2)(1+c)}{2},$$

$$g_3 = \frac{1}{2}\left(1 - \frac{c}{k}\right)(y_4 - y_3) \quad , \quad g_4 = \frac{1}{2}\left(1 + \frac{c}{k}\right)(y_3 - y_4).$$

From 4) we have

$$\frac{y - y_1}{y - y_2} = \frac{g_1(1-x)}{g_2(1+x)} = \frac{1-c}{1+c} \cdot \frac{x-1}{x+1}. \tag{5}$$

Set here $y = y_3$, $x = \frac{1}{k}$, we get

$$\frac{y_3 - y_1}{y_3 - y_2} = \frac{1-c}{1+c} \cdot \frac{1-k}{1+k}. \tag{6}$$

Also in 5) set

$$y = y_4,\ x = -\frac{1}{k},\ \text{we get}$$

$$\frac{y_4 - y_1}{y_4 - y_2} = \frac{1-c}{1+c} \cdot \frac{1+k}{1-k}. \tag{7}$$

From 6), 7) we find

$$\left(\frac{1-k}{1+k}\right)^2 = \frac{y_1 - y_3}{y_2 - y_3} \cdot \frac{y_2 - y_4}{y_1 - y_4} = \rho^2,\ \text{say.} \tag{8}$$

This gives

$$k = \frac{1-\rho}{1+\rho}. \tag{9}$$

From 6), 7) we have also

$$\left(\frac{1-c}{1+c}\right)^2 = \frac{y_1 - y_3}{y_2 - y_3} \cdot \frac{y_1 - y_4}{y_2 - y_4} = \sigma^2,\ \text{say.} \tag{10}$$

This gives

$$c = \frac{1-\sigma}{1+\sigma}. \tag{11}$$

To get a, b we start with 1) or

$$y + cxy - a - bx = 0.$$

For $x = 1$, $y = y_1$, this gives

$$y_1 + cy_1 - a - b = 0.$$

For $x = -1$, $y = y_2$ it gives

$$y_2 - cy_2 - a + b = 0.$$

Adding and subtracting these two relations give

$$\begin{aligned} a &= \tfrac{1}{2}(y_1 + y_2 + c(y_1 - y_2)), \\ b &= \tfrac{1}{2}(y_1 - y_2 + c(y_1 + y_2)). \end{aligned} \tag{12}$$

To find M we differentiate the second equation in 4), which gives

$$dy = g_2 \frac{(1-c)dx}{(1+cx)^2}.$$

The fourth equation of 4) gives

$$dy = g_4 \frac{(k-c)dx}{(1+cx)^2}.$$

Hence

$$dy^2 = g_2 g_4 \frac{(1-c)(k-c)}{(1+cx)^4} dx^2,$$

or

$$dy = \frac{\sqrt{g_2 g_4 (1-c)(k-c)}}{(1+cx)^2} dx. \tag{13}$$

Thus

$$\frac{dy}{\sqrt{Y}} = \frac{\sqrt{g_2 g_4 (1-c)(k-c)}}{(1+cx)^2} \cdot \frac{(1+cx)^2}{\sqrt{g_1 g_2 g_3 g_4}} \cdot \frac{dx}{\sqrt{X}}.$$

Hence

$$M = \tfrac{1}{2}\sqrt{\frac{(y_1-y_2)(y_3-y_4)}{k}}. \tag{14}$$

2. Students familiar with analytical geometry will recognize that ρ in 8) is the cross ratio of the four roots y_1, y_2, y_3, y_4. These four roots can be permuted in $4! = 24$ different ways, to which correspond 6 values of ρ^2. This the reader can verify without trouble. We find these 6 values are

$$\rho^2 \quad , \quad \frac{1}{\rho^2} \quad , \quad \frac{\rho^2}{\rho^2-1} \quad , \quad 1-\rho^2 \quad , \quad \frac{\rho^2-1}{\rho^2} \quad , \quad \frac{1}{1-\rho^2}. \tag{15}$$

We observe that three are reciprocals of the other three.

To illustrate our meaning, let us interchange y_1, y_2 in 8). The middle term becomes

$$\frac{y_2-y_3}{y_1-y_3} \cdot \frac{y_1-y_4}{y_2-y_4} = \frac{1}{\rho^2}. \tag{16}$$

Corresponding to this, the value of k in 9) is

$$\frac{1+\rho}{1-\rho}. \tag{17}$$

We observe that 9) and 17) are reciprocals. We have therefore established this important result:

By means of the linear transformation 1) *we can reduce*

$$\frac{dy}{\sqrt{Y}} \quad \textit{to} \quad \frac{dx}{M\sqrt{(1-x^2)(1-k^2x^2)}} \tag{18}$$

in such a way that the modulus k is numerically less than 1.

3. Let us return now to our general elliptic integral

$$\int \phi(x, \sqrt{P})dx. \tag{19}$$

We had

$$P = p_0x^4 + p_1x^3 + p_2x^2 + p_3x + p_4$$
$$= p_0(y - y_1)(y - y_2)(y - y_3)(y - y_4) = p_0Y.$$

The relations 4) show that the linear transformation 1) converts $\sqrt{P}$ into

$$C\frac{\sqrt{(1 - x^2)(1 - k^2x^2)}}{(1 + cx)^2} = C\frac{\sqrt{X}}{(1 + cx)^2}.$$

Thus this transformation converts the integral 19) into an integral of the same form

$$\int \psi(x, \sqrt{X})dx \tag{20}$$

except the radical $\sqrt{P}$ has been replaced by $\sqrt{X}$, which is the form used by Legendre.

If we had made this transformation at the start and had reasoned on the integral 20), the middle integral in 178, 18) would be

$$\int \frac{xdx}{\sqrt{(1 - x^2)(1 - k^2x^2)}}.$$

If we set $x^2 = u$, this becomes

$$\frac{1}{2}\int \frac{du}{\sqrt{(1 - u)(1 - k^2u)}},$$

which can be expressed by elementary functions.

The final result of our investigation may be summed up thus:

The general elliptic integral may be expressed in terms of the elementary functions and the integrals

$$\int \frac{dx}{\sqrt{X}}, \quad \int \frac{x^2dx}{\sqrt{X}}, \quad \int \frac{dx}{(x - a)\sqrt{X}}, \tag{21}$$

where

$$X = (1 - x^2)(1 - k^2x^2).$$

We have therefore established the statement made in 178, 1). The integrals 21) may be regarded as standard or *normal forms* of the three species of elliptic integrals.

180. Legendre's Normal Integrals. 1. Instead of the three integrals 21) of the last article, Legendre employed as normal integrals

$$\int \frac{dx}{\sqrt{(1-x^2)(1-k^2x^2)}}\ , \quad \int \frac{\sqrt{1-k^2x^2}}{\sqrt{1-x^2}}dx\ ,$$

$$\int \frac{dx}{(1+nx^2)\sqrt{(1-x^2)(1-k^2x^2)}}. \tag{1}$$

Let us show how the former integrals may be expressed in terms of these latter.

The integral of the 1° species is the same in both cases. To express the second integral of 179, 21) in terms of Legendre's integrals we observe that

$$\int \frac{x^2dx}{\sqrt{X}} = \int \frac{\frac{1}{k^2} - \frac{1}{k^2} + x^2}{\sqrt{X}} dx = \frac{1}{k^2}\int \frac{dx}{\sqrt{X}} - \frac{1}{k^2}\int \frac{\sqrt{1-k^2x^2}}{\sqrt{1-x^2}} dx.$$

Thus the normal integral of the the 2° species adopted in 179 is the sum of an integral of the 1° and of the 2° species as adopted by Legendre.

Turning to the third integral of 179, 21), we have

$$\int \frac{dx}{(x-a)\sqrt{X}} = \frac{x+a}{x^2-a^2}\int \frac{dx}{\sqrt{X}}$$

$$= \int \frac{xdx}{(x^2-a^2)\sqrt{X}} + a\int \frac{dx}{(x^2-a^2)\sqrt{X^2}}.$$

The first integral in the last member can be expressed by elementary functions, as we saw in 179, 3.

The last integral becomes, on setting $n = -\frac{1}{a^2}$,

$$-\frac{1}{a}\int \frac{1}{(1+nx^2)} \frac{dx}{\sqrt{(1-x^2)(1-k^2x^2)}},$$

which aside from a constant factor is Legendre's integral of the 3° species.

2. Let us set with Legendre

$$x = \sin \phi.$$

Then

$$\frac{dx}{\sqrt{1-x^2}} = d\phi.$$

The integrals 1) become, on putting in the limits 0, ϕ,

$$F(\phi, k) = \int_0^\phi \frac{d\phi}{\sqrt{1-k^2\sin^2\phi}} \quad , \quad E(\phi, k) = \int_0^\phi \sqrt{1-k^2\sin^2\phi} \cdot d\phi,$$

$$\Pi(\phi, n) = \int_0^\phi \frac{1}{1+n\sin^2\phi} \cdot \frac{d\phi}{\sqrt{1-k^2\sin^2\phi}}. \tag{2}$$

The radical which enters in these expressions and which is of constant occurrence in this theory is denoted by Legendre by $\Delta(\phi)$, thus

$$\Delta(\phi) = \sqrt{1-k^2\sin^2\phi}.$$

When $\phi = \frac{\pi}{2}$, the first two integrals in 2) are denoted by

$$K = \int_0^{\frac{\pi}{2}} \frac{d\phi}{\Delta(\phi)} \quad , \quad E = \int_0^{\frac{\pi}{2}} \Delta(\phi) d\phi. \tag{3}$$

They are called the *complete integrals* of the 1° and 2° species. Legendre denoted the integrals 3) by the letters F', E', but we shall follow the modern usage. As we shall see, they play the same rôle in the theory of Legendre and Jacobi as ω_1, η_1 do in Weierstrass' theory.

In practice the modulus k^2 is usually real and < 1. Legendre sets

$$k = \sin \theta \tag{4}$$

and calls θ the *modular angle*.

To make the elliptic integrals useful for numerical purposes Legendre calculated at great labor tables for the integrals $F(\phi)$, $E(\phi)$ for values of ϕ and θ for every degree from 0° to 90°. They are to be found in Vol. 2, p. 292 seq. of his great work: ***Traité des Fonctions Elliptiques***, Paris, 1826. Shorter tables are to be found in various works which treat of these integrals, for example in the Tables of B. O. Peirce referred to on p. 91.

The reader will note that the functions $F(\phi, k)$, $E(\phi, k)$ are unlike the functions $\log x$, $\sin x$, etc., in that they depend on two variables ϕ, k and so require tables of double entry. This makes their tabulation extremely laborious.

Turning to the elliptic integral of the 3° species, we see that this depends on the argument ϕ, the modulus k, and a number n which we call the *parameter;* in all on three variables. Its tabulation would thus require a table of triple entry, which is quite out of the question. Legendre, who had the numerical side of these integrals close to his heart, was delighted when Jacobi showed how they may be computed by means of the Θ functions.

3. *Example.* To illustrate the use of the tables let us compute the arc of an ellipse. We saw, 177, 7), that the length of an arc starting from the major axis is for $a = 1$,

$$s = \int_0^\phi \sqrt{1 - k^2 \sin^2 \phi}\, d\phi = E(\phi, k),$$

where k is the eccentricity of the ellipse

$$k = \sqrt{\frac{a^2 - b^2}{a^2}}.$$

Suppose

$$k = \sin \theta = \tfrac{1}{2},$$

then $\theta = 30°$. For $\phi = 45°$ we have from the tables

$$s = .76719.$$

For $\phi = 60°$,

$$s = 1.00755.$$

Thus the length l of an arc between $\phi = 60°$ and $\phi = 45°$ is

$$l = .24036.$$

181. Real Linear Transformations. In the foregoing reduction we have not been concerned whether the transformations employed were real or complex. In many of the applications our elliptic integrals are real, and it is often desirable to use only real transformations. With this in view let us show that:

If we set

$$x = \frac{p + qy}{1 + y} \tag{1}$$

we may reduce

$$\frac{dx}{\sqrt{\pm P}} = \frac{dx}{\sqrt{\pm (x - \alpha)(x - \beta)(x - \gamma)(x - \delta)}} \tag{2}$$

to the form

$$\frac{(q - p)\, dy}{\sqrt{a(y^2 - \eta_1)(y^2 - \eta_2)}}, \tag{3}$$

where

$$a = \pm (q - \alpha)(q - \beta)(q - \gamma)(q - \delta), \tag{4}$$

$$\eta_1 = -\frac{(p - \alpha)(p - \beta)}{(q - \alpha)(q - \beta)}, \tag{5}$$

$$\eta_2 = -\frac{(p - \gamma)(p - \delta)}{(q - \gamma)(q - \delta)}, \tag{6}$$

provided

$$D = \alpha + \beta - \gamma - \delta \tag{7}$$

is $\neq 0$. *In case* $D = 0$, *we set*

$$x = y + \tfrac{1}{2}(\alpha + \beta) = y + \tfrac{1}{2}(\gamma + \delta) \tag{8}$$

and then

$$a = \pm 1 \quad , \quad \eta_1 = \tfrac{1}{4}(\alpha - \beta)^2 \quad , \quad \eta_2 = \tfrac{1}{4}(\gamma - \delta)^2. \tag{9}$$

Moreover if the coefficients of the polynomial P *are real, the coefficients* p, q *of the transformation* 1) *will be real. Also the transformation* 8), *which is to be employed when* $D = 0$, *is real when* α, β *or* γ, δ *are real or conjugate imaginaries. Finally,* η_1 *and* η_2 *are real.*

The verification of these statements is purely algebraic and aside from its length involves no difficulty. We therefore sketch it only. Let us consider first the transformation 1). By direct calculation we find that

$$\frac{dx}{\sqrt{\pm P}} = \frac{(q - p)dy}{\sqrt{\pm Q}},$$

where

$$Q = \{p - \alpha + (q - \alpha)y\}\{p - \beta + (q - \beta)y\}\{p - \gamma + (q - \gamma)y\}$$
$$\{p - \delta + (q - \delta)y\}.$$

Let us now choose p and q so that the odd powers of y drop out of Q. This requires that

$$(p - \alpha)(q - \beta) + (p - \beta)(q - \alpha) = 0.$$

$$(p - \gamma)(q - \delta) + (p - \delta)(q - \gamma) = 0.$$

Let us set $\lambda = \frac{1}{2}(p + q) \quad , \quad \mu = \frac{1}{2}(p - q).$

We find

$$\lambda = \frac{\alpha\beta - \gamma\delta}{D},$$

$$\mu^2 = \frac{(\alpha - \gamma)(\alpha - \delta)(\beta - \gamma)(\beta - \delta)}{D^2} = \frac{M}{D^2}.$$

But

$$p = \lambda + \mu \quad , \quad q = \lambda - \mu.$$

To show that p and q are real, we observe that the coefficients of P being by hypothesis real, there are three cases to consider:

1° Roots all real. Take $\alpha < \beta < \gamma < \delta$.

2° Two roots real. Take $\alpha = a + ib, \quad \beta = a - ib$.

3° All roots imaginary. Take α, β as in 2° and $\gamma = c + id$, $\delta = c - id$.

Obviously in each case λ is real. Thus p, q are real if μ is real and > 0. We now consider the three cases separately.

Case 1° All the factors of M are < 0; hence $M > 0$, $D^2 > 0$, and thus μ is > 0.

Case 2° Here

$$M = (a - \gamma + ib)(a - \delta + ib)(a - \gamma - ib)(a - \delta - ib).$$

Now the product of two conjugate numbers is real and positive, as we saw in 2, 6. Thus M, being the product of two such pairs, is real and > 0.

As D is real, μ is real and > 0.

Case 3° This is treated in a precisely similar manner. Thus in every case μ is real and > 0.

Finally, p, q being real, we see that η_1, η_2 are real. Thus our theorem is proved for the case that $D \neq 0$. The case that $D = 0$ is at once disposed of, and needs no comment.

182. Real Quadratic Transformations. Let us now show how by a quadratic transformation we can convert

$$\frac{dy}{\sqrt{a(y^2-\eta_1)(y^2-\eta_2)}} = \frac{dy}{\sqrt{Y}}, \quad \eta_1, \eta_2 \text{ real} \tag{1}$$

into

$$\frac{Mdz}{\sqrt{(1-z^2)(1-k^2z^2)}} = \frac{Mdz}{\sqrt{Z}} \tag{2}$$

in such a way that *if the variable y ranges over some interval $\mathfrak{A}$ for which Y is real and positive, the variable z will range in the interval $\mathfrak{B} = (0, 1)$. Moreover M and k^2 will be real and* $0 < k^2 < 1$.

There are six cases, as indicated in the table.

Case	a	η_1	η_2
1	+	+	+
2	+	−	+
3	+	−	−
4	−	+	+
5	−	−	+
6	−	−	−

Case 1. Suppose $\eta_1 < \eta_2$. As Y is to be > 0, we must have either

$$y^2 < \eta_1 \quad \text{or} \quad y^2 > \eta_2.$$

If $y^2 < \eta_1$, we take

$$y = z\sqrt{\eta_1}. \tag{3}$$

Then

$$M = \frac{1}{\sqrt{a\eta_2}}, \quad k^2 = \frac{\eta_1}{\eta_2}. \tag{4}$$

If $y^2 > \eta_2$, we take

$$y = \frac{\sqrt{\eta_2}}{z}. \tag{5}$$

Then

$$M = -\frac{1}{\sqrt{a\eta_2}}, \quad k^2 = \frac{\eta_1}{\eta_2}. \tag{6}$$

Case 2. As Y is to be > 0, we must have $y^2 > \eta_2$.
We set

$$y = \frac{\sqrt{\eta_2}}{\sqrt{1 - z^2}}. \tag{7}$$

Then

$$M = \frac{1}{\sqrt{a(\eta_2 - \eta_1)}}, \quad k^2 = \frac{-\eta_1}{\eta_2 - \eta_1}. \tag{8}$$

Case 3. Here $Y > 0$ for all values of y.
Let

$$|\eta_1| < |\eta_2|.$$

We set

$$y = \sqrt{-\eta_1}\,\frac{z}{\sqrt{1 - z^2}}. \tag{9}$$

Then

$$M = \frac{1}{\sqrt{-a\eta_2}}, \quad k^2 = 1 - \frac{\eta_1}{\eta_2}. \tag{10}$$

Case 4. As Y is to be > 0, we must have

$$\eta_1 < y^2 < \eta_2.$$

We set

$$y = \frac{\sqrt{\eta_1}}{\sqrt{1 - \left(1 - \frac{\eta_1}{\eta_2}\right) z^2}}. \tag{11}$$

Then

$$M = \frac{1}{\sqrt{-a\eta_2}}, \quad k^2 = \frac{\eta_2 - \eta_1}{\eta_2}. \tag{12}$$

Case 5. For Y to be > 0 we must have

$$\eta_1 < y^2 < \eta_2.$$

We set

$$y = \sqrt{\eta_2}\,\sqrt{1 - z^2}. \tag{13}$$

Then

$$M = -\frac{1}{\sqrt{-a(\eta_2 - \eta_1)}}, \quad k^2 = \frac{\eta_2}{\eta_2 - \eta_1}. \tag{14}$$

Case 6. As Y is to be > 0, this case is impossible.

183. Rectification of the Hyperbola. As an example let us find the length of an arc of the hyperbola

$$b^2x^2 - a^2y^2 = a^2b^2.$$

We have

$$s=\int\left(1+\left(\frac{dx}{dy}\right)^2\right)^{\frac{1}{2}}dy=\frac{1}{b}\int\left(\frac{c^2y^2+b^4}{y^2+b^2}\right)^{\frac{1}{2}}dy, \qquad c^2=a^2+b^2,$$

$$=\frac{1}{bc}\int\frac{(c^2y^2+b^4)dy}{\sqrt{(y^2+b^2)\left(y^2+\frac{b^4}{c^2}\right)}}=\frac{1}{bc}H. \tag{1}$$

If we set

$$\eta_1=-\frac{b^4}{c^2}, \quad \eta_2=-b^2,$$

we have

$$|\eta_1|<|\eta_2|.$$

The integral 1) falls under Case 3 of 182. We set therefore

$$y=\frac{b^2}{c}\cdot\frac{z}{\sqrt{1-z^2}} \tag{2}$$

and get

$$\frac{dy}{\sqrt{(y^2+b^2)\left(y^2+\frac{b^4}{c^2}\right)}}=\frac{dz}{b\sqrt{(1-z^2)(1-k^2z^2)}}=\frac{1}{b}\cdot\frac{dz}{\sqrt{Z}}, \quad k^2=\frac{a^2}{c^2}.$$

We note that k is the reciprocal of the eccentricity of the hyperbola. Thus putting 2) in H we get

$$H=b^3\int\frac{dz}{(1-z^2)\sqrt{Z}}=b^3J.$$

Let us set

$$z=\sin\phi,$$

then

$$J=\frac{c^2}{b^2}\left\{\tan\phi\cdot\Delta\phi+\frac{b^2}{c^2}F(\phi)-E(\phi)\right\}.$$

Hence finally

$$s=c\tan\phi\cdot\Delta\phi+\frac{b^2}{c}F(\phi)-cE(\phi), \tag{3}$$

in which the modulus k has the value determined by

$$k^2=\frac{a^2}{c^2}.$$

184. Rectification of the Lemniscate. We saw in 177, 9) that the arc s of the lemniscate is given by

$$s = a\int_0^x \frac{dx}{\sqrt{(1-x^2)(1-2x^2)}}$$
$$= \frac{a}{\sqrt{2}}\int_0^x \frac{dx}{\sqrt{(x^2-1)(x^2-\frac{1}{2})}}.$$

Here $0 < x^2 \leq \frac{1}{2}$ if the arc falls in the first quadrant. We take $\eta_1 = \frac{1}{2}$, $\eta_2 = 1$ and use the transformation

$$x = y\sqrt{\tfrac{1}{2}}$$

of Case 1 in 182. We get

$$s = \frac{a}{\sqrt{2}}\int_0^y \frac{dy}{\sqrt{(1-y^2)(1-k^2y^2)}}\ , \quad k^2 = \frac{1}{2}$$
$$= \frac{a}{\sqrt{2}}F(\phi).$$

For $\phi = \frac{\pi}{2}$, the arc is just one quadrant of the lemniscate. If we set $k = \sin\theta$, we see $\theta = 45°$. The value of the complete integral K for this modular angle is given by Legendre's *Tables Traité*, vol. 2, p. 327, as

$$K = 1.85407.$$

185. Elliptic Integral of the First Species. 1. Let us now consider the function u of z defined by

$$u = \int_0^z \frac{dz}{\sqrt{(1-z^2)(1-k^2z^2)}}. \qquad (1$$

When the modulus $k = 0$, this function degenerates to

$$u = \int_0^z \frac{dz}{\sqrt{1-z^2}} = \text{arc}\sin z.$$

Now the many-valued arc sin function is of much less service to us than the inverse function $z = \sin u$ which is one-valued and periodic. So we shall find also here that it is not the many-valued function u of z defined by 1) which interests us most, but the inverse function z of u. This we shall see presently is one-valued and doubly periodic. In analogy to the sine function we denote this function by

$$z = sn(u, k) \text{ or more shortly by } z = sn\, u. \tag{2}$$

and read *s*, *n of u*. In analogy to the cosine function we write

$$\sqrt{1 - z^2} = \sqrt{1 - sn^2 u} = cu\, u. \quad \text{(read } c, n \text{ of } u\text{)}.$$

If we set $z = \sin\phi$, as we did in 178,

$$\sqrt{1 - k^2 z^2} = \sqrt{1 - k^2 \sin^2\phi} = \Delta\phi$$

in Legendre's notation. In memory of the Δ we set

$$\sqrt{1 - k^2 z^2} = dn\, u \text{ (read } d, n \text{ of } u\text{)}.$$

Thus with the integral 1) are connected three elliptic functions

$$sn\, u \quad , \quad cn\, u \quad , \quad dn\, u.$$

These are the functions of Legendre and more especially of Jacobi. It is these functions which occur in all the older literature of elliptic functions and which to-day are still used by many mathematicians.

In the same way as the basis of the Weierstrassian theory of the elliptic functions is the σ function, so the base of the Jacobian theory are the ϑ functions, which are integral transcendental functions differing from the σ function only by exponential factors.

After this slight outlook, let us return to the function u of z defined by 1). The integrand

$$f(z) = \frac{1}{\sqrt{(1 - z^2)(1 - k^2 z^2)}} \tag{3}$$

is one-valued and analytic except at

$$z = \pm 1, \quad \pm \frac{1}{k}.$$

Obviously each of these points is a branch point and the two values of f permute when z describes a small circle $\mathfrak{K}$ about one of them. Thus in any region acyclic relative to each of these points u is a one-valued function of z.

One of the values of u for $z = 0$ is $u = 0$; also one of the values of f for $z = 0$ is $+1$. Let us start with these values and find the value that u acquires, call it $\bar{u}$, when z describes a circuit $\mathfrak{C}$ about the branch point $z=1$. Without changing the value of $\bar{u}$ we may replace $\mathfrak{C}$ by the loop $C = (0, \alpha, \beta, \gamma, 0)$ as in Fig. 1. The circle C has a radius r as small as we please. Thus

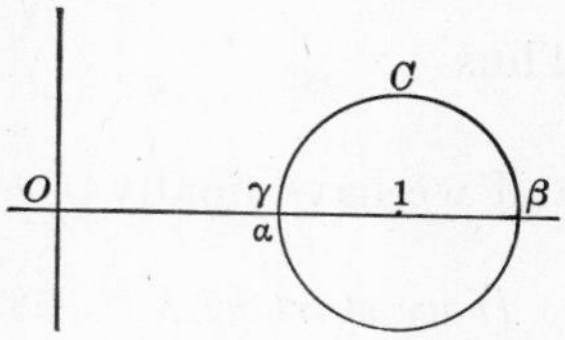

FIG. 1.

$$\bar{u} = \int_{\mathfrak{K}} = \int_0^\alpha + \int_C + \int^0 . \tag{4}$$

The first integral on the right differs from

$$K = \int_0^1 \frac{dz}{+\sqrt{(1-z^2)(1-k^2z^2)}} \tag{5}$$

by as little as we choose. Here the $+$ sign indicates that the radical has the value $+1$ for $z = 0$.

Let us look at the last integral in 4). When z leaves $z = 0$, f has the value $+1$. On reaching α it has a large positive value p. After z describes the circle C and arrives at γ, the two values which f has at this point have interchanged and the value of f is now $-p$. Thus as z describes the segment $\gamma, 0$, the integrand f has the same values as f had in describing the segment $0, \alpha$ except that its sign is changed. Hence as α and γ are really the same point,

$$\int_\gamma^0 = \int_\gamma^0 \frac{dz}{-\sqrt{}} = \int_0^\alpha \frac{dz}{+\sqrt{}} \doteq K \quad \text{as } r \doteq 0.$$

Turning now to the middle integral, we show this is 0. For let us set

$$z - 1 = re^{i\phi} \quad , \quad dz = rie^{i\phi}d\phi,$$

r being a constant on C. Then

$$\sqrt{(1-z^2)(1-k^2z^2)} = \sqrt{z-1} \cdot i\sqrt{(z+1)(1-k^2z^2)} = \sqrt{z-1} \cdot g(z),$$

where

$$|g(z)| > \text{some } G \quad , \quad \text{for all } z \text{ on } C.$$

Thus

$$\int_C f dz = \int_0^{2\pi} \frac{ir^{\frac{1}{2}}e^{\frac{1}{2}i\phi}}{g} d\phi,$$

and this is numerically

$$< \frac{2\pi}{G} \cdot r^{\frac{1}{2}} \quad \text{which} \doteq 0 \text{ as } r \doteq 0.$$

Thus

$$\int_C = 0,$$

and we have finally

$$\bar{u} = 2K. \qquad \text{Hence:}$$

If we start with the value $u=0$, $f=+1$ *at* $z=0$ *and let* z *describe a circuit about* $z=1$, u *will acquire the value* $2K$ *on returning to* $z=0$.

2. Let us set

$$L = \int_0^{\frac{1}{k}} \frac{dz}{+\sqrt{(1-z^2)(1-k^2z^2)}}, \tag{6}$$

where the + sign indicates that on starting out from $z=0$ the radical has the value $+1$. Precisely the same considerations show that if we start out from $z=0$ with the value $u=0$ and make a circuit $\mathfrak{L}$ about the branch point $z=\frac{1}{k}$, u acquires the value

$$\bar{u} = 2L$$

on reaching $z=0$ again.

3. We now suppose that z starts from $z=0$ and makes a circuit $\mathfrak{C}$ which includes both branch points $1, \frac{1}{k}$. We start with the values $u=0, f=+1$ and ask what value u has acquired on reaching $z=0$ again. If we denote it by $\bar{u}$, we have

$$\bar{u} = \int_{\mathfrak{C}} \frac{dz}{+\sqrt{\ }} = \int_{\mathfrak{K}} \frac{dz}{+\sqrt{\ }} + \int_{\mathfrak{L}} \frac{dz}{-\sqrt{\ }}. \tag{7}$$

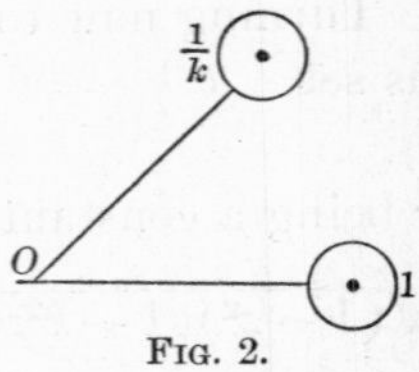

FIG. 2.

For in the first place $\mathfrak{C}$ may be replaced by $\mathfrak{K} \cdot \mathfrak{L}$ as in Fig. 2, since the region lying between these two curves contains no singular point of $f(z)$. Secondly, in the last integral in 7) we have the $-$ sign because when z reaches $z=0$ after the circuit $\mathfrak{K}$ about $z=1$, the radical has the value -1, and it is with this value, therefore, that we start out to make the circuit $\mathfrak{L}$ about $z=\frac{1}{k}$. Thus

$$\bar{u} = 2K - 2L. \tag{8}$$

Since we can deform any path of integration without changing the value of the integral u, provided that in so doing we do not pass a singular point of the integrand f, we see that the circuit $\mathfrak{K} \cdot \mathfrak{L}$ can be replaced by that in Fig. 3, which we will call $\mathfrak{M}$. Thus

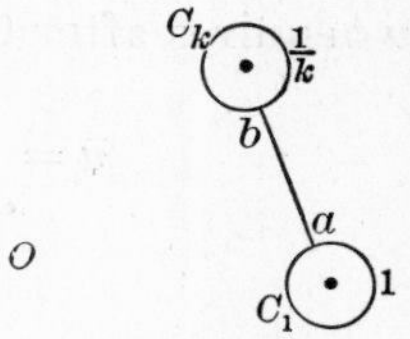

FIG. 3.

$$\bar{u} = \int_{\mathfrak{M}} = \int_{C_1} + \int_a^b \frac{dz}{+\sqrt{}} + \int_{C_k} + \int_b^a \frac{dz}{-\sqrt{}}. \tag{9}$$

Now as before

$$\int_{C_1} = 0 \quad , \quad \int_{C_k} = 0,$$

$$\int_b^a \frac{dz}{-\sqrt{}} = \int_a^b \frac{dz}{+\sqrt{}}.$$

If we let the radius r of the two circles C_1, C_k converge to 0, the last integral converges to a value denoted by Jacobi by

$$iK' = \int_1^{\frac{1}{k}} \frac{dz}{+\sqrt{(1-z^2)(1-k^2z^2)}}. \tag{10}$$

These results put in 9) give

$$\bar{u} = 2\,iK'. \tag{11}$$

To explain why the integral 10) is denoted by iK' instead of by K' we remark that in practice the modulus k is such that k^2 is real and <1. Then $(1-z^2)(1-k^2z^2)$ is real and negative in the segment $\left(1, \frac{1}{k}\right)$ and thus the integral 10) is purely imaginary. The notation iK' in 10) is therefore quite appropriate.

Equating the two values of $\bar{u}$ in 8), 11) shows that

$$2\,K - 2\,L = 2\,iK'. \tag{12}$$

4. Suppose next that z makes a circuit $\mathfrak{C}$ as in Fig. 4, which includes the two branch points $z = \pm 1$. If we start with $u = 0$, $f = +1$, let $\bar{u}$ be the value which

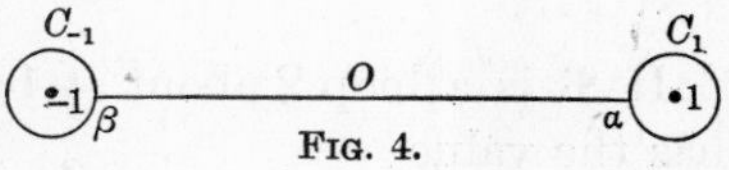

FIG. 4.

u acquires after $\mathfrak{C}$. Then

$$\bar{u} = \int_{\mathfrak{C}} \frac{dz}{+\sqrt{}} = \int_0^\alpha \frac{dz}{+\sqrt{}} + \int_{C_1} + \int_\alpha^0 \frac{dz}{-\sqrt{}}$$

$$+ \int_0^\beta \frac{dz}{-\sqrt{}} + \int_{C_{-1}} + \int_\beta^0 \frac{dz}{+\sqrt{}}.$$

As before $$\int_{C_1} = 0 \quad , \quad \int_{C_{-1}} = 0,$$

$$\int_\alpha^0 \frac{dz}{-\sqrt{}} = \int_0^\alpha \frac{dz}{+\sqrt{}} \doteq K \quad , \quad \text{as } \alpha \doteq 1.$$

Moreover since $f(-z) = f(z)$,

$$\int_0^\beta \frac{dz}{-\sqrt{}} = \int_0^\alpha \frac{dz}{+\sqrt{}} = \int_\beta^0 \frac{dz}{+\sqrt{}} \doteq K \quad , \quad \text{as } \beta \doteq -1.$$

Thus, $$\bar{u} = 4\,K.$$

5. Let us now ask what values u can acquire when beginning with the initial values $z = 0$, $z = +1$, $u = 0$, z describes any path $\mathfrak{P}$ not passing through a branch point, and ending at some point z.

Let U be its value along the path Oz as in Fig. 5. If $\mathfrak{P}$ is a loop $\mathfrak{L}$ about $z = 1$ followed by Oz, we have

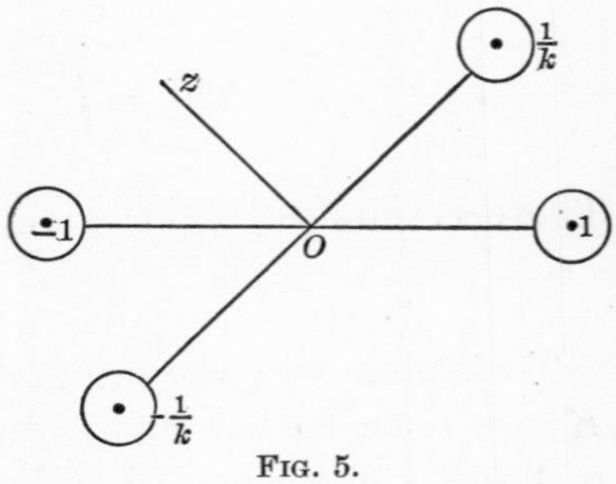

FIG. 5.

$$u = \int_{\mathfrak{P}} \frac{dz}{+\sqrt{}} = \int_{\mathfrak{L}} \frac{dz}{+\sqrt{}} + \int_0^z \frac{dz}{-\sqrt{}}.$$

In the last integral the radical has the $-$ sign as indicated, since on returning to $z = 0$ after $\mathfrak{L}$, f has acquired the value -1, instead of $+1$. Thus,

$$u = 2\,K - U. \qquad (13$$

If $\mathfrak{P}$ is a loop $\mathfrak{L}$ about $+1$ and -1, followed by the path Oz, u has the value

$$u = \int_{\mathfrak{L}} \frac{dz}{+\sqrt{}} + \int_0^z \frac{dz}{+\sqrt{}}.$$

For on returning to $z = 0$ after the loop $\mathfrak{L}$, the radical has changed its sign once in going about $z = 1$ and once about $z = -1$. It therefore reaches $z = 0$ at the end of $\mathfrak{L}$ with the value $+1$. Thus

$$u = 4K + U.$$

If $\mathfrak{P}$ is a loop $\mathfrak{L}$ about $z = 1$ and $z = \frac{1}{k}$, followed by Oz, we have

$$u = \int_{\mathfrak{L}} \frac{dz}{+\sqrt{\ }} + \int_0^z \frac{dz}{+\sqrt{\ }}$$
$$= 2iK' + U.$$

If $\mathfrak{P}$ is a loop $\mathfrak{L}$ about $z = 1$, followed by a loop $\mathfrak{M}$ about both $z = 1$ and $z = -1$ and finishing with Oz, we have

$$u = \int_{\mathfrak{L}} \frac{dz}{+\sqrt{\ }} + \int_{\mathfrak{M}} \frac{dz}{-\sqrt{\ }} + \int_0^z \frac{dz}{-\sqrt{\ }}$$
$$= 2K - 4K - U.$$
$$= 2K - U - 4K.$$

We see this differs by $-4K$ from the value of u in 13). By choosing various paths we find that all the values which u can acquire at a point z are given by

$$u = U + m\,4K + m'\,2iK'$$

and

$$u = 2K - U + m\,4K + m'\,2iK', \tag{14}$$

where m, m' are positive or negative integers or 0. Thus we may state:

The analytic function u defined by 1) *is an infinite many-valued function of z. If U is one value which u has at a point z, all the other values which u has at this point are represented by* 14).

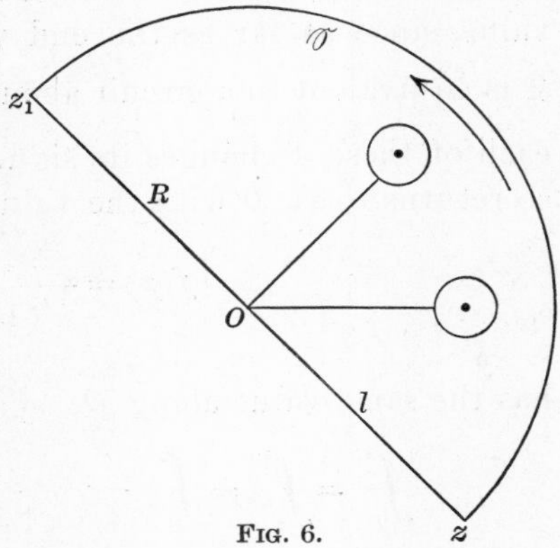

FIG. 6.

6. We have seen that u remains finite for finite z. Let us see what value u has as $z \doteq \infty$ along some line l as in Fig. 6. The calculation is easily effected

if we note that $0z\mathfrak{S}z_1 0$ is a circuit $\mathfrak{K}$ which embraces the two branch points $z = 1, \dfrac{1}{k}$. As this is the same circuit as considered in 3 we have

$$\int_{\mathfrak{K}} = 2\,iK'.\tag{15}$$

But

$$\int_{\mathfrak{K}+\sqrt{}}\frac{dz}{} = \int_0^z + \int_{\mathfrak{S}} + \int_{z_1}^0.\tag{16}$$

The second integral

$$\int_{\mathfrak{S}} \doteq 0 \quad \text{as} \quad R \doteq \infty.$$

For let us set

$$z = Re^{i\phi}$$

so that on the circle $\mathfrak{S}$

$$dz = Rie^{i\phi}d\phi = iz\,d\phi.$$

Hence

$$\int_{\mathfrak{S}} = i\int_{\phi_0}^{\phi_0+\pi} \frac{z\,d\phi}{\sqrt{(1-z^2)(1-k^2z^2)}}.$$

If R is taken sufficiently large,

$$\left|\frac{z}{\sqrt{(1-z^2)(1-k^2z^2)}}\right| < \epsilon$$

for all z on $\mathfrak{S}$. Thus

$$\left|\int_{\mathfrak{S}}\right| < \epsilon\pi \doteq 0 \quad \text{as} \quad R \doteq \infty.$$

Now, when z leaves $z = 0$, the integrand $f(z)$ has the value $+1$. After it describes the circuit $\mathfrak{K}$ it returns to $z = 0$ with the same value, since as far as the end value of f is concerned, the circuit $\mathfrak{K}$ is equivalent to a circuit about each branch point $\dfrac{1}{k}$ and 1. For each of these, f changes its sign. Thus it changes sign twice and so returns to $z = 0$ with the value $+1$. Thus

$$f(z) = \frac{1}{\sqrt{(1-z^2)(1-k^2z^2)}}$$

has the same value along Oz as along Oz_1. Hence

$$\int_0^z = \int_z^0 \doteq \int_0^\infty \frac{dz}{+\sqrt{(1-z^2)(1-k^2z^2)}}, \quad \text{as } z \doteq \infty.$$

This with 15), 16) gives

$$iK' = \int_0^\infty \frac{dz}{+\sqrt{(1-z^2)(1-k^2z^2)}}. \tag{17}$$

Thus the different values which u has for $z = \infty$ are

$$iK' + 2\,mK + 2\,m'iK'. \tag{18}$$

186. Inversion. 1. In the foregoing section we have considered the function u of z defined by

$$u = \int_0^z \frac{dz}{\sqrt{(1-z^2)(1-k^2z^2)}} = \int_0^z f(z)dz. \tag{1}$$

Let us now look at the inverse function z of u. This we said is denoted by

$$z = sn(u). \tag{2}$$

Since the integrand $f(z)$ is a one-valued analytic function about $z = 0$, u can be developed in a power series. It may be obtained thus: Since

$$f = (1-z^2)^{-\frac{1}{2}}(1-k^2z^2)^{-\frac{1}{2}},$$

we may develop each factor

$$(1-z^2)^{-\frac{1}{2}} \quad \text{and} \quad (1-k^2z^2)^{-\frac{1}{2}}$$

by the Binomial Theorem and get two power series in z. These two series when multiplied together give

$$f = 1 + \tfrac{1}{2}(1+k^2)z^2 + \tfrac{1}{8}(3 + 2\,k^2 + 3\,k^4)z^4 + \cdots$$

Integrating, we get

$$u = z + \tfrac{1}{6}(1+k^2)z^3 + \tfrac{1}{40}(3 + 2\,k^2 + 3\,k^4)z^5 + \cdots \tag{3}$$

which is valid for $|z| <$ *either* 1 *or* $\dfrac{1}{|k|}$.

If we invert this series by 125, we get

$$z = u - \frac{1}{3\,!}(1+k^2)u^3 + \frac{1}{5\,!}(1 + 14\,k^2 + k^4)u^5 - \cdots \tag{4}$$

which is valid in some circle $\mathfrak{c}$ whose center is $u = 0$.

By analytic continuation we may extend the function so as to define it for values of u outside $\mathfrak{c}$. It can be shown in various ways that the analytic function defined by 1) is an elliptic function, having $4K$, $2iK'$ as a primitive pair of periods. Its zeros are $\equiv 0$ and its poles are $\equiv iK'$ mod $2K$, $2iK'$, each of order 1.

It was by inverting the integral 1) that Legendre, Abel, and Jacobi were led to consider the elliptic functions. We have seen that Legendre set

$$z = \sin \phi.$$

From this point of view it was at once evident that z admits the period $4K$. But Legendre, using for the most part real variables, failed to notice that z possesses also an imaginary period, that in fact z is a double periodic function.

The discovery of this property by Abel about 1825 enabled him and Jacobi to develop the theory of elliptic functions in the next few years far more than their predecessors had done in half a century.

Because of the fundamental nature of the double periodicity of the elliptic functions, we began our treatment of these functions in the preceding chapter from this point of view. At the same time the older theory is so interwoven in the modern that we have not hesitated in treating the functions of Legendre and Jacobi to start from the elliptic integrals and work up to the elliptic functions. This point of view is also useful in those applications which lead at once to an an elliptic integral.

2. To show that the inverse function $z = sn\ u$ is in fact an elliptic function, let us actually write down such a function which satisfies the differential equation

$$\frac{dz}{du} = \sqrt{(1 - z^2)(1 - k^2 z^2)}, \qquad (5$$

the radical having the plus sign for $z = 0$. The constant of integration we will determine by taking $z = 0$ for $u = 0$. There cannot be two such analytic functions. For both having the same derivative 5) about $u = 0$, they can differ only by an additive constant and as $z = 0$ for $u = 0$, this constant must be 0.

3. To this end we consider the function q of 176. We saw that q is an elliptic function which satisfies the differential equation

$$\frac{dq}{du} = \sqrt{(1-(e_1-e_2)q^2)(1-(e_3-e_2)q^2)}. \tag{6}$$

Let us choose e_1, e_2, e_3 so that

$$k^2 = \frac{e_3 - e_2}{e_1 - e_2} \tag{7}$$

and set

$$z = \sqrt{e_1 - e_2} \cdot q.$$

Then z satisfies the equation

$$\frac{dz}{du} = \sqrt{e_1 - e_2}\sqrt{(1-z^2)(1-k^2z^2)}.$$

To remove the factor on the right we set

$$u = \frac{v}{\sqrt{e_1 - e_2}},$$

which gives

$$\frac{dz}{dv} = \sqrt{(1-z^2)(1-k^2z^2)}. \tag{8}$$

Thus

$$z = \sqrt{e_1 - e_2} \cdot \sigma_{02}\left(\frac{v}{\sqrt{e_1 - e_2}}\ ,\ \omega_1\ ,\ \omega_2\right) \tag{9}$$

is a solution of 5). As $z = 0$ for $v = 0$, the function 9) must be 4), replacing u by v, or $sn\, v$.

We saw in 176 that $\sigma_{02}(u)$ is a homogeneous function of z, ω_1, ω_2 of degree 1. We can thus write 9)

$$z = \sigma_{02}(v\ ,\ \omega_1\sqrt{e_1 - e_2}\ ,\ \omega_2\sqrt{e_1 - e_2}), \tag{10}$$

whose periods are

$$4\,K = 4\,\omega_1\sqrt{e_1 - e_2}\ ,\quad 2\,iK' = 2\,\omega_2\sqrt{e_1 - e_2}, \tag{11}$$

whose zeros are $\equiv 0$, and whose poles are $\equiv iK'$, mod $2\,K$, $2\,iK'$.

4. Having assured ourselves that the inverse function $z = sn\, u$ is a *one-valued* function throughout the whole plane, $z = \infty$ included, let us see how the study of the integral

$$u = \int_0 \frac{dz}{\sqrt{(1-z^2)(1-kz^{22})}} \tag{12}$$

shows us:

1° z is a double periodic function with the periods

$$4\,K = 4\int_0^1 \frac{dz}{\sqrt{(1-z^2)(1-k^2z^2)}},$$

$$2\,iK' = 2\int_1^{\frac{1}{k}} \frac{dz}{\sqrt{(1-z^2)(1-k^2z^2)}}, \qquad (13$$

2° z has as simple zeros the points $\equiv 0$,

3° and as simple poles the points $\equiv iK'$ both mod $2\,K$, $2\,iK'$.

This will be an *a posteriori* verification, but it is very instructive. Precisely this path was followed by Cauchy and his successors.

5. To begin, the relations 185, 14) show that $sn\,u$ admits $4\,K$ and $2\,iK'$ as periods, while the reasoning of 185, 6 shows that $sn\,u$ remains finite except in the vicinity of the points

$$c = iK' + 2\,mK + 2\,m'iK'. \qquad (14$$

Let us show that these are poles of the first order for $sn\,u$. We write 12)

$$u = \int_0^{\infty} + \int_{\infty}^{z} = c + w, \qquad (15$$

where c has the value given in 14). We wish to see how w behaves about $z = \infty$.

If we set $z = \frac{1}{t}$, it becomes

$$w = -\int_0^t \frac{dt}{\sqrt{(k^2-t^2)(1-t^2)}} = \int_0^t \frac{1}{k}\{-1 + c_1t^2 + c_2t^4 + \cdots\}dt$$

$$= -\frac{1}{k}\cdot t + \frac{1}{3}\frac{c_1}{k}t^3 + \cdots$$

This shows, using 125, that t considered as a function of w is a one-valued analytic function.

$$t = w(-k + b_1w + b_2w^2 + \cdots). \qquad (16$$

Hence

$$z = \frac{1}{t} = \frac{1}{u-c}\left\{-\frac{1}{k} + d_1(u-c) + d_2(u-c)^2 + \cdots\right\}, \qquad (17$$

and $u = c$ is a pole of the first order.

6. Let us show that the points $u \equiv 0 \mod 2K,\ 2iK'$ at which $sn\, u = 0$ are simple zeros. In the vicinity of $z = 0$ we have

$$\frac{1}{\sqrt{(1-z^2)(1-k^2z^2)}} = 1 + a_1 z + a_2 z^2 + \cdots$$

Hence

$$u = \int \frac{dz}{\sqrt{\quad}} = c + c_1 z + c_2 z^2 + \cdots \qquad c_1 = 1, \tag{18}$$

where c is given in 14). The relation 18) shows that

$$z = (u-c)\{e_0 + e_1(u-c) + e_2(u-c)^2 + \cdots\} \tag{19}$$

and thus $u = c$ is a simple zero.

7. Let us show that z is a one-valued analytic function about the point u for which $z = \pm 1,\ \pm\frac{1}{k}$. These latter points are points in whose vicinity the integrand of 12) becomes infinite.

Let us set

$$z - 1 = t^2 \quad ; \quad \text{then } dz = 2\,tdt.$$

Also

$$\sqrt{(1-z^2)(1-k^2z^2)} = \sqrt{z-1}\,\sqrt{(z+1)(k^2z^2-1)} = t\{a_0 + a_1 t + \cdots\}.$$

Thus

$$\frac{1}{\sqrt{\quad}} = \frac{1}{t}\{b_0 + b_1 t + \cdots\},$$

$$du = 2(b_0 + b_1 t + \cdots)dt,$$

$$u = c_0 + c_1 t^2 + c_2 t^3 + \cdots \quad , \quad c_1 \neq 0, \tag{20}$$

where c_0 is one of the values which u has for $t = 0$, that is, for $z = 1$. These values are all $\equiv \pm K$.

The relation 20) defines t as a one-valued function of u in the vicinity of $u = c_0$. As $z = 1 + t^2$ this gives

$$z - 1 = d_1(u - c_0) + d_2(u - c_0)^2 + \cdots \tag{21}$$

Thus z is a one-valued function of u about $u = c_0$.

187. The *sn*, *cn* and *dn* Functions. 1. We have now two definitions of $z = sn\, u$; one as the inverse of

$$u = \int_0^z \frac{dz}{\sqrt{(1-z^2)(1-k^2z^2)}}, \tag{1}$$

the other as

$$z = sn u = \sqrt{e_1 - e_2} \cdot \sigma_{02}(v, \omega_1, \omega_2) \quad , \quad v = \frac{u}{\sqrt{e_1 - e_2}} \tag{2}$$

$$= \frac{\sqrt{e_1 - e_2}}{\sqrt{p(v) - e_2}}, \tag{3}$$

where

$$k^2 = \frac{e_3 - e_2}{e_1 - e_2}. \tag{4}$$

The radicals

$$\sqrt{1 - z^2} \quad , \quad \sqrt{1 - k^2 z^2},$$

although two-valued functions of z, are one-valued functions of u. For from 3) we have

$$1 - z^2 = \frac{p - e_1}{p - e_2} = \frac{\sigma_1^2(v)}{\sigma_2^2(v)} = \sigma_{12}^2(v).$$

Hence

$$cn\, u = \sqrt{1 - z^2} = \frac{\sigma_1(v)}{\sigma_2(v)} \quad , \quad cn(0) = 1. \tag{5}$$

Similarly

$$dn\, u = \sqrt{1 - k^2 z^2} = \frac{\sigma_3(v)}{\sigma_2(v)} \quad , \quad dn(0) = 1. \tag{6}$$

If we set

$$z = \sin \phi,$$

the integral 1) becomes

$$u = \int_0^\phi \frac{d\phi}{\sqrt{1 - k^2 \sin^2 \phi}} = \int_0^\phi \frac{d\phi}{\Delta\phi}. \tag{7}$$

Then

$$sn\, u \quad , \quad cn\, u \quad , \quad dn\, u \tag{8}$$

become in Legendre's notation

$$\sin \phi \quad , \quad \cos \phi \quad , \quad \Delta\phi, \tag{9}$$

as already remarked.

2. We wish now to deduce a number of properties of the functions 8) from the definition of $sn\, u$ as the inverse of the integral 1), and from the definition of $cn\, u$, $dn\, u$ by the relations

$$cn\, u = \sqrt{1 - sn^2\, u} \quad , \quad dn\, u = \sqrt{1 - k^2 sn^2\, u}. \tag{10}$$

This is the older point of view and will accustom the reader to the use of integrals as an instrument of research. Later we propose to study these functions from the standpoint of the ϑ functions.

Let us first find the periods of $cn\,u$. We take up the considerations of 185. Allowing z to describe a circuit about $z = 1$, u goes over into $u + 2K$, while $\sqrt{1 - z^2}$ changes its sign. Thus

$$cn(u + 2K) = -cn\,u.$$

Hence $cn\,u$ has $4K$ as a period.

If we let z describe a circuit which contains both $z = 1$ and $\frac{1}{k}$, u goes over into $u + 2iK'$, while $\sqrt{1 - z^2}$ changes sign. Hence

$$cn(u + 2iK') = -cn\,u.$$

Thus $cn\,u$ has the period $2K + 2iK'$. In a similar manner we may reason on $dn\,u$. Thus we can draw up the table:

	Periods
$sn\,u$	$4K, 2iK'$
$cn\,u$	$4K, 2K + 2iK'$
$dn\,u$	$2K, 4iK'$

The poles of $cn\,u$, $dn\,u$ are obviously the same as those of $sn\,u$, as seen from 10), and they are of order 1.

From 10) we see that $cn\,u = 0$ when $sn^2 u = 1$. But $sn\,K = 1$. Hence by 185, 10) all the points u at which $sn\,u = 1$ are given by $K + 4mK + 2m'iK'$. As $sn^2 u$ is even, the points at which $sn^2 u = 1$ are $K + 2mK + 2m'iK'$. In a similar manner we may reason on $dn\,u$.

We may thus draw up the table:

	Zeros	Poles
$sn\,u$	$2mK + 2m'iK'$	$2mK + (2m' + 1)iK'$
$cn\,u$	$(2m + 1)K + 2m'iK'$	$2mK + (2m' + 1)iK'$
$dn\,u$	$(2m + 1)K + (2m' + 1)iK'$	$2mK + (2m' + 1)iK'$

Since $sn\,u$, $cn\,u$, $dn\,u$ have each two poles only in a parallelogram formed of the periods given in the first table, these periods are *primitive* pairs of periods.

3. Let z move from 0 to 1, at which point $u = K$. Hence

$$sn\,K = 1 \quad , \quad cn\,K = 0 \quad , \quad dn\,K = \sqrt{1-k^2} = k', \tag{11}$$

if with Legendre we set

$$k' = \sqrt{1-k^2}, \tag{12}$$

taking the positive determination of the radical for $k = 0$. This is called the *complementary modulus*. The introduction of k' is quite natural from Legendre's point of view. For as we have seen, he set $k = \sin\theta$; hence $\cos\theta$ would be k'.

Next let z move from 0 to $\frac{1}{k}$, at which point $u = K + iK'$. Then

$$\begin{aligned} sn(K+iK') &= \frac{1}{k}, \\ cn(K+iK') &= \sqrt{1-\frac{1}{k^2}} = \pm\frac{ik'}{k}, \\ dn(K+iK') &= 0. \end{aligned} \tag{13}$$

To determine the sign in the second equation let us take k real positive and < 1. We let z move over the path $0\,azc\frac{1}{k}$ in the figure. When $z = 0$, $\sqrt{1-z^2}$ has the value $+1$. Thus at $z = a$, $\sqrt{1-z^2}$ is real and positive. We set

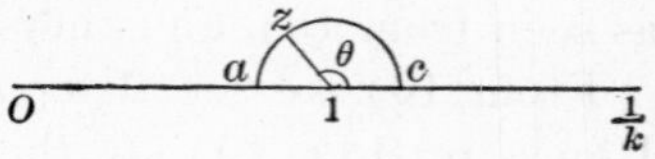

$$1 - z = re^{i(\theta-\pi)}.$$

Then

$$\sqrt{1-z} = r^{\frac{1}{2}}e^{\frac{1}{2}i(\theta-\pi)},$$

and take $\sqrt{1+z}$ with positive sign. Then $\sqrt{1-z^2}$ is real and positive at a, as it must be; but at c, $\sqrt{1-z}$ becomes

$$r^{\frac{1}{2}}e^{-\frac{\pi i}{2}} = -ir^{\frac{1}{2}},$$

which is negative imaginary. Thus at $z = \frac{1}{k}$, the radical is negative imaginary. Hence we must take the $-$ sign in 13).

Thus from the foregoing we may write down the following table:

	0	K	$2K$	$3K$
0	0 1 1	1 0 k'	0 -1 1	-1 0 k'
iK'	∞	$1/k$ $-ik'/k$ 0	∞	$-1/k$ ik'/k 0
$2iK'$	0 -1 -1	1 0 $-k'$	0 1 -1	-1 0 $-k'$
$3iK'$	∞	$1/k$ ik'/k 0	∞	$-1/k$ $-ik'/k$ 0

In each square the values of $sn\,u$, $cn\,u$, $dn\,u$ are given in order for

$$\mu = mK + m'iK' \quad , \quad m,\ m' = 0,\ 1,\ 2,\ 3.$$

In the table m refers to the columns and m' to the rows. Thus for $u = 3\,K + iK'$

$$sn\,u \quad , \quad cn\,u \quad , \quad dn\,u$$

$$= -\frac{1}{k} \quad , \quad \frac{ik'}{k} \quad , \quad 0.$$

188. The Addition Formulæ. 1. If we set

$$u = \int_1^x \frac{dx}{x} \quad , \quad v = \int_1^y \frac{dy}{y} \quad , \quad w = \int_1^{xy} \frac{dz}{z},$$

the addition theorem

$$\log xy = \log x + \log y$$

states that

$$w = u + v,$$

or that

$$\int_1^x + \int_1^y = \int_1^{xy}. \tag{1}$$

2. Let us set

$$u = \int_0^x \frac{dx}{\sqrt{1 - x^2}}. \tag{2}$$

The inverse function defined by this relation is $x = \sin u$. The addition theorem for the sine function is

$$\sin w = \sin(u+v) = \sin u \cos v + \cos u \sin v. \tag{3}$$

Let us therefore set

$$v = \int_0^y \frac{dy}{\sqrt{1-y^2}}, \quad w = \int_0^z \frac{dz}{\sqrt{1-z^2}}.$$

The relation 3) states that

$$z = x\sqrt{1-y^2} + y\sqrt{1-x^2}, \tag{4}$$

and hence

$$\int_0^x + \int_0^y = \int_0^{x\sqrt{1-y^2}+y\sqrt{1-x^2}}. \tag{5}$$

3. Let us set

$$u = \int_0^x \frac{dx}{\sqrt{(1-x^2)(1-k^2x^2)}} = \int_0^x \frac{dx}{\Delta(x)}. \tag{6}$$

For $k=0$ this integral reduces to 2). It occurred to Euler that the integrals 6) might have an addition theorem, that is, the sum of two integrals

$$\int_0^x + \int_0^y$$

might be expressed as a single integral

$$\int_0^z$$

in which z is some algebraic function of x, y as in 4). This relation he found to exist; it is in fact

$$z = \frac{x\sqrt{(1-y^2)(1-k^2y^2)} + y\sqrt{(1-x^2)(1-k^2x^2)}}{1-k^2x^2y^2}. \tag{7}$$

Thus if we set, similar to 2

$$v = \int_0^y \frac{dy}{\sqrt{(1-y^2)(1-k^2y^2)}},$$

$$w = u + v = \int_0^z \frac{dz}{\sqrt{(1-z^2)(1-k^2z^2)}},$$

we may write 7)

$$sn(u+v) = \frac{sn\,u\;cn\,v\;dn\,v + sn\,v\;cn\,u\;dn\,u}{1 - k^2 sn^2\,u\;sn^2\,v}$$

$$= \frac{sn\,u\;sn'v + sn\,v\;sn'u}{1 - k^2 sn^2\,u\;sn^2\,v}. \tag{8}$$

To obtain the relation 7) we notice that the differential equation

$$\frac{dx}{\Delta x} + \frac{dy}{\Delta y} = 0 \tag{9}$$

admits as integral

$$\int_0^x \frac{dx}{\Delta x} + \int_0^y \frac{dy}{\Delta y} = C. \tag{10}$$

If this integral is determined by the condition that when $x = 0$, y shall have the value z, the relation 10) shows that the constant C of integration must have the value

$$C = \int_0^z \frac{dz}{\Delta z}. \tag{11}$$

The value of C may also be obtained, as Darboux has shown, as follows:

Let us introduce a new variable defined by

$$ds = \frac{dx}{\Delta x}. \tag{12}$$

Then 9) becomes

$$ds + \frac{dy}{\Delta y} = 0,$$

or

$$\frac{dx}{ds} = \Delta x \;, \quad \frac{dy}{ds} = -\Delta y. \tag{13}$$

Hence

$$\frac{d^2x}{ds^2} = 2\,k^2x^3 - (1+k^2)x,$$

$$\frac{d^2y}{ds^2} = 2\,k^2y^3 - (1+k^2)y,$$

$$y\frac{d^2x}{ds^2} - x\frac{d^2x}{ds^2} = 2\,k^2xy(x^2 - y^2),$$

$$y^2\left(\frac{dx}{ds}\right)^2 - x^2\left(\frac{dy}{ds}\right)^2 = -(1 - k^2x^2y^2)(x^2 - y^2).$$

Thus

$$\frac{y\dfrac{d^2x}{ds^2}-x\dfrac{d^2y}{ds^2}}{y^2\left(\dfrac{dx}{ds}\right)^2-x^2\left(\dfrac{dy}{ds}\right)^2}=-\frac{2\,k^2xy}{1-k^2x^2y^2}.$$

If we multiply this by

$$y\frac{dx}{ds}+x\frac{dy}{ds},$$

we get

$$\frac{y\dfrac{d^2x}{ds^2}-x\dfrac{d^2y}{ds^2}}{y\dfrac{dx}{ds}-x\dfrac{dy}{ds}}=-\frac{2\,k^2xy\left(y\dfrac{dx}{ds}+x\dfrac{dy}{ds}\right)}{1-k^2x^2y^2},$$

or

$$d\log\left(y\frac{dx}{ds}-x\frac{dy}{ds}\right)=d\log(1-k^2x^2y^2).$$

Integrating, we get

$$\log\left(y\frac{dx}{ds}-x\frac{dy}{ds}\right)=\log(1-k^2x^2y^2)+\log c,$$

or using 13), we have

$$y\Delta x+x\Delta y=c(1-k^2x^2y^2). \tag{14}$$

This is an integral of 9). To determine c we must have $y=z$ for $x=0$. This in 14) gives $c=z$. Hence by 14)

$$z=\frac{y\Delta x+x\Delta y}{1-k^2x^2y^2},$$

which is 7).

4. By means of simple but rather lengthy reductions we get

$$cn(u+v)=\frac{cn\,u\,cn\,v-sn\,u\,dn\,u\,sn\,v\,dn\,v}{1-k^2sn^2\,u\,sn^2\,v}, \tag{15}$$

$$dn(u+v)=\frac{dn\,u\,dn\,v-k^2sn\,u\,cn\,u\,sn\,v\,cn\,v}{1-k^2sn^2\,u\,sn^2\,v}. \tag{16}$$

From 8), 15), 16) we may also derive :

$$sn(u+v)sn(u-v) = \frac{sn^2 u - sn^2 v}{1 - k^2 sn^2 u\, sn^2 v}, \tag{17}$$

$$cn(u+v)cn(u-v) = \frac{cn^2 v - sn^2 u\, dn^2 v}{1 - k^2 sn^2 u\, sn^2 v}, \tag{18}$$

$$dn(u+v)dn(u-v) = \frac{dn^2 v - k^2 sn^2 u\, cn^2 v}{1 - k^2 sn^2 u\, sn^2 v}. \tag{19}$$

189. Differential Equation for K and K'. 1. We saw that

$$K = \int_0^{\frac{\pi}{2}} \frac{d\phi}{\sqrt{1 - k^2 \sin^2\phi}}. \tag{1}$$

When $|k^2| < 1$ we can develop the integrand, getting

$$(1 - k^2 \sin^2\phi)^{-\frac{1}{2}} = 1 + \sum_{n=1}^{\infty} \frac{1 \cdot 3 \cdot 5 \cdots (2n-1)}{2 \cdot 4 \cdot 6 \cdots 2n} k^{2n} \sin^{2n}\phi. \tag{2}$$

But from the calculus we know that

$$\int_0^{\frac{\pi}{2}} \sin^{2n}\phi\, d\phi = \frac{1 \cdot 3 \cdot 5 \cdots (2n-1)}{2 \cdot 4 \cdot 6 \cdots 2n} \cdot \frac{\pi}{2}.$$

Thus integrating 2) termwise gives

$$K = \frac{\pi}{2}\left\{1 + \left(\frac{1}{2}\right)^2 k^2 + \left(\frac{1 \cdot 3}{2 \cdot 4}\right)^2 k^4 + \left(\frac{1 \cdot 3 \cdot 5}{2 \cdot 4 \cdot 6}\right)^2 k^6 + \cdots\right\} \tag{3}$$

valid for $|k^2| < 1$.

Comparing this with 103, 5) we see that

$$K = \frac{\pi}{2} F\left(\frac{1}{2}, \frac{1}{2}, 1, k^2\right). \tag{4}$$

This relation, holding for $|k^2| < 1$, must hold throughout its analytic continuation.

2. The other period $2iK'$ we saw in 186, 13) is defined by

$$2iK' = 2\int_1^{\frac{1}{k}} \frac{dx}{\sqrt{(1-x^2)(1-k^2x^2)}} = 2i\int_1^{\frac{1}{k}} \frac{dx}{\sqrt{(x^2-1)(1-k^2x^2)}}.$$

Let us set

$$x = \frac{1}{\sqrt{1 - k'^2 u^2}} \quad , \quad k'^2 = 1 - k^2.$$

Then to $x = 1$, $x = \frac{1}{k}$ correspond $u = 0$ and $u = 1$. We thus get

$$K' = \int_0^1 \frac{du}{\sqrt{(1 - u^2)(1 - k'^2 u^2)}}. \tag{5}$$

Comparing with 4) we see that

$$K' = \frac{\pi}{2} F\left(\frac{1}{2}, \frac{1}{2}, 1, k'^2\right). \tag{6}$$

3. We saw in 103, 4 that $F(\alpha\beta\gamma z)$ satisfies the differential equation

$$z(z-1)F'' + \{(\alpha + \beta + 1)z - \gamma\}F' + \alpha\beta F = 0. \tag{7}$$

If we take

$$\alpha = \beta = \tfrac{1}{2} \quad , \quad \gamma = 1 \quad , \quad z = k^2,$$

the relation 4) shows that K satisfies the equation.

$$z(z-1)\frac{d^2y}{dz^2} + (2z - 1)\frac{dy}{dz} + \frac{1}{4}y = 0 \quad , \quad z = k^2. \tag{8}$$

If we replace z by $1 - z = k'^2$ this equation is not changed. This shows that not only K but K' as given in 6) is a solution of 8). Thus both K and K' are integrals of 8). We shall return to this subject later.

CHAPTER XII

THE THETA FUNCTIONS

190. Historical. These functions were first considered by Abel. We have seen, 186, 4), that the inversion of

$$u=\int_0^z \frac{dz}{\sqrt{(1-z^2)(1-k^2z^2)}}$$

leads to an infinite series

$$z=u-\frac{1}{3!}(1+k^2)u^3+\cdots \tag{1}$$

which gives the value of $sn\,u$ within a circle passing through iK', which is the nearest pole of z.

In a similar manner the inversion of

$$u=\int_0^z \frac{dz}{1+z^2}$$

leads to a series

$$z=\tan u=u+\tfrac{1}{3}u^3+\tfrac{2}{15}u^5+\cdots$$

which gives the value of $\tan u$ within a circle passing through $\frac{\pi}{2}$, its nearest pole.

But we know that there exists an analytic expression

$$\frac{z\Pi\left(1-\dfrac{z^2}{n^2\pi^2}\right)}{\Pi\left(1-\dfrac{4z^2}{(2n-1)^2\pi^2}\right)} \qquad n=1, 2, \cdots \tag{2}$$

which is valid for the entire domain of definition of the tangent function. It occurred to Abel that a similar expression might be obtained for the sn function. This is the way he found it.

From the addition theorem we may express $sn\,nu$ in terms of $sn\,u$, $cn\,u$, $dn\,u$ just as in trigonometry the addition theorem of the sine function enables us to express $\sin nu$ in terms of $\sin u$, cos u. If in the expression for $sn\, nu$, n being an odd integer, we replace u by $\frac{u}{n}$ we get

$$sn\, u = n\, sn \frac{u}{n} \frac{\Pi \left\{ 1 - \dfrac{sn\, \dfrac{u}{n}}{sn\left(\dfrac{2\, mK + 2\, m' iK'}{n}\right)} \right\}}{\Pi \left\{ 1 - \dfrac{sn\, \dfrac{u}{n}}{sn\left(\dfrac{2\, mK + (2\, m' + 1) iK'}{n}\right)} \right\}}. \tag{3}$$

This expression is entirely analogous to that obtained for the sine function in 136, 6).

From 1) we have

$$\lim_{n=\infty} \frac{sn\, \dfrac{u}{n}}{sn\left(\dfrac{2\, mK + 2\, m' iK'}{n}\right)} = \frac{u}{2\, mK + 2\, m' iK'},$$

etc. Abel therefore concluded that

$$sn\, u = u \frac{\Pi\left(1 - \dfrac{u}{2\, mK + 2\, m' iK'}\right)}{\Pi\left(1 - \dfrac{u}{2\, mK + (2\, m' + 1) iK'}\right)}. \tag{4}$$

This passage to the limit is not rigorous and the infinite products which enter 4) are not even convergent in the sense that we have given this term in 128, 2. Let us therefore regard the relation 4) merely as a stepping stone to get infinite products which do converge; these will be the ϑ's.

To this end we write the products which figure in 4) as double iterated products, and for brevity we will set

$$u = 2\, Kv \quad , \quad \tau = \frac{iK'}{K}. \tag{5}$$

Then

$$sn\, 2Kv = \frac{T_1(v)}{T_0(v)}, \tag{6}$$

where

$$T_1 = 2\, Kv \prod_n \left(1 - \frac{v}{n}\right) \prod_{m'} \prod_m \left(1 - \frac{v}{m + m'\tau}\right), \tag{7}$$

and a similar expression for T_0. Here

$$n = \pm 1, \pm 2, \dots$$

$$m = 0, \pm 1, \pm 2 \dots \quad ; \quad m' = \pm 1, \pm 2, \dots$$

Now

$$\Pi\left(1 - \frac{v}{n}\right) = \frac{\sin \pi v}{\pi v},$$

$$\Pi_m\left(1 - \frac{v}{m + m'\tau}\right) = \frac{\sin \pi(m'\tau - v)}{\sin m'\pi\tau}.$$

Hence

$$T_1(v) = 2\,Kv \frac{\sin \pi v}{\pi v} \Pi_{m'} \frac{\sin \pi(m'\tau - v)}{\sin m'\pi\tau}$$

$$= 2\,K \frac{\sin \pi v}{\pi} \prod_{n=1}^{\infty} \frac{\sin \pi(n\tau - v)}{\sin n\pi\tau} \cdot \frac{\sin \pi(n\tau + v)}{\sin n\pi\tau}$$

$$= 2\,K \frac{\sin \pi v}{\pi} \Pi \frac{\{e^{\pi i(n\tau - v)} - e^{-\pi i(n\tau - v)}\}\{e^{\pi i(n\tau + v)} - e^{-\pi i(n\tau + v)}\}}{(e^{\pi i n\tau} - e^{-\pi i n\tau})^2}$$

$$= \frac{2\,K}{\pi} \sin \pi v\, \Pi \frac{1 - e^{2\pi i n\tau}(e^{2\pi i v} + e^{-2\pi i v}) + e^{4\pi i n\tau}}{(1 - e^{2\pi i n\tau})^2}.$$

Thus finally

$$T_1(v) = \frac{2\,K}{\pi} \sin \pi v \frac{\Pi(1 - 2\,q^{2n} \cos 2\,\pi v + q^{4n})}{\Pi(1 - q^{2n})^2}, \quad n = 1, 2 \dots \tag{8}$$

where

$$q = e^{\pi i \tau} = e^{-\pi \frac{K'}{K}}. \tag{9}$$

Here the infinite products in the numerator and denominator of 8) are absolutely convergent when $|q| < 1$. This last is no essential restriction because we would merely need to interchange K, K' in 9) to get a q which is numerically < 1.

A similar reduction of $T_0(v)$ leads to

$$T_0(v) = \frac{\Pi(1 - 2\,q^{2n+1} \cos 2\,\pi v + q^{4n+2})}{\Pi(1 - q^{2n+})^2}, \quad n = 1, 2 \dots \tag{10}$$

Similarly, we can express $cn\, 2\,Kv$, $dn\, 2\,Kv$ as the quotient products whose numerators T_2, T_3 are slightly different from T_1, and whose denominators are T_0 as before.

Thus the development of sn, cn, dn into infinite products leads us to four integral transcendental functions T_0. T_1, T_2, T_3, which play the same role in the theory of Jacobi that the four functions σ, σ_1, σ_2, σ_3 play in the theory of Weierstrass. It is one of the immortal achievements of Abel to have introduced these functions into analysis. Although his method of deduction is not rigorous, we can and will in fact show that when T_1, T_0 as given in 8), 10) are put in 6), the resulting function satisfies the differential equation

$$\frac{dz}{du} = \sqrt{(1-z^2)(1-k^2z^2)}, \tag{11}$$

which defines the *sn* function.

Here, as often happens, a method which is not rigorous, and cannot perhaps be made rigorous, leads to results whose correctness can be established *a posteriori* very simply. Such methods have a great heuristic value and are not to be despised by the pioneer.

191. The ϑ's as Infinite Products. 1. It is convenient to replace the T's introduced in the last article by four new functions which differ from them by constant factors. With Jacobi we set

$$q = e^{\pi i \omega}. \tag{1}$$

$$\begin{aligned}
\vartheta_1(v) &= 2\,q^{\frac{1}{4}} \sin \pi v \prod_1^\infty (1-q^{2n})(1-2\,q^{2n}\cos 2\,\pi v + q^{4n}),\\
\vartheta_2(v) &= 2\,q^{\frac{1}{4}} \cos \pi v \prod_1^\infty (1-q^{2n})(1+2\,q^{2n}\cos 2\,\pi v + q^{4n}),\\
\vartheta_3(v) &= \prod_1^\infty (1-q^{2n})(1+2\,q^{2n-1}\cos 2\,\pi v + q^{4n-2}),\\
\vartheta_0(v) &= \prod_1^\infty (1-q^{2n})(1-2\,q^{2n-1}\cos 2\,\pi v + q^{4n-2}).
\end{aligned} \tag{2}$$

We do not need to regard them in any way related to the elliptic functions, but simply as integral transcendental functions whose properties are to be investigated. The only restriction we make is that

$$|q| < 1 \tag{3}$$

in order that the products 2) converge absolutely.

We first show that these four functions are very closely related to each other by the formulæ:

$$\begin{aligned}
\vartheta_3(v+\tfrac{1}{2}) &= \vartheta_0(v),\\
\vartheta_3\left(v+\frac{\omega}{2}\right) &= e^{-\pi i v} q^{-\frac{1}{4}} \vartheta_2(v),\\
\vartheta_3\left(v+\frac{1+\omega}{2}\right) &= i e^{-\pi i v} q^{-\frac{1}{4}} \vartheta_1(v).
\end{aligned} \tag{4}$$

To prove the first relation we have, setting

$$Q=\prod_1^\infty(1-q^{2n}),$$

$$\begin{aligned}\vartheta_3(v+\tfrac{1}{2}) &= Q\Pi(1+2q^{2n-1}\cos 2\pi(v+\tfrac{1}{2})+q^{4n-2})\\ &= Q\Pi(1-2q^{2n-1}\cos 2\pi v+q^{4n-2})\\ &= \vartheta_0(v).\end{aligned}$$

To prove the second relation in 4) we have

$$\vartheta_3(v)=Q\Pi(1+q^{2n-1}e^{2\pi iv})(1+q^{2n-1}e^{-2\pi iv}).$$

Hence

$$\begin{aligned}\vartheta_3\left(v+\frac{\omega}{2}\right) &= Q\Pi(1+q^{2n-1}e^{2\pi i\left(v+\frac{\omega}{2}\right)})(1+q^{2n-1}e^{-2\pi i\left(v+\frac{\omega}{2}\right)})\\ &= Q(1+e^{-2\pi iv})\Pi(1+q^{2n}e^{2\pi iv})(1+q^{2n}e^{-2\pi iv})\\ &= Qe^{-\pi iv}q^{-\frac{1}{4}}q^{\frac{1}{4}}\cdot 2\cos\pi v\Pi(1+2q^{2n}\cos 2\pi v+q^{4n})\\ &= q^{-\frac{1}{4}}e^{-\pi iv}\vartheta_2(v).\end{aligned}$$

2. In a similar manner we may prove the following relations:

$$\begin{aligned}\vartheta_1(v+\tfrac{1}{2}) &= \vartheta_2(v),\\ \vartheta_1\left(v+\frac{\omega}{2}\right) &= iq^{-\frac{1}{4}}e^{-\pi iv}\vartheta_0(v),\\ \vartheta_1\left(v+\frac{1+\omega}{2}\right) &= q^{-\frac{1}{4}}e^{-\pi iv}\vartheta_3(v).\end{aligned} \qquad (5$$

$$\begin{aligned}\vartheta_2(v+\tfrac{1}{2}) &= -\vartheta_1(v),\\ \vartheta_2\left(v+\frac{\omega}{2}\right) &= q^{-\frac{1}{4}}e^{-\pi iv}\vartheta_3(v),\\ \vartheta_2\left(v+\frac{1+\omega}{2}\right) &= -iq^{-\frac{1}{4}}e^{-\pi iv}\vartheta_0(v).\end{aligned} \qquad (6$$

$$\begin{aligned}\vartheta_0(v+\tfrac{1}{2}) &= \vartheta_3(v),\\ \vartheta_0\left(v+\frac{\omega}{2}\right) &= iq^{-\frac{1}{4}}e^{-\pi iv}\vartheta_1(v),\\ \vartheta_0\left(v+\frac{1+\omega}{2}\right) &= q^{-\frac{1}{4}}e^{-\pi iv}\vartheta_2(v).\end{aligned} \qquad (7$$

3. By repeated application of the foregoing or directly we find:

$$\begin{aligned}\vartheta_1(v+1) &= -\vartheta_1(v),\\ \vartheta_2(v+1) &= -\vartheta_2(v),\\ \vartheta_3(v+1) &= \vartheta_3(v),\\ \vartheta_0(v+1) &= \vartheta_0(v).\end{aligned} \tag{8}$$

$$\begin{aligned}\vartheta_1(v+\omega) &= -q^{-1}e^{-2\pi iv}\vartheta_1(v),\\ \vartheta_2(v+\omega) &= q^{-1}e^{-2\pi iv}\vartheta_2(v),\\ \vartheta_3(v+\omega) &= q^{-1}e^{-2\pi iv}\vartheta_3(v),\\ \vartheta_0(v+\omega) &= -q^{-1}e^{-2\pi iv}\vartheta_0(v).\end{aligned} \tag{9}$$

192. The ϑ's as Infinite Series. The relation 191, 8)

$$\vartheta_3(v+1) = \vartheta_3(v)$$

shows that $\vartheta_3(v)$ admits the period 1, and can therefore be developed in Fourier's Series by 126. Thus

$$\vartheta_3(v) = \sum_{-\infty}^{\infty} a_n e^{2\pi inv}. \tag{1}$$

To determine the coefficients a_n we use 191, 9)

$$\vartheta_3(v+\omega) = q^{-1}e^{-2\pi iv}\vartheta_3(v). \tag{2}$$

For putting 1) in 2) gives

$$\begin{aligned}\vartheta_3(v+\omega) &= \Sigma a_n e^{2\pi in(v+\omega)} = \Sigma a_n q^{2n} e^{2\pi inv}\\ &= q^{-1}e^{-2\pi iv}\Sigma a_n e^{2\pi inv}\\ &= \Sigma a_n q^{-1} e^{2\pi i(n-1)v}.\end{aligned}$$

Comparing the coefficients of $e^{2\pi inv}$ gives

$$a_n q^{2n} = a_{n+1} q^{-1}$$

or

$$a_n = q^{n^2} a_0.$$

Thus

$$\begin{aligned}\vartheta_3(v) &= a_0 \sum_{-\infty}^{\infty} q^{n^2} e^{2\pi inv}\\ &= a_0\{1 + \sum_1^{\infty} q^{n^2}(e^{2\pi inv} + e^{-2\pi inv})\}\\ &= a_0(1 + 2\sum_1^{\infty} q^{n^2} \cos 2\,\pi nv).\end{aligned}$$

To determine a_0 set $q=0$. Then $\vartheta_3(v)=1$. Hence $a_0=1$. In this way we get

$$\begin{aligned}\vartheta_3(v) &= 1 + 2\sum_1^\infty q^{n^2}\cos 2\pi n v,\\ \vartheta_2(v) &= 2\sum_0^\infty q^{(n+\frac{1}{2})^2}\cos(2n+1)\pi v,\\ \vartheta_1(v) &= 2\sum_0^\infty(-1)^n q^{(n+\frac{1}{2})^2}\sin(2n+1)\pi v,\\ \vartheta_0(v) &= 1+2\sum_1^\infty(-1)^n q^{n^2}\cos 2\pi n v.\end{aligned} \qquad (3$$

The representation of the ϑ's as infinite series is due to Jacobi (1825). As they converge with extreme rapidity for the values of q ordinarily employed, they are of immense value in all questions of numerical calculations of the elliptic functions, as we shall see.

193. The Zeros of the ϑ's. 1. The infinite products 191, 2), being convergent, cannot vanish unless one of their factors vanish. From this we have at once that the zeros of the ϑ's are as follows:

$$\begin{aligned}&\vartheta_1(v); && v = m + n\omega,\\ &\vartheta_2(v); && v=(m+\tfrac{1}{2})+n\omega,\\ &\vartheta_3(v); && v=(m+\tfrac{1}{2})+(n+\tfrac{1}{2})\omega,\\ &\vartheta_0(v); && v=m+(n+\tfrac{1}{2})\omega,\end{aligned} \qquad (1$$

where $m, n = 0, \pm 1, \pm 2, \cdots$.

To illustrate the proof, let us find the zeros of $\vartheta_3(v)$. We have

$$1+2q^{2n-1}\cos 2\pi v + q^{4n-2} = (1+q^{2n-1}e^{2\pi i v})(1+q^{2n-1}e^{-2\pi i v}).$$

Let us find the values of v for which

$$1+q^{2n-1}e^{2\pi i v}=0.$$

This gives, since $q=e^{\pi i \omega}$,

$$e^{2\pi i v} = -\frac{1}{q^{2n-1}} = -\frac{1}{e^{\pi i(2n-1)\omega}}.$$

Hence
$$2\pi i v = \log(-1) - \pi i(2n-1)\omega.$$

As
$$\log(-1) = \pi i + 2s\pi i,$$

$$v=(m+\tfrac{1}{2})+(n+\tfrac{1}{2})\omega \qquad m, n \text{ any integers},$$

as required by 1).

2. Another method of getting the zeros of the ϑ's is the following, it uses the infinite series 192, 3). From the series for $\vartheta_1(v)$ we see that it vanishes at the points $m + n\omega$, since each term of the series vanishes.

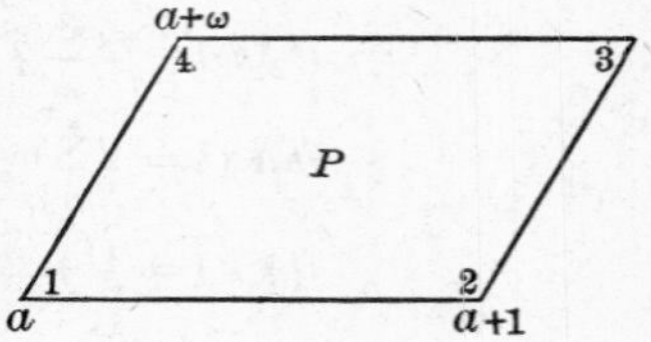

To show that the ϑ's vanish at no other points let us consider $\vartheta_1(v)$ for example. We take a parallelogram P as in the figure not passing through one of the points $m + n\omega$. Then by 124, 8),

$$\frac{1}{2\pi i}\int_P d \log \vartheta_1(v) = M - N. \tag{2}$$

As $\vartheta_1(v)$ is nowhere infinite in the finite part of the plane, $N = 0$. Now

$$\int_P = \int_{12} + \int_{23} + \int_{34} + \int_{41} \cdot \tag{3}$$

From 191, 8)
$$\frac{d \log \vartheta_1(v+1)}{dv} = \frac{d \log \vartheta_1(v)}{dv},$$

while from 191, 9)

$$\frac{d \log \vartheta_1(v+\omega)}{dv} = -2\pi i + \frac{d \log \vartheta_1(v)}{dv}.$$

Thus
$$\int_{23} = \int_{14} \cdot$$

$$\int_{43} = -2\pi i \int_a^{a+1} dv + \int_a^{a+1} d \log \vartheta_1(v)$$

$$= -2\pi i + \int_{12} \cdot$$

These in 3) give
$$\int_P = 2\pi i.$$

Putting this in 2) gives $M = 1$. Thus $\vartheta_1(v)$ has just one zero and this of order 1 in the parallelogram P. The first equations of 191, 8), 9) show that $\vartheta_1(v)$ has a zero of order 1 in each of the congruent parallelograms, mod 1, ω. From 191, 5) we may now find the zeros of the other thetas.

194. The ϑ's with Zero Argument. 1. If in the infinite series and products of the ϑ's given in 191, 2) and 192, 3) we set $v = 0$, we get

$$\vartheta_0 = 1 + 2\sum_1^\infty(-1)^n q^{n^2} = \Pi(1 - q^{2n})\Pi(1 - q^{2n-1})^2. \tag{1}$$

$$\vartheta_2 = 2\sum_0^\infty q^{(n+\frac{1}{2})^2} = 2q^{\frac{1}{4}}\Pi(1 - q^{2n})\Pi(1 + q^{2n})^2. \tag{2}$$

$$\vartheta_3 = 1 + 2\sum_1^\infty q^{n^2} = \Pi(1 - q^{2n})\Pi(1 + q^{2n-1})^2. \tag{3}$$

Here, as is customary, we set ϑ_0 instead of $\vartheta_0(0)$, etc. As $\vartheta_1 = 0$, let us take the derivative of

$$\begin{aligned}\vartheta_1(v) &= 2\,q^{\frac{1}{4}}\sin \pi v \Pi(1 - q^{2n})\Pi(1 - 2\,q^{2n}\cos 2\,\pi v + q^{4n})\\ &= \sin \pi v \cdot \phi(v).\end{aligned}$$

Then
$$\vartheta_1'(v) = \pi \cos \pi v \cdot \phi(v) + \sin \pi v \cdot \phi'(v).$$

Hence
$$\vartheta_1'(0) = \pi\phi(0),$$

since
$$\sin \pi v = 0 \quad \text{for} \quad v = 0.$$

Thus
$$\vartheta_1' = 2\pi\sum_0^\infty(-1)^n(2\,n + 1)q^{(n+\frac{1}{2})^2} = 2\,\pi q^{\frac{1}{4}}\Pi(1 - q^{2n})^3. \tag{4}$$

These four functions ϑ_1', ϑ_0, ϑ_2, ϑ_3 considered as functions of the complex variable q are of extraordinary interest from the standpoint of the theory of functions. As we have already seen, for these series or products to converge absolutely it is necessary that $|q| < 1$. There is nothing remarkable about this. The series

$$\log(1 + z) = \frac{z}{1} - \frac{z^2}{2} + \frac{z^3}{3} - \cdots$$

does not converge absolutely unless $|z| < 1$; but by analytic continuation it is possible to extend the function represented by this series beyond the unit circle. The thing which is so remarkable about the series 1), 2), 3), 4) is that it is quite impossible to extend them by analytic continuation beyond the unit circle in the q-plane for the reason that the functions defined by them become infinite in the vicinity of every point on this circle. Here, then, is a class of functions utterly different from all the functions of elementary analysis. These latter are defined for the whole plane, isolated points excepted. The four functions

$\vartheta_0, \vartheta_1, \vartheta_2, \vartheta_1'$ are, on the other hand, defined only for points which lie within the unit circle.

If we replace q by its value $q = e^{\pi i \omega}$ and consider these functions as functions of ω, we find that they behave in a most remarkable manner when ω is replaced by

$$\omega' = \frac{a\omega + b}{c\omega + d}, \tag{5}$$

a, b, c, d being integers such that $ad - bc = 1$.

The ∞^3 transformations 5) form a group G, and by the aid of the functions $\vartheta_0, \vartheta_1, \vartheta_2, \vartheta_1'$ we can construct functions which remain unaltered for G or for some subgroup of G.

One of the simplest of these functions is the modulus k^2 of the *sn* function. We shall show directly that

$$k^2 = \frac{\vartheta_2^4}{\vartheta_3^4}.$$

This function remains unaltered by the subgroup of G characterized by

$$a \equiv 1, \quad b \equiv 0, \quad c \equiv 0, \quad d \equiv 1, \text{ mod } 2. \tag{6}$$

For this reason all functions of this class, that is, one-valued analytic functions which remain unaltered for the substitutions of G or for one of its subgroups, have received the name of *elliptic modular functions*. Their theory has already reached imposing proportions, yet the modular functions form only a small part of a still vaster class of functions called the *automorphic functions*. For these functions the coefficients in 5) are not restricted to integers.

2. Returning now to our ϑ's with zero arguments, let us prove a relation of *great importance:*

$$\vartheta_1' = \pi \vartheta_0 \vartheta_2 \vartheta_3. \tag{7}$$

From 1), 2), 3), we have

$$\vartheta_0 \vartheta_2 \vartheta_3 = 2\, q^{\frac{1}{4}} \Pi (1 - q^{2n})^3 (1 + q^{2n})^2 (1 + q^{2n-1})^2 (1 - q^{2n-1})^2.$$

Now from 135, 1),

$$\Pi (1 + q^{2n})(1 + q^{2n-1})(1 - q^{2n-1}) = 1.$$

Thus

$$\vartheta_0 \vartheta_2 \vartheta_3 = 2\, q^{\frac{1}{4}} \Pi\, (1 - q^{2n})^3.$$

Comparing this with 4) gives 7).

195. Definition of *sn*, *cn*, *dn* as ϑ Quotients. 1. With the four ϑ functions we can form 12 quotients

$$\frac{\vartheta_r(v)}{\vartheta_s(v)} \qquad r, s = 0, 1, 2, 3,$$

six of which are reciprocals of the other six. Of the remaining six, three are quotients of the other three. Let us therefore consider

$$\frac{\vartheta_1(v)}{\vartheta_0(v)}\,, \quad \frac{\vartheta_2(v)}{\vartheta_0(v)}\,, \quad \frac{\vartheta_3(v)}{\vartheta_0(v)}. \tag{1}$$

These admit as periods, respectively,

$$2, \omega \quad ; \quad 2, 1 + \omega \quad ; \quad 1, 2\,\omega. \tag{2}$$

The poles of these functions are the zeros of the denominators. In a parallelogram constructed on the above periods, each of the above quotients has two simple poles respectively. They are thus elliptic functions of order 2, and the above parallelograms are primitive.

Without assuming any knowledge whatever of the functions *sn*, *cn*, *dn*, let us study the three elliptic functions 1).

We will begin with

$$q(v) = \frac{\vartheta_1(v)}{\vartheta_0(v)}$$

and find the differential equation which this satisfies. To this end we use 165, 14. Here the poles are

$$p_1 = \frac{\omega}{2}\,, \quad p_2 = 1 + \frac{\omega}{2}.$$

Hence the zeros of $\dfrac{dq}{dv}$ are

$$\equiv \frac{1+\omega}{2}\,, \quad 1 + \frac{1+\omega}{2}\,, \quad \tfrac{1}{2} + \omega\,, \quad 1 + \omega + \tfrac{1}{2}, \qquad \text{mod } 2, \omega.$$

To find the values of $q(v)$ at these points let us set

$$\frac{\vartheta_2}{\vartheta_3} = \sqrt{k} \tag{3}$$

and use the relations in 191. Then

$$q\left(\frac{1+\omega}{2}\right)=\frac{\vartheta_3}{\vartheta_2}=\frac{1}{\sqrt{k}}.$$

$$q\left(1+\frac{1+\omega}{2}\right)=-q\left(\frac{1+\omega}{2}\right)=-\frac{1}{\sqrt{k}}.$$

$$q\left(\tfrac{1}{2}+\omega\right)=q\left(\tfrac{1}{2}\right)=\frac{\vartheta_2}{\vartheta_3}=\sqrt{k}.$$

$$q(1+\omega+\tfrac{1}{2})=-q(\tfrac{1}{2})=-\sqrt{k}.$$

Thus

$$\left(\frac{dq}{dv}\right)^2=C(1-kq^2)(k-q^2).$$

Let us set

$$s=\frac{1}{\sqrt{k}}q=\frac{1}{\sqrt{k}}\frac{\vartheta_1(v)}{\vartheta_0(v)}. \qquad (4$$

We get

$$\frac{ds}{dv}=c\sqrt{(1-s^2)(1-k^2s^2)}. \qquad (5$$

To determine c we have from 4)

$$\frac{ds}{dv}=\frac{1}{\sqrt{k}}\frac{\vartheta_0(v)\vartheta_1'(v)-\vartheta_1(v)\vartheta_0'(v)}{\vartheta_0^2(v)}.$$

For $v=0$, this gives

$$\left(\frac{ds}{dv}\right)_{v=0}=\frac{1}{\sqrt{k}}\frac{\vartheta_1'}{\vartheta_0}.$$

The right side of 5) reduces to c for $v=0$. Hence

$$c=\frac{1}{\sqrt{k}}\frac{\vartheta_1'}{\vartheta_0},$$

or using 3) and 194, 7), we get

$$c=\frac{\vartheta_3}{\vartheta_2}\cdot\frac{\pi\vartheta_0\vartheta_2\vartheta_3}{\vartheta_0}=\pi\vartheta_3^2.$$

Putting this value of c in 5) and setting

$$u=\pi v\vartheta_3^2 \qquad (6$$

we get

$$\frac{ds}{du}=\sqrt{(1-s^2)(1-k^2s^2)}. \qquad (7$$

Let us therefore define three functions of u by the relations

$$sn\, u = \frac{\vartheta_3}{\vartheta_2} \cdot \frac{\vartheta_1(v)}{\vartheta_0(v)}, \tag{8}$$

$$cn\, u = \frac{\vartheta_0}{\vartheta_2} \cdot \frac{\vartheta_2(v)}{\vartheta_0(v)}, \tag{9}$$

$$dn\, u = \frac{\vartheta_0}{\vartheta_3} \cdot \frac{\vartheta_3(v)}{\vartheta_0(v)}, \tag{10}$$

where v is related to u by 6). Then if k is defined by 3), we have shown that $z = sn\, u$ satisfies the differential equation 7). As $z = 0$ for $u = 0$ we see that u considered as a function of z satisfies the relation

$$u = \int_0^z \frac{dz}{\sqrt{(1-z^2)(1-k^2z^2)}}.$$

The function 8) is therefore indeed the old *sn* function studied in Chapter XI.

2. Before showing that 9), 10) are our old *cn*, *dn* studied in Chapter XI let us note the periods, zeros, and poles of the functions 8), 9), 10).

The periods may be read off from 2). If we set

$$2\, K = \pi\vartheta_3^2 \quad , \quad 2\, iK' = \pi\omega\vartheta_3^2, \tag{11}$$

we have as primitive pairs of periods:

	Periods
$sn\, u$	$4\, K,\ 2\, i\, K'$
$cn\, u$	$4\, K,\ 2\, K + 2\, iK'$
$dn\, u$	$2\, K,\ 4\, iK'$

As zeros and poles we have

	Zeros	Poles
$sn\, u$	$2\, mK + 2\, m'iK'$	$2\, mK + (2\, m' + 1)iK'$
$cn\, u$	$(2\, m + 1)K + 2\, m'iK'$	$2\, mK + (2\, m' + 1)iK'$
$dn\, u$	$(2\, m + 1)K + (2\, m' + 1)iK'$	$2\, mK + (2\, m' + 1)iK'$

3. We also note that from 191 we have

$$\begin{aligned} sn\,(u+2K) &= -\,sn\,u, \\ cn\,(u+2K) &= -\,cn\,u, \\ dn\,(u+2K) &= dn\,u. \end{aligned} \tag{12}$$

$$\begin{aligned} sn\,(u+2iK') &= sn\,u, \\ cn\,(u+2iK') &= -\,cn\,u, \\ dn\,(u+2iK') &= -\,dn\,u. \end{aligned} \tag{13}$$

$$\begin{aligned} sn(u+K) &= \frac{cn\,u}{dn\,u}, \\ cn(u+K) &= -\,k'\,\frac{sn\,u}{dn\,u} \quad , \quad \sqrt{k'} = \frac{\vartheta_0}{\vartheta_3}, \\ dn(u+K) &= \frac{k'}{dn\,u}. \end{aligned} \tag{14}$$

$$\begin{aligned} sn(u+iK') &= \frac{1}{k\,sn\,u}, \\ cn(u+iK') &= \frac{dn\,u}{ik\,sn\,u}, \\ dn(u+iK') &= \frac{cn\,u}{i\,sn\,u}. \end{aligned} \tag{15}$$

$$\begin{aligned} sn(u+K+iK') &= \frac{dn\,u}{k\,cn\,u}, \\ cn(u+K+iK') &= \frac{-\,ik'}{k\,cn\,u}, \\ dn(u+K+iK') &= \frac{ik'\,sn\,u}{cn\,u}. \end{aligned} \tag{16}$$

4. We now show that the functions 9), 10) are the *cn*, *dn* functions considered in Chapter XI, that is, we show that the functions 9), 10) satisfy the relations

$$cn^2\,u = 1 - sn^2\,u, \tag{17}$$

$$dn^2\,u = 1 - k^2\,sn^2\,u. \tag{18}$$

Let us prove 18); the proof of 17) is similar.

The function $dn^2\,u$ has $2K$, $2iK'$ as a primitive pair of periods as seen from 12), 13).

The zeros of $dn^2 u$ are $\equiv K + iK'$. Its poles $\equiv iK'$. Both zeros and poles are of order 2.

On the other hand, $1 - k^2 sn^2 u$ has the same periods, zeros, and poles and to the same order. Thus the two members of 18) can differ only by a constant factor C. To determine this, we set $u = 0$. This gives at once $C = 1$.

5. Finally let us show that k^2, k'^2 as defined in 3), 14) satisfy the relation

$$k^2 + k'^2 = 1. \qquad (19$$

In fact, setting $u = K$ in 18), we get

$$dn^2 K = 1 - k^2 sn^2 K. \qquad (20$$

But from 14) $\quad dn^2 K = k'^2 \quad , \quad sn^2 K = 1.$

This in 20) gives 19).

196. Numerical Calculation. 1. Let us now show how to calculate K, K', $sn\,u$, etc., by means of the ϑ's when the modulus k is given. We have

$$\sqrt{k'} = \frac{\vartheta_0}{\vartheta_3} = \frac{1 - 2q + 2q^4 - 2q^9 + \cdots}{1 + 2q + 2q^4 + 2q^9 + \cdots}. \qquad (1$$

When q is small, we have approximately

$$\sqrt{k'} = \frac{1-2q}{1+2q}, \qquad (2$$

or

$$q = \frac{1}{2}\frac{1-\sqrt{k'}}{1+\sqrt{k'}}. \qquad (3$$

To get a closer approximation, we note that

$$2l = \frac{1-\sqrt{k'}}{1+\sqrt{k'}} = \frac{\vartheta_3 - \vartheta_0}{\vartheta_3 + \vartheta_0} = 2\frac{q + q^9 + q^{25} + \cdots}{1 + 2q^4 + 2q^{16} + \cdots}. \qquad (4$$

If we develop the right side of 4) in a power series in q and invert this series, we get

$$q = l + 2l^5 + 15l^9 + 150l^{13} + \cdots \qquad (5$$

This series converges with great rapidity. For example let $k^2 = \frac{1}{2}$. We find that

$$q = .0432139 \cdots$$

On the other hand

$$l = .0432136 \cdots$$

This shows that the first term of 5) gives q correctly to 6 decimals for this value of k.

Having found q, we get K by the relation

$$\sqrt{\frac{2K}{\pi}} = \vartheta_3 = 1 + 2q + 2q^4 + 2q^9 + \cdots \tag{6}$$

As

$$1 + \sqrt{k'} = 1 + \frac{\vartheta_0}{\vartheta_3}$$

we can write 6)

$$\sqrt{\frac{2K}{\pi}} = \frac{\vartheta_3 + \vartheta_0}{1 + \sqrt{k'}} = 2\,\frac{1 + 2q^4 + 2q^{16} + \cdots}{1 + \sqrt{k'}}, \tag{7}$$

which converges more rapidly than 6).

To get K' we use 191, 1) and 195, 11), which give

$$q = e^{-\pi\frac{K'}{K}}$$

or

$$K' = \frac{K}{\pi}\log\left(\frac{1}{q}\right) = \frac{1}{2}\,\vartheta_3^2 \cdot \log\left(\frac{1}{q}\right). \tag{8}$$

The values of $sn\,u$, $cn\,u$, $dn\,u$ for a given u and k are now found from 195, 8), 9), 10).

2. Suppose on the contrary the value of z in

$$z = sn\,(u, k) \tag{9}$$

is given, and we wish to find the corresponding values of u. We start from the relation 195, 10)

$$dn\,u = \sqrt{k'}\,\frac{\vartheta_3(v)}{\vartheta_0(v)}\quad,\quad u = 2\,Kv. \tag{10}$$

From this we get

$$V = \frac{\sqrt{k'}}{\sqrt{1 - k^2 z^2}} = \frac{\vartheta_0(v)}{\vartheta_3(v)} = \frac{1 - 2q\cos 2\pi v + 2q^4\cos 4\pi v - \cdots}{1 + 2q\cos 2\pi v + 2q^4\cos 4\pi v + \cdots}. \tag{11}$$

As a first approximation, this gives,

$$V = \frac{1 - 2q\cos 2\pi v}{1 + 2q\cos 2\pi v}$$

or

$$\cos 2\pi v = \frac{1}{2}\cdot\frac{1}{q}\,\frac{1 - V}{1 + V}. \tag{12}$$

To get a formula which converges still more rapidly, we set

$$W=\frac{\vartheta_3(v)-\vartheta_0(v)}{\vartheta_3(v)+\vartheta_0(v)}=\frac{\sqrt{1-k^2z^2}-\sqrt{k'}}{\sqrt{1-k^2z^2}+\sqrt{k'}}$$

$$=\frac{2(q\cos 2\pi v+q^9\cos 6\pi v+\cdots)}{1+(2q^4\cos 4\pi v+2q^{16}\cos 8\pi v+\cdots)}. \qquad (13$$

As a first approximation, this gives

$$\cos 2\pi v=\frac{1}{2q}\cdot W. \qquad (14$$

197. The Θ and Z Functions. 1. The ϑ functions depend upon two variables u and q. Let us set

$$\Theta_r(u, K, K')=\vartheta_r\left(\frac{u}{2K}, q\right), \quad r=0, 1, 2, 3, \qquad (1$$

where as usual

$$q=e^{-\pi\frac{K'}{K}}, \quad \text{Ord}\,\frac{K'}{K}>0. \qquad (2$$

The properties of the Θ's may be read off at once from those of the ϑ's; in particular:

The $\Theta_r(u, K, K')$ are homogenous functions of 0 degree in u, K, K'.

Jacobi denoted $\Theta_0(u)$ by $\Theta(u)$ and $\Theta_1(u)$ by $\mathrm{H}(u)$; H is Greek eta. We shall not use the H notation, but shall at times write Θ for Θ_0.

2. By means of any one of these Θ's we may express an elliptic function by virtue of the following theorem:

Let $f(u)$ be of order m and have $2K$, $2iK'$ as a primitive pair of periods. Let

$$c_1, c_2, \cdots c_m \quad ; \quad p_1, p_2, \cdots p_m$$

be a system of incongruent zeros and poles. Then

$$f(u)=Ce^{-\mu\frac{\pi i u}{K}}\frac{\Theta_1(u-c_1)\cdots\Theta_1(u-c_m)}{\Theta_1(u-p_1)\cdots\Theta_1(u-p_m)}, \qquad (3$$

where μ is determined by Abel's relation

$$\Sigma c_n-\Sigma p_n=2\lambda K+2\mu iK'. \qquad (4$$

The proof of this follows along the same lines as 166, 3.

Example 1. Let us prove the *important relation*

$$sn^2 u - sn^2 v = \frac{\Theta_0^2}{k} \frac{\Theta_1(u+v)\Theta_1(u-v)}{\Theta_0^2(u)\Theta_0^2(v)}, \tag{5}$$

which for brevity we will write

$$L(u) = CR(u),$$

v being regarded as a constant.

For $L(u)$ having the periods $\omega_1 = 2K$, $\omega_2 = 2iK'$, vanishes at the points

$$c_1 \equiv v, \qquad c_2 \equiv -v.$$

The poles of L are

$$p_1 \equiv iK' \equiv p_2,$$

being double. Thus 4) becomes

$$0 - 2iK' = \lambda\ 2K + \mu\ 2iK'.$$

Hence $\mu = -1$. Thus 3) gives

$$L = Ce^{\frac{\pi i u}{K}} \frac{\Theta_1(u-v)\Theta_1(u+v)}{\Theta_1^2(u-iK')}.$$

Replacing $\Theta_1(u)$ by its value expressed in terms of $\Theta_0(u)$, or

$$\Theta_1(u) = -iq^{\frac{1}{4}} e^{\frac{\pi i u}{2K}} \Theta_0(u+iK')$$

found from 191, we get 5). The constant is found by setting $u=0$.

Example 2. In a similar manner we may establish another *important formula:*

$$1 - k^2\, sn^2 u\, sn^2 v = \frac{\Theta_0^2 \Theta_0(u+v)\,\Theta_0(u-v)}{\Theta_0^2(u)\Theta_0^2(v)}. \tag{6}$$

3. With the Θ's we can define four new functions

$$Z_r(u) = \frac{d \log \Theta_r(u)}{du} = \frac{\Theta_r'(u)}{\Theta_r(u)}, \quad r = 0, 1, 2, 3. \tag{7}$$

For $Z_0(u)$ Jacobi wrote $Z(u)$, and we shall adopt this notation at times. In developing his theory of elliptic functions Weierstrass defined the $\zeta(u)$ function analogous to Jacobi's $Z(u)$.

The properties of the Z's may be read off from the corresponding ϑ relations. Thus we have:

$$\begin{aligned} Z(u+2K) &= Z(u), \\ Z(u+2iK') &= Z(u) - \frac{i\pi}{K}. \end{aligned} \tag{8}$$

These show that $\frac{dZ}{du}$ is an elliptic function having $2K$, $2iK'$ as periods. This function is analogous to Weierstrass' p function. In a moment we shall show that $Z'(u)$ differs from $dn^2\,u$ only by a constant.

The addition theorem of $Z(u)$ is obtained from 6) by logarithmic differentiation. Thus

$$Z(u+v) + Z(u-v) - 2\,Z(u) = -\frac{2\,k^2\,sn^2\,v\;sn\,u\;cn\,u\;dn\,u}{1 - k^2\,sn^2\,u\;sn^2\,v}. \tag{9}$$

Interchanging u and v gives, on noting that

$$Z(-u) = -Z(u), \tag{10}$$

$$Z(u+v) - Z(u-v) - 2\,Z(v) = -\frac{2\,k^2\,sn^2\,u\;sn\,v\;cn\,v\;dn\,v}{1 - k^2\,sn^2\,u\,sn^2\,v}.$$

Adding, we get

$$Z(u+v) - Z(u) - Z(v) = -k^2\,sn\,u\;sn\,v\;sn(u+v). \tag{11}$$

By logarithmic differentiation of the ϑ relations in 191 we get, without trouble:

$$Z(u \pm K) = Z(u) - k^2\frac{sn\,u\;cn\,u}{dn\,u} = Z_3(u), \tag{12}$$

$$Z(u \pm iK') = Z(u) + \frac{cn\,u\;dn\,u}{sn\,u} \mp \frac{\pi i}{2\,K}, \tag{13}$$

$$= Z_1(u) \mp \frac{\pi i}{2\,K}.$$

We have also

$$Z(0) = 0\;,\; Z(K) = 0\;,\; Z(K+iK') = -\frac{\pi i}{2\,K}\;,\; Z(iK') = \infty. \tag{14}$$

198. Hermite's Formula. The reasoning used to establish 168, 2) may be applied at once to Jacobi's Z and gives, using the same notation as before, a celebrated formula due to Hermite:

$$g(u)=A_1Z_1(u-a)-A_2Z_1'(u-a)+\cdots+\frac{(-1)^{\lambda-1}A_\lambda}{(\lambda-1)!}Z_1^{(\lambda-1)}(u-a)$$

$$+B_1Z_1(u-b)-B_2Z^1(u-b)+\cdots+\frac{(-1)_1^{\mu-1}B_\mu}{(\mu-1)!}Z_1{}^{(\mu-1)}(u-b) \quad (1$$

$+\cdots+$ constant.

Example 1. Let us make use of 1) to show that

$$dn^2 u=Z'(u)-Z'(K+iK'). \quad (2$$

For the poles of $dn^2 u$ are $\equiv iK'$ and are double. By 195, 15),

$$dn(u+iK')=\frac{cn\, u}{i\, sn\, u}=-\frac{i}{u}+\cdots$$

Thus the characteristic of $dn^2 u$ at the point $u=iK'$ is $-\dfrac{1}{u^2}$. Hence in 1), $A_1=0$, $A_2=-1$ and thus

$$dn^2 u=Z_1'(u-iK')+C$$
$$=Z'(u)+C, \text{ using 197, 13)}. \quad (3$$

To determine C set $u=K+iK'$ and recall that $dn(K+iK')=0$. This gives $C=-Z'(K+iK')$, which in 3) gives 2).

Example 2. In the same manner we show that

$$\frac{1}{sn^2 u}=Z'(0)-Z'(u+iK'). \quad (4$$

Example 3. Let us show that

$$\frac{1}{sn^2 u-sn^2 v}=\frac{1}{sn\, v\, cn\, v\, dn\, v}\{Z_0(v)+\tfrac{1}{2}Z_1(u-v)-\tfrac{1}{2}Z_1(u+v)\}. \quad (5$$

To this end we note that the poles of the function of u on the left, call it $g(u)$, are $u\equiv\pm v$. To find the characteristic of $g(u)$ at the point $u=v$ we have

$$g(u)=\frac{1}{sn\, u-sn\, v}\cdot\frac{1}{sn\, u+sn\, v}=\frac{1}{sn\, u-sn\, v}\cdot\frac{1}{h(u)}.$$

Let us set $u=v+w$. Then,

$$sn\, u=sn(v+w)=sn\, v+w\, sn'\, v+\cdots$$
$$h(u)=h(v+w)=h(v)+wh'(v)+\cdots$$
$$=2\, sn\, v+\cdots$$

Thus

$$g(u) = \frac{1}{w\, sn'\, v + \cdots} \cdot \frac{1}{2\, sn\, v + \cdots}$$

$$= \frac{1}{2\, sn\, v\, cn\, v\, dn\, v} \cdot \frac{1}{u - v} + \text{higher powers of } u - v.$$

Thus

$$\operatorname*{Char}_{u=v} g(u) = \frac{1}{2\, sn\, v\, cn\, v\, dn\, v} \cdot \frac{1}{u-v}.$$

The characteristic of g at the point $u = -v$ is the same term with a minus sign. Hence 1) becomes

$$\frac{1}{sn^2 u - sn^2 v} = \frac{1}{2\, sn\, v\, cn\, v\, dn\, v}\{C + Z_1(u - v) - Z_1(u + v)\}. \qquad (6$$

In this let us replace u by $u + iK'$, we get

$$\frac{k^2\, sn^2 u}{1 - k^2\, sn^2 u\, sn^2 v} = \frac{1}{2\, sn\, v\, cn\, v\, dn\, v}\{C + Z(u - v) - Z(u + v)\}. \qquad (7$$

If we set here $u = 0$, we get

$$C = 2\, Z(v).$$

This in 6) gives 5). From 7) we get

$$\frac{k^2\, sn\, v\, cn\, v\, dn\, v\, sn^2 u}{1 - k^2\, sn^2 u\, sn^2 v} = Z(v) + \tfrac{1}{2} Z(u - v) - \tfrac{1}{2} Z(u + v). \qquad (8$$

199. Elliptic Integrals expressed by Θ Functions. Let

$$F = \int f(x, y)\,dx \qquad (1$$

where f is a rational function of x and y and

$$y = \sqrt{(1 - x^2)(1 - k^2x^2)}. \qquad (2$$

In 178, 10) we saw that we can write

$$F = \int E\,dx + \int \frac{G}{y}\,dx \qquad (3$$

where E and G are rational functions of x. The first integral on the right can be expressed by the elementary functions. Let us look at the second. We have

$$G = xH(x^2) + L(x^2),$$

where H, L are rational functions of x^2. Hence

$$\int \frac{G}{y}\,dx = \int H\,\frac{xdx}{y} + \int L\frac{dx}{y}. \tag{4}$$

In the first integral on the right let us set $t = x^2$, it becomes

$$\frac{1}{2}\int H(t)\frac{dt}{\sqrt{(1-t)(1-k^2t)}},$$

which can be expressed by elementary functions. Thus the general elliptic integral 1) reduces to the elementary functions and the integral

$$\phi = \int \frac{Ldx}{y}, \tag{5}$$

where L is a rational function of x^2.

Let us change the variable by setting

$$x = sn(u, k).$$

Then

$$dx = \sqrt{(1-x^2)(1-k^2x^2)}\,du = ydu,$$

and 5) becomes

$$\phi = \int R(x^2)du. \tag{6}$$

Here, R being a rational function of x^2, is an elliptic function admitting $2K$, $2iK'$ as periods. Hence by 198, 1),

$$\begin{aligned} R = {} & A_1 Z_1(u-a) - A_2 Z_1'(u-a) + \cdots \\ & + B_1 Z_1(u-b) - B_2 Z_1'(u-b) + \cdots \\ & + \cdots + C. \end{aligned}$$

This in 6) gives

$$\begin{aligned} \phi = {} & A_1 \log \Theta_1(u-a) - A_2 Z_1(u-a) + \cdots \\ & + B_1 \log \Theta(u-b) - B_2 Z_1(u-b) + \cdots \\ & + \cdots + Cu + D. \end{aligned} \tag{7}$$

200. The Elliptic Integral of the 2° Species. This we saw in 180, 1) is

$$\int \frac{\sqrt{1-k^2x^2}}{\sqrt{1-x^2}}\,dx. \tag{1}$$

If we set $x = sn\,u$ it becomes, putting in the limits 0, u,

$$E(u) = \int_0^u dn^2\,u\,du$$
$$= Z(u) - uZ'(K + iK') \qquad (2$$

on using 198, 2).

We have already called

$$E = \int_0^K dn^2\,u\,du$$

the complete integral of the 2° species. This corresponds to K, the complete integral of the 1° species.

Let us set in analogy to iK',

$$iH = \int_K^{K+iK'} dn^2\,u\,du.$$

If we set $u = K$ in 2), we get

$$Z'(K + iK') = -\frac{E}{K}.$$

Thus

$$E(u) = Z(u) + u\frac{E}{K}. \qquad (3$$

Replacing u by $u + 2K$, and $u + 2iK'$ and using 197, 8), we find

$$E(u + 2K) = E(u) + 2E,$$
$$E(u + 2iK') = E(u) + 2iH. \qquad (4$$

Thus

$$E(K + iK') = E + iH. \qquad (5$$

In 3) let us set $u = K + iK'$, we get, using 197, 14),

$$EK' - HK = \frac{\pi}{2}, \qquad (6$$

which is the *Legendrian Relation*, whose analogue in Weierstrass' theory is 171, 8).

From 197, 11) we have the addition theorem of the elliptic integral of the 2° species,

$$E(u + v) = E(u) + E(v) - k^2\,sn\,u\,sn\,v\,sn\,(u + v). \qquad (7$$

To calculate E we differentiate 3), getting

$$dn^2\,u = Z'(u) + \frac{E}{K}.$$

Setting $u = 0$ gives

$$1 - \frac{E}{K} = \frac{\Theta''(0)}{\Theta(0)} = \frac{2\pi^2}{K^2} \frac{q - 4q^4 + 9q^9 - 16q^{16} + \cdots}{1 - 2q + 2q^4 - 2q^9 + \cdots}. \tag{8}$$

201. The Elliptic Integral of the 3° Species. 1. We saw in 180, 1) that the elliptic integral of the 3° species used by Legendre is

$$\int \frac{1}{(1 + nx^2)} \frac{dx}{\sqrt{(1 - x^2)(1 - k^2x^2)}}.$$

This differs only by a constant from

$$\int \frac{1}{(x^2 - a^2)} \cdot \frac{dx}{\sqrt{(1 - x^2)(1 - k^2x^2)}}. \tag{1}$$

Let us set

$$x = sn\, u \quad , \quad a = sn\, v.$$

Then we can write 1), putting in the limits 0, u,

$$\int_0^u \frac{du}{sn^2 u - sn^2 v}.$$

Making use of 198, 5) gives

$$\int_0^u \frac{du}{sn^2 u - sn^2 v} = \frac{1}{sn\, v\, cn\, v\, dn\, v} \left\{ uZ(v) + \frac{1}{2} \log \frac{\Theta_1(v - u)}{\Theta_1(v + u)} \right\}, \tag{2}$$

taking that branch of the log which $= 1$ when $u = 0$.

The relation 2) shows how the calculation of the integral 1) may be effected by means of the Θ series, which, as we remember, converge in general with great rapidity.

2. Instead of the integral 2), Jacobi took as normal integral of the 3° species

$$\Pi(u, v) = \int_0^u \frac{k^2\, sn\, v\, cn\, v\, dn\, v\, sn^2 u}{1 - k^2\, sn^2 u\, sn^2 v}\, du. \tag{3}$$

Using 198, 8), we find that

$$\Pi(u, v) = uZ(v) + \frac{1}{2} \log \frac{\Theta(v - u)}{\Theta(u + v)}, \tag{4}$$

taking that branch of the log which $= 1$ when $u = 0$.

From 4) we have a remarkable *theorem due to Jacobi*, which states that when the argument u is interchanged with the parameter v in 3) we have

$$\Pi(u, v) - uZ(v) = \Pi(v, u) - vZ(u). \tag{5}$$

It follows at once from 4).

From 4) we have at once the *addition theorem* of the integrals of the 3° species. Denoting the parameter now by a, we get

$$\begin{aligned}&\Pi(u+v, a) - \Pi(u, a) - \Pi(v, a)\\ &= \frac{1}{2}\log\frac{\Theta(u+v-a)\Theta(u+a)\Theta(v+a)}{\Theta(u+v+a)\Theta(u-a)\Theta(v-a)}.\end{aligned} \tag{6}$$

Relation between the Functions of Jacobi and Weierstrass

202. Relation between *sn* and *p*. 1. We have now developed the two kinds of elliptic functions which are in current use to-day. To have two parallel theories may seem an *embarras de richesse;* it might seem better to choose one theory and discard the other. Perhaps one day that will be done, but at present we stand too near the time when only the functions of Jacobi were employed to neglect these latter. Besides, each set of functions has its good points, and each suffers from the defects of its very virtues. Since then we have these two classes of functions,

$$\begin{matrix} sn\, u, & \vartheta(u), & Z(u), \cdots k^2, \cdots \\ pu, & \sigma(u), & \zeta(u), \cdots g_2, g_3, \cdots \end{matrix}$$

we must ask what is their relation to one another. Let us begin with pu, $sn\, u$.

In 186, 9) we saw that

$$sn(u, k) = \sqrt{e_1 - e_2}\,\sigma_{0,2}\left(\frac{u}{\sqrt{e_1 - e_2}}, \omega_1, \omega_2\right), \tag{1}$$

where e_1, e_2, e_3 are such that

$$k^2 = \frac{e_3 - e_2}{e_1 - e_2} \tag{2}$$

as given in 186, 7). From 172, 16) we can also write

$$sn(u, k) = \frac{\sqrt{e_1 - e_2}}{\sqrt{p\left(\frac{u}{\sqrt{e_1 - e_2}}, \omega_1, \omega_2\right) - e_2}}. \tag{3}$$

The periods of $sn\,u$ are

$$4\,K = 4\,\omega_1\sqrt{e_1 - e_2}\quad , \quad 2\,iK' = 2\,\omega_2\sqrt{e_1 - e_2}. \tag{4}$$

From 3) we have

$$p(u, \omega_1, \omega_2) = e_2 + \frac{e_2 - e_1}{sn^2(u\sqrt{e_1 - e_2}, k)}. \tag{5}$$

2. Let $sn\,u$ have the periods $4\,K$, $2\,iK'$, then $sn^2 u$ has the periods $2\,K$, $2\,iK'$. Let $p(u)$ be a p function constructed on these periods. Then

$$p(u)\quad , \quad \frac{1}{sn^2 u} \tag{6}$$

have a double pole in their common parallelogram of periods. Their characteristics at $u = 0$ are both $\frac{1}{u^2}$. Hence the two functions 6) differ only by an additive constant. To find this we develop both functions 6) about the point $u = 0$. We have

$$p(u) = \frac{1}{u^2} + * + au^2 + \cdots$$

$$sn\,u = u\left(1 - \frac{1+k^2}{6}u^2 + \cdots\right).$$

$$sn^2 u = u^2\left(1 - \frac{1+k^2}{3}u^2 + \cdots\right).$$

$$\frac{1}{sn^2 u} = \frac{1}{u^2} + \frac{1+k^2}{3} + \cdots$$

Thus by 165, 10

$$p(u) = \frac{1}{sn^2 u} - \frac{1}{3}(1 + k^2). \tag{7}$$

From 7) we can get the relation between $p(u)$ and $sn\,u$ when p has the periods $2\,\omega_1$, $2\,\omega_2$ and sn the periods $4\,K$, $2\,iK'$.

For let us suppose, as we always do, that the indices 1, 2 are so chosen that if we set

$$\tau = \frac{\omega_2}{\omega_1} \tag{8}$$

then Ord $\tau > 0$. We then set

$$q = e^{\pi i \tau}\quad , \quad 2\,K = \pi\vartheta_3^2\quad , \quad 2\,iK' = 2\,K\tau,$$

$$\sqrt{k} = \frac{\vartheta_2(0, \tau)}{\vartheta_3(0, \tau)}\quad , \quad sn\,u = \frac{1}{\sqrt{k}}\frac{\vartheta_1\left(\frac{u}{2\,K}, \tau\right)}{\vartheta_0\left(\frac{u}{2\,K}, \tau\right)}. \tag{9}$$

Then 7) gives

$$p(u) = \frac{K^2}{\omega_1^2}\left\{\frac{1}{sn^2\frac{Ku}{\omega_1}} - \frac{1+k^2}{3}\right\}. \quad (10$$

Differentiating 10) gives

$$p'(u) = -\frac{2\,K^3}{\omega_1^3}\frac{cn\,v\;dn\,v}{sn^3 v}\quad,\quad v = \frac{Ku}{\omega_1}. \quad (11$$

203. The e_1, e_2, e_3 in Terms of the ϑ's. In 202, 10) let us set $u = \omega_1, \omega_2, \omega_3$. Then

$$\frac{Ku}{\omega_1} \text{ becomes } K \quad , \quad iK' \quad , \quad -(K+iK').$$

$$pu \text{ becomes } e_1 \quad , \quad e_2 \quad , \quad e_3.$$

$$\frac{1}{sn^2\frac{Ku}{\omega_1}} \text{ becomes } 1 \quad , \quad 0 \quad , \quad k^2.$$

Hence

$$e_1 = \frac{K^2}{\omega_1^2}\frac{1+k'^2}{3},$$
$$e_2 = -\frac{K^2}{\omega_1^2}\frac{1+k^2}{3}, \quad (1$$
$$e_3 = \frac{K^2}{\omega_1^2}\frac{k^2-k'^2}{3},$$

and

$$e_1 + e_2 + e_3 = 0.$$

From 1) we get

$$e_1 - e_2 = \frac{K^2}{\omega_1^2}\quad,\quad e_1 - e_3 = k'^2\frac{K^2}{\omega_1^2}\quad,\quad e_3 - e_2 = k^2\frac{K^2}{\omega_1^2}. \quad (2$$

Hence

$$k^2 = \frac{e_3 - e_2}{e_1 - e_2}\quad,\quad k'^2 = \frac{e_1 - e_3}{e_1 - e_2}. \quad (3$$

If now we put in the values of k^2, k'^2, K in terms of the ϑ's, we find

$$e_1 = \frac{1}{3}\left(\frac{\pi}{2\,\omega_1}\right)^2\{\vartheta_3^4 + \vartheta_0^4\},$$
$$e_2 = -\frac{1}{3}\left(\frac{\pi}{2\,\omega_1}\right)^2\{\vartheta_2^4 + \vartheta_3^4\}, \quad (4$$
$$e_3 = \frac{1}{3}\left(\frac{\pi}{2\,\omega_1}\right)^2\{\vartheta_2^4 - \vartheta_0^4\}.$$

Their differences give

$$e_3 - e_2 = \left(\frac{\pi}{2\,\omega_1}\right)^2 \vartheta_2^4,$$

$$e_1 - e_3 = \left(\frac{\pi}{2\,\omega_1}\right)^2 \vartheta_0^4, \qquad (5$$

$$e_1 - e_2 = \left(\frac{\pi}{2\,\omega_1}\right)^2 \vartheta_3^4.$$

204. Relation between σ's and ϑ's. The two functions

$$\sigma(u,\, 2\,\omega_1,\, 2\,\omega_2) \quad , \quad \vartheta_1(v,\, \tau),$$

where

$$v = \frac{u}{2\,\omega_1} \quad , \quad \tau = \frac{\omega_2}{\omega_1}$$

are integral transcendental functions having the same zeros. Thus by Weierstrass' theorem, 140, 1,

$$\vartheta_1(v) = e^{g(u)}\sigma(u),$$

where g is an integral function.

If we take the second logarithmic derivative, we find as in 166, 1 that $g'' =$ constant. Hence

$$\vartheta_1(v) = e^{a+bu+cu^2}\sigma(u)$$
$$= Ae^{bu+cu^2}\sigma(u). \qquad (1$$

As $\vartheta_1(v)$, $\sigma(u)$ are both odd functions,

$$e^{-bu+cu^2} = e^{bu+cu^2},$$

or

$$e^{2bu} = 1 \quad , \quad \text{hence } b = 0.$$

To determine A and c let us develop both sides of 1) about $u = 0$. We have

$$\vartheta_1(v) = v\vartheta_1' + \frac{v^3}{3!}\vartheta_1''' + \cdots$$

$$e^{cu^2} = 1 + cu^2 + \cdots$$

$$e^{cu^2}\sigma(u) = u + cu^3 + \cdots$$

These in 1) give

$$u\frac{\vartheta_1'}{2\,\omega_1} + \frac{u^3}{6}\frac{\vartheta_1'''}{8\,\omega_1^3} + \cdots = Au + cAu^3 + \cdots$$

Hence

$$A = \frac{\vartheta_1'}{2\,\omega_1} \quad , \quad c = \frac{1}{24}\frac{\vartheta_1'''}{\omega_1^2\vartheta_1'}.$$

Thus 1) becomes

$$\vartheta_1\left(\frac{u}{2\,\omega_1},\ \tau\right) = \frac{\vartheta_1'}{2\,\omega_1} e^{\frac{1}{6}\frac{\vartheta_1'''}{\vartheta_1'}\left(\frac{u}{2\omega_1}\right)^2} \sigma(u). \tag{2}$$

We can give this relation another form. We have

$$\sigma(u + 2\,\omega_1) = -\,e^{2\eta_1(u+\omega_1)}\sigma(u),$$
$$\vartheta_1(u + 1,\ \tau) = -\,\vartheta_1(u).$$

Thus

$$\vartheta_1\left(\frac{u + 2\,\omega_1}{2\,\omega_1},\ \tau\right) = -\,\vartheta_1\left(\frac{u}{2\,\omega_1}\right) = \frac{\vartheta_1'}{2\,\omega_1} e^{\frac{1}{6}\frac{\vartheta_1'''}{\vartheta_1'}\left(\frac{u}{2\omega_1}+1\right)^2} \sigma(u + 2\,\omega_1),$$

or

$$\frac{\vartheta_1'}{2\,\omega_1} e^{\frac{1}{6}\frac{\vartheta_1'''}{\vartheta_1}\left(\frac{u}{2\omega_1}\right)^2} \sigma(u) = \frac{\vartheta_1'}{2\,\omega_1} e^{\frac{1}{6}\frac{\vartheta_1'''}{\vartheta_1'}\left[\left(\frac{u}{2\omega_1}\right)^2 + \frac{u}{\omega_1} + 1\right]} e^{2\eta_1(u+\omega_1)}\sigma(u).$$

This gives

$$e^{\frac{1}{6}\frac{\vartheta_1'''}{\vartheta_1'}\left[\frac{u}{\omega_1}+1\right]} e^{2\eta_1(u+\omega_1)} = 1,$$

or

$$2\,\eta_1\omega_1 = -\frac{1}{6}\frac{\vartheta_1'''}{\vartheta_1'}. \tag{3}$$

This in 2) gives

$$\vartheta_1\left(\frac{u}{2\,\omega_1}\right) = \frac{\vartheta_1'}{2\,\omega_1} e^{-2\,\eta_1\omega_1\left(\frac{u}{2\,\omega_1}\right)^2} \sigma(u). \tag{4}$$

As

$$\sigma_r(u) = e^{-\eta_r u}\frac{\sigma(u + \omega_r)}{\sigma\omega_r},$$

we have at once

$$\sigma_1(u) = e^{2\eta_1\omega_1\left(\frac{u}{2\omega_1}\right)^2} \frac{\vartheta_2\left(\frac{u}{2\,\omega_1}\right)}{\vartheta_2},$$

$$\sigma_2(u) = e^{2\eta_1\omega_1\left(\frac{u}{2\omega_1}\right)^2} \frac{\vartheta_0\left(\frac{u}{2\,\omega_1}\right)}{\vartheta_0}, \tag{5}$$

$$\sigma_3(u) = e^{2\eta_1\omega_1\left(\frac{u}{2\omega_1}\right)^2} \frac{\vartheta_3\left(\frac{u}{2\,\omega_1}\right)}{\vartheta_3}.$$

From these relations we get

$$sn(u, \tau) = \frac{K}{\omega_1} \frac{\sigma\left(\frac{\omega_1 u}{K}, \omega_1, \omega_2\right)}{\sigma_2\left(\frac{\omega_1 u}{K}, \omega_1, \omega_2\right)},$$

$$cn(u, \tau) = \frac{\sigma_1\left(\frac{\omega_1 u}{K}, \omega_1, \omega_2\right)}{\sigma_2\left(\frac{\omega_1 u}{K}, \omega_1, \omega_2\right)}, \qquad (6$$

$$dn(u, \tau) = \frac{\sigma_3\left(\frac{\omega_1 u}{K}, \omega_1, \omega_2\right)}{\sigma_2\left(\frac{\omega_1 u}{K}, \omega_1, \omega_2\right)}.$$

Also we find

$$sn(v, \tau) = \frac{\sqrt{e_1 - e_2}}{\sqrt{pu - e_2}},$$

$$cn(v, \tau) = \frac{\sqrt{pu - e_1}}{\sqrt{pu - e_2}}, \qquad u = \frac{v}{\sqrt{e_1 - e_2}}, \qquad (7$$

$$dn(v, \tau) = \frac{\sqrt{pu - e_3}}{\sqrt{pu - e_2}}.$$

CHAPTER XIII

LINEAR DIFFERENTIAL EQUATIONS

205. Introductory. 1. In the last three chapters we have given a brief account of the elliptic functions. These functions are of great importance in themselves; they also furnish a striking and brilliant example of the great power and usefulness of the theory of functions of a complex variable. As usually happens, these two theories have mutually aided each other. The function theory has furnished the viewpoint and instruments of research; the elliptic functions in return have furnished fresh problems which have given rise to a broadening and deepening of the function theory. Without the notion of a complex variable, the imaginary period of the elliptic functions would never have been discovered, and without this period, there would be no theory of double periodic functions. Yet the double periodicity is their most important and characteristic property.

2. Another theory which has been revolutionized and put on an entirely new basis by the advent of the theory of functions is the theory of differential equations. In the old days, a differential equation meant merely this: Find some combination of the elementary functions which satisfies it. The simplest type of differential equation has the form

$$dy = f(x)dx,$$

whose integral is formally given by

$$y = \int f(x)dx.$$

But already the simple differential equation

$$dy = \frac{dx}{\sqrt{(1-x^2)(1-k^2x^2)}} \tag{1}$$

could not be integrated in terms of the elementary functions. The problem of integrating a differential equation was a kind of game of hide and seek, the solution being usually so well hidden that no amount of seeking could discover it.

We owe to Cauchy an entirely new point of view. He first taught us to regard a differential equation as defining a function whose properties are to be unfolded by a study of the equation itself. This method we have already illustrated in studying the differential equation 1). We propose now to apply it to a broad class of equations called *linear homogeneous differential equations.* They have the form

$$p_0 \frac{d^n y}{dx^n} + p_1 \frac{d^{n-1} y}{dx^{n-1}} + \cdots + p_n y = 0, \tag{2}$$

the coefficients p being analytic functions of the complex variable x. Such an equation is said to be of *order n.* We shall restrict ourselves to $n = 2$; moreover we shall generally suppose the coefficients to be rational.

A number of important functions in analysis satisfy such equations, and we have chosen these equations for the same twofold reason that induced us to choose the elliptic functions, viz. to illustrate the general principles of the function theory, and to develop the properties of certain functions of great importance.

Examples of this type of equations are the following:

Example 1. The *polynomials of Legendre* satisfy

$$(1 - x^2) \frac{d^2 y}{dx^2} - 2x \frac{dy}{dx} + n(n+1) y = 0. \tag{3}$$

Example 2. The *associated Legendrean functions* satisfy

$$(1 - x^2) \frac{d^2 y}{dx^2} - 2(m+1) x \frac{dy}{dx} + \{n(n+1) - m(m+1)\} y = 0. \tag{4}$$

Example 3. *Bessel's functions* satisfy

$$x^2 \frac{d^2 y}{dx^2} + x \frac{dy}{dx} + (x^2 - n^2) y = 0. \tag{5}$$

Example 4. The *functions of Lamé* satisfy

$$\frac{d^2 y}{dx^2} + \frac{1}{2} \left\{ \frac{1}{x - e_1} + \frac{1}{x - e_2} + \frac{1}{x - e_3} \right\} \frac{dy}{dx}$$
$$- \frac{1}{4} \frac{ax + b}{(x - e_1)(x - e_2)(x - e_3)} y = 0. \tag{6}$$

Example 5. The *hypergeometric function* satisfies

$$x(x-1)\frac{d^2y}{dx^2}+\{x(\alpha+\beta+1)-\gamma\}\frac{dy}{dx}+\alpha\beta y=0. \qquad (7$$

We notice that all these equations have rational coefficients.

3. The general theory of linear homogeneous differential equations was first studied by Riemann. It owes, however, its present perfection largely to L. Fuchs, who began his researches in this field about 1866, and to a stately array of mathematicians who have followed in his wake. Prior to Riemann we may mention as especially important the early investigations of Gauss and Kummer of the hypergeometric differential equation 7).

206. Existence Theorem. 1. Instead of the general equation 2) of the last article let us consider one of the second order

$$y''=p_1y'+p_2y, \qquad (1$$

the coefficients p_1, p_2 being analytic about the point $x=a$. We propose to show that 1) admits an *analytic solution*

$$y=b_0+b_1(x-a)+b_2(x-a)^2+\cdots \qquad (2$$

which is uniquely determined by the *initial conditions* that y and y' shall have assigned values $y=\alpha$, $y'=\beta$ at $x=a$. The reasoning we shall employ can be easily generalized so as to apply to the general case of order n. By using an equation 1) of second order we simplify our calculations without sacrificing the general method.

Suppose for the moment that 1) admits the analytic solution 2). The coefficients b_n are determined as follows. From 2) we have

$$y(a)=b_0\quad,\quad y'(a)=b_1,\cdots y^{(n)}(a)=n!\,b_n.$$

This gives at once $\quad b_0=\alpha,\qquad b_1=\beta.$

From 1) we have

$$y''(a)=p_1(a)y'(a)+p_2(a)y(a).$$

Let us set $\quad A_1=p_1(a)\quad,\quad A_2=p_2(a),$

then the last relation gives

$$2!\,b_2=b_1A_1+b_0A_2=\beta A_1+\alpha A_2. \qquad (3$$

Differentiating 1) we get y''' in terms of y, y', y'' or

$$y'''=p_1y''+p_1'y'+p_2y'+p_2'y. \qquad (4$$

If we set here $x = a$, we get b_3. In this way we may continue and so determine one coefficient b after another.

This shows that only one analytic solution 2) with a given set of initial conditions is possible. The form of these b's is important. To determine it let us set

$$p_1 = \sum_{n=0}^{\infty} p_{1n}(x-a)^n \quad , \quad p_2 = \sum_{n=0}^{\infty} p_{2n}(x-a)^n. \tag{5}$$

These are simply the development of p_1, p_2 in power series, since by hypothesis they are regular at $x = a$.

The relation 3) shows that b_2 is an integral rational function of α, β and p_{10}, p_{20}. The relation 4) shows that b_3 is an integral rational function of α, β, p_{10}, p_{20}, p_{11}, p_{21}. Thus in general

$$b_n = F_n(b_0, b_1, p_{10}, p_{11}, p_{20}, p_{21} \cdots) \tag{6}$$

is an integral rational function of the enclosed letters with *positive* coefficients.

2. Having shown how to determine a solution 2) which *formally* satisfies 1), let us show that this solution converges for all x which lie within a circle $\mathfrak{K}$ about $x = a$, and which reaches to the nearest singular point of the coefficients $p_1(x)$, $p_2(x)$ of 1).

To this end we seek a simple differential equation of the same type as 1), which we know admits an integral

$$z = c_0 + c_1(z-a) + c_2(z-a)^2 + \cdots \tag{7}$$

converging within $\mathfrak{K}$, such that

$$\beta_n \leq \gamma_n. \tag{8}$$

Here, as we have so often done before when dealing with series, we denote the absolute values by the corresponding Greek or German letters. Thus in particular $\beta_n = |b_n|$, $\gamma_n = |c_n|$.

Let this auxiliary equation be

$$z'' = q_1 z' + q_2 z, \tag{9}$$

where

$$q_1 = \sum_0^{\infty} q_{1n}(x-a)^n \quad , \quad q_2 = \sum_0^{\infty} q_{2n}(x-a)_n \tag{10}$$

are the development of q_1, q_2 in power series about $x = a$.

Now whatever the $q_1(x)$, $q_2(x)$ are, the coefficients c_n must satisfy the relations

$$c_n = F_n(c_0, c_1, q_{10}, q_{11} \cdots q_{20}, q_{21} \cdots), \tag{11}$$

where F_n is the same function as in 6), only with different arguments.

As the coefficients are positive in **11)**, the c_n will be real and positive when the arguments in 11) are real and positive.

Now c_0, c_1 being arbitrary, we take them real and positive and such that

$$c_0 \geq \beta_0 \quad , \quad c_1 \geq \beta_1.$$

If now

$$\mathfrak{q}_{1n} \geq \mathfrak{p}_{1n} \quad , \quad \mathfrak{q}_{2n} \geq \mathfrak{p}_{2n}, \tag{12}$$

then

$$\beta_n \leq F_n(\beta_0,\ \beta_1,\ \mathfrak{p}_{10} \cdots \mathfrak{p}_{20} \cdots)$$
$$\leq F_n(\gamma_0,\ \gamma_1,\ \mathfrak{q}_{10} \cdots \mathfrak{q}_{20} \cdots) = \gamma_n,$$

or

$$\beta_n \leq \gamma_n.$$

Let us now try to choose the coefficients q_1, q_2 in 9) so that 12) holds. By Cauchy's inequality

$$\mathfrak{p}_{mn} \leq \frac{P_m}{R^n} \quad , \quad m = 1,\ 2,$$

where

$$P_m \geq \text{Max} \mid p_m(x) \mid$$

on $\mathfrak{R}$ whose radius, say, is R.

But then if we only take $\displaystyle q_{mn} = \frac{P_m}{R^n}$,

the condition 12) is satisfied. In this case

$$q_m = P_m \left\{ 1 + \frac{x-a}{R} + \frac{(x-a)^2}{R^2} + \cdots \right\}$$
$$= \frac{P_m}{1 - \dfrac{x-a}{R}} \quad , \quad | x - a | < R.$$

Thus our auxiliary equation 9) becomes

$$\left(1 - \frac{x-a}{R}\right) z'' = P_1 z' + P_2 z. \tag{13}$$

We need only to show that 7) is convergent. The ratio of two successive terms of its adjoint series is

$$\frac{\gamma_{n+2}}{\gamma_{n+1}} \mid x - a \mid.$$

Thus 7) will converge within $\mathfrak{R}$ if we show that

$$\lim_{n=\infty} R\frac{\gamma_{n+2}}{\gamma_{n+1}} = 1. \tag{14}$$

To do this we derive a recursion formula to determine the γ's, or what is the same, the c's.

Differentiating 13) gives

$$\left(1 - \frac{x-a}{R}\right)z''' - \frac{1}{R}z'' = P_1 z'' + P_2 z'.$$

Differentiating again, we get

$$\left(1 - \frac{x-a}{R}\right)z^{\text{IV}} - \frac{2}{R}z''' = P_1 z''' + P_2 z''.$$

In general we see that

$$\left(1 - \frac{x-a}{R}\right)z^{(n+2)} - \frac{n}{R}z^{(n+1)} = P_1 z^{(n+1)} + P_2 z^{(n)}.$$

Setting $x = a$ and noting that $c_n = \frac{1}{n!}z^{(n)}(a)$

we get

$$(n+2)!c_{n+2} - \frac{n(n+1)!}{R}c_{n+1} = (n+1)!P_1 c_{n+1} + n!P_2 c_n.$$

Thus
$$R(n+2)!c_{n+2} = (n+1)!\{n + RP_1\}c_{n+1} + n!RP_2 c_n,$$
or
$$Rc_{n+2} = \frac{n+RP_1}{n+2}c_{n+1} + \frac{1}{(n+1)(n+2)}RP_2 c_n. \tag{15}$$

Let us now take P_1 so that

$$RP_1 > 2.$$

As the last term in 15) is positive, this shows that

$$Rc_{n+2} > c_{n+1}$$

or

$$\frac{c_n}{c_{n+1}} \cdot \frac{1}{R} < 1. \tag{16}$$

Let us now write 15)

$$R\frac{c_{n+2}}{c_{n+1}} = \frac{n+RP_1}{n+2} + \frac{R^2P_2}{(n+1)(n+2)} \cdot \frac{1}{R}\frac{c_n}{c_{n+1}}.$$

Letting $n \doteq \infty$ and using 16) we get 14).

3. The form of proof here given is entirely general, and holds for any n. We have thus proved the

Existence Theorem. The differential equation

$$\frac{d^n y}{dx^n} + p_1 \frac{d^{n-1} y}{dx^{n-1}} + \cdots + p_n y = 0 \qquad (17$$

admits one and only one analytic solution which together with its first $n-1$ *derivatives takes on assigned values at* $x = a$. *This solution is valid within a circle* $\mathfrak{K}$ *which extends to the nearest singular point of the coefficients* $p_1 \cdots p_n$ *which are regular about the point* $x = a$.

4. Let

$$y = b_0 + b_1(x-a) + b_2(x-a)^2 + \cdots \qquad (18$$

be a solution valid in $\mathfrak{K}$. Let a_1 be a point within $\mathfrak{K}$. We can write 18)

$$y = b_0' + b_1'(x-a_1) + b_2'(x-a_1)^2 + \cdots \qquad (19$$

which is convergent within some circle $\mathfrak{K}_1$ about $x = a_1$ which certainly extends up to the edge of $\mathfrak{K}$ and may go beyond. If we develop the coefficients $p_m(x)$ about $x = a_1$ and put 19) in 17), we get a power series about $x = a_1$. Since 19) satisfies 17) within $\mathfrak{K}$, it will continue to satisfy it for all points within $\mathfrak{K}_1$; moreover $\mathfrak{K}_1$ will reach to the nearest singular point of the coefficients p. In this way we may extend the solution 18) by analytic continuation. Thus we have the theorem:

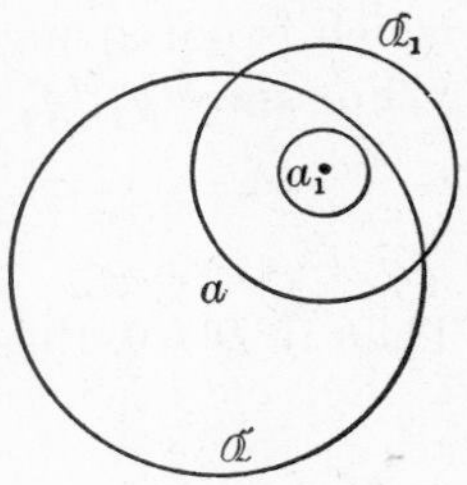

If the function 18) *is a solution of the differential equation* 17), *all its analytical continuations are still solutions of* 17).

207. Fundamental System. To each particular set of initial conditions $y = \alpha$, $y' = \beta$ for $x = a$ will correspond a *particular* solution of

$$y'' + p_1 y' + p_2 y = 0. \qquad (1$$

Let y_1, y_2 be two such particular solutions. Then

$$y = c_1 y_1 + c_2 y_2 \qquad (2$$

is obviously a solution of 1) also. Let us show that we may pick out particular solutions y_1, y_2 such that every solution of 1) has the form 2).

For suppose that y is to satisfy the initial conditions

$$y(a)=\alpha \quad , \quad y'(a)=\beta.$$

On the other hand, suppose the initial conditions of y_1 are

$$y_1(a)=\alpha_1 \quad , \quad y_1'(a)=\beta_1,$$

of y_2 are

$$y_2(a)=\alpha_2 \quad , \quad y_2'(a)=\beta_2.$$

Then 2) shows that we must have

$$\alpha=c_1\alpha_1+c_2\alpha_2 \quad , \quad \beta=c_1\beta_1+c_2\beta_2.$$

These two relations determine c_1, c_2 when

$$\begin{vmatrix} \alpha_1 & \alpha_2 \\ \beta_1 & \beta_2 \end{vmatrix} \neq 0. \tag{3}$$

Let us set

$$D(x)=\begin{vmatrix} y_1 & y_2 \\ y_1' & y_2' \end{vmatrix}. \tag{4}$$

We note that $D(a)$ is nothing but the left side of 3).

Let us show that if $D\neq 0$ at $x=a$, it is also $\neq 0$ at any point x which is not a singular point of the coefficients p in 1).

For since y_1, y_2 are solutions of 1), we have

$$y_1''+p_1y_1'+p_2y_1=0,$$
$$y_2''+p_1y_2'+p_2y_2=0.$$

Then if $D\neq 0$, these give

$$p_1=\frac{\begin{vmatrix} y_1' & y_1 \\ y_2'' & y_2 \end{vmatrix}}{D(x)}=\frac{D_1(x)}{D(x)}. \tag{5}$$

Now we note that

$$\frac{d}{dx}D(x)=-D_1(x).$$

Thus 5) gives

$$p_1=-\frac{d}{dx}\log D(x),$$

or

$$D(x)=Ce^{-\int p_1(x)dx}. \tag{6}$$

At $x=a$, D is $\neq 0$, hence $C\neq 0$. Thus D is always $\neq 0$ since D cannot vanish unless $p_1(x)=\infty$. But this point would be a singular point of p_1. The reasoning being entirely general we see that:

If

$$y_1, y_2 \cdots y_n \tag{7}$$

are particular solutions of

$$\frac{d^n y}{dx^n} + p_1 \frac{d^{n-1}y}{dx^{n-1}} + \cdots + p_n y = 0, \tag{8}$$

for which

$$D(x) = \begin{vmatrix} y_1, & y_2 & \cdots y_n \\ y_1', & y_2' & \cdots y_n' \\ \cdot & \cdot & \cdot \\ y_1^{(n-1)}, & y_2^{(n-1)} & \cdots y_n^{(n-1)} \end{vmatrix} \tag{9}$$

is $\neq 0$ *at a point* $x = a$ *at which all the coefficients* $p_1 \cdots p_n$ *in* 8) *are regular, then* $D \neq 0$ *at all such points in a connected region.*

Such a system 7) is called a *fundamental system*, and we have the theorem:

Every analytic solution of the differential equation 8) *is a linear function of any fundamental system* 7) *with constant coefficients.*

208. Linear Independence. We have just seen that a fundamental system $y_1, y_2, \cdots y_n$ is characterized by the fact that

$$D = \begin{vmatrix} y_1 & \cdots y_n \\ y_1' & \cdots y_n' \\ \cdot & \cdot \\ y_1^{(n-1)} & \cdots y_n^{(n-1)} \end{vmatrix} \tag{1}$$

is $\neq 0$. We now prove the theorem:

For a linear relation with constant coefficients

$$c_1 y_1 + c_2 y_2 + \cdots + c_n y_n = 0 \tag{2}$$

to hold, it is necessary and sufficient that $D = 0$ *identically.*

It is necessary. For if 2) holds, we get on differentiating

$$c_1 y_1' + c_2 y_2' + \cdots + c_n y_n' = 0$$

$$\cdot \quad \cdot \quad \cdot \quad \cdot \quad \cdot \quad \cdot \quad \cdot \quad \cdot \quad \cdot \quad \cdot \quad \cdot$$

$$c_1 y_1^{(n-1)} + c_2 y_2^{(n-1)} + \cdots + c_n y_n^{(n-1)} = 0.$$

From these equations and 2) we have necessarily $D = 0$.

It is sufficient. For let $D = 0$. Now $y_1, y_2 \cdots y_n$ are all solutions of the differential equation of order $n - 1$, viz.:

$$\begin{vmatrix} u, & y_2, & y_3 & \cdots y_n \\ u', & y_2', & y_3' & \cdots y_n' \\ \cdot & \cdot & \cdot & \cdot \\ u^{(n-1)}, & y_2^{(n-1)}, & y_3^{(n-1)} & \cdots y_n^{(n-1)} \end{vmatrix} = \frac{d^{n-1}u}{dx^{n-1}} + \phi_1 \frac{d^{n-2}u}{dx^{n-2}} + \cdots + \phi_{n-1} u = 0. \tag{3}$$

For setting $u = y_1$, this determinant reduces to D which $= 0$ by hypothesis. If we set $u = y_2$, for example, two columns of this determinant are the same; it therefore vanishes in this case.

Let then $u_1, u_2, \cdots u_{n-1}$ form a fundamental system of 3). Then $y_1 \cdots y_n$ being solutions of 3) are linear functions of the u's. Thus

$$y_1 = a_{11}u_1 + \cdots + a_{1,\,n-1}u_{n-1}$$
$$\cdot \quad \cdot \quad \cdot \quad \cdot \quad \cdot \quad \cdot \quad \cdot \quad \cdot \quad \cdot \quad \cdot \quad \cdot$$
$$y_n = a_{n1}u_1 + \cdots + a_{n,\,n-1}u_{n-1}.$$

If we eliminate the u's from these equations, we get a relation of the type 2).

In the exceptional case that the coefficients $\phi_1, \phi_2 \cdots$ in 3) vanish, it reduces to an identity. Then by using a smaller number of the y's we would still get a linear relation between them; but we shall not urge this point here.

Thus we may state that:

Any set $y_1, y_2 \cdots y_n$ of linearly independent solutions of a differential equation of order n form a fundamental solution.

209. Simple Singular Points. 1. Having seen that

$$\frac{d^2y}{dx^2} + p_1\frac{dy}{dx} + p_2 y = 0 \qquad (1$$

admits a solution taking on assigned initial conditions at any non-singular point of the coefficients p_1, p_2, we now turn to these singular points and ask how the solution of y behaves about one of them as $x = a$. We shall restrict ourselves to the case that p_1, p_2 have at most poles at $x = a$ whose orders are not greater than one and two respectively. Then we can write 1) in a *normal form*,

$$(x-a)^2\, q_0 \frac{d^2y}{dx^2} + (x-a)\, q_1 \frac{dy}{dx} + q_2 y = 0. \qquad (2$$

Here we suppose that the new coefficients q_0, q_1, q_2 are regular at $x = a$ and that q_0 does not vanish at this point. Then we have, developing about $x = a$,

$$q_m(x) = \sum_0^\infty q_{mn}(x-a)^n \qquad m = 0, 1, 2 \qquad (3$$

and at least $q_{00} \neq 0$.

The equation 2) may be written

$$\sum_{m=0}^{2} (x-a)^m q_{2-m} y^{(m)} = 0. \tag{4}$$

Let us try to satisfy 4) by setting

$$y = (x-a)^r \Sigma\, c_k (x-a)^k \quad , \quad c_0 \neq 0. \tag{5}$$

Our problem is to determine the unknown exponent r which in general is not a positive integer, and the coefficients c_n.

From 5) we get, on differentiating,

$$y' = (r+k)\Sigma c_k (x-a)^{r+k-1},$$
$$y'' = (r+k)(r+k-1)\,\Sigma c_k (x-a)^{r+k-2}.$$

These in 4) give

$$(x-a)^2 \sum_n q_{0n}(x-a)^n \sum_k (r+k)(r+k-1)c_k(x-a)^{r+k-2}$$
$$+ (x-a)\sum_n q_{1n}(x-a)^n \sum_k (r+k)c_k(x-a)^{r+k-1}$$
$$+ \sum_n q_{2n}(x-a)^n \sum_k c_k(x-a)^{r+k} = 0. \tag{6}$$

The coefficient of $(x-a)^{r+n}$ can be written, as Frobenius remarked, as follows. Let us set

$$f(x, r) = q_2 + r q_1 + r(r-1) q_0$$
$$= \sum_0^\infty \{q_{2n} + r q_{1n} + r(r-1) q_{0n}\}(x-a)^n$$
$$= \sum_0^\infty f_n(r)(x-a)^n. \tag{7}$$

Then 6) can be written

$$\Sigma f_{n-k}(r+k) c_k (x-a)^{r+n} = 0 \qquad \begin{array}{l} n = 0, 1, 2 \cdots \infty, \\ k = 0, 1, 2 \cdots n. \end{array} \tag{8}$$

As this power series $= 0$ identically, the coefficients of the different powers $(x-a)^{r+n}$ must all $= 0$. Hence

$$\begin{array}{l} c_0 f_0(r) = 0 \\ c_0 f_1(r) + c_1 f_0(r+1) = 0 \\ c_0 f_2(r) + c_1 f_1(r+1) + c_2 f_0(r+2) = 0 \\ c_0 f_3(r) + c_1 f_2(r+1) + c_2 f_1(r+2) + c_3 f_0(r+3) = 0 \\ \cdot \quad \cdot \quad \cdot \quad \cdot \quad \cdot \quad \cdot \quad \cdot \quad \cdot \quad \cdot \quad \cdot \quad \cdot \quad \cdot \quad \cdot \quad \cdot \quad \cdot \quad \cdot \quad \cdot \quad \cdot \quad \cdot \end{array} \tag{9}$$

Thus when 2) admits a solution of the type 5), the coefficients c_0, $c_1 \cdots$ and the exponent r must satisfy 9).

As $c_0 \neq 0$, the first equation requires r to satisfy $f_0(r) = 0$; or using its definition in 7),

$$f_0(r) = q_2(a) + rq_1(a) + r(r-1)q_0(a) = 0. \qquad (10$$

This equation for determining r is of fundamental importance; it is called the *indicial equation.* It is a quadratic in r.

Let now r be a root of 10). The coefficients $c_1, c_2 \cdots$ may be obtained in succession provided

$$f_0(r+1) \quad , \quad f_0(r+2) \quad , \quad f_0(r+3) \cdots \qquad (11$$

are all $\neq 0$. But for that root r_1 of 10) whose abscissa is greatest, none of the coefficients 11) can vanish. Neither can they vanish when the two roots of 10) do not differ by an integer.

Thus when the indicial equation admits two distinct roots r_1, r_2 which do not differ by an integer, there exist two series

$$\begin{aligned} y_1 &= (x-a)^{r_1}\{c_{10} + c_{11}(x-a) + c_{12}(x-a)^2 + \cdots\} \quad , \quad c_{10} \neq 0 \\ y_2 &= (x-a)^{r_2}\{c_{20} + c_{21}(x-a) + c_{22}(x-a)^2 + \cdots\} \quad , \quad c_{20} \neq 0, \end{aligned} \qquad (12$$

which *formally* satisfy the given differential equation. These series converge within a circle whose center is $x = a$ and which passes through the nearest singular point of the coefficients p_1, p_2 in 1).

This may be shown by the method employed in 206. As the reader has been through one existence proof it is not worth while here to repeat the proof.

2. The foregoing results can be extended to the general case. Let the coefficients of

$$\frac{d^n y}{dx^n} + p_1 \frac{d^{n-1}y}{dx^{n-1}} + \cdots + p_n y = 0 \qquad (13$$

have at $x = a$ at most poles of orders not greater than $1, 2, \cdots n$ respectively. Then we can write 13) in the normal form

$$(x-a)^n q_0 \frac{d^n y}{dx^n} + (x-a)^{n-1} q_1 \frac{d^{n-1}y}{dx^{n-1}} + \cdots + q_n y = 0 \qquad (14$$

where the q's are regular at $x = a$. They therefore have the form given in 3), where now $m = 0, 1, \cdots n$, and as before we suppose $q_{00} = q_0(a) \neq 0$. If we now try to satisfy 14) by a series of the form 5), we are led to a system of equations of the form 9). The indicial equation which determines the exponent r is here

$$f_0(r)=q_n(a)+rq_1(a)+r(r-1)q_2(a)+\cdots+r(r-1)\cdots (r-n+1)q_0(a)=0, \tag{15}$$

which we see is entirely similar to 10). Since by hypothesis $q_{00}(a)$ is $\neq 0$, the indicial equation is of degree n.

Let us arrange its roots in groups

$$\begin{array}{ccc} r_1 , & r_2' , & r_2'' \cdots \\ r_2 , & r_2' , & r_1'' \cdots \\ \cdot\ \cdot & \cdot\ \cdot & \cdot\ \cdot\ \cdot \end{array} \tag{16}$$

Here r_1 is the root whose abscissa is greatest and the first row embraces all the roots of 15) which differ from r_1 by an integer. Of all the remaining roots let r_2 have the greatest abscissa; then the second row embraces all the roots which differ from r_2 by an integer, and so on. The roots

$$r_1 , \quad r_2 \cdots \tag{17}$$

which head their respective rows are called *prime roots*. And now the existence theorem states that:

To each prime root 17) *corresponds an integral of* 13)

$$y_m=(x-a)^{r_m}\{c_{m0}+c_m(x-a)_1+c_{m2}(x-a)^2+\cdots\}, \tag{18}$$

$c_{m0}\neq 0$, *whose circle of convergence reaches up to the nearest singular point of the coefficients* p.

3. In case that each group in 16) contains but a single root, all the roots of 15) are prime roots. As to each prime root corresponds an integral 18), the foregoing method gives us n integrals of our differential equation 13). Let us now show that:

When the roots of indicial equation 15) *are all prime, the* n *integrals* 18) *form a fundamental system.*

For suppose there exists a linear relation

$$a_1y_1+a_2y_2+\cdots+a_ny_n=0 \tag{19}$$

between them. If we put the values y_1, $y_2\cdots$ as given by 18) in 19), we get a power series; the exponents of course are not integers in general. If $a_m \neq 0$ in 19), our power series contains the term

$$a_m c_{m0}(x-a)^{r_m},$$

and this is the only term with the exponent r_m. Thus $a_m c_{m0} = 0$, and hence $a_m = 0$, or $c_{m0} = 0$. Both of these are contrary to hypothesis. Hence a relation of the type 19) is impossible.

The case we have just treated is the simplest case that can arise at a singular point. We therefore call such points *simple singular points.*

210. The Hypergeometric Equation. 1. This is, as remarked in 205, 7),

$$x(x-1)\frac{d^2y}{dx^2} + \{x(\alpha+\beta+1)-\gamma\}\frac{dy}{dx} + \alpha\beta y = 0. \qquad (1$$

Its singular points in the finite part of the plane are $x = 0$, $x = 1$. Let us find the indicial equation for these points.

The point $x = 0$. Bringing 1) to the normal form

$$(x-1)x^2y'' + \{x(\alpha+\beta+1)-\gamma\}xy' + \alpha\beta xy = 0,$$

we have

$$q_0(x) = x-1 \quad , \quad q_1(x) = (\alpha+\beta+1)x-\gamma \quad , \quad q_2(x) = \alpha\beta x. \qquad (2$$

The indicial equation for $x = 0$ is, therefore,

$$r^2 + (\gamma-1)r = 0,$$

or

$$r\{r-(1-\gamma)\} = 0, \qquad (3$$

whose roots are $r_1 = 0$, $r_2 = 1-\gamma$.

The point $x = 1$. The normal form of 1) at this point is

$$x(x-1)^2y'' + \{(\alpha+\beta+1)x-\gamma\}(x-1)y' + \alpha\beta(x-1)y = 0.$$

Here

$$q_0(x) = x \quad , \quad q_1(x) = (\alpha+\beta+1)x-\gamma \quad , \quad q_2(x) = \alpha\beta(x-1).$$

The indicial equation is, therefore,

$$r\{r-(\gamma-\alpha-\beta)\} = 0, \qquad (4$$

whose roots are

$$r_1 = 0 \quad , \quad r_2 = \gamma-\alpha-\beta.$$

2. Let us investigate the nature of the point $x=\infty$. To this end we set

$$x=\frac{1}{u},$$

and 1) becomes

$$\frac{d^2y}{du^2}+\left\{\frac{2}{u}+\frac{\gamma u-(\alpha+\beta+1)}{u(1-u)}\right\}\frac{dy}{du}+\frac{\alpha\beta}{u^2(1-u)}y=0. \tag{5}$$

Obviously $u=0$ is a singular point.

The normal form of 5) at $u=0$ is

$$(1-u)u^2\frac{d^2y}{du^2}+\{2(1-u)+\gamma u-(\alpha+\beta+1)\}u\frac{dy}{du}+\alpha\beta y=0.$$

Here

$$q_0(u)=1-u \quad , \quad q_1(u)=2(1-u)+\gamma u-(\alpha+\beta+1) \quad , \quad q_2(u)=\alpha\beta.$$

Thus the indicial equation for $u=0$ is (6

$$r^2-(\alpha+\beta)r+\alpha\beta=0,$$

whose roots are

$$r_1=\alpha \quad , \quad r_2=\beta.$$

3. Let us now calculate the coefficients of our solution by the formulæ of 209, 9). We consider first *the point* $x=0$.

Now by definition

$$f_n(r)=r(r-1)\frac{q_0^{(n)}(0)}{n\,!}+r\frac{q_1^{(n)}(0)}{n\,!}+\frac{q_2^{(n)}(0)}{n\,!}. \tag{7}$$

As the q's are linear functions as shown by 2), all derivatives beyond the first vanish. Thus

$$f_2(r)=0 \quad , \quad f_3(r)=0 \quad \cdots$$

Hence the equations 209, 9) are all two-term equations and they give

$$c_n=-c_{n-1}\frac{f_1(r+n-1)}{f_0(r+n)}. \tag{8}$$

Let us now use the root $r=0$ of 3). Then

$$f_0(n)=-n\{\gamma+(n-1)\},$$

$$f_1(n-1)=\alpha\beta+(n-1)(\alpha+\beta+1)+(n-1)(n-2)$$

$$=(n+\alpha-1)(n+\beta-1).$$

Hence

$$c_n = \frac{(n+\alpha-1)(n+\beta-1)}{n(\gamma+n-1)} c_{n-1} \quad , \quad n = 1, 2, \cdots \tag{9}$$

We thus get

$$c_1 = \frac{\alpha \cdot \beta}{1 \cdot \gamma} c_0 \quad , \quad c_2 = \frac{(\alpha+1)(\beta+1)}{2\cdot(\gamma+1)} c_1 = \frac{\alpha \cdot \alpha+1 \cdot \beta \cdot \beta+1}{1 \cdot 2 \cdot \gamma \cdot \gamma+1} c_0,$$

etc. Hence taking $c_0 = 1$,

$$\begin{aligned} y_1 &= \left\{1 + \frac{\alpha \cdot \beta}{1 \cdot \gamma} x + \frac{\alpha \cdot \alpha+1 \cdot \beta \cdot \beta+1}{1 \cdot 2 \cdot \gamma \cdot \gamma+1} x^2 + \cdots \right\} \\ &= F(\alpha, \beta, \gamma, x). \end{aligned} \tag{10}$$

Let us now use the other root $r = 1-\gamma$ of 3). As

$$f_1(r) = r(r-1) + r(\alpha+\beta+1) + \alpha\beta = r^2 + (\alpha+\beta)r + \alpha\beta,$$
$$f_0(r) = -r(r-1+\gamma),$$

we have, from 8), on taking $r = 1-\gamma$,

$$\begin{aligned} c_n &= \frac{(n-\gamma)^2 + (n-\gamma)(\alpha+\beta) + \alpha\beta}{n(1-\gamma+n)} c_{n-1} \\ &= \frac{(n+\alpha-\gamma)(n+\beta-\gamma)}{n(1-\gamma+n)} c_{n-1}. \end{aligned} \tag{11}$$

Let us compare 9) and 11). We see that 9) goes over into 11) on replacing

$$\alpha \quad , \quad \beta \quad , \quad \gamma$$

by

$$\alpha+1-\gamma \quad , \quad \beta+1-\gamma \quad , \quad 2-\gamma.$$

Thus the integral corresponding to $r = 1-\gamma$ is

$$y_2 = x^{1-\gamma} F(\alpha+1-\gamma, \beta+1-\gamma, 2-\gamma, x). \tag{12}$$

4. Let us now turn to the *point* $x = 1$. The recursion formula is found to be for the root $r = 0$ of 4)

$$c_n = -\frac{(n+\alpha-1)(n+\beta-1)}{n(n+\alpha+\beta-\gamma)} c_{n-1}. \tag{13}$$

We see that 9) goes over into 13) on replacing

$$\alpha \quad , \quad \beta \quad , \quad \gamma$$

by

$$\alpha \quad , \quad \beta \quad , \quad \alpha+\beta-\gamma+1,$$

aside from the sign which can be made right by replacing $x-1$ by $1-x$. Thus the solution corresponding to the root $r = 0$ is

$$y_1 = F(\alpha, \beta, \alpha+\beta-\gamma+1, 1-x). \tag{14}$$

The solution corresponding to the other root $r = \gamma - \alpha - \beta$ of 4) is found to be

$$y_2 = (1-x)^{\gamma-\alpha-\beta} F(\gamma-\beta, \gamma-\alpha, \gamma-\alpha-\beta+1, 1-x). \quad (15$$

5. Finally we consider the *point* $x = \infty$. The recursion formula for the coefficients corresponding to the root $r = \alpha$ of 6) is

$$c_n = \frac{(\alpha+n-1)(\alpha+n-\gamma)}{n(\alpha+n-\beta)} c_{n-1}.$$

We see that 9) goes over into this on replacing

$$\alpha \quad , \quad \beta \quad , \quad \gamma$$

by

$$\alpha \quad , \quad \alpha-\gamma+1 \quad , \quad \alpha-\beta+1.$$

Thus the solution corresponding to the root $r = \alpha$ is

$$y_1 = \frac{1}{x^\alpha} F\left(\alpha, \alpha-\gamma+1, \alpha-\beta+1, \frac{1}{x}\right). \quad (16$$

The solution corresponding to the other root $r = \beta$ of 6) is similarly

$$y_2 = \frac{1}{x^\beta} F\left(\beta, \beta-\gamma+1, \beta-\alpha+1, \frac{1}{x}\right). \quad (17$$

211. Bessel's Equation. This is, as remarked in 205, 5),

$$x^2y'' + xy' + (x^2 - m^2)y = 0. \quad (1$$

The only singular point in the finite part of the plane is $x = 0$. Let us consider the integrals of 1) for this point. The equation is already in the normal form. Here

$$q_0(x) = 1 \quad , \quad q_1(x) = 1 \quad , \quad q_2(x) = x^2 - m^2.$$

The indicial equation for $x = 0$ is therefore

$$f_0(r) = -m^2 + r + r(r-1) = 0,$$

or

$$f_0(r) = r^2 - m^2 = 0. \quad (2$$

Also here

$$f_1(r) = 0 \quad , \quad f_2(r) = 1 \quad , \quad f_n(r) = 0 \quad , \quad n > 2.$$

Thus the equations 209, 9) become

$$c_1 = 0 \quad , \quad c_0 + c_2 f_2(r+2) = 0 \quad , \quad c_3 = 0,$$

and in general,

$$c_{2n} f_0(r+2n) + c_{2n-2} = 0 \quad , \quad c_{2n+1} = 0. \quad (3$$

One root of the indicial equation 2) is $r = m$. For this root 3) gives

$$n(2m + n)c_n + c_{n-2} = 0 \quad , \quad n \text{ even.}$$

Hence

$$c_2 = -\frac{c_0}{2(2m+2)},$$

$$c_4 = -\frac{c_2}{4(2m+4)} = \frac{c_0}{2 \cdot 4(2m+2)(2m+4)},$$

etc. Thus the integral corresponding to $r = m$ is

$$y_1 = c_0 x^m \left\{ 1 - \frac{x^2}{2(2m+2)} + \frac{x^4}{2 \cdot 4(2m+2)(2m+4)} - \frac{x^6}{2 \cdot 4 \cdot 6(2m+2)(2m+4)(2m+6)} + \cdots \right\}. \quad (4$$

In case m is not an integer, the other root $r = -m$ of 2) also furnishes a solution y_2 since the coefficient $f_0(r + 2n)$ of c_{2n} does not vanish for any n.

Let us take the constant c_0 so that

$$c_0 = \frac{1}{2^m \Pi(m)}.$$

Then as solutions of 1) we have

$$y_1 = J_m(x) = \sum_{n=0}^{\infty} \frac{(-1)^n}{\Pi(n)\Pi(m+n)} \left(\frac{x}{2}\right)^{m+2n} \quad (5$$

and

$$y_2 = J_{-m}(x) = \sum_{n=0}^{\infty} \frac{(-1)^n}{\Pi(n)\Pi(n-m)} \left(\frac{x}{2}\right)^{2n-m}. \quad (6$$

They are called *Bessel functions* of order m and $-m$ respectively.

212. The Logarithmic Case. 1. We have seen that when the indicial equation

$$F(r) = r(r-1)q_0(a) + rq_1(a) + q_2(a) = 0 \quad (1$$

has its first coefficient $q_0(a) \neq 0$, our differential equation, which we write in the normal form

$$L(y) = (x-a)^2 q_0(x) y'' + (x-a) q_1(x) y' + q_2(x) y = 0, \quad (2$$

has one solution of the form

$$y_1 = (x-a)^{r_1}\{c_0 + c_1(x-a) + c_2(x-a)^2 + \cdots\}, \quad (3$$

where r_1 is that root of 1) whose abscissa is greatest. Suppose now the roots of 1) are equal, or at least differ by an integer. The method developed in 209 gives *in general* only one integral 2), viz. the integral 3).

To obtain another linearly independent solution Fuchs proceeds as follows. We set

$$y = y_1 \int z dx \tag{4}$$

in 2). This leads to a linear homogeneous equation of order 1. Let z be a particular solution of this equation, and let y_2 be the value of 4) for this value of z. *Then y_1, y_2 form a fundamental system of our original equation.*

For if

$$c_1 y_1 + c_2 y_2 = 0, \tag{5}$$

we have, on using 4),

$$c_1 y_1 + c_2 y_1 \int z dx = 0,$$

or

$$c_1 + c_2 \int z dx = 0.$$

Differentiating this, we get

$$c_2 z = 0,$$

and this requires that $c_2 = 0$. Putting this in 5), we see that $c_1 = 0$. Thus y_1, y_2 are linearly independent as stated.

2. Let us now set 4) in 2) and find the resulting equation which z satisfies. We have, differentiating 4) and setting for brevity

$$z_1 = \int z dx,$$

$$y' = y_1' z_1 + y_1 z,$$
$$y'' = y_1'' z_1 + 2 y_1' z + y_1 z'.$$

These in 2) give

$$z_1 L(y_1) + (x-a)\{q_1 y_1 + 2(x-a) q_0 y_1'\} z + (x-a)^2 q_0 y_1 z' = 0. \tag{6}$$

But $L(y_1) = 0$ since y_1 is a solution of 2). Writing 6) in the normal form, we get

$$(x-a) q_0 z' + \left\{ q_1 + 2(x-a) q_0 \frac{y_1'}{y_1} \right\} z = 0. \tag{7}$$

If we write 3)

$$y_1 = (x-a)^{r_1} \eta,$$

we have

$$\log y_1 = r_1 \log (x-a) + \log \eta.$$

Hence

$$(x-a)\frac{y_1'}{y_1} = r_1 + (x-a)\psi(x),$$

where $\psi(a) \neq 0$. Thus we may write 7)

$$M(z) = (x-a)s_0 z' + s_1 z = 0, \tag{8}$$

where

$$s_0(x) = q_0(x),$$
$$s_1(x) = q_1(x) + 2\,q_0(x)\{r_1 + (x-a)\psi(x)\}.$$

Thus the indicial equation of 8) is

$$rs_0(a) + s_1(a) = 0,$$

or

$$G(r) = rq_0(a) + q_1(a) + 2\,q_0(a)r_1 = 0. \tag{9}$$

Then

$$(r+1)\,G(r) = q_0(a)\{-r_1(r_1-1) + (r+r_1+1)(r+r_1)\}$$
$$+\,q_1(a)\{-r_1 + (r+r_1+1)\},$$

as is seen by actually multiplying out. This we may write

$$(r+1)\,G(r) = -\{r_1(r_1-1)q_0(a) + r_1q_1(a)\}$$
$$+\{(r+r_1+1)(r+r_1)q_0(a) + (r+r_1+1)q_1(a)\}.$$

But the first term on the right is $q_2(a)$, since r_1 is a root of $F(r) = 0$. Thus the last equation becomes

$$(r+1)\,G(r) = (r+r_1+1)(r+r_1)q_0(a) + (r+r_1+1)q_1(a) + q_2(a)$$
$$= F(r+r_1+1)$$
$$= (r+1)\{r-(r_2-r_1-1)\}.$$

Hence the root of $G(r) = 0$ is

$$r_2 - r_1 - 1 = -m, \quad \text{an integer,}$$

since by hypothesis r_1 and r_2 differ by an integer, which may be 0.

From this we have as result that the differential equation 7) admits a solution,

$$z = (x-a)^{-m}\{e_0 + e_1(x-a) + \cdots\},$$

whose coefficients may be obtained as before. Then

$$\int zdx = \frac{h_{m-1}}{(x-a)^{m-1}} + \cdots + \frac{h_1}{x-a} + h \log(x-a)$$
$$+ k_1(x-a) + k_2(x-a)^2 + \cdots \qquad (10$$

But we have seen that

$$y_2 = y_1 \int zdx$$

is a second solution of 2). Putting in the value of y_1 as given by 3), we get

$$y_2 = (x-a)^{r_2}\phi(x) + (x-a)^{r_1}\phi_1(x) \log(x-a), \qquad (11$$

which may also be written

$$y_2 = (x-a)^{r_2}\{\phi(x) + h(x-a)^{m-1}\psi(x) \log(x-a)\}, \qquad (12$$

where $\phi(x)$, $\psi(x)$ are regular at $x = a$ and do not vanish at this point.

3. Thus when the indicial equation at the point $x = a$ has two roots which differ by an integer, there exist always two linearly independent solutions of the form 2) and 11) or 2) and 12).

Let us note that the logarithmic term in y_2 may not be present. This takes place, as 12) shows, when $h = 0$.

That the two roots of the indicial equation may differ by an integer without y_2 containing a logarithmic term, is illustrated by Bessel's equation 211. For let $m = l + \frac{1}{2}$ in 1) of that article, l being an integer. Then the two roots of the indicial equation are

$$l + \tfrac{1}{2} \quad , \quad -l - \tfrac{1}{2},$$

whose difference is $2l + 1$, an integer. However, the recursion formula 211, 3) for determining the coefficients c_n is such that the c_n of odd index vanish, and thus c_n for even index are uniquely determined if only m is not an integer.

4. There is no difficulty of generalizing the foregoing result. We may therefore state the theorem:

At the point $x = a$ let the indicial equation of

$$y^{(n)} + p_1 y^{n-1} + \cdots + p_n y = 0 \qquad (13$$

be of degree n. Let

$$r \quad , \quad r' \quad , \quad r'' \quad \cdots r^{(s)} \qquad (14$$

be the group of roots belonging to a prime root r, arranged according to diminishing abscissæ. Then

$$\begin{aligned} y &= (x-a)^r\phi(x), \\ y_1 &= (x-a)^{r'}\{\phi_{10}(x)+\phi_{11}\log(x-a)\}, \\ y_2 &= (x-a)^{r''}\{\phi_{20}(x)+\phi_{21}\log(x-a)+\phi_{22}\log^2(x-a)\}, \\ &\cdots\cdots\cdots\cdots\cdots \\ y_s &= (x-a)^{r^{(s)}}\{\phi_{s0}(x)+\phi_{s1}(x)\log(x-a)+\cdots+\phi_{ss}\log^s(x-a)\} \end{aligned} \qquad (15$$

are solutions of 13). *The functions* ϕ *are one-valued analytic functions within a circle about the point* $x=a$, *and passing through the nearest singular point of the coefficients* p *of* 13). *Each group of roots as* 14) *of the indicial equation furnishes a group of integrals as* 15). *The total number of integrals obtained in this manner is* n. *They form a fundamental system.*

5. When the degree of the indicial equation at a singular point $x=a$ is n, the same as the order of the differential equation, we say $x=a$ is a *regular point*. They include the simple singular points of 209.

When the indicial equation at the singular point $x=a$ is of degree less than n, the foregoing method does not give us all the integrals of 13). Such singular points are called *irregular*, and their theory is too difficult to treat in this work. We shall soon see that Bessel's equation has $x=\infty$ as an irregular point.

213. Method of Frobenius. 1. In the foregoing article we have established the existence of a fundamental system when the roots of the indicial equation differ by an integer, using a method due to Fuchs. Knowing the form of the solution, the coefficients may be obtained in any given case by the method of undetermined coefficients. Frobenius has given a method which leads more quickly to the desired result.

Let us take the singular point $x=a$ at the origin; we write our equation in the form

$$L(y)=x^2\frac{d^2y}{dx^2}+xp(x)\frac{dy}{dx}+q(x)y=0. \qquad (1$$

Using still the notation of 209, 9) let us set

$$c_0 f_1(s) + c_1 f_0(s+1) = 0,$$
$$c_0 f_2(s) + c_1 f_1(s+1) + c_2 f_0(s+2) = 0, \qquad (2$$
$$\cdots\cdots\cdots\cdots$$

where s is not necessarily a root of the indicial equation, but an arbitrary parameter.

Then c_n will have the form

$$c_n(s) = \frac{l_n(s)}{f_0(s+1) f_0(s+2) \cdots f_0(s+n)} \cdot c_0(s). \qquad (3$$

Let us now set

$$y = x^s \sum_{n=0}^{\infty} c_n x^n = g(x, s) \qquad (4$$

in 1). It becomes

$$L[g(x, s)] = x^s \sum_{n=0}^{\infty} \{c_n f_0(s+n) + c_{n-1} f_1(s+n-1) + \cdots + c_0 f_n(s)\} x^n$$
$$= c_0 f_0(s) x^s, \qquad (5$$

since all the terms on the right vanish except that which corresponds to $n = 0$, by reason of the relations 2).

Thus when s is a root of the indicial equation

$$f_0(r) = r(r-1) + p(0) r + q(0) = 0, \qquad (6$$

we see that

$$y_1 = x^{r_1} \sum_0^{\infty} c_n x^n \qquad (7$$

satisfies the equation 1).

Suppose that the two roots r_1, r_2 of the indicial equation differ by an integer, say $r_1 = r_2 + m$, $m \geq 0$. Then 6) has the form

$$f_0(r) = (r - r_1)(r - r_1 + m).$$

For c_0 let us take

$$c_0 = C f_0(s+1) f_0(s+2) \cdots f_0(s+m). \qquad (8$$

Then the c_n in 3) will have the form

$$c_n = \frac{C l_n(s)}{f_0(s+m+1) \cdots f_0(s+n)}, \qquad (9$$

in which the denominator does not vanish. Also the coefficient of x^s in 5) has the form

$$c_0 f_0(s) = (s - r_1)(s - r_1 + m)^2 S.$$

Hence in this case

$$L[g(x, s)] = (s - r_1)(s - r_1 + m)^2 S x^s. \tag{10}$$

Now

$$\frac{\partial}{\partial s} L(g) = x^2 \frac{\partial}{\partial s}\frac{d^2 g}{dx^2} + xp\frac{\partial}{\partial s} \cdot \frac{dg}{dx} + q\frac{\partial}{\partial s} \cdot g = L\left(\frac{\partial g}{\partial s}\right).$$

$$\frac{\partial}{\partial s}(s - r_1)(s - r_1 + m)^2 S = (s - r_1 + m)^2 S + 2(s - r_1)(s - r_1 + m)S$$
$$+ (s - r_1)(s - r_1 + m)^2 \frac{dS}{ds}.$$

Hence differentiating 10) with respect to s and then setting $s = r_2$, we see that

$$\left[\frac{\partial y}{\partial s}\right]_{s=r_2}$$

is a solution. Thus, provided the series 4) can be differentiated termwise, we have as a second solution of 1)

$$y_2 = \frac{\partial y}{\partial r_2} = x^{r_2} \log x \sum_0^\infty c_n x^n + x^{r_2} \sum_0^\infty \left(\frac{\partial c_n}{\partial s}\right)_{s=r_2} x^n. \tag{11}$$

2. When the coefficients of 4) are determined by 3) and $s = r_1$, the first prime root of the indicial equation, the series 4) is a solution. But if we give the c_n values as determined by 9) and take $s = r_2$ the second root of the indicial equation, we see that the series 4) will also be a solution in the case that r_1, r_2 differ by an integer.

214. Logarithmic Case of the Hypergeometric Equation. 1. We saw in 210 that the two roots of the indicial equation at $x = 0$ are 0 and $1 - \gamma$. Thus when

$$g = \gamma - 1$$

is an integer, we have the logarithmic case.

To fix the ideas *let us suppose that* $\gamma \geq 1$. Then our two integrals have the form

$$y_1 = F(\alpha, \beta, \gamma, x), \tag{1}$$
$$y_2 = F(\alpha, \beta, \gamma, x) \log x + x^{1-\gamma} G(x),$$

where G is regular at $x=0$. We proceed to apply the method of Frobenius given in 213 to find G. We have here

$$\begin{aligned} f_0(s) &= -s(s-1)-\gamma s = -s(s+g), \\ f_1(s) &= s(s-1)+s(\alpha+\beta+1)+\alpha\beta, \\ f_2(s) &= f_3(s) = \cdots = 0. \end{aligned} \tag{2}$$

Thus the relations 213, 2) become

$$c_n f_0(s+n)+c_{n-1}f_1(s+n-1)=0,$$

or

$$c_n = \frac{(s+n+\alpha-1)(s+n+\beta-1)}{(n+s)(s+n+\gamma-1)}c_{n-1}. \tag{3}$$

The coefficient c_0 is by 213, 8)

$$\begin{aligned} c_0(s) &= Cf_0(s+1)\cdots f_0(s+g) \\ &= (-1)^g C(s+1)\cdots(s+g)(s+g+1)\cdots(s+2g). \end{aligned} \tag{4}$$

As C is arbitrary, let us take, in order to get simple formulæ,

$$C = \frac{(-1)^g}{(s+\alpha)\cdots(s+\alpha+g-1)(s+\beta)\cdots(s+\beta+g-1)}. \tag{5}$$

Then 3), 4), 5) give

$$c_n(s) = c_0(s)\,C_n(s), \tag{6}$$

where

$$c_0(s) = \frac{(s+1)\cdots(s+g)(s+g+1)\cdots(s+2g)}{(s+\alpha)\cdots(s+\alpha+g-1)(s+\beta)\cdots(s+\beta+g-1)}, \tag{7}$$

$$C_n(s) = \frac{(s+\alpha)\cdots(s+\alpha+n-1)(s+\beta)\cdots(s+\beta+n-1)}{(s+1)\cdots(s+n)(s+\gamma)\cdots(s+\gamma+n-1)}, \tag{8}$$

$$C_0(s)=1.$$

Thus

$$y = c_0(s)x^s\sum_{n=0}^{\infty}C_n(s)x^n \quad , \quad C_0 = 1 \tag{9}$$

is a solution for $s = 1-\gamma$. *We call this* y_1.

From 8) we have

$$\begin{aligned} c_0(s)\,C_{n+g}(s) &= \frac{(s+1)\cdots(s+2g)(s+\alpha)\cdots(s+\alpha+g+n-1)(s+\beta)\cdots}{(s+\alpha)\cdots(s+\alpha+g-1)(s+\beta)\cdots(s+\beta+g-1)(s+1)} \\ &\qquad \frac{}{\cdots(s+g+n)(s+\gamma)\cdots(s+g+\gamma+n-1)} \\ &= \frac{(s+g+\alpha)\cdots(s+\alpha+g+n-1)(s+g+\beta)\cdots(s+\beta+g+n-1)}{(s+g+1)\cdots(s+g+n)(s+g+\gamma)\cdots(s+g+\gamma+n-1)} \\ &= C_n(s+g). \end{aligned}$$

Thus we can write 9),

$$y = c_0(s)x^s \sum_{n=0}^{g-1} C_n(s)x^n + x^s \sum_{n=0}^{\infty} C_n(s+g)x^{n+g}. \tag{10}$$

This series satisfies formally the hypergeometric equation for $s = 1 - \gamma = -g$.

As $c_0(s)$ contains the factor $(s+g)$, $c_0 = 0$ for $s = 1 - \gamma$. Thus 10) becomes

$$y_1 = \sum_{n=0}^{\infty} C_n(0)x^n = F(\alpha, \beta, \gamma, x), \tag{11}$$

since the recursion formula 3) goes over into 210, 11) for $s = 1 - \gamma$.

In order to apply 213, 11), let us show that 10) may be differentiated termwise with respect to s at the point $s = 1 - \gamma$. To this end we show that the series

$$G = \sum_{n=0}^{\infty} C_n(s+g)x^{n+g} = \Sigma g_n(s)$$

is steadily convergent in a small circle $\mathfrak{c}$ about the point $s = 1 - \gamma$.

In $\mathfrak{c}$ we will have $\quad 0 < \sigma < |s + g| \leq \tau.$

Thus if we set $|\alpha| = a$, $|\beta| = b$, we have

$$|C_n| \leq \frac{(\tau + a) \cdots (\tau + a + n - 1)(\tau + b) \cdots (\tau + b + n - 1)}{(\sigma + 1) \cdots (\sigma + n)(\sigma + \gamma) \cdots (\sigma + \gamma + n - 1)} = e_n.$$

Let us now consider the series,

$$E = e_0 + e_1 R + e_2 R^2 + \cdots \qquad 0 < R < 1.$$

This series is convergent since the ratio of two successive terms is

$$\frac{(\tau + a + n)(\tau + b + n)}{(\sigma + n + 1)(\sigma + \gamma + n)} R,$$

and this $\doteq R$ as $n \doteq \infty$.

Thus 10) converges steadily and we may differentiate it termwise. The new series so obtained is a solution of our differential equation for $s = 1 - \gamma$ by 213.

We get thus

$$\frac{\partial y}{\partial s} = y \log x + c_0'(s)x^s \sum_{n=0}^{g-1} C_n(s)x^n + c_0(s)x^s \sum_{n=0}^{g-1} C_n'(s)x^n$$
$$+ x^s \sum_{n=0}^{\infty} C_n'(s+g)x^{n+g}. \tag{12}$$

Let us now set $s = 1 - \gamma = -g$. Then

$$c_0(s) = 0 \quad , \qquad y = F(\alpha, \beta, \gamma, x).$$

To find $C'_n(0)$ we take the logarithm of 8) and then differentiate with respect to s. This gives

$$C'_n(s) = C_n(s)\left\{\frac{1}{s+\alpha} + \cdots \frac{1}{s+\beta} + \cdots - \frac{1}{s+1} - \cdots - \frac{1}{s+\gamma}\cdots\right\}.$$

Setting in this $s = 0$ gives

$$C'_n(0) = C_n(0)\left\{\frac{1}{\alpha} + \cdots + \frac{1}{\alpha+n-1} + \frac{1}{\beta} + \cdots + \frac{1}{\beta+n-1}\right\}$$
$$- C_n(0)\left\{\frac{1}{1} + \cdots + \frac{1}{n} + \frac{1}{\gamma} + \cdots + \frac{1}{\gamma+n-1}\right\}.$$

To find $C'_n(-g)$ we note that

$$c'_0(-g) = \lim_{s=-g} \frac{c_0(s) = c_0(-g)}{s+g} = \lim_{s=-g} \frac{c_0(s)}{s+g}$$
$$= \frac{-(1)^\gamma(\gamma-2)!(\gamma-1)!}{(\alpha-1)\cdots(\alpha-\gamma+1)(\beta-1)\cdots(\beta-\gamma+1)}.$$

We have thus a second solution.

$$y_2 = F(\alpha, \beta, \gamma, x) \log x + F_1(\alpha, \beta, \gamma, x),$$

where

$$F_1(\alpha, \beta, \gamma, x) = \frac{(-1)^\gamma(\gamma-2)!(\gamma-1)!}{(\alpha-1)\cdots(\alpha-\gamma+1)(\beta-1)\cdots(\beta-\gamma+1)} \cdot \frac{1}{x^{\gamma-1}}$$
$$+ \cdots + \frac{\gamma-1}{(\alpha-1)(\beta-1)} \cdot \frac{1}{x} + \frac{\alpha\cdot\beta}{1\cdot\gamma}\left(\frac{1}{\alpha} + \frac{1}{\beta} - \frac{1}{1} - \frac{1}{\gamma}\right)x \qquad (13$$
$$+ \frac{\alpha(\alpha+1)\beta(\beta+1)}{1\cdot 2\cdot\gamma(\gamma+1)}\left\{\frac{1}{\alpha} + \frac{1}{\alpha+1} + \frac{1}{\beta} + \frac{1}{\beta+1} - \frac{1}{1} - \frac{1}{2} - \frac{1}{\gamma} - \frac{1}{\gamma+1}\right\}x^2$$
$$+ \cdots$$

2. In the foregoing we supposed $\gamma \geq 1$. *If we suppose γ is 0 or a negative integer*, we have a fundamental system

$$y_1 = x^{1-\gamma} F(\alpha+1-\gamma, \beta+1-\gamma, 2-\gamma, x),$$
$$y_2 = y_1 \log x + x^{1-\gamma} F_1(\alpha+1-\gamma, \beta+1-\gamma, 2-\gamma, x). \qquad (14$$

3. Let us now consider the *point* $x=1$. *If* $\gamma-\alpha-\beta$ *is an integer*, we have the logarithmic case. *If* $\gamma-\alpha-\beta\leq 0$, a fundamental system is

$$y_1=F(\alpha,\beta,\alpha+\beta-\gamma+1,1-x),$$
$$y_2=y_1\log(1-x)+F_1(\alpha,\beta,\alpha+\beta-\gamma+1,1-x).$$

If $\gamma-\alpha-\beta>0$, a fundamental system is

$$y_1=(1-x)^{\gamma-\alpha-\beta}F(\gamma-\beta,\gamma-\alpha,\gamma-\alpha-\beta+1,1-x), \tag{15}$$
$$y_2=y_1\log(1-x)+(1-x)^{\gamma-\alpha-\beta}F_1(\gamma-\beta,\gamma-\alpha,\gamma-\alpha-\beta+1,1-x).$$

4. Finally let us consider the *point* $x=\infty$. *If* $\alpha-\beta$ *is a positive integer*, we have

$$y_1=x^{-\alpha}F\left(\alpha,\alpha-\gamma+1,\alpha-\beta+1,\frac{1}{x}\right), \tag{16}$$

$$y_2=y_1\log\frac{1}{x}+x^{-\alpha}F_1\left(\alpha,\alpha-\gamma+1,\alpha-\beta+1,\frac{1}{x}\right).$$

If $\alpha-\beta$ *is* 0 *or a negative integer*, we have

$$\begin{aligned} y_1&=x^{-\beta}F\left(\beta,\beta-\gamma+1,\beta-\alpha+1,\frac{1}{x}\right),\\ y_2&=y_1\log\frac{1}{x}+x^{-\beta}F_1\left(\beta,\beta-\gamma+1,\beta-\alpha+1,\frac{1}{x}\right).\end{aligned} \tag{17}$$

215. Logarithmic Case of Bessel's Equation. 1. The indicial equation of Bessel's equation

$$x^2\frac{d^2y}{dx^2}+x\frac{dy}{dx}+(x^2-m^2)y=0 \tag{1}$$

has, at $x=0$, the two roots $\pm m$, as we saw in 211. When m is an integer, we have the logarithmic case. As in most applications m is an integer, we wish to find a fundamental system in this case.

Applying Frobenius' method given in 213, we have here

$$f_0(s)=s^2-m^2 \quad , \quad f_1(s)=0 \quad , \quad f_2(s)=1$$

and

$$f_n(s)=0 \qquad \text{for } n>2.$$

The equations 213, 2) have the form

$$c_nf_0(s+n)+c_{n-2}=0,$$

or

$$c_n\{(s+n)^2-m^2\}+c_{n-2}=0.$$

Thus

$$c_2 = \frac{-c_0}{(s+2)^2 - m^2},$$

$$c_4 = \frac{c_0}{\{(s+4)^2 - m^2\}\{(s+2)^2 - m^2\}},$$

etc. We notice that $f_0(s+n)$ occurs in these denominators only for even n. We may therefore modify the formula for c_0 in 213, 9) and take

$$c_0 = Cf_0(s+2)f_0(s+4)\cdots f_0(s+2m). \qquad (2$$

Let us set $P(s) = (-1)^m\{(s+2)^2 - m^2\}\cdots\{(s+2m-2)^2 - m^2\}$

so that

$$c_0 = (-1)^m C\{(s+2m)^2 - m^2\}P(s). \qquad (3$$

Then the series

$$y = x^s \sum_{n=0}^{\infty} c_n x^n \qquad (4$$

becomes here

$$y = c_0 x^s\left[1 - \frac{x^2}{(s+2)^2 - m^2} + \frac{x^4}{\{(s+2)^2 - m^2\}\{(s+4)^2 - m^2\}} - \cdots - \frac{x^{2m-2}}{P}\right] + Cx^{s+2m}\left[1 - \frac{x^2}{(s+2m+2)^2 - m^2} + \frac{x^4}{\{(s+2m+2)^2 - m^2\}\{(s+2m+4)^2 - m^2\}} - \cdots\right]$$

$$= c_0 x^s u + Cx^{s+2m} v = U + V. \qquad (5$$

Here U embraces only a finite number of terms. The series v is steadily convergent for every x and for any $s > -(m+1)$.

For let $|x| < R$. Then

$$(s+2m+2)^2 - m^2 > \sigma > 0.$$

Hence each term in v is numerically $\leq$ the corresponding term in

$$1 + \frac{R^2}{\sigma} + \frac{R^{2\cdot 2}}{\sigma(\sigma+1^2)} + \frac{R^{2\cdot 3}}{\sigma(\sigma+1^2)(\sigma+2^2)} + \cdots$$

The ratio of two successive terms is here

$$\frac{R^2}{\sigma + n^2}$$

and this $\doteq 0$ as $n \doteq \infty$.

Hence from the general theory of 213, if y_1 denote the value of 4) for $s = -m$,

$$y_1 = U_1 + V_1 \text{ and } \left(\frac{\partial y}{\partial s}\right)_{s=-m}$$

are solutions of 1).

From 3) we note that $c_0 = 0$ for $s = -m$, thus $U_1 = 0$. Referring to 211, 5), we see that

$$V_1 = \frac{C}{2^n \Pi(n)} J_n(x). \tag{6}$$

2. Let us now turn to the logarithmic integral. We have

$$\frac{\partial U}{\partial s} = x^s u c_0'(s) + c_0\{x^s u \log x + x^s u'\}.$$

Hence

$$\frac{\partial U_1}{\partial s} = x^{-m}\left\{1 + \frac{1}{m-1}\left(\frac{x}{2}\right)^2 + \frac{1}{2(m-1)(m-2)}\left(\frac{x}{2}\right)^4 + \cdots\right\} c_0'(-m)$$

$$= (-1)^m \frac{2\, mP(-m)}{\Pi(m-1)} \cdot \frac{C}{x^m} \sum_{k=0}^{m-1} \frac{\Pi(m-1-k)}{\Pi(k)} \left(\frac{x}{2}\right)^{2k},$$

where

$$P(-m) = (-1)^{2m-1} 2^{2m-2} \Pi^2(m-1).$$

Similarly

$$\frac{\partial V_1}{\partial s} = C\Pi(m) J_m(x) \log x + \frac{1}{2} C J_m(x)$$

$$+ \frac{1}{2} C x^m \sum_{k=0}^{\infty} (-1)^{k+1} \frac{\Pi(m)}{\Pi(k)\Pi(m+k)} \{\omega(k) + \omega(k+m)\} \left(\frac{x}{2}\right)^{2k},$$

where

$$\omega(k) = 1 + \frac{1}{2} + \cdots + \frac{1}{k}, \quad \omega(0) = 1.$$

Here we can neglect the term $\frac{1}{2} C J_m(x)$, as we are seeking a fundamental system and this term is y_1 aside from a constant factor. Also for simplicity let us set

$$C = \frac{-1}{2^{m-1}\Pi(m)}.$$

Thus the solution

$$\left(\frac{\partial y}{\partial s}\right)_{s=-m} = \frac{\partial U_1}{\partial s} + \frac{\partial V_1}{\partial s}$$

leads us to take as second independent integral

$$y_2 = \left(\frac{2}{x}\right)^m \sum_{k=0}^{m-1} \frac{\Pi(m-1-k)}{\Pi(k)} \left(\frac{x}{2}\right)^{2k} - J_m(x) \log x$$

$$+ \left(\frac{x}{2}\right)^m \sum_{k=0}^{\infty} \frac{(-1)^k}{\Pi(m)\Pi(m+k)} \{\omega(k) + \omega(k+m)\}. \quad (7$$

216. The Differential Equation for *K*, *K'*. 1. In 189 we saw that

$$K = \frac{\pi}{2} F\left(\frac{1}{2}, \frac{1}{2}, 1, k^2\right) \quad , \quad K' = \frac{\pi}{2} F\left(\frac{1}{2}, \frac{1}{2}, 1, 1-k^2\right).$$

Thus K and K' satisfy a special case of the hypergeometric equation for which $\alpha = \beta = \frac{1}{2}$, $\gamma = 1$, viz.:

$$x(x-1)\frac{d^2y}{dx^2} + (2x-1)\frac{dy}{dx} + \frac{1}{4}y \quad , \quad x = k^2. \quad (1$$

Referring now to 214, we see that a fundamental system of integrals of 1) for $x = 0$ is

$$y_1 = F(\tfrac{1}{2}, \tfrac{1}{2}, 1, x), \quad (2$$

$$y_2 = y_1 \log x + F_1(\tfrac{1}{2}, \tfrac{1}{2}, 1, x). \quad (3$$

Here

$$F_1\left(\frac{1}{2}, \frac{1}{2}, 1, x\right) = 2\left\{\left(\frac{1}{2}\right)^2 x + \left(\frac{1\cdot 3}{2\cdot 4}\right)^2\left(1 + \frac{2}{3\cdot 4}\right)x^2\right.$$

$$\left. + \left(\frac{1\cdot 3\cdot 5}{2\cdot 4\cdot 6}\right)^2\left(1 + \frac{2}{3\cdot 4} + \frac{2}{5\cdot 6}\right)x^3 + \cdots\right\} \quad (4$$

2. Let us find the development of K' about $x = 0$. Since K' is a solution of 1), we must have

$$K' = Ay_1 + By_2, \quad (5$$

or since

$$K = \frac{\pi}{2} F\left(\frac{1}{2}, \frac{1}{2}, 1, x\right),$$

$$\pi K' = 2AK + 2BK \log k^2 + \pi B F_1. \quad (6$$

From 196, 2) we find $\quad k'^2 = 1 - 16q + \cdots$

Hence

$$x = k^2 = 16q + \cdots = 16 e^{-\pi\frac{K'}{K}} + \cdots$$

or
$$\frac{\pi K'}{K} = \log 16 - \log k^2 + \cdots \tag{7}$$

Also
$$\pi B \frac{F_1}{K} = \pi B \frac{\frac{1}{2}k^2 + \cdots}{\frac{\pi}{2}\left(1 + \frac{1}{4}k^2 + \cdots\right)}$$
$$= Bk^2 + \cdots \tag{8}$$

In 6) let us divide by K and put in 7), 8); we get

$$(4 \log 2 - 2A) - (1 + 2B) \log k^2 + \cdots = 0.$$

Thus
$$A = 2 \log 2, \qquad B = -\tfrac{1}{2}.$$

Hence 5) gives

$$K' = (2 \log 2 - \tfrac{1}{2} \log k^2) F(\tfrac{1}{2}, \tfrac{1}{2}, 1, k^2) - \tfrac{1}{2} F_1(\tfrac{1}{2}, \tfrac{1}{2}, 1, k^2). \tag{9}$$

217. Criterion for a Regular Point. We saw in 212 that $x = a$ is a regular point of
$$\frac{d^2y}{dx^2} + p(x)\frac{dy}{dx} + q(x)y = 0, \tag{1}$$

if p, q have the form
$$p = \frac{g(x)}{x-a}, \quad q = \frac{h(x)}{(x-a)^2}, \tag{2}$$

where g, h are regular at $x = a$. When $x = a$ is a regular point, 1) admits a fundamental system of integrals,

$$y_1 = (x-a)^{r_1}\phi_1(x) \tag{3}$$
$$y_2 = (x-a)^{r_2}\{\phi_{21}(x) + \phi_{22}(x) \log (x-a)\},$$

where r_1, r_2 are roots of the indicial equation at this point.

We wish now to establish conversely:

If 1) *admits* 3) *as a fundamental system of integrals at the point* $x = a$, *it is necessary that* p, q *have the form* 2).

For we saw in 212 that if we set

$$y_2 = y_1 \int z dx, \tag{4}$$

then z satisfies the equation
$$\frac{dz}{dx} + gz = 0, \text{ where } g = p + 2\frac{y_1'}{y_1}. \tag{5}$$

From 4) we have

$$z = \frac{d}{dx}\left(\frac{y_2}{y_1}\right).$$

Thus from 3) we see that z must have the form

$$z = (x-a)^s\{\phi(x) + \psi(x)\log(x-a)\},$$

where ϕ, ψ are one-valued about $x = a$.

Let now x make a circuit about $x = a$. If z acquires the value $\bar{z}$, this must be a solution of 5). Hence

$$\bar{z} = cz. \tag{6}$$

But

$$\bar{z} = e^{2\pi is}(x-a)^s[\phi + \psi\{\log(x-a) + 2\pi i\}]$$
$$= e^{2\pi is}z + 2\pi i e^{2\pi is}(x-a)^s\psi.$$

Putting this in 6) gives

$$z(c - e^{2\pi is}) + 2\pi i e^{2\pi is}(x-a)^s\psi = 0.$$

This requires that $\psi = 0$. Hence

$$z = (x-a)^s\phi(x).$$

Thus

$$\frac{1}{z}\frac{dz}{dx} = \frac{s}{x-a} + f(x), \tag{7}$$

where f is regular at $x = a$.

On the other hand, 5) gives

$$\frac{1}{z}\frac{dz}{dx} = g = p + 2\frac{y_1'}{y_1}$$
$$= p + \frac{2r_1}{x-a} + k(x), \tag{8}$$

where k is regular at a.

Thus 7), 8) show that $p(x)$ has at most a pole of order 1) at $x = a$.

From 1) we have, setting $y = y_1$,

$$q(x) = -\frac{y_1''}{y_1} - p\frac{y_1'}{y_1}.$$

Now

$$\frac{y_1''}{y_1} = \frac{l(x)}{(x-a)^2},$$

where l is regular at a. Hence q has at most a pole of order 2.

218. Differential Equations of the Fuchsian Class. 1. When all the singular points of a linear homogeneous differential equation are regular, it is said to belong to the *Fuchsian class.*

Now in order that $x = a$ is a regular point of

$$\frac{d^2y}{dx^2} + p(x)\frac{dy}{dx} + q(x)y = 0, \tag{1}$$

the coefficients p, q being one-valued, it is necessary that $x = a$ is at most a pole of p and q. Hence p, q having only poles, even at $x = \infty$, must be rational functions of x. As the poles of p cannot be of order > 1, and those of q of order > 2, we can write

$$p = \frac{f(x)}{h(x)} \quad , \quad q = \frac{g(x)}{h^2(x)}, \tag{2}$$

where f, g are polynomials and

$$\begin{aligned} h &= x^m + c_1 x^{m-1} + \cdots + c_m \\ &= (x - a_1)(x - a_2) \cdots (x - a_m). \end{aligned}$$

To find the degrees of these polynomials we use the fact that $x = \infty$ must be a regular point. Let

$$\begin{aligned} f(x) &= a_0 x^r + a_1 x^{r-1} + \cdots + a_r, \\ g(x) &= b_0 x^s + b_1 x^{s-1} + \cdots + b_s. \end{aligned}$$

We set now $x = \frac{1}{u}$ in 1). Since

$$\frac{dy}{dx} = -u^2\frac{dy}{du} \quad , \quad \frac{d^2y}{dx^2} = u^4\frac{d^2y}{du^2} + 2\,u^3\frac{dy}{du},$$

we find as transformed equation

$$\frac{d^2y}{du^2} + \left\{\frac{2\,u^3 - u^2p}{u^4}\right\}\frac{dy}{du} + \frac{q}{u^4}y = 0.$$

As

$$p = \frac{a_0 + a_1 u + \cdots + a_r u^r}{1 + c_1 u + \cdots + c_m u^m} \cdot u^{m-r},$$

$$q = \frac{b_0 + b_1 u + \cdots + b_s u^s}{1 + d_1 u + \cdots + d_{2m} u^{2m}} \cdot u^{2m-s},$$

we see that
$$p_1 = \frac{2u^3 - u^2 p}{u^4} = \frac{P(u)}{u^{r-m+2}},$$
$$q_1 = \frac{q}{u^4} = \frac{Q(u)}{u^{s-2m+4}},$$
where P, Q are regular at $u = 0$.

As p_1 cannot have a pole of order > 1, and q_1 one of order > 2, we have
$$r - m + 2 \leq 1 \quad , \quad s - 2m + 4 \leq 2,$$
or
$$r \leq m - 1 \quad , \quad s \leq 2m - 2.$$
Thus
$$m - r = 1 + k \quad , \quad 2m - s = 2 + l \quad , \quad k, l \geq 0.$$
Also
$$p_1 = \frac{1}{u}\{2 - a_0 u^k + \cdots\},$$
$$q_1 = \frac{1}{u^2}\{b_0 u^l + \cdots\}.$$
Hence
$$P(u) = 2 - a_0 u^k + \cdots \quad ; \quad Q(u) = b_0 u^l + \cdots \tag{3}$$
Let us set
$$\lambda = \lim_{u=0} \frac{p}{u} = \lim_{x=\infty} xp, \tag{4}$$
$$\mu = \lim_{u=0} \frac{q}{u^2} = \lim_{x=\infty} x^2 q. \tag{5}$$

Then we see from 3) that
$$P(0) = 2 - \lambda \quad , \quad Q(0) = \mu. \tag{6}$$

2. At the singular point $x = a_i$ let r_i, ρ_i be the roots of the indicial equation. The roots at $x = \infty$ we will denote by r_∞, ρ_∞. Fuchs showed that these roots must satisfy the relation
$$\Sigma(r_i + \rho_i) = m - 1, \qquad i = 1, 2, \cdots m, \infty. \tag{7}$$
This is called *Fuchs' relation*.

Let us find the indicial equation at $x = a_i$. We bring 1) to the normal form
$$(x - a_i)^2 h_i^2(x) \frac{d^2 y}{dx^2} + (x - a_i) h_i(x) f(x) \frac{dy}{dx} + g(x) y = 0.$$

The indicial equation is
$$r(r-1) h_i^2(a_i) + r h_i(a_i) f(a_i) + g(a_i) = 0. \tag{8}$$
Now
$$h(x) = (x - a_i) h_i(x).$$

Hence

$$h'(x) = h(x) + (x - a_i)h_i'(x).$$

Thus

$$h_i(a_i) = h'(a_i).$$

We may thus write 5)

$$r(r-1) + \frac{f(a_i)}{h'(a_i)} r + \frac{g(a_i)}{h'(a_i)^2} = 0.$$

Hence

$$r_i + \rho_i = 1 - \frac{f(a_i)}{h'(a_i)}. \tag{9}$$

Let us now write 1) in *the normal form for* $x = \infty$. Setting $x = \frac{1}{u}$, we saw that it takes the form

$$u^2 \frac{d^2y}{du^2} + uP\frac{dy}{du} + Qy = 0.$$

Its indicial equation is therefore

$$r(r-1) + rP(0) + Q(0) = 0,$$

or, using 4),

$$r^2 + (1 - \lambda)r + \mu = 0.$$

Thus

$$r_\infty + \rho_\infty = \lambda - 1.$$

From elementary algebra we have

$$p = \frac{f(x)}{h(x)} = \sum_{i=1}^{m} \frac{f(a_i)}{h'(a_i)} \cdot \frac{1}{x - a_i}.$$

Hence from 4),

$$\lambda = \lim_{x=\infty} xp = \sum \frac{f(a_i)}{h'(a_i)}.$$

Thus

$$r_\infty + \rho_\infty = \sum_i \frac{f(a_i)}{h'(a_i)} - 1. \tag{10}$$

From 9), 10) we have 7).

219. Expression of $F(\alpha, \beta, \gamma, x)$ as an Integral. We leave now the general theory of linear differential equations and return to the hypergeometric function. Let us show that when

$$|x| < 1 \quad , \quad 0 < \beta < \gamma, \tag{1}$$

we may express $F(\alpha, \beta, \gamma, x)$ as a definite integral, viz.:

$$F(\alpha, \beta, \gamma, x) = \frac{1}{B(\beta, \gamma - \beta)} \int_0^1 u^{\beta-1}(1-u)^{\gamma-\beta-1}(1-xu)^{-\alpha} du \tag{2}$$

$$= \frac{J}{B(\beta, \gamma - \beta)},$$

where $B(p, q)$ is the Beta function

$$B(p, q) = \int_0^1 u^{p-1}(1-u)^{q-1}du. \tag{3}$$

For by the binomial theorem

$$(1-xu)^{-\alpha} = 1 + \frac{\alpha}{1}xu + \frac{\alpha \cdot \alpha+1}{1 \cdot 2}x^2u^2 + \cdots$$

when $|xu| < 1$. Hence the integral J in 2) may be written

$$J = \int_0^1 u^{\beta-1}(1-u)^{\gamma-\beta-1}du + \frac{\alpha \cdot x}{1}\int_0^1 u^{\beta}(1-u)^{\gamma-\beta-1}du$$
$$+ \frac{\alpha \cdot \alpha+1}{1 \cdot 2}x^2 \int_0^1 u^{\beta+1}(1-u)^{\gamma-\beta-1}du + \cdots$$
$$= B(\beta, \gamma-\beta) + \alpha x B(\beta+1, \gamma-\beta)$$
$$+ \frac{\alpha \cdot \alpha+1}{1 \cdot 2}x^2 B(\beta+2, \gamma-\beta) + \cdots \tag{4}$$

Now

$$B(\beta+1, \gamma-\beta) = \frac{\beta}{\gamma}B(\beta, \gamma-\beta).$$

Hence

$$B(\beta+2, \gamma-\beta) = \frac{\beta+1}{\gamma+1}B(\beta+1, \gamma-\beta) = \frac{\beta \cdot \beta+1}{\gamma \cdot \gamma+1}B(\beta, \gamma-\beta),$$

etc. Putting these values in 4), we get 2).

220. Loop Integrals of the Hypergeometric Equation. 1. In the last article we have shown that the hypergeometric equation

$$x(1-x)\frac{d^2y}{dx^2} + \{\gamma - (\alpha+\beta+1)x\}\frac{dy}{dx} - \alpha\beta y = 0 \tag{1}$$

admits as solution the integral 2) when the conditions 1) of that article are satisfied. Let us replace the path of integration (0, 1) by a more general path L, properly chosen; we proceed to show that 1) admits a solution of the form

$$y = \int_L (z-x)^{-\alpha}u(z)dz. \tag{2}$$

In fact, putting 2) in 1), we get

$$\int_L v\frac{dF}{dz}dz + \int_L \frac{dG}{dz}dz = 0, \tag{3}$$

where

$$v = (z - x)^{-\alpha}. \tag{4}$$

$$F = z(1-z)\frac{du}{dz} - \{\alpha - \gamma + (\beta - \alpha + 1)z\}u, \tag{5}$$

$$G = z(1-z)\left\{u\frac{dv}{dz} - v\frac{du}{dz}\right\} + \{\alpha - \gamma + (\beta - \alpha + 1)z\}uv. \tag{6}$$

To prove this we may proceed as follows. From 5) we have

$$v\frac{dF}{dz} = z(1-z)vu'' + \{1 - \alpha + \gamma + z(\alpha - \beta - 3)\}vu' - (\beta - \alpha + 1)uv.$$

From 6) we have

$$\frac{dG}{dz} = -z(1-z)vu'' + \{\alpha - \gamma - 1 + (\beta - \alpha + 3)z\}vu'$$
$$+\{\alpha(\alpha+1)z(1-z)(z-x)^{-\alpha-2} + \alpha(\gamma - \alpha - 1 + (\alpha - \beta + 1)z)(z-x)^{-\alpha-1}$$
$$+(\beta - \alpha + 1)v\}u.$$

Thus

$$v\frac{dF}{dz} + \frac{dG}{dz} = \{\alpha(\alpha+1)z(1-z)(z-x)^{-\alpha-2}$$
$$+\alpha[\gamma - \alpha - 1 + (\alpha - \beta + 1)z](z-x)^{-\alpha-1}\}u = Hu.$$

On the other hand we have from 2)

$$\frac{dy}{dx} = \alpha\int_L (z-x)^{-\alpha-1}u\,dz,$$

$$\frac{d^2y}{dx^2} = \alpha(\alpha+1)\int_L (z-x)^{-\alpha-2}u\,dz.$$

Thus 1) becomes

$$\int_L u\{\alpha(\alpha+1)x(1-x)(z-x)^{-\alpha-2} + \alpha(\gamma - (\alpha+\beta+1)x)(z-x)^{-\alpha-1}$$
$$-\alpha\beta(z-x)^{-\alpha}\}dz.$$

Now we have identically

$$x(1-x) = z(1-z) + (2z-1)(z-x) - (z-x)^2,$$
$$\gamma - (\alpha + \beta + 1)x = \gamma - (\alpha + \beta + 1)z + (\alpha + \beta + 1)(z - x).$$

Thus the brace in the foregoing integral reduces to the function H above, and this establishes 3).

An integral of

$$F = 0$$

is

$$u = e^{\int \frac{\alpha - \gamma + (\beta - \alpha + 1)z}{z(1-z)}dz}$$
$$= z^{\alpha - \gamma}(z-1)^{\gamma - \beta - 1}. \tag{7}$$

This in 6) gives

$$G = \alpha z^{\alpha-\gamma+1}(z-1)^{\gamma-\beta}(z-x)^{-\alpha-1}. \tag{8}$$

Thus when u is chosen as in 7), $F=0$ and hence the first integral in 3) vanishes for any path. Also if L is so chosen that G in 8) takes on the same value at the end of L that it had at the start, the second integral in 3) vanishes.

In this case 2), or what is the same,

$$y = \int_L z^{\alpha-\gamma}(z-1)^{\gamma-\beta-1}(z-x)^{-\alpha}dz = \int_L w(z)dz, \tag{9}$$

is an integral of 1). Here

$$w = z^{\alpha-\gamma}(z-1)^{\gamma-\beta-1}(z-x)^{-\alpha}. \tag{10}$$

2. Let l_0, l_1, l_x, l_∞ denote loops about the points $z = 0, 1, x, \infty$, respectively, each circuit being described about the corresponding point in the positive sense.

Let $\overline{G}_0, \overline{w}_0$ be the end values of G_0, w_0 after describing l_0, etc.

After a circuit about $z=0$,

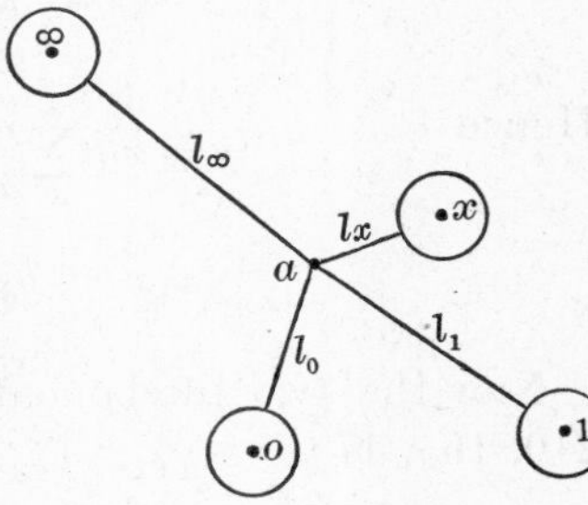

$$z^{\alpha-\gamma+1} = e^{(\alpha-\gamma+1)\log z}$$

goes over into

$$e^{(\alpha-\gamma+1)(\log z + 2\pi i)} = e^{2\pi i(\alpha-\gamma+1)}z^{\alpha-\gamma+1}$$
$$= e^{2\pi i(\alpha-\gamma)}z^{\alpha-\gamma+1}.$$

Thus $\qquad \overline{G}_0 = e^{2\pi i(\alpha-\gamma)}G_0.$

Similarly $\qquad \overline{w}_0 = e^{2\pi i(\alpha-\gamma)}w_0.$

In the same manner we find

$$\overline{G}_1 = e^{2\pi i(\gamma-\beta)}G_1 \quad , \quad \overline{w}_1 = e^{2\pi i(\gamma-\beta)}w_1$$
$$\overline{G}_x = e^{-2\pi i\alpha}G_x \quad , \quad \overline{w}_x = e^{-2\pi i\alpha}w_x$$
$$\overline{G}_\infty = e^{2\pi i\beta}G_\infty \quad , \quad \overline{w}_\infty = e^{2\pi i\beta}w_\infty.$$

Let a, b be any two of the four points $0, 1, x, \infty$. Let L_{ab} be a path about a, b as in Fig. 2, § 150. Obviously, as far as the values of G and the integral 9) are concerned, this path is equivalent to

$$l_a l_b l_a^{-1} l_b^{-1}.$$

As G returns to its original value,

$$y_{ab} = \int_{L_{ab}} wdz$$

is a solution of 1). Since we can choose the points a, b in

$$\frac{4 \cdot 3}{1 \cdot 2} = 6$$

ways, we get in this manner six solutions of 1). They must of course be linear functions of a fundamental system, as shown in 210.

3. As an illustration let us consider y_{01}. For simplicity let us take $|x| > 1$ and suppose that α, β do not differ by an integer.

As the loop L_{01} let us take a double loop $\mathfrak{L}$ running over two little circles about $z = 0$, $z = 1$ and the segment of the real axis joining them.

Then on $\mathfrak{L}$, $\left|\frac{z}{x}\right| < 1$ and

$$(z - x)^{-\alpha} = a_0 x^{-\alpha}\left(1 - \frac{z}{x}\right)^{-\alpha}$$

$$= x^{-\alpha}\left\{ a_0 + a_1\frac{z}{x} + a_2\frac{z^2}{x^2} + \cdots\right\}.$$

Hence

$$\begin{aligned} y &= x^{-\alpha}\sum_0^\infty \frac{a_n}{x^n}\int_{\mathfrak{L}} z^{n+\alpha-\gamma}(z-1)^{\gamma-\beta-1}dz \\ &= x^{-\alpha}\left\{ b_0 + \frac{b_1}{x} + \frac{b_2}{x^2} + \cdots\right\}. \end{aligned} \tag{11}$$

Now the two fundamental integrals at $x = \infty$ are, as we saw in 210, 16), 17),

$$\eta_1 = x^{-\alpha}F\left(\alpha,\ \alpha - \gamma + 1,\ \alpha - \beta + 1,\ \frac{1}{x}\right),$$

$$\eta_2 = x^{-\beta}F\left(\beta,\ \beta - \gamma + 1,\ \beta - \alpha + 1,\ \frac{1}{x}\right).$$

Hence y must have the form

$$y = c_1\eta_1 + c_2\eta_2.$$

As y does not contain any powers of x in common with η_2, we see that c_2 must $= 0$. Hence 11) differs from η_1 only by a constant factor.

CHAPTER XIV

FUNCTIONS OF LEGENDRE AND LAPLACE

Functions of Legendre

221. The Potential. 1. We wish in the present chapter to develop some of the more important properties of these functions which are of great importance in mathematical physics. We begin with the polynomials introduced by Legendre, who was led to study them while treating of the attraction exerted by the earth on a mass exterior to it. Such questions arise in celestial mechanics and in geodesy.

Let us find the attraction exerted by a body B on a unit mass μ situated at the point A.

The force exerted by an element of mass dm situated at P on μ is, by Newton's law,

$$f = c\frac{dm}{\delta^2},$$

$$\delta^2 = (x-a)^2 + (y-b)^2 + (z-c)^2.$$

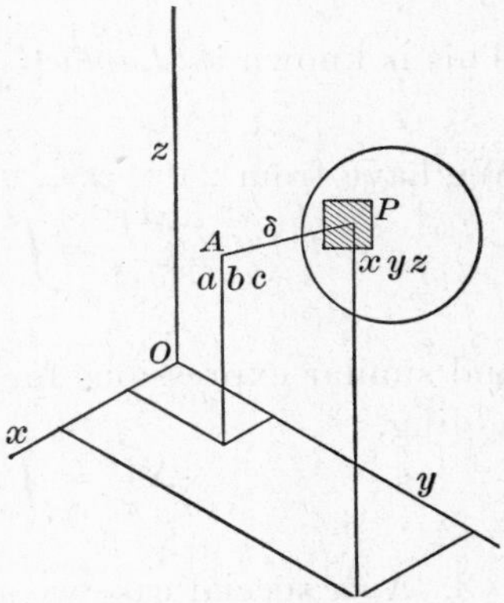

If AP makes the angles α, β, γ with the x, y, z axes, we have

$$\cos\alpha = \frac{x-a}{\delta}, \quad \cos\beta = \frac{y-b}{\delta},$$

$$\cos\gamma = \frac{z-c}{\delta}.$$

The x, y, z components of f are therefore

$$c\frac{dm}{\delta^2}\cdot\frac{x-a}{\delta}, \quad c\frac{dm}{\delta^2}\cdot\frac{y-b}{\delta}, \quad c\frac{dm}{\delta^2}\cdot\frac{z-c}{\delta}.$$

If we denote the total force of attraction exerted by B on μ by F and the x, y, z components of F by X, Y, Z, we have

$$X = c\int\frac{x-a}{\delta^3}\,dm, \quad Y = c\int\frac{y-b}{\delta^3}\,dm, \quad Z = c\int\frac{z-c}{\delta^3}\,dm.$$

Let us consider the function

$$V = c\int \frac{dm}{\delta}. \tag{1}$$

We have

$$\frac{\partial V}{\partial x} = c\int dm \cdot \frac{\partial}{\partial x}\left(\frac{1}{\delta}\right) = -c\int \frac{dm}{\delta^2} \cdot \frac{x-a}{\delta} = -X. \tag{2}$$

Similarly

$$\frac{\partial V}{\partial y} = -Y \quad , \quad \frac{\partial V}{\partial z} = -Z.$$

Thus the function 1) has the remarkable property that its first partial derivatives are, aside from sign, the components of the force exerted by the body B on a unit mass μ situated at A. This function V is called the *potential* of the body B with respect to the point A. It is of extraordinary importance in many parts of applied mathematics. For simplicity we shall set $c = 1$.

2. Let us now show that V satisfies the partial differential equation

$$\frac{\partial^2 V}{\partial x^2} + \frac{\partial^2 V}{\partial y^2} + \frac{\partial^2 V}{\partial z^2} = 0. \tag{3}$$

This is known as *Laplace's equation* and is often written

$$\Delta V = 0. \tag{4}$$

We have from 2)

$$\frac{\partial^2 V}{\partial x^2} = \int \left\{ \frac{3(x-a)^2}{\delta^5} - \frac{1}{\delta^3} \right\} dm,$$

and similar expressions for the two other derivatives in 3). Thus adding,

$$\Delta V = \int \left\{ \frac{3\,\delta^2}{\delta^5} - \frac{3}{\delta^3} \right\} dm = 0.$$

3. As a special case we see that

$$V = \frac{1}{\delta} \tag{5}$$

is a solution of 3).

4. As an exercise in the calculus the student may transform 3) to polar coördinates,

$$x = r\cos\theta\cos\phi \quad , \quad y = r\sin\theta\sin\phi \quad , \quad z = r\cos\theta. \tag{6}$$

It is convenient to call θ the *altitude* and ϕ the *azimuth* of the point x, y, z.

After a lengthy calculation we find that the left side of 3) becomes

$$\Delta V = \frac{\partial}{\partial r}\left(r^2 \frac{\partial V}{\partial r}\right) + \frac{1}{\sin\theta}\frac{\partial}{\partial\theta}\left(\sin\theta\frac{\partial V}{\partial\theta}\right) + \frac{1}{\sin^2\theta}\frac{\partial^2 V}{\partial\phi^2}. \tag{7}$$

When the attracting masses are symmetric with respect to an axis, we may take this to be the z-axis. Then V cannot change when ϕ changes. Hence

$$\frac{\partial V}{\partial\phi} = 0,$$

and in this case 7) becomes

$$\Delta V = \frac{\partial}{\partial r}\left(r^2 \frac{\partial V}{\partial r}\right) + \frac{1}{\sin\theta}\frac{\partial}{\partial\theta}\left(\sin\theta\frac{\partial V}{\partial\theta}\right). \tag{8}$$

222. Definition of Legendre's Coefficients. 1. In many investigations it is useful to develop the quantity $\frac{1}{\delta}$ in a series. In doing this we are led directly to Legendre's coefficients.

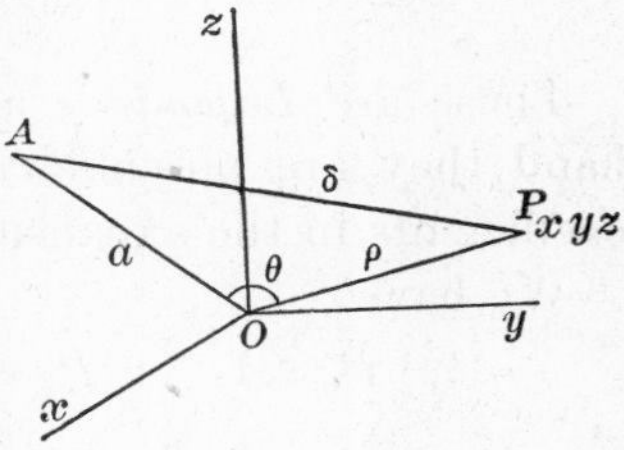

Let θ be the angle between a and ρ. Then

$$\delta^2 = a^2 + \rho^2 - 2\,a\rho\cos\theta.$$

Let

$$r = \frac{a}{\rho}\ , \quad \text{when } a < \rho$$

$$= \frac{\rho}{a}\ , \quad \text{when } a > \rho.$$

Then

$$\begin{aligned}\delta &= a^2(1 - 2\,r\cos\theta + r^2)\quad , \quad a > \rho\\ &= \rho^2(1 - 2\,r\cos\theta + r^2)\quad , \quad a < \rho.\end{aligned} \tag{1}$$

In either case the development of $\frac{1}{\delta}$ leads us to develop

$$V = \frac{1}{\sqrt{1 - 2\,r\cos\theta + r^2}}\ , \quad 0 \le r < 1. \tag{2}$$

This we now do, using the binomial series

$$(1-u)^{-\frac{1}{2}} = 1 + \frac{1}{2}u + \frac{1\cdot 3}{2\cdot 4}u^2 + \frac{1\cdot 3\cdot 5}{2\cdot 4\cdot 6}u^3 + \cdots \tag{3}$$

which is valid when $|u| < 1$. Let us therefore set

$$x = \cos\theta \quad , \quad u = 2rx - r^2,$$

whence

$$u^m = \sum_{s=0}^{m} (-1)^s \frac{m!}{s!(m-s)!} (2x)^{m-s} r^{m+s}.$$

This in 2), 3) gives

$$V = \sum_{m=0} \sum_{s=0}^{m} (-1)^s \frac{(2m)!}{2^{m+s} m!\, s!\,(m-s)!} r^{m+s} x^{m-s}$$

$$= \sum_{m=0}^{\infty} r^m \sum_{s=0}^{m} (-1)^s \frac{(2m-2s)!}{2^m (m-s)!\,(m-2s)!\,s!} \cdot x^{m-2s} \quad , \quad 0 \leq 2s \leq m.$$

Thus

$$V = \sum_{m=0}^{\infty} P_m(x) r^m = P_0 + P_1 r + P_2 r^2 + \cdots \tag{4}$$

where

$$P_m(x) = \frac{1 \cdot 3 \cdot 5 \cdots (2m-1)}{m!}$$

$$\left\{ x^m - \frac{m \cdot m-1}{2(2m-1)} x^{m-2} + \frac{m \cdot m-1 \cdot m-2 \cdot m-3}{2 \cdot 4 \cdot 2m-1 \cdot 2m-3} x^{m-4} - \cdots \right\}. \tag{5}$$

These are *Legendre's coefficients* or *polynomials*, for on the one hand they are polynomials in x, and on the other they are the coefficients in the expansion 4).

We have

$$P_0 = 1 \quad , \quad P_1 = x \quad , \quad P_2 = \tfrac{3}{2} x^2 - \tfrac{1}{2}, \tag{6}$$

$$P_3 = \tfrac{5}{2} x^3 - \tfrac{3}{2} x \quad , \quad P_4 = \tfrac{35}{8} x^4 - \tfrac{15}{4} x^2 + \tfrac{3}{8}, \text{ etc.}$$

2. From 5) we see that

$$P_m(-x) = (-1)^m P_m(x). \tag{7}$$

Thus $P_m(x)$ is an odd or even function as m is odd or even.

3. When $\theta = 0$, $x = \cos\theta = 1$. Then

$$V = \frac{1}{1-r} = 1 + r + r^2 + \cdots$$

Comparing with 4), we see

$$P_m(1) = 1, \quad m = 1, 2, \ldots \tag{8}$$

4. From 5), 6), we have

$$P_{2m}(0) = (-1)^m \frac{1 \cdot 3 \cdot 5 \cdots 2m-1}{2 \cdot 4 \cdot 6 \cdots 2m}, \tag{9}$$

$$P_{2m+1}(0) = 0. \tag{10}$$

5. The equations 6) enable us to express $x, x^2, x^3 \cdots$ in terms of $P_0, P_1, P_2, \cdots$.

Thus we find

$$x = P_1(x),$$
$$x^2 = \tfrac{2}{3} P_2(x) + \tfrac{1}{3} P_0(x),$$
$$x^3 = \tfrac{2}{5} P_3(x) + \tfrac{3}{5} P_1(x), \text{ etc.}$$

In general we see x^n has the form

$$x^n = a_0 P_0(x) + a_1 P_1(x) + \cdots + a_n P_n(x), \tag{11}$$

the coefficients being constants.

223. Development of P_m in Multiple Angles. 1. We have

$$1 - 2r\cos\theta + r^2 = (1 - re^{i\theta})(1 - re^{-i\theta}).$$

But

$$(1 - re^{i\theta})^{-\frac{1}{2}} = a_0 + a_1 re^{i\theta} + a_2 r^2 e^{2i\theta} + \cdots$$

where

$$a_0 = 1,\ a_1 = \tfrac{1}{2},\ a_2 = \frac{1 \cdot 3}{2 \cdot 4},\quad a_3 = \frac{1 \cdot 3 \cdot 5}{2 \cdot 4 \cdot 6} \cdots$$

Hence

$$V = \frac{1}{\sqrt{1 - 2r\cos\theta + r^2}} = (a_0 + a_1 re^{i\theta} + \cdots)(a_0 + a_1 re^{-i\theta} + \cdots)$$
$$= 1 + P_1 r + P_2 r^2 + \cdots$$

Thus

$$P_n(\cos\theta) = 2a_0 a_n \cos n\theta + a_1 a_{n-1}\cos(n-2)\theta$$
$$+ a_2 a_{n-2}\cos(n-4)\theta + \cdots$$
$$= 2\frac{1 \cdot 3 \cdot 5 \cdots 2n-1}{2 \cdot 4 \cdot 6 \cdots 2n}\left\{\cos n\theta + \frac{1}{1}\cdot\frac{n}{2n-1}\cos(n-2)\theta \right. \tag{1}$$
$$\left. + \frac{1 \cdot 3}{1 \cdot 2}\cdot\frac{n \cdot n-1}{2n-1 \cdot 2n-3}\cos(n-4)\theta + \cdots\right\}.$$

From this we have

$$P_0 = 1 \quad, \quad P_1 = \cos\theta \quad, \quad P_2 = \tfrac{1}{4}(3\cos 2\theta + 1) \cdots \tag{2}$$

2. We note that all the coefficients in 1) are positive. Thus $P_n(\cos\theta)$ has its greatest value when $\theta = 0$, for then

$$\cos n\theta,\ \cos(n-2)\theta,\ \cdots \qquad (3$$

all take on their maximum positive value 1.

Thus $P_n(x)$ has its maximum value for $x = 1$. On the other hand P_n is certainly greater than the right side of 1) when we replace the quantities 3) by -1. Thus

$$-P_n(1) \overline{<} P_n(\cos\theta) \overline{<} P_n(1),$$

or using 222, 8),

$$-1 \leq P_n(\cos\theta) \leq 1. \qquad (4$$

224. Differential Equation for $P_n(x)$. Let A be on the z-axis. Then

$$V = \frac{1}{\sqrt{1 - 2r\cos\theta + r^2}}, \quad r = \frac{\rho}{a} < 1,$$

is independent of ϕ. Now V satisfies Laplace's equation $\Delta V = 0$ as we saw in 221, 3. This we saw in 221, 8) is here

$$\frac{\partial}{\partial r}\left(r^2\frac{\partial V}{\partial r}\right) + \frac{1}{\sin\theta}\frac{\partial}{\partial\theta}\left(\sin\theta\frac{\partial V}{\partial\theta}\right) = 0. \qquad (1$$

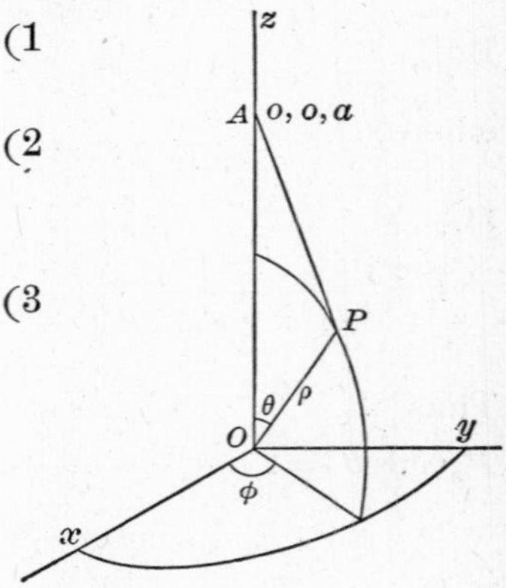

Let us set

$$x = \cos\theta. \qquad (2$$

Then 1) becomes

$$\frac{\partial}{\partial r}\left(r^2\frac{\partial V}{\partial r}\right) + \frac{\partial}{\partial x}\cdot(1-x^2)\frac{\partial V}{\partial x} = 0. \qquad (3$$

Now by 222, 4)

$$V = \sum_{n=0}^{\infty} P_n(x) r^n.$$

Putting this in 3) gives

$$\Sigma r^n\left\{n(n+1)P_n + \frac{d}{dx}\cdot(1-x^2)\frac{dP_n}{dx}\right\} = 0.$$

Hence P_n satisfies

$$n(n+1)P_n + \frac{d}{dx}(1-x^2)\frac{dP_n}{dx} = 0. \qquad (4$$

or

$$(1-x^2)\frac{d^2y}{dx^2} - 2x\frac{dy}{dx} + n(n+1)y = 0. \qquad (5$$

If in this we set

$$u = x^2,$$

it becomes

$$u(1-u)\frac{d^2y}{du^2} + (\tfrac{3}{2}u - \tfrac{1}{2})\frac{dy}{du} + n(n+1)y = 0. \tag{6}$$

This is a special case of the hypergeometric differential equation. Comparing with 210, 1) we get

$$\alpha = -\frac{n}{2} \quad , \quad \beta = \frac{n+1}{2} \quad , \quad \gamma = \tfrac{1}{2}.$$

A fundamental system of integrals of 6) is, as we saw, 210, 10), 12),

$$y_1 = F\left(-\frac{n}{2}, \frac{n+2}{2}, \frac{1}{2}, x^2\right),$$

$$y_2 = xF\left(-\frac{n-1}{2}, \frac{n+2}{2}, \frac{3}{2}, x^2\right).$$

Now when α or β is a negative integer, $F(\alpha, \beta, \gamma, x)$ reduces to a polynomial. Hence when n is an even integer, y_1 is a polynomial and y_2 is an infinite series; while when n is odd, y_2 is a polynomial and y_1 is an infinite series. This shows that

$$P_n(x) = c_1 y_1 \quad , \quad n \text{ even}$$
$$= c_2 y_2 \quad , \quad n \text{ odd}.$$

Comparing with 222, 5), we get

$$P_{2n}(x) = (-1)^n \frac{1 \cdot 3 \cdot 5 \dots 2n-1}{2 \cdot 4 \cdot 6 \dots 2n} F(-n, n+\tfrac{1}{2}, \tfrac{1}{2}, x^2), \tag{7}$$

$$P_{2n+1}(x) = (-1)^n \frac{3 \cdot 5 \cdot 7 \dots 2n+1}{2 \cdot 4 \cdot 6 \dots 2n} xF(-n, n+\tfrac{3}{2}, \tfrac{3}{2}, x^2). \tag{8}$$

225. Integral Properties of $P_n(x)$. 1. In 224, 4) let us set

$y = P_m$ and then $y = P_n$; we get

$$m(m+1)P_m + \frac{d}{dx}(1-x^2)\frac{dP_m}{dx} = 0,$$

$$n(n+1)P_n + \frac{d}{dx}(1-x^2)\frac{dP_n}{dx} = 0.$$

Multiply the first by P_n, the second by P_m, and subtracting, we get on integrating

$$(m-n)(m+n+1)\int_{-1}^{1} P_m P_n dx = 0.$$

Thus

$$\int_{-1}^{1} P_m P_n dx = 0 \quad , \quad m \neq n. \tag{1}$$

From this follows the theorem:

Let $F_m(x)$ be a polynomial of degree $m < n$. Then

$$\int_{-1}^{1} F_m(x) P_n(x) dx = 0. \tag{2}$$

For by 222, 5, 11)

$$F_m = c_0 P_0 + c_1 P_1 + \cdots + c_m P_m.$$

Thus the left side of 2)

$$= \sum_{s=0}^{m} c_s \int_{-1}^{1} P_s(x) P_n(x) dx$$

$$= 0 \quad , \quad \text{by 1)}.$$

2. We have

$$\frac{1}{\sqrt{1-2xr+r^2}} = 1 + rP_1(x) + r^2 P_2(x) + \cdots = \sum_{m=0}^{\infty} r^m P_m(x).$$

Squaring, we get

$$\frac{1}{1-2xr+r^2} = \Sigma\, r^{m+n} P_m(x) P_n(x) \quad , \quad m, n = 0, 1, 2, \cdots \tag{3}$$

Now

$$\int_{-1}^{1} \frac{dx}{1-2xr+r^2} = \frac{1}{r}\log\frac{1+r}{1-r} = 2\left\{1 + \frac{1}{3}r^2 + \frac{1}{5}r^4 + \cdots\right\}. \tag{4}$$

Hence, integrating 3) and using 1), 4), we have

$$\Sigma \frac{2}{2n+1} r^{2n} = \sum_{n=0}^{\infty} r^{2n} \int_{-1} P_n^2(x) dx.$$

Hence, equating the coefficients of like powers of r, we have

$$\int_{-1}^{1} P_n^2(x) dx = \frac{2}{2n+1} n = 1, 2, \cdots \tag{5}$$

3. We have

$$\frac{1}{\sqrt{1-2\,xz+z^2}}=1+zP_1(x)+z^2P_2(x)+\cdots$$

Hence, C denoting a small circle about the origin in the z-plane,

$$\int_C\frac{dz}{z^{n+1}\sqrt{1-2\,xz+z^2}}=\int_C\frac{dz}{z^{n+1}}+P_1(x)\int_C\frac{dz}{z^n}+\cdots+P_n(x)\int_C\frac{dz}{z}+\cdots$$
$$=2\,\pi iP_n(x).$$

Thus

$$P_n(x)=\frac{1}{2\,\pi i}\int_C\frac{dz}{z^{n+1}\sqrt{1-2\,xz+z^2}},\tag{6}$$

the radical having the value $+1$ for $z=0$.

Let us set $z=\frac{1}{u}$ in 6), we get

$$P_n(x)=\frac{1}{2\,\pi i}\int_D\frac{u^n du}{\sqrt{1-2\,xu+u^2}},\tag{7}$$

where D is a large circle about $u=0$, which u describes in the positive direction.

4. In 7) let us set

$$\sqrt{1-2\,xu+u^2}=w-u \quad , \quad \text{or } 1-2\,xu+u^2=(w-u)^2.$$

Then

$$u=\frac{w^2-1}{2(w-x)} \quad , \quad du=\frac{w-u}{w-x}\,dw.$$

While u describes the large circle D, w will describe a curve $\mathfrak{K}$ which is approximately a circle of radius $2\,R$. Thus 7) gives

$$P_n(x)=\frac{1}{2\,\pi i}\int_{\mathfrak{K}}\frac{(w^2-1)^n}{2^n(w-x)^{n+1}}\,dw.\tag{8}$$

Since the integrand has no singular points in the distant part of the w-plane, $\mathfrak{K}$ can be regarded as a large circle whose center is x. The relation 8) is due to *Schläfli*.

226. Rodrigue's Formula. 1. Let

$$f(x) = (x^2 - 1)^n.$$

Then by Cauchy's integral formula

$$f(x) = \frac{1}{2\pi i}\int_{\mathfrak{K}} \frac{(w^2-1)^n}{w-x}\,dw,$$

where $\mathfrak{K}$ is a circle about the point $w = x$. Hence

$$f^{(n)}(x) = \frac{n!}{2\pi i}\int_{\mathfrak{K}} \frac{(w^2-1)^n}{(w-x)^{n+1}}\,dw$$

$$= 2^n n!\, P_n(x) \quad , \quad \text{by 225, 8).}$$

Thus

$$P_n(x) = \frac{1}{2^n \cdot n!}\frac{d^n}{dx^n}(x^2-1)^n, \tag{1}$$

a relation due to *Rodrigue.*

2. From this relation we can prove the theorem:

The n roots of $P_n(x) = 0$ are all real, and lie in the interval $\mathfrak{A} = (-1, 1)$.

We start with

$$f(x) = (x^2-1)^n = (x-1)^n(x+1)^n.$$

This shows that $x = 1$ is an n-tuple root, and the same is true of $x = -1$. As f is of degree $2n$, $f(x)$ has no other roots.

By Rolle's theorem

$$f(1) - f(-1) = 0 = 2f'(a_1) \quad , \quad -1 < a_1 < 1.$$

Hence $f'(x)$ vanishes at $x = a_1$, a point within $\mathfrak{A}$. But

$$f'(x) = 2n(x^2-1)^{n-1}x$$

has $x = \pm 1$ as roots of order $n - 1$. Thus $f'(x) = 0$ at $x = \pm 1$ and at $x = a_1$, and only at these points. We may reason in the same way on $f''(x)$. We have

$$f''(x) = 4n(n-1)(x^2-1)^{n-2}x^2 + 2n(x^2-1)^{n-1}.$$

This has $x = \pm 1$ as roots of order $n - 2$. Rolle's theorem again shows that $f''(x)$ must $= 0$ at some point b_1 within $(-1, a_1)$, and at some point b_2 within $(a_1, 1)$. We have thus found $2n - 2$

roots of $f''(x)$. Since the degree of $f''(x)$ is $2n-2$, there are no other roots. Thus $f''(x)$ vanishes at just two points b_1, b_2 within $\mathfrak{A}$.

Continuing in this way, we see that $f^{(n)}(x)$ vanishes at n and only n points within $\mathfrak{A}$. By Rodrigue's relation 1), $P_n(x)$ and $f^{(n)}(x)$ differ only by a constant factor. Hence $P_n(x)$ vanishes n times within $\mathfrak{A}$. As P_n is of degree n, these are all the roots of $P_n(x)$.

227. Development of $f(x)$ in Terms of $P_n(x)$. 1. Let $f(x)$ be a one-valued continuous function of x having only a finite number of oscillations in the interval $\mathfrak{A}=(-1,1)$. Then it can be shown that $f(x)$ can be developed in a series of Legendrian functions

$$f(x)=c_0+c_1P_1(x)+c_2P_2(x)+\cdots \qquad (1$$

which is valid for any x in $\mathfrak{A}$. Moreover this series can be integrated termwise in $\mathfrak{A}$.

Admitting this, let us show how the coefficients c_n may be found. Multiplying both sides by $P_n(x)$ and integrating, we get

$$\int_{-1}^{1} f(x)P_n(x)\,dx=\sum_n\int_{-1}^{1}c_nP_mP_n dx.$$

All the terms on the right vanish by 225, 1), 5) except that corresponding to c_n. Thus

$$\int_{-1}^{1} f(x)P_n dx=c_n\int_{-1}^{1}P_n^2(x)\,dx=\frac{2c_n}{2n+1}.$$

Hence

$$c_n=\frac{2n+1}{2}\int_{-1}^{1}f(x)P_n(x)dx. \qquad (2$$

Thus we have the theorem:

Let $f(x)$ be a one-valued continuous function having only a finite number of oscillations in the interval $(-1,1)$. Then

$$f(x)=\sum_{n=0}^{\infty}\frac{2n+1}{2}P_n(x)\int_{-1}^{1}f(x)P_n(x)dx. \qquad (3$$

2. Since $P_n'(x)$ satisfies the condition of this theorem, we have

$$\frac{dP_n(x)}{dx}=P_n'(x)=a_{n-1}P_{n-1}+a_{n-2}P_{n-2}+\cdots$$

Since P_n' is odd or even with $n-1$, we must have

$$P_n'(x) = a_{n-1}P_{n-1} + a_{n-3}P_{n-3} + \cdots$$

Here by 2)

$$a_m = \frac{2m+1}{2}\int_{-1}^{1} P_m P_n' dx.$$

Integrating by parts gives

$$a_m = \frac{2m+1}{2}\left\{2 - \int_{-1}^{1} P_n P_m' dx\right\}$$

$$= 2m+1$$

since the integral vanishes as $P_m'(x)$ is the sum of P's whose index is $< n$. Thus

$$P_n'(x) = (2n-1)P_{n-1} + (2n-5)P_{n-3} + (2n-9)P_{n-5} + \cdots \qquad (4$$

3. Let us show that $f(x)$ can be developed in a series of Legendrian functions

$$f(x) = a_0 + a_1P_1(x) + a_2P_2(x) + \cdots \qquad (5$$

in but one way. For suppose that

$$f(x) = b_0 + b_1P_1(x) + b_2P_2(x) + \cdots \qquad (6$$

were a second development valid in $(-1, 1)$. Subtracting we get

$$0 = c_0 + c_1P_1(x) + c_2P_2(x) + \cdots \qquad (7$$

where

$$c_n = a_n - b_n.$$

Let us multiply 7) by $P_n(x)$ and integrate between -1 and 1. Granting we can integrate the resulting series termwise, we get

$$0 = c_0\int_{-1}^{1} P_n dx + c_1\int_{-1}^{1} P_1P_n dx + c_2\int_{-1}^{1} P_2P_n dx + \cdots \qquad (8$$

Here each term is 0 by 225 except the term corresponding to c_n. Thus 8) reduces to

$$0 = c_n\int_{-1}^{1} P_n^2 dx = \frac{2c_n}{2n+1}.$$

Hence

$$c_n = 0,$$

and thus

$$a_n = b_n \qquad n = 1, 2 \cdots$$

228. Recurrent Relations. 1.

$$(n+1)P_{n+1} - (2n+1)xP_n + nP_{n-1} = 0. \tag{1}$$

$$(1-x^2)P'_n + nxP_n - nP_{n-1} = 0. \tag{2}$$

$$(1-x^2)P'_{n-1} + nP_n - nxP_{n-1} = 0. \tag{3}$$

$$xP'_n - P'_{n-1} - nP_n = 0. \tag{4}$$

$$P'_{n+1} - P'_{n-1} - (2n+1)P_n = 0. \tag{5}$$

These may be proved by putting in the values of P_m, P'_m as given by 222, 5). There results a polynomial in x whose coefficients are all zero. A more expeditious method is the following. Let

$$\begin{aligned} V &= (1 - 2xz + z^2)^{-\frac{1}{2}} \\ &= P_0(x) + zP_1(x) + {}^2zP_2(x) + \cdots \end{aligned} \tag{6}$$

Thus

$$\frac{\dfrac{\partial V}{\partial z}}{V} = \frac{x - z}{1 - 2xz + z^2},$$

or

$$(1 - 2xz + z^2)\frac{\partial V}{\partial z} + (z - x)V = 0. \tag{7}$$

On the other hand, we get from 6)

$$\frac{\partial V}{\partial z} = P_1 + 2zP_2 + 3z^2P_3 + \cdots \tag{8}$$

Putting 6) and 8) in 7) gives

$$\Sigma z^n\{(n+1)P_{n+1} - 2xnP_n + (n-1)P_{n-1} + P_{n-1} - xP_n\} = 0.$$

As all the coefficients are 0, the coefficient of z^n here gives 1).

2. To get 5) we use 227, 4). Thus

$$\begin{aligned} P'_{n+1} &= (2n+1)P_n + (2n-3)P_{n-2} + \cdots \\ P'_{n-1} &= \qquad * \qquad + (2n-3)P_{n-2} + \cdots \end{aligned}$$

Subtracting gives 5).

3. To get 4) we have only to differentiate 1) with respect to x and use 5).

4. To get 2) we multiply 4) by x, getting

$$x^2P'_n = xP'_{n-1} + nxP_n.$$

Hence

$$(1-x^2)P_n' = P_n' - xP_{n-1}' - nxP_n,$$

or

$$(1-x^2)P_n' + nxP_n = P_n' - xP_{n-1}'$$

$$= nP_{n-1},$$

on using 4), 5).

229. Legendre's Functions of the Second Kind. We saw in 224, 6) that $P_n(x)$ satisfies the equation

$$u(1-u)\frac{d^2y}{du^2} + \left(\frac{3}{2}u - \frac{1}{2}\right)\frac{dy}{du} + n(n+1)y = 0 \quad , \quad u = x^2. \qquad (1$$

This equation admits, by 210, 16), 17), two integrals about $u = \infty$, viz.:

$$y_1 = x^n F\left(-\frac{n}{2}, -\frac{n-1}{2}, -\frac{2n-1}{2}, \frac{1}{x^2}\right), \qquad (2$$

$$y_2 = \frac{1}{x^{n+1}} F\left(\frac{n+1}{2}, \frac{n+2}{2}, \frac{2n+3}{2}, \frac{1}{x^2}\right). \qquad (3$$

Since $F(\alpha, \beta, \gamma, x)$ is a polynomial when α or β is a negative integer, we see that whether n is odd or even

$$F\left(-\frac{n}{2}, -\frac{n-1}{2}, -\frac{2n-1}{2}, w\right)$$

is a polynomial in w, and thus 2) is aside from a constant factor nothing but $P_n(x)$.

The other integral 3) multiplied by a constant factor gives rise to Legendre's Functions of the second kind, viz.:

$$Q_n(x) = \frac{1 \cdot 2 \cdot 3 \cdots n}{3 \cdot 5 \cdot 7 \cdot \cdots 2n+1} \cdot \frac{1}{x^{n+1}} F\left(\frac{n+1}{2}, \frac{n+2}{2}, \frac{2n+3}{2}, \frac{1}{x^2}\right),$$

$$|x| > 1. \qquad (4$$

230. Recurrent Relations for Q_n. 1. If in 229, 4) we set $n = 0$, we get

$$Q_0(x) = \frac{1}{x} F\left(\frac{1}{2}, 1, \frac{3}{2}, \frac{1}{x^2}\right),$$

or

$$Q_0(x) = \frac{1}{2}\log\frac{x+1}{x-1}. \qquad (1$$

Using 229, 4) we prove at once that

$$Q_1 - xQ_0 + 1 = 0 \tag{2}$$

and

$$(n+1)Q_{n+1} - (2n+1)xQ_n + nQ_{n-1} = 0. \tag{3}$$

These show that

$$Q_n(x) = S_n(x)\log\frac{x+1}{x-1} + T_n(x) \tag{4}$$

when S, T are polynomials. We can go further by observing that the recursion formula 3) for Q_n is the same as that for P_n in 228, 1). Let us set

$$L = \log\frac{x+1}{x-1} \quad , \quad Z_1 = 1$$

in 2), 3), we get $\qquad Q_1 = xQ_0 - 1 = \frac{1}{2}P_1L - Z_1.$

Then $\qquad 2Q_2 = 3xQ_1 - Q_0 \quad ; \quad 2P_2 = 3xP_1 - P_0.$

Hence

$$Q_2 = \tfrac{1}{2}P_2L - Z_2$$

if we set

$$Z_2 = \tfrac{3}{2}P_1 = \tfrac{3}{2}x.$$

This is perfectly general. For let us admit that

$$Q_n = \tfrac{1}{2}P_nL - Z_n \tag{5}$$

is true for n and show that it holds for $n+1$. Here Z_n is a polynomial of degree $n-1$.

For by 3),

$$\begin{aligned}(n+1)Q_{n+1} &= (2n+1)xQ_n - nQ_{n-1}, \text{ or using 5)},\\ &= (2n+1)x\{\tfrac{1}{2}P_nL - Z_n\} - n\{\tfrac{1}{2}P_{n-1}L - Z_{n-1}\}\\ &= \tfrac{1}{2}L\{(2n+1)xP_n - nP_{n-1}\} - (2n+1)xZ_n + nZ_{n-1}\\ &= \tfrac{1}{2}(n+1)LP_{n+1} + \{nZ_{n-1} - (2n+1)xZ_n\},\end{aligned}$$

which goes over into 5) on setting

$$-(n+1)Z_{n+1} = nZ_{n-1} - (2n+1)xZ_n. \tag{6}$$

This is a *recursion formula for* Z_n and shows that Z_n is odd or even according as $n-1$ is odd or even.

2. Since L is a logarithm and P_n, Z_n are polynomials, we see that Legendre's equation 224, 6) does not define any new class of functions, that is, its general integral is a combination of polynomials and logarithms.

231. Development of Z_n in Terms of the P_m. Since Z_n is a polynomial, we can develop it in terms of $P_0, P_1, P_2 \cdots$ by 227, 1, or by 222, 5. Thus

$$Z_n = a_1 P_{n-1} + a_3 P_{n-3} + \cdots \tag{1}$$

the a_{2m} being all 0 on account of the parity of Z_n. To determine the coefficients in 1) we use the fact that Q_n is a solution of Legendre's equation 224, 4)

$$\frac{d}{dx}\left[(1-x^2)\frac{dy}{dx}\right] + n(n+1)y = 0.$$

This gives

$$\frac{d}{dx}\left[(1-x^2)\frac{d}{dx}Z_n\right] + n(n+1)Z_n - 2P'_n = 0. \tag{2}$$

But by 227, 4)

$$P'_n = (2n-1)P_{n-1} + (2n-5)P_{n-3} + \cdots \tag{3}$$

Thus 1) and 3) in 2) give

$$a_{2m+1} = \frac{2n-4m-1}{(2m+1)(n-m)}, \quad m = 0, 1, 2, \cdots$$

Hence

$$Z_n = \frac{2n-1}{1 \cdot n}P_{n-1} + \frac{2n-5}{3(n-1)}P_{n-3} + \frac{2n-9}{5(n-2)}P_{n-5} + \cdots \tag{4}$$

232. Laplace's Equation. 1. One of the most important equations in mathematical physics is Laplace's equation

$$\Delta u = \frac{\partial^2 u}{\partial x^2} + \frac{\partial^2 u}{\partial y^2} + \frac{\partial^2 u}{\partial z^2} = 0. \tag{1}$$

Example 1. Suppose heat is passing into a body at certain points of its surface S, and leaving at other points. It is easy to show that the temperature u at any interior point P of the body satisfies the partial differential equation

$$\frac{\partial u}{\partial t} = c\Delta u, \tag{2}$$

where c is a constant. In many cases a stationary state sets in; as much heat leaves an elementary cube described about the point P as enters it. In this case the temperature u is constant, and hence $\frac{\partial u}{\partial t} = 0$. Thus u satisfies in such a case Laplace's equation.

It can be shown that when u is known on the surface S in this case, the value of u can be found at any point P within the body; in other words, the solution of 1) is uniquely determined when u is given on the boundary S.

Any function u satisfying 1) is called a *harmonic function.*

Example 2. Suppose a fluid, that is, a liquid or a gas, is in motion. At the time t, the particle at the point P is moving with a certain velocity $\mathfrak{u}$ whose components call u, v, w. Let V be the volume of an element of the fluid at the time t; at the time $t + dt$, this volume has changed to $V + dV$. Thus the rate at which V is changing is $\frac{dV}{dt}$; it is called the *divergence of the vector* $\mathfrak{u}$. It is denoted by

$$\text{div } \mathfrak{u}.$$

One finds easily that

$$\text{div } \mathfrak{u} = \frac{\partial u}{\partial x} + \frac{\partial v}{\partial y} + \frac{\partial w}{\partial z}. \tag{3}$$

If the fluid is incompressible, as it is sensibly for liquids like water

$$\text{div } \mathfrak{u} = 0. \tag{4}$$

In an important class of problems the velocity $\mathfrak{u}$ is such that its components are the derivatives of some function $\phi(x, y, z)$, that is

$$u = \frac{\partial \phi}{\partial x}, \quad v = \frac{\partial \phi}{\partial y}, \quad w = \frac{\partial \phi}{\partial z}. \tag{5}$$

We call ϕ the *velocity potential.*

If the fluid is incompressible and its velocity has a velocity potential ϕ, then ϕ satisfies Laplace's equation 1) as is seen at once by putting 5) in 4).

The surfaces

$$\phi(x, y, z) = C \tag{6}$$

are called *equal potential surfaces.*

A curve in space such that the tangent at each point of it has the direction of the vector $\mathfrak{u}$ at that point is called a *stream line.*

These cut the surfaces 6) orthogonally. For the normal at a a point of 6) has direction cosines which are proportional to

$$\frac{\partial \phi}{\partial x}, \quad \frac{\partial \phi}{\partial y}, \quad \frac{\partial \phi}{\partial z};$$

but these by 5) are proportional to the direction cosines of the vector $\mathfrak{u}$.

2. When the particles of the fluid are all moving parallel to a plane, which we take as the x, y plane, we may neglect the component w of the motion since it is 0. Let

$$f(z) = U + iV \tag{7}$$

be an analytic function not necessarily one-valued. Then, as we have seen, the Cauchy-Riemann relations hold, or

$$\frac{\partial U}{\partial x} = \frac{\partial V}{\partial y}, \quad \frac{\partial U}{\partial y} = -\frac{\partial V}{\partial x}. \tag{8}$$

From these follow that

$$\frac{\partial^2 U}{\partial x^2} + \frac{\partial^2 U}{\partial y^2} = 0, \quad \frac{\partial^2 V}{\partial x^2} + \frac{\partial^2 V}{\partial y^2} = 0. \tag{9}$$

Thus U, V satisfy Laplace's equation for two variables. Let us take one of the functions U, V (to fix the ideas, say U) as a velocity potential. Then by definition the components of the velocity $\mathfrak{u}$ are

$$u = \frac{\partial U}{\partial x}, \quad v = \frac{\partial U}{\partial y}.$$

The relation 9) shows that $\operatorname{div} \mathfrak{u} = 0$, thus the fluid is incompressible.

From 8) we now have

$$\frac{\partial U}{\partial x}\frac{\partial V}{\partial x} + \frac{\partial U}{\partial y}\frac{\partial V}{\partial y} = 0.$$

Thus the two families of curves

$$U = \text{const}, \quad V = \text{const} \tag{10}$$

cut each other orthogonally. This gives the theorem:

The two components of an analytic function 7) *may be used to define two families of curves* 10), *such that one family represents the stream lines of the motion, the other the curves of equal potential.*

3. To illustrate this theorem let us take as analytic function

$$f(z) = z^2 = x^2 - y^2 + i \cdot 2\,xy.$$

Then

$$U = x^2 - y^2 \quad , \quad V = 2\,xy.$$

These give rise to two families of equilateral hyperbolas whose asymptotes are the lines

$$y = x \quad , \quad y = -x \quad \text{and} \quad y = 0 \quad , \quad x = 0.$$

233. Theorems of Gauss and Green. 1. In studying the solution of Laplace's equation we shall find it extremely useful to use some theorems relating to surface and volume integrals due to Gauss and Green.

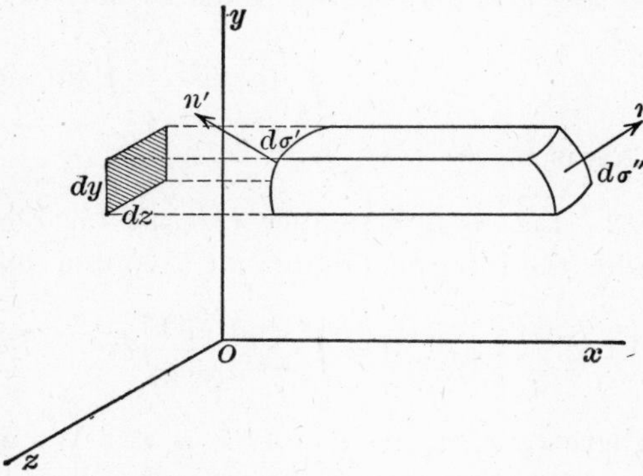

Let S be an ordinary closed surface. Let us effect a rectangular division of the yz-plane. Each rectangle $dydz$ may be used as the base of a cylinder which cuts out elements of surface $d\sigma'$, $d\sigma''$, $d\sigma'''$ ··· on S whose normals call n', n'', n''' ····.

Then as the figure shows

$$dydz = -\,d\sigma' \cos(n'x) = d\sigma'' \cos(n''x) = \ldots$$

Let

$$d\tau = dxdydz$$

be an element of volume. Let $\mathfrak{u}$ be a vector whose components are u, v, w. Then if $\frac{\partial u}{\partial x}$ is one-valued and continuous,

$$\int_S \frac{\partial u}{\partial x}\, d\tau = \int dydz \int \frac{\partial u}{\partial x}\, dx = \int_S udydz = \int_S u \cos(nx) d\sigma. \qquad (1$$

We get similar relations for $\frac{\partial v}{\partial y}, \frac{\partial w}{\partial z}$. Thus adding,

$$\int_S \left(\frac{\partial u}{\partial x} + \frac{\partial v}{\partial y} + \frac{\partial w}{\partial z}\right) d\tau = \int_S \operatorname{div} \mathfrak{u} \cdot d\tau$$

$$= \int (u \cos(nx) + v \cos(ny) + w \cos(nz)) d\sigma. \quad (2$$

Now the component of the vector $\mathfrak{u}$ normal to S is

$$\mathfrak{u}_n = u \cos(nx) + v \cos(ny) + w \cos(nz). \quad (3$$

If $\mathfrak{u}$ denoted the velocity of a fluid, $\mathfrak{u}_n dS$ would denote the amount of fluid which passes across the element of surface dS per unit of time. For this reason we call quite in general

$$\mathfrak{u}_n dS$$

the flux of $\mathfrak{u}$ *across* dS. Thus 2) may be written

$$\int_S \operatorname{div} \mathfrak{u} d\tau = \int_S \operatorname{flux} \mathfrak{u} \cdot d\sigma. \quad (4$$

This is *Gauss' theorem.*

2. Let us now deduce *Green's theorems.* To this end we consider the integral taken over a volume bounded by S,

$$J = \int_S \sum \frac{\partial U}{\partial x_i} \frac{\partial V}{\partial x_i} d\tau \qquad i = 1, 2, 3 \quad (5$$

where x_1, x_2, x_3 are simply x, y, z. We use the subscript notation in order to use the Σ sign on account of brevity.

We have now

$$\frac{\partial U}{\partial x_i} \frac{\partial V}{\partial x_i} = \frac{\partial}{\partial x_i} \cdot U \frac{\partial V}{\partial x_i} - U \frac{\partial^2 V}{\partial x_i^2}.$$

Let $\mathfrak{g}$ be the vector whose three components are $U \frac{\partial V}{\partial x_i}$. Then 5) becomes

$$J = \int_S \operatorname{div} \mathfrak{g} \, d\tau - \int_S U \Delta V d\tau.$$

By Gauss' relation 4)

$$\int_S \operatorname{div} \mathfrak{g} \, d\tau = \int_S \operatorname{flux} \mathfrak{g} \, d\sigma = - \int_S U \frac{\partial V}{\partial n} d\sigma$$

if we reckon the normal n inward. Thus

$$J = -\int_S U\frac{\partial V}{\partial n}d\sigma - \int_S U\Delta V d\tau, \qquad (6$$

or interchanging U, V

$$= \int_S V\frac{\partial U}{\partial n}d\sigma - \int_S V\Delta U d\tau.$$

Equating these two values of J gives

$$\int_S\left(U\frac{\partial V}{\partial n} - V\frac{\partial U}{\partial n}\right)d\sigma = \int_S (V\Delta U - U\Delta V)d\tau. \qquad (7$$

If we set $U = 1$ in 7), we get

$$\int_S \frac{\partial V}{\partial n}d\sigma = -\int_S \Delta V d\tau. \qquad (8$$

If we set $U = V$ in 6) it becomes

$$\int_S \sum \frac{\partial V^2}{\partial x_i^2}d\tau = -\int_S V\frac{\partial V}{\partial n}d\sigma - \int_S V\Delta V d\tau. \qquad (9$$

If V is harmonic, that is, if $\Delta V = 0$, this gives

$$\int_S \sum \frac{\partial V^2}{\partial x_i^2}d\tau = -\int_S V\frac{\partial V}{\partial n}d\sigma. \qquad (10$$

If U and V are both harmonic, 7) becomes

$$\int_S U\frac{\partial V}{\partial n}d\sigma = \int_S V\frac{\partial U}{\partial n}d\sigma. \qquad (11$$

If V is harmonic, the relation 11) gives for $U = 1$

$$\int_S \frac{\partial V}{\partial n}d\sigma = 0. \qquad (12$$

These relations are due to *Green*.

234. Potential Expressed in Terms of Boundary Values. 1. Let a be a point within the surface S. The distance from a to any point x in S is

$$r = \sqrt{(x_1 - a_1)^2 + (x_2 - a_2)^2 + (x_3 - a_3)^2}.$$

Then

$$U = \frac{1}{r}$$

is not continuous in S. Let us therefore describe a small sphere K of radius k about a and let T denote the remaining volume, as well as the surface bounding this volume. The normals n we will reckon inward as in the figure.

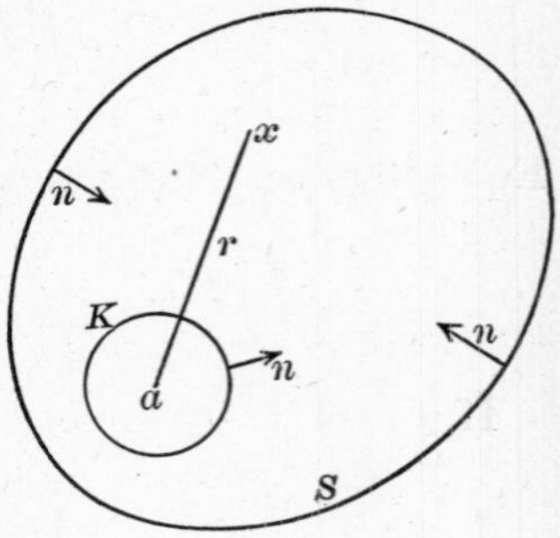

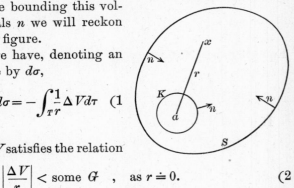

From 233, 7) we have, denoting an element of surface by $d\sigma$,

$$\int_T \left(\frac{1}{r} \frac{\partial V}{\partial n} - V \frac{\partial \frac{1}{r}}{\partial u} \right) d\sigma = - \int_T \frac{1}{r} \Delta V d\tau \quad (1$$

since $\Delta U = 0$.

Let us suppose V satisfies the relation

$$\left| \frac{\Delta V}{r} \right| < \text{some } G \quad , \quad \text{as } r \doteq 0. \quad (2$$

Then

$$\left| \int_K \frac{\Delta V}{r} d\tau \right| < G \int_K d\tau \doteq 0 \quad , \quad \text{as } k \doteq 0.$$

Hence the integral on the right of 1) converges to

$$- \int_S \frac{1}{r} \Delta V d\tau \quad , \quad \text{as } k \doteq 0.$$

Let us turn to the integral on the left of 1). We have, taking account of the sign of the normals,

$$\int_T (\quad) d\sigma = \int_S (\quad) d\sigma - \int_K (\quad) d\sigma.$$

Now relative to K, $\quad \frac{\partial}{\partial n} \cdot \frac{1}{r} = \frac{\partial r}{\partial n} \cdot \frac{\partial}{\partial r} \frac{1}{r} = - \frac{1}{r^2}.$

Let now V_1, V_2 be the minimum and maximum of V on K. Then

$$4 \pi k^2 V_1 \leq \int_K V d\sigma \leq 4 \pi k^2 V_2,$$

or

$$\int_K V d\sigma = 4 \pi k^2 V_m,$$

where V_m is a mean value of V on K.

Let now $k \doteq 0$, then $V_m \doteq V_a$, the value of V at a. Thus

$$\int V \frac{\partial}{\partial r} \frac{1}{r} d\sigma \doteq 4 \pi V_a.$$

Let us now look at

$$\int_K \frac{1}{r} \frac{\partial V}{\partial n} d\sigma.$$

Since the first partial derivatives of V are continuous, so is $\frac{\partial V}{\partial n}$. Hence

$$\left| \frac{\partial V}{\partial n} \right| < \text{some } H \text{ on } K.$$

Thus

$$\left| \int_K \frac{1}{r} \frac{\partial V}{\partial n} d\sigma \right| < \frac{4 \pi k^2}{k} H \doteq 0, \text{ as } k \doteq 0.$$

We thus get, *the point a being within S*,

$$4 \pi V_a = \int_S \left(V \frac{\partial}{\partial n} \frac{1}{r} - \frac{1}{r} \frac{\partial V}{\partial n} \right) d\sigma - \int_S \frac{1}{r} \Delta V d\tau. \qquad (3$$

In case *V is a harmonic function*, this gives

$$V_a = \frac{1}{4 \pi} \int_S \left(V \frac{\partial}{\partial n} \frac{1}{r} - \frac{1}{r} \frac{\partial V}{\partial n} \right) d\sigma. \qquad (4$$

2. In the foregoing, the point a was taken inside the surface; *let us now take a without S.*

Let $\mathfrak{K}$ be a sphere of radius $K \doteq \infty$. About a as a center let us describe a sphere $\mathfrak{k}$ of radius $k \doteq 0$. The three surfaces $\mathfrak{K}$, S, $\mathfrak{k}$ limit a region T whose boundary may be denoted by the same letter.

Let x be any point in T. Then

$$U = \frac{1}{r}$$

is continuous in T and we have again

$$\int_T \left(\frac{1}{r} \frac{\partial V}{\partial n} - V \frac{\partial}{\partial n} \frac{1}{r} \right) d\sigma = - \int_T \frac{1}{r} \Delta V d\tau.$$

Then if we reckon n inward as in Fig. 2 we have

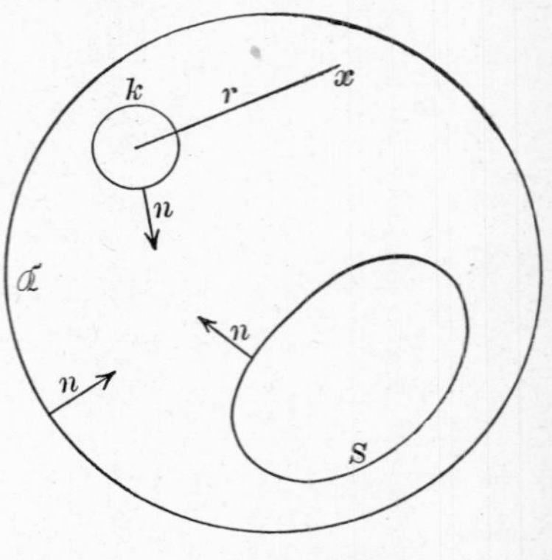

$$\int_{\mathfrak{K}}(\quad) + d\sigma \int_{\mathfrak{k}}(\quad)d\sigma$$

$$+\int_S(\quad)d\sigma = \int_T \frac{1}{r}\Delta V d\tau. \quad (5$$

We have already seen that

$$\int_{\mathfrak{k}} \frac{1}{r}\frac{\partial V}{\partial n}d\tau \doteq 0,$$

$$\int_{\mathfrak{k}} V\frac{\partial}{\partial n}\frac{1}{r}d\sigma \doteq 4\pi V_a.$$

Let us suppose now that V is such that 2) still holds and that also

$$V \doteq 0, \text{ and } \left| R^2 \frac{\partial V}{\partial n}\right| < \text{some } G \text{ as } R \doteq \infty. \qquad (6$$

Then
$$\int_{\mathfrak{K}} \frac{1}{r}\frac{\partial V}{\partial n} d\sigma \doteq 0 \quad , \quad \int_{\mathfrak{K}} V\frac{\partial}{\partial n}\frac{1}{r} d\sigma \doteq 0 \quad \text{as } K \doteq \infty.$$

Thus 5) gives, *the point a being without S*,

$$4\pi V_a = \int_S \left(V\frac{\partial}{\partial n}\frac{1}{r} - \frac{1}{r}\frac{\partial V}{\partial n}\right)d\sigma - \int_\Sigma \frac{1}{r}\Delta V d\tau, \qquad (7$$

where Σ denotes all space outside of S.

If V is harmonic, this gives

$$4\pi V_a = \int_S \left(V\frac{\partial}{\partial n}\frac{1}{r} - \frac{1}{r}\frac{\partial V}{\partial n}\right)d\sigma. \qquad (8$$

We notice that 4) and 8) are the same in form.

235. Outline of a Solution of Laplace's Equation. The following method is applicable to the sphere, the cylinder, and the ellipsoid. It depends upon the fact that each of these three surfaces belongs to a family of triply orthogonal surfaces, viz.:

1° *Sphere*, cone, meridian plane.

2° *Cylinder*, meridian plane, plane perpendicular to the axis.

3° Confocal *ellipsoid*, hyperboloid of one and two sheets.

In passing let us note that the rectangular xyz coördinates are also defined by a system of triply orthogonal surfaces, viz.: planes. To solve

$$\frac{\partial^2 u}{\partial x^2} + \frac{\partial^2 u}{\partial y^2} + \frac{\partial^2 u}{\partial z^2} = 0, \tag{1}$$

by the method we have here in view, we first pass from the rectangular coördinates x, y, z to a system of coördinates determined by the triply orthogonal surfaces.

To illustrate this let us consider the case of the sphere. Here the family of surfaces are given by

$$\begin{aligned} x^2 + y^2 + z^2 - r^2 &= 0, \\ x^2 + y^2 - z^2 \tan^2 \theta &= 0, \\ y - x \tan \phi &= 0. \end{aligned} \tag{2}$$

If we solve these, we get

$$\begin{aligned} f_1(x, y, z) &= \sqrt{x^2 + y^2 + z^2} = r, \\ f_2(x, y, z) &= \operatorname{arctg} \frac{\sqrt{x^2 + y^2}}{z} = \theta, \\ f_3(x, y, z) &= \operatorname{arctg} \frac{y}{x} = \phi. \end{aligned} \tag{3}$$

Giving r, θ, ϕ definite values, we can solve 2) for x, y, z, getting

$$x = g_1(r, \theta, \phi) \quad , \quad y = g_2(r, \theta, \phi) \quad , \quad z = g_3(r, \theta, \phi).$$

In the case of the sphere these are

$$x = r \sin \theta \cos \phi \quad , \quad y = r \sin \theta \sin \phi \quad , \quad z = r \cos \theta.$$

The new coördinates are polar coördinates.

In general the family of orthogonal surfaces corresponding to 3) may be written

$$f_1(x, y, z) = \xi \quad , \quad f_2(x, y, z) = \eta \quad , \quad f_3(x, y, z) = \zeta.$$

To each triplet ξ, η, ζ will correspond one surface in each family. Their intersection, taking account of the octant, will be the required point. The next step is to take ξ, η, ζ as new independent variables and transform Laplace's equation 1) to this set of variables. For polar coördinates this has been done already.

We saw, 221, 7), that 1) becomes

$$\Delta u = \frac{\partial}{\partial r}\left(r^2 \frac{\partial u}{\partial r}\right) + \frac{1}{\sin\theta}\frac{\partial}{\partial\theta}\left(\sin\theta\frac{\partial u}{\partial\theta}\right) + \frac{1}{\sin^2\theta}\frac{\partial^2 u}{\partial\phi^2} = 0. \quad (4$$

Having transformed 1) to the new coördinates ξ, η, ζ we try to find solutions of the very special form

$$u = F(\xi)\, G(\eta) H(\zeta), \quad (5$$

where F, G, H depend respectively on a *single* variable as indicated. With this end in view we set 5) in the transformed Laplace equation $\Delta u = 0$ and find that it is possible to break it into three ordinary linear differential equations of the second order, of the type

$$\frac{d^2F}{d\xi^2} + p\frac{dF}{d\xi} + qF = 0, \quad (6$$

and similar equations for η and ζ.

Let $F_1(\xi)$ be a particular solution of 6), while $G_1(\eta)$, $H_1(\zeta)$ may denote particular solutions of the equations analogous to 6). Then

$$u_1 = F_1 G_1 H_1 \quad (7$$

is a solution of $\Delta u = 0$.

As we shall see, it is possible to get an infinity of solutions

$$u_1 \;,\; u_2 \;,\; u_3 \;\cdots$$

of $\Delta u = 0$ of the type 7). Then

$$u = c_1 u_1 + c_2 u_2 + c_3 u_3 + \cdots \quad (8$$

is found to be a solution and it is possible to determine the constants c which enter so as to satisfy the given boundary values. All this will be made clear in the following.

236. Solution of $\Delta u = 0$ for the Sphere. Axial Symmetry. 1. Let us apply the method outlined in the last article to find a solution of $\Delta u = 0$ for the case that u must assume given values on a sphere S of radius R, which are the same on all meridians having the same axis. This axis we call the *axis of symmetry*, and we say the boundary conditions have *axial symmetry*.

Let us take this axis as the z-axis. Since the boundary values are symmetrical, we take u as independent of ϕ. Then $\frac{\partial u}{\partial \phi} = 0$ and Laplace's equation becomes

$$\frac{\partial}{\partial r}\left(r^2 \frac{\partial u}{\partial r}\right) + \frac{1}{\sin \theta} \frac{\partial}{\partial \theta}\left(\sin \theta \frac{\partial u}{\partial \theta}\right) = 0. \tag{1}$$

According to the general scheme we now set

$$u = F(r) G(\theta) \tag{2}$$

where F depends only on r, and G only on θ. We find 1) becomes

$$\frac{1}{F} \frac{d}{dr}\left(r^2 \frac{dF}{dr}\right) = -\frac{1}{G} \cdot \frac{1}{\sin \theta} \frac{d}{d\theta}\left(\sin \theta \frac{dG}{d\theta}\right). \tag{3}$$

Here the left side is a function of r alone, the right side is a function of θ alone. Suppose then that we determine F so that

$$\frac{1}{F} \frac{d}{dr}\left(r^2 \frac{dF}{dr}\right) - a = 0 \tag{4}$$

and G so that

$$\frac{1}{G} \frac{1}{\sin \theta} \frac{d}{d\theta}\left(\sin \theta \frac{dG}{d\theta}\right) + a = 0. \tag{5}$$

The corresponding values of F, G put in 2) will obviously satisfy 1).

2. Let us look at 4). This may be written

$$r^2 \frac{d^2 F}{dr^2} + 2r \frac{dF}{dr} - aF = 0, \tag{6}$$

which is a linear homogeneous differential equation and so belongs to the class of equations treated in the previous chapter.

Its only singular point in the finite part of the plane is $r = 0$. At this point the indicial equation is

$$s^2 + s - a = 0. \tag{7}$$

Let s be one of its roots. We then set

$$y = r^s(c_0 + c_1 r + c_2 r^2 + \cdots). \tag{8}$$

Here the c's are determined by 209, 5), viz.:

$$c_0 f_1(s) + c_1 f_0(s+1) = 0$$

$$c_0 f_2(s) + c_1 f_1(s+1) + c_2 f_0(s+2) = 0, \text{ etc.}$$

Now in the present case $f_1, f_2 \cdots$ are all zero. Thus $c_1, c_2 \cdots$ are all zero. Thus 8) reduces to

$$y = r^s.$$

Since we are seeking only particular solutions of 1), let us choose a in 7) so that its roots are integers. Then if n is one root, the other must be $-(n+1)$. Hence

$$a = n(n+1). \tag{9}$$

For this value of a, 6) admits the two integrals

$$r^n \text{ and } \frac{1}{r^{n+1}}, \quad n = 1, 2, \cdots \tag{10}$$

Both types of solution are useful, as we shall see.

3. Let us now turn to 5), which becomes on giving a its value in 9), and setting

$$x = \cos\theta,$$

$$(1-x^2)\frac{d^2G}{dx^2} - 2x\frac{dG}{dx} + n(n+1)G = 0. \tag{11}$$

But this is Legendre's equation for which

$$P_n(x), \quad Q_n(x)$$

form a fundamental system.

Thus by 2)

$$u_n = r^n P_n(\cos\theta)$$

$$u_n = \frac{1}{r^{n+1}} P_n(\cos\theta) \qquad n = 1, 2, \cdots \tag{12}$$

are solutions of Laplace's equation $\Delta u = 0$.

The boundary values being symmetrical with respect to the z-axis, the value of u is known on S when it is known on a meridian. Call this value v, it is a function of θ. If continuous and having only a finite number of oscillations in the interval $(0, \pi)$, it can be developed in a series

$$v = a_0 + a_1 P_1(\cos\theta) + a_2 P_2(\cos\theta) + \cdots \quad (13$$

where

$$a_n = \frac{2n+1}{2}\int_0^\pi v P_n(\cos\theta)\sin\theta d\theta \quad (14$$

as we saw in 227, 1.

According to the general scheme we now set

$$u = c_1 u_1 + c_2 u_2 + c_3 u_3 + \cdots$$

and try to determine the coefficients c so that u reduces to v when the point $P = x, y, z$ is on the sphere S.

There are two cases. *If P is within S*, we take

$$u = c_0 + c_1 \frac{r}{R} P_1(\cos\theta) + c_2\left(\frac{r}{R}\right)^2 P_2(\cos\theta) + \cdots \quad (15$$

If P is without S, we take

$$u = c_0 \frac{R}{r} + c_1\left(\frac{R}{r}\right)^2 P_1(\cos\theta) + c_2\left(\frac{R}{r}\right)^3 P_2(\cos\theta) + \cdots \quad (16$$

To determine the c's we take $r = R$. Then 15), 16) give, since $u = v$ now,

$$v = c_0 + c_1 P_1(\cos\theta) + c_2 P_2(\cos\theta) + \cdots \quad (17$$

Comparing this with 13), we see that the boundary condition is satisfied if we take

$$c_n = a_n$$

where a_n is given in 14).

Functions of Laplace

237. Spherical Harmonics. 1. We have just seen how to solve $\Delta u = 0$ when the values assigned to u on the surface of a sphere S are symmetrical with respect to an axis. We wish now to consider the case that the values assigned to u on S have no such symmetry. This general case was considered first by Laplace, and the functions he introduced to effect the solution have been named after him. We begin by proving a number of theorems.

2. *The equation*

$$\Delta V = \frac{\partial^2 V}{\partial x^2} + \frac{\partial^2 V}{\partial y^2} + \frac{\partial^2 V}{\partial z^2} = 0, \quad (1$$

admits as a solution the homogeneous polynomial

$$U = \Sigma a_{ijk} x^i y^j z^k \tag{2}$$

of degree $n = i + j + k$ *containing* $2n + 1$ *parameters.*

For 2) contains

$$\frac{(n+1)(n+2)}{2}$$

terms. Putting 2) in 1) we get a homogeneous integral rational function of degree $n - 2$ which contains

$$\frac{n(n-1)}{2}$$

terms. As ΔU must $= 0$ identically, the coefficients of all its terms must $= 0$. The number of independent parameters is therefore

$$\frac{(n+1)(n+2)}{2} - \frac{n(n-1)}{2} = 2n + 1.$$

We call such polynomials *harmonic polynomials of order n.*

3. We have at once the following theorem:

There exist $2n + 1$ *linearly independent harmonic polynomials of order n.*

As examples of such linearly independent harmonic polynomials, we add the following table:

$n = 0$	a constant.
$n = 1$	$x, y, z.$
$n = 2$	$x^2 - y^2,\ y^2 - z^2,\ xy,\ yz,\ xz.$
$n = 3$	$3x^2y - y^3,\ 3x^2z - z^3,\ 3yx^2 - y^3,\ 3y^2z - z^3,\ 3z^2x - x^3,\ 3z^2y - y^3,\ xyz.$

4. Let us pass to polar coördinates,

$$x = r \sin\theta \cos\phi \quad , \quad y = r \sin\theta \sin\phi \quad , \quad z = r \cos\theta. \tag{3}$$

Then the harmonic polynomial U of order n becomes

$$U = r^n Y_n, \tag{4}$$

where Y_n is a homogeneous polynomial of degree n in

$$\sin\theta \cos\phi \quad , \quad \sin\theta \sin\phi \quad , \quad \cos\theta. \tag{5}$$

We call Y_n *a spherical harmonic of order n*, and have the theorem:

There exist $2n+1$ *linearly independent spherical harmonics of order n.*

If we transform 1) to polar coördinates 3), we get, as already seen,

$$\frac{\partial^2 V}{\partial r^2}+\frac{1}{r^2}\frac{\partial^2 V}{\partial \theta^2}+\frac{1}{r^2\sin^2\theta}\frac{\partial^2 V}{\partial \phi^2}+\frac{2}{r}\frac{\partial V}{\partial r}+\frac{\cot\theta}{r^2}\frac{\partial V}{\partial \theta}=0. \tag{6}$$

If we put 4) in 6), we see that Y_n satisfies

$$\frac{\partial^2 Y}{\partial \theta^2}+\frac{1}{\sin^2\theta}\frac{\partial^2 Y}{\partial \phi^2}+\cot\theta\frac{\partial Y}{\partial \theta}+n(n+1)Y=0. \tag{7}$$

Let us also note in passing that

$$\frac{\partial U}{\partial r}=nr^{n-1}Y_n. \tag{8}$$

5. *If U, V are two harmonic polynomials or two spherical harmonics of orders* $m\neq n$, *then*

$$\int_S UV d\sigma = 0, \tag{9}$$

the integration extended over the sphere S.

Let us first suppose that U, V are polynomials. By Green's relation 233, 7)

$$\int_S\left(U\frac{\partial V}{\partial n}-V\frac{\partial U}{\partial n}\right)d\sigma=0.$$

Using 4) and 8) this gives

$$\int_S(nR^{n-1}Y_mY_n-mR^{m-1}Y_mY_n)d\sigma=0,$$

or

$$\int Y_mY_n d\sigma=0. \tag{10}$$

If we multiply this by R^{m+n}, it goes over into 9). If we suppose, on the other hand, that U, V are spherical harmonics, say $U=Y_m$, $V=Y_n$, they may be converted into harmonic polynomials by multiplying by r^m, r^n respectively. Then we are led to 10) again.

238. Integral Relations between Y_m and P_n.

Let
$$V = \rho^m Y_m \tag{1}$$
be a harmonic polynomial. Let $P(\rho', \phi', \theta')$ be a point inside the sphere S, and $Q(\rho, \phi, \theta)$ a point on its surface. Let

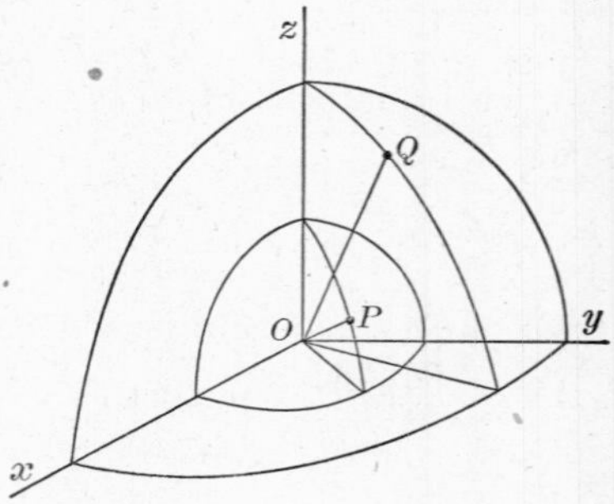

$$r = \text{Dist}\,(P, Q).$$

Then by 234, 4)
$$4\pi V_P = \int_S \left(V \frac{\partial}{\partial n} \frac{1}{r} - \frac{1}{r} \frac{\partial V}{\partial n} \right) d\sigma. \tag{2}$$

Let
$$\mu = \cos(\rho, \rho') = \cos\omega = \cos\theta\cos\theta' + \sin\theta\sin\theta'\cos(\phi - \phi'). \tag{3}$$

Then by 222, 4)
$$\frac{1}{r} = \frac{1}{\rho} \sum_0^\infty \left(\frac{\rho'}{\rho}\right)^s P_s(\mu). \tag{4}$$

Hence
$$\frac{\partial}{\partial n} \cdot \frac{1}{r} = -\frac{\partial}{\partial \rho} \cdot \frac{1}{r} = \sum_0^\infty \left(s+1\right) \frac{\rho'^s}{\rho^{s+2}} P_s(\mu).$$

Also
$$\frac{\partial V}{\partial n} = -m\rho^{m-1} Y_m,$$
$$d\sigma = \rho^2 \sin\theta d\theta d\phi.$$

These in 1), 2) give
$$4\pi V_P = 4\pi\rho'^m Y_m(\theta', \phi')$$
$$= \int_S \left\{ \rho^m Y_m \sum_{n=0}^\infty (n+1) \frac{\rho'^n}{\rho^{n+2}} P_n(\mu) \right.$$
$$\left. + m\rho^{m-2} Y_m \sum_{n=0}^\infty \left(\frac{\rho'}{\rho}\right)^n P_n(\mu) \right\} \rho^2 \sin\theta d\theta d\phi$$
$$= \sum_{n=0}^\infty \rho'^n \left\{ \frac{\rho^m}{\rho^n} \int_S (m+n+1) Y_m P_n(\mu) \sin\theta d\theta d\phi \right\}.$$

The right side is a power series in ρ'. Equating coefficients of like powers gives

$$\int_0^{2\pi} d\phi \int_0^\pi Y_m(\theta, \phi) P_n(\mu) \sin\theta d\theta = 0 \quad , \quad m \neq n \tag{5}$$

$$Y_m(\theta', \phi') = \frac{2m+1}{4\pi} \int_0^{2\pi} d\phi \int_0^\pi Y_m(\theta, \phi) P_n(\mu) \sin\theta d\theta \tag{6}$$

where μ is given by 3).

239. Development of $f(\theta, \phi)$ in Terms of Y_m. Suppose the values of a function f are given at all the points θ, ϕ of a sphere S. If f is continuous and has only a finite number of oscillations along any great circle, it can be proved that f admits a development of the form

$$f = Y_0(\theta, \phi) + Y_1(\theta, \phi) + Y_2(\theta, \phi) + \cdots \tag{1}$$

where the Y_m are spherical harmonics of order m. Moreover this series may be integrated termwise.

Admitting this, we can easily show how to determine the terms in 1). Let $P(\theta, \phi)$ be an arbitrary but fixed point on S; let $Q(\alpha, \beta)$ be a variable point on S; let

$$\mu = \cos\omega = \cos\alpha\cos\theta + \sin\alpha\sin\theta\cos(\beta - \phi). \tag{2}$$

We multiply 1) by $\quad P_n(\mu)\sin\alpha d\alpha d\beta$

and integrate over S. Then by 238, 5) every term on the right will drop out except that with the index n. Thus

$$\int_0^{2\pi} d\beta \int_0^{\pi} f \cdot P_n \cdot \sin\alpha d\alpha = \int_0^{2\pi} d\beta \int_0^{\pi} Y_n P_n \sin\alpha d\alpha$$

$$= \frac{4\pi}{2n+1} Y_n(\theta, \phi), \text{ by 238, 6)}. \tag{3}$$

Hence

$$f(\theta, \phi) = \sum \frac{2n+1}{4\pi} \int_0^{2\pi} d\beta \int_0^{\pi} f \cdot P_n(\cos\omega)\sin\alpha d\alpha, \tag{4}$$

where $\cos\omega$ is given by 2).

For later reference we note that 3) gives

$$Y_n(\theta, \phi) = \frac{2n+1}{4\pi} \int_0^{2\pi} d\beta \int_0^{\pi} f(\alpha, \beta) P_n(\cos\omega)\sin\alpha d\alpha. \tag{5}$$

240. Fundamental System of Harmonics of Order *n*. 1. We saw in 237, 2 that there are $2n+1$ linearly independent spherical harmonics of order n. Such a system we call *fundamental*. We show how to form them.

We saw in 237, 4 that any spherical harmonic Y_n of order n is homogeneous in

$$\sin\theta\cos\phi \quad , \quad \sin\theta\sin\phi \quad , \quad \cos\theta. \tag{1}$$

Thus $$Y_n = \Sigma A_{p,q}(\sin\theta\cos\phi)^p(\sin\theta\sin\phi)^q\cos^{n-p-q}\theta$$
$$= \Sigma A_{p,q}\cos^p\phi\sin^q\phi\sin^{p+q}\theta\cos^{n-p-q}\theta. \qquad (2$$

Now $\cos^p\phi\sin^q\phi$ can be expressed as a linear function of sines and cosines of the angles

$$(p+q)\phi \quad , \quad (p+q-2)\phi \quad , \quad \cdots$$

In fact
$$\cos^p\phi\sin^q\phi = \left(\frac{e^{i\phi}+e^{-i\phi}}{2}\right)^p\left(\frac{e^{i\phi}-e^{-i\phi}}{2i}\right)^q.$$

Expanding this gives

$$2^{p+q}i^q\cos^p\phi\sin^q\phi = e^{i(p+q)\phi} + (p-q)e^{i(p+q-2)\phi} + \cdots + (-1)^q e^{-i(p+q)\phi}.$$

Hence, when q is even,

$$\cos^p\phi\sin^q\phi = a_0\cos(p+q)\phi + a_1\cos(p+q-2)\phi + \cdots$$
$$= \sum_j a_j\cos(p+q-2j)\phi.$$

When q is odd, we get similarly

$$\cos^p\phi\sin^q\phi = \sum_j b_j\sin(p+q-2j)\phi.$$

If we set these in 2), we get

$$Y_n = \Sigma C_{m,j}\sin^m\theta\cos^{n-m}\theta\begin{cases}\cos(m-2j)\phi \\ \sin(m-2j)\phi\end{cases}. \qquad (3$$

Now
$$\sin^m\theta\cos^{n-m}\theta = \sin^{m-2j}\theta(1-\cos^2\theta)^j\cos^{n-m}\theta.$$

This in 3) gives, on setting $n-m=k$,

$$Y_n = \sum_{k=0}^{n}\{F_k\cos k\phi + G_k\sin k\phi\}, \qquad (4$$

where
$$F_k = L_k\sin^k\theta \quad , \quad G_k = M_k\sin^k\theta \qquad (5$$

and L_k, M_k are polynomials in $\cos\theta$.

Now we saw in 237, 7) that Y_n satisfies

$$\frac{\partial^2 Y}{\partial\theta^2} + \frac{1}{\sin^2\theta}\frac{\partial^2 Y}{\partial\phi^2} + \cot\theta\frac{\partial Y}{\partial\theta} + n(n+1)Y = 0. \qquad (6$$

Putting 3) in 6), we get

$$\sum_{n=0}^{\infty} \left\{ \sin^2\theta \frac{d^2F_k}{d\theta^2} + \sin\theta\cos\theta \frac{dF_k}{d\theta} + [n(n+1)\sin^2\theta - k^2]F_k \right\} \cos k\phi$$
$$+ \sum_{n=0}^{\infty} \{\text{similar expression in } G_k\} \sin k\phi = 0.$$

This relation holding for any ϕ requires that F_k, G_k are solutions of

$$\sin^2\theta \frac{d^2y}{d\theta^2} + \sin\theta\cos\theta \frac{dy}{d\theta} + \{n(n+1)\sin^2\theta - k^2\} y = 0.$$

If now we set

$$y = u \sin^k \theta,$$

we get by 5) the equation that L_k, M_k satisfy, viz.:

$$\sin^2\theta \frac{d^2u}{d\theta^2} + (2k+1)\sin\theta\cos\theta \frac{du}{d\theta}$$
$$+ \{n(n+1) - k(k+1)\} \sin^2\theta \cdot u = 0.$$

If we set

$$x = \cos\theta,$$

this becomes

$$(1-x^2)\frac{d^2u}{dx^2} - 2(k+1)x\frac{du}{dx} + \{n(n+1) - k(k+1)\} u = 0. \qquad (7$$

This is closely related to Legendre's equation

$$(1-x^2)\frac{d^2v}{dx^2} - 2x\frac{dv}{dx} + n(n+1)v = 0. \qquad (8$$

For if we differentiate 8) k times, we get 7).

Thus one solution of 7) is

$$u = \frac{d^{(k)}P_n(x)}{dx^k} = P_n^{(k)}(x). \qquad (9$$

Since now every solution of 7) is the kth derivative of a solution of 8), it follows that L_k, M_k are.

But L, M are polynomials in x. Now we have seen that 8) admits no solution besides $cP_n(x)$, which is a polynomial. Hence L_k, M_k are aside from constant factors the function given in 9). Thus by 5), F_k, G_k have the form

$$\sin^k\theta P_n^{(k)}(\cos\theta) = (1-x^2)^{\frac{k}{2}} P_n^{(k)}(x) = P_{n,k}(x). \qquad (10$$

They are called *associated Legendrian Functions.*

Thus we have:

$$P_{1,1} = \sqrt{1-x^2}.$$

$$P_{2,1} = 3x\sqrt{1-x^2} \quad , \quad P_{2,2} = 3(1-x^2),$$

$$P_{3,1} = \tfrac{3}{2}(5x^2-1)\sqrt{1-x^2} \quad , \quad P_{3,2} = 15x(1-x^2),$$

$$P_{3,3} = 15(1-x^2)\sqrt{1-x^2}.$$

2. Returning now to 4) we see that Y_n has the form

$$Y_n = \sum_{k=0}^{n} \{a_{n,k} P_{n,k}(\cos\theta)\sin k\phi + b_{n,k} P_{n,k}(\cos\theta)\cos k\phi\}. \qquad (11$$

Since $\sin k\phi = 0$ for $k = 0$, Y_n is the sum of $2n+1$ terms of the type

$$\sin k\phi P_{n,k}(\cos\theta) \quad , \quad \cos k\phi P_{n,k}(\cos\theta). \qquad (12$$

It is easy to show that the functions 12) are homogeneous in the quantities 1) of degree n. To do this we reverse the process used in 1. Thus each of the $2n+1$ terms 12) which enter 11) being homogeneous and also satisfying 6), is by definition a spherical harmonic.

Since any spherical harmonic Y_n of order n can be expressed linearly in terms of the $2n+1$ harmonics 12), these latter form a fundamental system of order n.

We have thus the theorem:

The $2n+1$ harmonics

$$P_n(\cos\theta) \quad , \qquad (13$$

$$\cos\phi P_{n,1}(\cos\theta) \quad , \quad \cos 2\phi P_{n,2}(\cos\theta) \quad , \quad \cdots \cos n\phi P_{n,n}(\cos\theta),$$

$$\sin\phi P_{n,1}(\cos\theta) \quad , \quad \sin 2\phi P_{n,2}(\cos\theta) \quad , \quad \cdots \sin n\phi P_{n,n}(\cos\theta),$$

form a fundamental system of order n.

241. Integral Relations between $P_{n,k}$, $P_{n,m}$. We now prove the important relations

$$\int_{-1}^{1} P_{mk}(x) P_{nk}(x)\,dx = 0 \qquad m \neq n \qquad (1$$

$$\int_{-1}^{1} P_{nk}^2(x)\,dx = \frac{(n+k)!}{(n-k)!}\cdot\frac{2}{2n+1}. \qquad (2$$

To this end we consider

$$J = \int_{-1}^{1} P_{mk} P_{nk} dx$$

$$= \int_{-1}^{1} (1 - x^2)^k \frac{d^k P_m}{dx^k} \cdot \frac{d^k P_n}{dx^k} dx.$$

To fix the ideas suppose $n \geq m$. We integrate by parts, using the formula

$$\int_{-1}^{1} u dv = [uv]_{-1}^{1} - \int_{-1}^{1} v du.$$

We take

$$u = (1 - x^2)^k P_m^{(k)} \quad , \quad v = P_n^{(k-1)}.$$

Then

$$[uv]_{-1}^{1} = 0$$

and hence

$$J = -\int_{-1}^{1} P_n^{(k-1)} \frac{d}{dx} (1 - x^2)^k P_m^{(k)} dx.$$

Repeating this process k times gives

$$J = (-1)^k \int_{-1}^{1} P_n \frac{d^k}{dx^k} (1 - x^2)^k P_m^{(k)} dx$$

$$= (-1)^k \int_{-1}^{1} P_n F_m dx, \qquad (3$$

where F_m is a polynomial of degree m.
Thus when $n > m$, $J = 0$ by 225, 2), which gives 1). *Suppose* $n = m$. We have from 222, 5)

$$P_n(x) = \frac{1 \cdot 3 \cdots 2n - 1}{1 \cdot 2 \cdots n} x^n - \cdots = Ax^n + \cdots$$

Hence

$$P_n^{(k)}(x) = An(n-1) \cdots (n-k+1) x^{n-k} + \cdots$$

Also

$$(1 - x^2)^k = (-1)^k x^{2k} + \cdots$$

Hence

$$G_{n+k} = P_n^{(k)}(x)(1 - x^2)^k = (-1)^k An(n-1) \cdots (n-k+1) x^{n+k} + \cdots$$

$$F_n = \frac{d^k}{dx^k} G_{n+k} = (-1) \, An(n-1) \cdots (n-k+1)(n+k)(n+k-1) \cdots (n+1) x^n + \cdots$$

$$= (-1)^k \frac{(n+k)!}{(n-k)!} Ax^n + \cdots$$

Now F_n is a polynomial of degree n; it can therefore by 227 be expressed in terms of $P_0, P_1 \cdots P_n$. We get

$$F_n = (-1)^k \frac{(n+k)!}{(n-k)!} P_n + A_1 P_{n-1} + A_2 P_{n-2} + \cdots$$

Thus 3) becomes

$$J = \frac{(n+k)!}{(n-k)!} \int_{-1}^{1} P_n^2 dx,$$

since each of the other terms $= 0$ by 225, 1). If we now use 225, 5), we get 2) at once.

242. Development of $f(\theta, \phi)$ in Terms of P_{nk}. In 239 we saw that when $f(\theta, \phi)$ is a one-valued continuous function of θ, ϕ having but a finite number of oscillations along any great circle, it could be developed in a series of spherical harmonics

$$f(\theta, \phi) = Y_0 + Y_1 + Y_2 + \cdots \tag{1}$$

But in 240, 10) we saw that each Y_n is a linear combination of certain fundamental harmonics. Thus

$$f(\theta, \phi) = \sum_{n=0}^{\infty} \sum_{k=0}^{n} \{A_{nk} \cos k\phi + B_{nk} \sin k\phi\} P_{nk}(x), \tag{2}$$

where

$$x = \cos \theta.$$

To determine the A's and B's we note that

$$\int_0^{2\pi} \cos m\phi \sin n\phi d\phi = 0, \qquad \text{always}$$

$$\int_0^{2\pi} \cos m\phi \cos n\phi d\phi = 0, \qquad m \neq n,$$

$$\int_0^{2\pi} \cos^2 n\phi d\phi = \pi\,, \int_0^{2\pi} \cos n\phi d\phi = 0\;, \int_0^{2\pi} \sin n\phi d\phi = 0\,, n > 0.$$

Let us multiply 1) by $d\phi$ and integrate, we get

$$\int_0^{2\pi} f d\phi = 2\,\pi \sum_{n=0}^{\infty} A_{n0} P_n(x).$$

This we multiply by $P_m dx$ and integrate, getting

$$\int_{-1}^{1} dx \int_0^{2\pi} f P_m d\phi = 2\pi \sum_n A_{n0} \int_{-1}^{1} P_m P_n dx$$
$$= \frac{4\pi}{2n+1} A_{n0}$$

since all the terms on the right $= 0$ except when $m = n$. Hence

$$A_{n0} = \frac{2n+1}{4\pi} \int_0^{2\pi} d\beta \int_0^{\pi} f P_m \sin\alpha d\alpha \quad , \quad n = 0, 1, 2 \cdots \quad (3$$

Let us now multiply 1) by $\cos k\phi d\phi$, $k > 0$, and integrate, we get

$$\int_0^{2\pi} f \cos k\phi d\phi = \pi \sum_{n=0}^{\infty} A_{nk} P_{nk}.$$

We now multiply this by $P_{nk} dx$ and integrate. We get, using 241, 1), 2),

$$\int_{-1}^{1} dx \int_0^{2\pi} f \cos k\phi P_{nk} d\phi = \frac{2\pi}{2n+1} \cdot \frac{(n+k)!}{(n-k)!} A_{nk}.$$

Thus

$$A_{nk} = \frac{2n+1}{2\pi} \frac{(n-k)!}{(n+k)!} \int_0^{2\pi} d\beta \int_0^{\pi} f \cos k\beta P_{nk}(\cos\alpha) \sin\alpha d\alpha. \quad (4$$

Similarly we get

$$B_{nk} = \frac{2n+1}{2\pi} \frac{(n-k)!}{(n+k)!} \int_0^{2\pi} d\beta \int_0^{\pi} f \sin k\beta P_{nk}(\cos\alpha) \sin\alpha d\alpha. \quad (5$$

There are no coefficients B_{n0} since the factor $\sin k\phi = 0$ for $k = 0$.

Putting in these values of the A's and B's in Y_n we get

$$Y_n = \int_0^{\pi} d\alpha \int_0^{2\pi} \sum_{k=0}^{n} \eta_k P_{nk}(\cos\theta) \frac{2n+1}{2\pi} \frac{(n-k)!}{(n+k)!} f(\alpha, \beta)$$
$$\{\cos k\phi \cos k\beta + \sin k\phi \sin k\beta\} P_{nk}(\cos\alpha) \sin\alpha d\beta,$$

where

$$\eta_k = \tfrac{1}{2} \quad \text{when} \quad k = 0$$
$$= 1 \quad \text{when} \quad k > 0.$$

Thus we have

$$Y_n = \int_0^{\pi} d\alpha \int_0^{2\pi} \sum_{k=0}^{n} \frac{(n-k)!}{(n+k)!} \frac{2n+1}{2\pi} \eta_k f(\alpha, \beta) P_{nk}(\cos\alpha) P_{nk}(\cos\theta)$$
$$\cos k(\phi - \beta) \sin\alpha d\beta. \quad (6$$

243. Expression of $P_n(\cos\omega)$ in Terms of P_n, P_{nk}. Let

$$P(\alpha, \beta) \quad , \quad Q(\theta, \phi)$$

be two points on a sphere whose center is 0. If ω is the angle between OP, OQ we have

$$\cos\omega = \cos\alpha\cos\theta + \sin\alpha\sin\theta\cos(\beta-\phi).$$

Now in 239, 5) we saw

$$Y_n(\theta, \phi) = \frac{2n+1}{4\pi}\int_0^\pi \sin\alpha d\alpha \int_0^{2\pi} f(\alpha, \beta) P_n(\cos\omega) d\beta.$$

If we compare this with 242, 6) we get

$$P_n(\cos\omega) = P_n(\cos\alpha)P_n(\cos\theta)$$
$$+ 2\sum_{k=1}^{n}\frac{(n-k)!}{(n+k)!}P_{nk}(\cos\alpha)P_{nk}(\cos\theta)\cos k(\beta-\phi). \quad (1$$

244. Solution of Dirichlet's Problem for the Sphere. 1. This problem is to find a solution V of Laplace's equation $\Delta V = 0$ which takes on assigned values $f(\theta, \phi)$ on a sphere S of radius R.

If the point P is in S, we set

$$V = Y_0 + Y_1\frac{r}{R} + Y_2\left(\frac{r}{R}\right)^2 + \cdots \qquad r \leq R. \quad (1$$

Each term is a solution of $\Delta V = 0$ and hence 1) is. For $r = R$ it reduces to

$$V_s = Y_0 + Y_1 + Y_2 + \cdots \quad (2$$

Thus V_s must $= f(\theta, \phi)$ if 1) is to satisfy the boundary conditions. Thus the coefficients Y_0, $Y_1 \cdots$ in 1) are the terms of the development of $f(\theta, \phi)$ given in 242, 6).

If the point P is outside S, we set

$$V = Y_0 + Y_1\frac{R}{r} + Y_2\left(\frac{R}{r}\right)^2 + \cdots \qquad r > R \quad (3$$

and reason as before.

2. By the above we have solved the problems:

1° Determine the temperature at any point in a sphere S which is in a stationary state, the temperature being given on the surface of S.

2° Determine the potential for any point outside a sphere S, knowing its value on the surface of S.

3° Determine the motion of an incompressible fluid having a velocity potential V, knowing V on the surface of S.

CHAPTER XV

BESSEL AND LAMÉ FUNCTIONS

Bessel Functions

245. The Integrals of Bessel's Equation. 1. This equation was studied in Chapter XIII; it is

$$x^2\frac{d^2y}{dx^2}+x\frac{dy}{dx}+(x^2-m^2)y=0. \qquad (1$$

When $2m$ is not an integer, we saw in 211 that 1) has two linearly independent integrals

$$J_m(x)=\sum_{n=0}^{\infty}\frac{(-1)^n}{\Pi(n)\Pi(m+n)}\left(\frac{x}{2}\right)^{m+2n}, \qquad (2$$

and

$$J_{-m}(x)=\sum_{n=0}^{\infty}\frac{(-1)^n}{\Pi(n)\Pi(n-m)}\left(\frac{x}{2}\right)^{2n-m}. \qquad (3$$

The first converges for every x, the second for every $x\neq 0$.

In the applications m is usually an integer. For $m=0, 1$, we have

$$J_0(x)=1-\frac{x^2}{2\cdot 2}+\frac{x^4}{2^2\cdot 4^2}-\frac{x^6}{2^2\cdot 4^2\cdot 6^2}+\cdots \qquad (4$$

$$J_1(x)=\frac{x}{2}-\frac{x^3}{2^2\cdot 4}+\frac{x^5}{2^2\cdot 4^2\cdot 6}-\frac{x^7}{2^2\cdot 4^2\cdot 6^2\cdot 8}+\cdots \qquad (5$$

The function defined by the series 2) is called a *Bessel's function of order m.*

2. When m is an integer, we have

$$J_m(x)=(-1)^mJ_{-m}(x). \qquad (6$$

For k being an integer or 0,

$$\frac{1}{\Pi(-k)}=0.$$

Hence the first m terms in 3) vanish. Let us therefore change the index of summation in 3), setting $\nu = n - m$. Then 3) becomes

$$J_{-m}(x) = \sum_{\nu=0}^{\infty} \frac{(-1)^{m+\nu}}{\Pi(m+\nu)\Pi(\nu)} \left(\frac{x}{2}\right)^{2\nu+m}$$

$$= (-1)^m J_m(x).$$

3. Since 2) is a power series, we may differentiate it termwise, which gives

$$J'_m(x) = \sum_{n=0}^{\infty} \frac{(-1)^n (m+2n)}{2^{m+2n}\Pi(n)\Pi(m+n)} \cdot x^{m+2n-1}. \qquad (7$$

4. When x is complex,

$$x = r(\cos\theta + i\sin\theta), \qquad (8$$

we may write

$$J_m(x) = \left(\frac{x}{2}\right)^m j_m(x).$$

Now

$$\left(\frac{x}{2}\right)^{2n} = \left(\frac{r}{2}\right)^{2n} (\cos 2n\theta + i \sin 2n\theta).$$

Thus

$$j_m(x) = \sum_{n=0}^{\infty} \frac{(-1)^n \cos 2n\theta}{\Pi(n)\Pi(m+n)} \left(\frac{r}{2}\right)^{2n} + i \sum_{n=0}^{\infty} \frac{(-1)^n \sin 2n\theta}{\Pi(n)\Pi(m+n)} \left(\frac{r}{2}\right)^{2n}. \qquad (9$$

When m is real, this enables us to write $J_m(x)$ in the form

$$J_m(x) = U_m + iV_m,$$

where U, V are real.

5. From 2), 3) we have

$$J_{\frac{1}{2}}(x) = \sqrt{\frac{2}{\pi x}} \sin x, \qquad (10$$

$$J_{-\frac{1}{2}}(x) = \sqrt{\frac{2}{\pi x}} \cos x. \qquad (11$$

246. Relations between the J_m and the J'_n. 1. The following recursion relation exists between three consecutive Bessel's Functions.

$$J_{n+1}(x) = \frac{2n}{x} J_n(x) - J_{n-1}(x). \qquad (1$$

For

$$J_{n-1} = \frac{x^{n-1}}{2^{n-1}\Pi(n-1)} + \sum_{s=1}^{\infty}(-1)^s \frac{x^{2s+n-1}}{2^{n+2s-1}\Pi(s)\Pi(n-1+s)}, \tag{2}$$

$$J_{n+1} = -\sum_{s=1}^{\infty}(-1)^s \frac{x^{2s+n-1}}{2^{n+2s-1}\Pi(s-1)\Pi(n+s)}. \tag{3}$$

Hence

$$J_{n-1} + J_{n+1} = \frac{x^{n-1}}{2^{n-1}\Pi(n-1)}$$

$$+ \sum_{s=1}^{\infty}(-1)^s \frac{x^{2s+n-1}}{2^{n+2s-1}}\left\{\frac{1}{\Pi(s)\Pi(n-1+s)} - \frac{1}{\Pi(s-1)\Pi(n+s)}\right\}$$

$$= \frac{x^{n-1}}{2^{n-1}\Pi(n-1)} + n\sum_{s=1}^{\infty}(-1)^s \frac{x^{2s+n-1}}{2^{n+2s-1}\Pi(s)\Pi(n+s)}$$

$$= \frac{n}{x}\sum_{s=0}^{\infty}(-1)^s \frac{x^{2s+n}}{2^{n+2s-1}\Pi(s)\Pi(n+s)}$$

$$= \frac{2n}{x}J_n(x).$$

2. We show next that

$$2J_n'(x) = J_{n-1}(x) - J_{n+1}(x). \tag{4}$$

For subtracting 3) from 2) gives

$$J_{n-1} - J_{n+1} = \frac{x^{n-1}}{2^{n-1}\Pi(n-1)} + \sum_{s=1}^{\infty}(-1)^s \frac{x^{2s+n-1}}{2^{n+2s-1}} \cdot \frac{n+2s}{\Pi(s)\Pi(n+s)}$$

$$= \sum_{0}^{\infty}(-1)^s \frac{(n+2s)x^{2s+n-1}}{2^{n+2s-1}\Pi(s)\Pi(n+s)}$$

$$= 2J_n'(x).$$

3. From 4) we get, on replacing J_{n+1} by its value given by 1),

$$J_n'(x) = -\frac{n}{x}J_n(x) + J_{n-1}(x). \tag{5}$$

From 1) we also get

$$J_n'(x) = \frac{n}{x}J_n(x) - J_{n+1}(x). \tag{6}$$

4. From 245, 7) we have

$$J_0'(x) = -J_1(x). \qquad (7$$

5. We have also

$$\frac{d}{dx}(x^n J_n) = nx^{n-1}J_n + x^n J_n',$$

or using 5),

$$\frac{d}{dx}(x^n J_n) = x^n J_{n-1}(x). \qquad (8$$

6. By means of 1) and 245, 10), 11) we have the theorem:

When n is a positive or negative odd integer, $J_n(x)$ can be expressed in terms of the elementary functions.

Thus in particular the recursion formula 1) gives

$$J_{\frac{3}{2}}(x) = \sqrt{\frac{2}{\pi x}}\left\{\frac{\sin x}{x} - \cos x\right\},$$

$$J_{\frac{5}{2}}(x) = \sqrt{\frac{2}{\pi x}}\left\{\sin x\left(\frac{3}{x^2} - 1\right) - \frac{3}{x}\cos x\right\},$$

$$J_{-\frac{3}{2}}(x) = -\sqrt{\frac{2}{\pi x}}\left\{\frac{\cos x}{x} + \sin x\right\},$$

$$J_{-\frac{5}{2}}(x) = \sqrt{\frac{2}{\pi x}}\left\{\cos x\left(\frac{3}{x^2} - 1\right) + \frac{3}{x}\sin x\right\}.$$

247. Integral Relations. 1. As a first such relation let us prove

$$\int_0^x xJ_0(x)dx = xJ_1(x). \qquad (1$$

For $n = 0$ Bessel's equation becomes

$$x\frac{d^2y}{dx^2} + \frac{dy}{dx} + xy = 0.$$

This is satisfied by J_0; it therefore gives

$$\frac{d}{dx}\left(xJ_0'\right) + xJ_0 = 0.$$

Integrating this gives

$$xJ_0'(x) + \int_0^x xJ_0 dx = 0.$$

Using 246, 7), this goes over into 1).

2. To get other relations let us set in Bessel's equation

$$x^2\frac{d^2y}{dx^2} + x\frac{dy}{dx} + (x^2 - m^2)y = 0. \qquad (2$$

$$u = \sqrt{x} \cdot y(\alpha x).$$

It becomes

$$\frac{d^2u}{dx^2} + \left(\alpha^2 - \frac{4\,m^2 - 1}{4\,x^2}\right)u = 0. \qquad (3$$

Thus

$$u = \sqrt{x}J_n(\alpha x) \quad , \quad v = \sqrt{x}J_n(\beta x) \qquad (4$$

are solutions of equations of the form

$$\frac{d^2u}{dx^2} + gu = 0,$$

$$\frac{d^2v}{dx^2} + hv = 0. \qquad (5$$

From 5) we have

$$v\frac{d^2u}{dx^2} - u\frac{d^2v}{dx^2} = (h - g)uv. \qquad (6$$

On the other hand the left side of 6)

$$= \frac{d}{dx}\left(v\frac{du}{dx} - u\frac{dv}{dx}\right).$$

Thus 6) gives

$$v\frac{du}{dx} - u\frac{dv}{dx} = \int (h - g)uvdx + C. \qquad (7$$

Substituting 4) in 7) gives

$$(\beta^2 - \alpha^2)\int_0^x xJ_n(\alpha x)J_n(\beta x)dx$$
$$= x\{\alpha J_n(\beta x)J_n'(\alpha x) - \beta J_n(\alpha x)J_n'(\beta x)\}. \qquad (8$$

If we use 246, 6), we get from 8)

$$(\beta^2 - \alpha^2)\int_0^x xJ_n(\alpha x)J_n(\beta x)dx$$
$$= x\{\beta J_n(\alpha x)J_{n+1}(\beta x) - \alpha J_n(\beta x)J_{n+1}(\alpha x)\}. \qquad (9$$

Let us differentiate 8) with respect to β and then set $\beta = \alpha$. We get

$$2\alpha \int_0^x x J_n^2(\alpha x) dx$$
$$= x\{\alpha x J_n'^2(\alpha x) - J_n(\alpha x) J_n'(\alpha x) - \alpha x J_n(\alpha x) J_n''(\alpha x)\}. \quad (10$$

Expressing $J_n''(\alpha x)$ by means of 1) this gives

$$\int_0^x x J_n^2(\alpha x) dx = \frac{x^2}{2} \left\{ J_n'^2(\alpha x) + \left(1 - \frac{n^2}{\alpha^2 x^2}\right) J_n^2(\alpha x) \right\}. \quad (11$$

Using 246, 6, this gives

$$\int_0^x x J_n^2(\alpha x) dx = \frac{x^2}{2} \{J_n^2(\alpha x) + J_{n+1}^2(\alpha x)\} - \frac{nx}{\alpha} J_n(\alpha x) J_{n+1}(\alpha x). \quad (12$$

Similarly if we differentiate 9) with respect to β and then set $\beta = \alpha$ we get

$$2\alpha \int_0^x x J_n^2(\alpha x) dx = x J_n(\alpha x) J_{n+1}(\alpha x)$$
$$+ \alpha x^2 \{J_n(\alpha x) J_{n+1}'(\alpha x) - J_n'(\alpha x) J_{n+1}(\alpha x)\}. \quad (13$$

248. The Roots of $J_m(x)$, m Real. 1. In many of the applications it is important to know that $J_m(x)$ has an infinite number of real roots. Let us consider the general question of the nature of the roots of $J_m(x)$.

The roots of $J_m(x) = 0$ are all real when m is real. For suppose $J_m = 0$ for $x = a + ib$, $b \neq 0$. Then the series

$$J_m(x) = \left(\frac{x}{2}\right)^m \sum_{n=0}^{\infty} \frac{(-1)^n}{\Pi(n)\Pi(m+n)} \cdot \left(\frac{x}{2}\right)^{2n} \quad (1$$

would give

$$A + iB = 0,$$

whence

$$A = 0 \quad , \quad B = 0.$$

This shows that then the conjugate number $x' = a - ib$ must be a root. Let us therefore suppose that

$$\alpha = a + ib \quad , \quad \beta = a - ib$$

are two roots of J_m. Then

$$\alpha^2 - \beta^2 = 4iab.$$
$$J_m(\alpha x) = P + iQ \quad , \quad J_m(\beta x) = P - iQ.$$

These in 247, 9 give

$$-4\,iab\int_0^1 x(P^2+Q^2)dx=0 \tag{2}$$

since

$$J_m(\alpha)=0 \quad , \quad J_m(\beta)=0.$$

But the integrand in 2) is positive. Hence the left side cannot vanish unless a or $b=0$.

Suppose $a=0$, so that $\alpha=ib$, $b>0$ is purely imaginary. Then 1) becomes

$$J_m(ib)=\left(\frac{ib}{2}\right)^m\sum_{n=0}^{\infty}\frac{1}{\Pi(n)\Pi(m+n)}\left(\frac{b}{2}\right)^{2n}$$

$$=\left(\frac{ib}{2}\right)^m j_m.$$

Here j_m is a series all of whose terms are positive. It cannot vanish. As $b>0$, J_m does not vanish. Thus J_m has only real roots.

2. The development 1) shows that:

$$J_m(0)=0 \quad , \quad \textit{when } m>0.$$

It also shows that:

If $x=\alpha>0$ is a root, so is $x=-\alpha$ a root.

3. *No two consecutive functions $J_m(x)$, $J_{m+1}(x)$ have a root in common, aside from $x=0$.*

For if α were such a root, 247, 9) gives

$$\int_0^1 xJ_n(\alpha x)J_n(\beta x)\,dx=0.$$

In this relation let $\beta \doteq \alpha$; we get

$$\int_0^1 xJ_n^2(\alpha x)\,dx=0.$$

This is impossible as the integrand is >0 for $x>0$.

4. *The roots of $J_m(x)$ are all simple, aside from $x=0$.*

For consider

$$f(x)=x^mJ_m(x).$$

This does not vanish for $x\neq 0$, unless $J_m=0$.

But from 246, 8),
$$f'(x) = x^m J_{m-1}(x).$$
As J_m, J_{m-1} have no root $\neq 0$ in common, $f'(x)$ does not vanish for any non-zero root of J_m.

5. *$J_m(x)$ has an infinity of roots.*

For we have seen in 247, 2 that
$$u = \sqrt{x} J_m(x)$$
satisfies
$$\frac{d^2u}{dx^2} + gu = 0,$$
where
$$g = 1 - \frac{4m^2 - 1}{4x^2}.$$

The index m being fixed, let us take $\xi > 0$ so that
$$0 < g < 1 \text{ for } x \geq \xi.$$
The equation
$$\frac{d^2v}{dx^2} + v = 0$$
admits
$$v = \sin x$$
as a solution. Then by 247, 2
$$\left[v\frac{du}{dx} - u\frac{dv}{dx} \right]_\alpha^\beta = \int_\alpha^\beta (1-g)\, uvdx.$$
If we take
$$\alpha = 2n\pi \quad , \quad \beta = (2n+1)\pi,$$
we get
$$u(\beta) + u(\alpha) = -\int_\alpha^\beta (1-g)\, uvdx. \tag{3}$$
Suppose now u is positive in the interval $\mathfrak{A} = (\alpha, \beta)$. Then the left side is positive and the right side is negative, since $1 - g > 0$ in any case, and v is positive except at the end points of $\mathfrak{A}$. Thus the two sides of 3) have opposite signs, which is a contradiction.

Similarly, if u is negative in $\mathfrak{A}$, we are led to a contradiction. Thus u must vanish at least once in $\mathfrak{A}$. Hence in any interval (a, b) of length π, $J_m(x)$ vanishes at least once, provided $a \geq \xi$.

249. Bessel Functions as Loop Integrals. We have seen that Bessel's equation

$$x^2\frac{d^2y}{dx^2} + x\frac{dy}{dx} + (x^2 - m^2)y = 0 \tag{1}$$

admits J_m as a solution. As J_m has the form

$$J_m = x^m(a_0 + a_1x + \cdots),$$

let us set

$$y = x^m u$$

in 1). We get

$$x\frac{d^2u}{dx^2} + (2m+1)\frac{du}{dx} + xu = 0. \tag{2}$$

This is a special case of a class of equations

$$(a_0 + b_0x)\frac{d^nu}{dx^n} + (a_1 + b_1x)\frac{d^{n-1}u}{dx^{n-1}} + \cdots + (a_n + b_nx)u = 0, \tag{3}$$

whose integral may be expressed in the form

$$u = \int_L e^{xz}w(z)dz. \tag{4}$$

Let us suppose $n = 2$ in 3) and let us change the independent variable x by setting

$$x' = a_0 + b_0x.$$

If we make this substitution in 3) and then drop the prime from x', we get an equation of the form

$$x\frac{d^2u}{dx^2} + (a + bx)\frac{du}{dx} + (c + dx)u = 0. \tag{5}$$

Comparing 5) with Bessel's equation 2), we see that

$$a = 2m + 1 \quad , \quad b = 0 \quad , \quad c = 0 \quad , \quad d = 1. \tag{6}$$

If we divide through by x, the equation 5) becomes

$$\frac{d^2u}{dx^2} + \left(\frac{a}{x} + b\right)\frac{du}{dx} + \left(\frac{c}{x} + d\right)u = 0. \tag{7}$$

Here the coefficients have poles of order 1 at $x = 0$. Hence the integrals are regular at this point.

Let us now consider *the point* $x = \infty$. If we set

$$x = \frac{1}{z},$$

we get

$$\frac{d^2u}{dz^2} + \left(\frac{2-a}{z} - \frac{b}{z^2}\right)\frac{du}{dz} + \left(\frac{c}{z^3} + \frac{d}{z^4}\right)u = 0. \tag{8}$$

As the coefficient of $\frac{du}{dz}$ can have a pole of order at most 1, and the coefficient of u, a pole of order at most 2 when $x = \infty$ is regular, we see this point is an irregular point of 5).

Bessel's equation 2) becomes, on setting 6) in 8),

$$\frac{d^2u}{dz^2} - \frac{2m-1}{z}\frac{du}{dz} + \frac{1}{z^4}u = 0. \tag{9}$$

2. Suppose we try to satisfy 5) by a power series of the form

$$u = x^r \left\{ h_0 + \frac{h_1}{x} + \frac{h_2}{x^2} + \cdots \right\} \tag{10}$$

which shall be valid about $x = \infty$. We shall find it possible to determine the coefficients h_0, $h_1 \cdots$ so that 5) is *formally* satisfied, but we shall find that 10) is divergent.

To illustrate this let us consider the equation 2) for $m=0$ which is satisfied by $J_0(x)$.

If we set

$$y = e^{ix}u,$$

it becomes

$$\frac{d^2u}{dx^2} + \left(\frac{1}{x} + 2i\right)\frac{du}{dx} + \frac{i}{x}u = 0. \tag{11}$$

Comparing this with 7), we see that

$$a = 1 \quad , \quad b = 2i \quad , \quad c = i \quad , \quad d = 0.$$

If we put 10) in 11), we find

$$r = -\tfrac{1}{2}$$

and

$$2inh_n = \frac{(2n-1)^2}{4}h_{n-1}.$$

The ratio of two successive terms in the adjoint of 10) is

$$|x|\left|\frac{h_n}{h_{n-1}}\right| = \frac{1}{8}\frac{n}{|x|}\left(2-\frac{1}{n}\right)^2 \doteq \infty.$$

The series 10) diverges therefore for every x.

3. Returning now to 5), let us try to determine w and L in 4) so that the resulting integral satisfies 5). Putting 4) in 5), we get

$$\int e^{xz}Fdz + \int_L dG = 0, \tag{12}$$

where

$$F = (az+c)w - \frac{d}{dz}\cdot w(z^2+bz+d), \tag{13}$$

$$G = e^{xz}(z^2+bz+d)w. \tag{14}$$

Thus if we determine w so that $F=0$ and choose L so that G takes on the same value at the beginning and end of L, the integral 4) will be a solution of 5).

Let us write 13)

$$\frac{d}{dz}(pw) = qw.$$

Then

$$\frac{\frac{d}{dz}(pw)}{pw} = \frac{q}{p}.$$

Hence

$$\log pw = \int \frac{q}{p}dz,$$

or

$$w = \frac{1}{p}e^{\int\frac{q}{p}dz}.$$

Let us now decompose $\frac{q}{p}$ into partial fractions. We have

$$\frac{q}{p} = \frac{az+c}{z^2+bz+d} = \frac{\lambda}{z-\alpha} + \frac{\mu}{z-\beta}$$

where α, β are the roots of $p=0$, which we will *suppose unequal.* Thus we may take

$$w = \frac{1}{p}(z-\alpha)^\lambda(z-\beta)^\mu = (z-\alpha)^{\lambda-1}(z-\beta)^{\mu-1}. \tag{15}$$

This in 14) gives

$$G = e^{xz}(z-\alpha)^\lambda(z-\beta)^\mu. \tag{16}$$

As a path of integration L we may take a double loop about α, β as in 220.

Hence, remembering that

$$e^{xz} = 1 + \frac{xz}{1!} + \frac{x^2z^2}{2!} + \cdots$$

we get from 4)

$$u_{\alpha\beta} = \int_L e^{xz}(z-\alpha)^{\lambda-1}(z-\beta)^{\mu-1}dz \tag{17}$$

$$= \sum_{n=0}^{\infty} \frac{x^n}{n!}\int_L z^n(z-\alpha)^{\lambda-1}(z-\beta)^{\mu-1}dz.$$

4. For Bessel's equation 5), 6)

$$p = z^2 + 1 = 0 \text{ gives } \alpha = i \quad , \quad \beta = -i,$$

$$q = (2m+1)z.$$

Hence

$$\frac{q}{p} = \frac{\frac{1}{2}(2m+1)}{z-i} + \frac{\frac{1}{2}(2m+1)}{z+i}$$

which gives

$$\lambda = \mu = m + \tfrac{1}{2}.$$

Thus 4), 17) become

$$u_{\alpha\beta} = \int_L e^{xz}(z^2+1)^{m-\frac{1}{2}}dz \tag{18}$$

$$= \sum_{n=0}^{\infty} \frac{x^n}{n!}\int_L z^n(z^2+1)^{m-\frac{1}{2}}dz. \tag{19}$$

Now

$$L = lkl^{-1}k^{-1},$$

where l, k are loops about $z = i$, $z = -i$.

When z describes a small circle about $z = i$, the end value of

$$Z_n = z^n(z^2+1)^{m-\frac{1}{2}} = z^n(z-i)^{m-\frac{1}{2}}(z+i)^{m-\frac{1}{2}}$$

is

$$e^{(m-\frac{1}{2})2\pi i}Z_n = -e^{2\pi i m}Z_n = -\eta Z_n.$$

Thus

$$\int_L = \int_l + \eta\int_k + \eta^2\int_{l^{-1}} + \eta\int_{k^{-1}}. \tag{20}$$

But obviously

$$\int_l + \eta\int_{l^{-1}} = 0 \quad , \quad \int_k + \eta\int_{k^{-1}} = 0$$

since the integrand has the same values, while the direction of integration is reversed in l and l^{-1}, etc.

Thus 20) can be written

$$\int_L Z_n dz = (1-\eta)\{\int_l Z_n dz - \int_k Z_n dz\}. \qquad (21$$

Now when n is odd,

$$\int_l Z_n dz = \int_k Z_n dz;$$

when n is even,

$$\int_l Z_n dz = -\int_k Z_n dz.$$

Thus

$$\int_L Z_n dz = 0 \quad , \quad n \text{ odd},$$

$$= 2(1-\eta)\int_l Z_n dz \quad , \quad n \text{ even}.$$

To compute the integrals we set

$$z = iy^{\frac{1}{2}}.$$

Then the loop l will go over into a loop j about $y=1$, and

$$2\int_l Z_{2n} dz = (-1)^n i \int_j y^{n-\frac{1}{2}}(1-y)^{m-\frac{1}{2}} dy.$$

Now

$$\int_j = \int_0^1 - \eta\int_1^0 = (1+\eta)\int_0^1 y^{n-\frac{1}{2}}(1-y)^{m-\frac{1}{2}} dy$$

$$= (1+\eta)B(n+\tfrac{1}{2},\ m+\tfrac{1}{2}).$$

Thus finally 19) gives

$$u_{\alpha\beta} = (1+e^{2\pi i m})^2 i\,\Gamma(\tfrac{1}{2})\Gamma(m+\tfrac{1}{2})\sum_{n=0}^{\infty}\frac{(-1)^n}{\Gamma(n+1)\Gamma(m+n+1)}\left(\frac{x}{2}\right)^{2n} \qquad (22$$

$$= i(1+e^{2\pi i m})^2\Gamma(\tfrac{1}{2})\Gamma(m+\tfrac{1}{2})\cdot\frac{2^m}{x^m}J_m(x) \qquad (23$$

by 245, 2).

Thus $x^m u_{\alpha\beta}$ aside from a constant factor is nothing but $J_m(x)$.

250. Other Loop Integrals for $x>0$. 1. A second path of integration L for which the function

$$G = e^{xz}(z-\alpha)^{\lambda}(z-\beta)^{\mu}, \qquad (1$$

considered in 249, 16) takes on the same value at the beginning and end is indicated in Fig. 1. We will denote them by A and B;

both are parallel to the real axis and pass about the points α, β respectively.

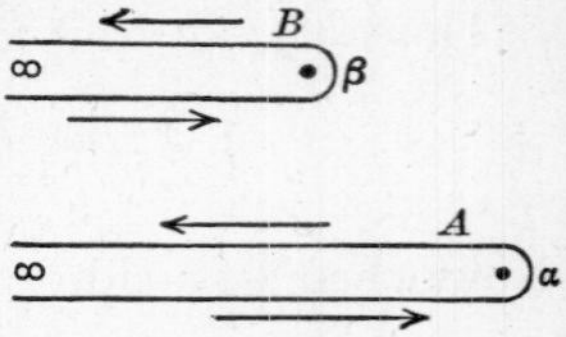

FIG. 1.

On A for example the real and imaginary parts of

$$z = u + iv$$

are such that $|v| <$ some η while u comes from $-\infty$, moves up to α, and recedes again to $-\infty$.

If we set

$$z - \alpha = re^{i\theta} \quad , \quad z - \beta = se^{i\phi},$$

we have

$$G = e^{xu}r^{\lambda}s^{\mu}e^{i(xv+\lambda\theta+\mu\phi)}.$$

Thus

$$|G| = e^{xu}r^{\lambda}s^{\mu} \doteq 0 \text{ as } u \doteq -\infty,$$

and G takes on the same value at the beginning and end of A or B.

2. Let us now consider the integral

$$u_\alpha = \int_A e^{xz}wdz = \int_A e^{xz}(z-\alpha)^{\lambda-1}(z-\beta)^{\mu-1}dz \quad (2$$

where w is given by 249, 15). Similar results hold for the other integral u_β for the loop B.

Setting

$$z - \alpha = y, \quad \alpha - \beta = a,$$

2) becomes

$$u_\alpha = \int_{\mathfrak{A}} e^{x(y+\alpha)}y^{\lambda-1}(y+a)^{\mu-1}dy \quad (3$$

where $\mathfrak{A}$ is the new path.

As y approaches indefinitely near 0 for a part of $\mathfrak{A}$, call it $\mathfrak{A}_1$, we have

$$\left|\frac{y}{a}\right| < 1. \quad (4$$

Then

$$(y+a)^{\mu-1} = a^{\mu-1}\left(1+\frac{y}{a}\right)^{\mu-1}$$

$$= a^{\mu-1}\left\{1 + \frac{\mu-1}{1}\frac{y}{a} + \frac{\mu-1\cdot\mu-2}{1\cdot 2}\frac{y^2}{a^2} + \cdots\right\}$$

$$= \sum_{n=0}^{\infty} c_n y^n, \quad (5$$

where

$$c_n = \frac{\mu-1\cdot\mu-2\cdots\mu-n}{1\cdot 2\cdots n}a^{\mu-n-1}. \quad (6$$

For the other part of $\mathfrak{A}$, call it $\mathfrak{A}_2$, the relation 4) does not hold, and we write 5)

$$(y+a)^{\mu-1} = c_0 + c_1 y + \cdots + c_s y^s + R_s. \qquad (7$$

This in 3) gives

$$u_a = e^{ax} \sum_{n=0}^{s} c_n \int_{\mathfrak{A}} e^{xy} y^{\lambda+n-1} dy + e^{ax} \int_{\mathfrak{A}} e^{xy} y^{\lambda-1} R_s dy \qquad (8$$

$$= e^{ax}(U+V).$$

We set now

$$xy = -t$$

in the U integral. Then $\mathfrak{A}$ goes over into a loop $\mathfrak{L}$ as in Fig. 2.

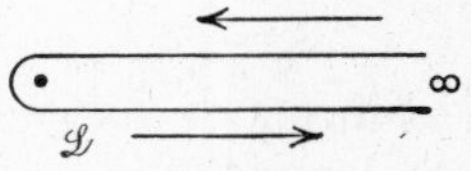

FIG. 2.

We get now

$$U = (-1)^{\lambda} x^{-\lambda} \sum_{n=0}^{s} (-1)^n c_n x^{-n} \int_{\mathfrak{L}} e^{-t} t^{\lambda+n-1} dt. \qquad (9$$

But, as we have seen in 149, 2),

$$\int_{\mathfrak{L}} e^{-t} t^{\lambda+n-1} dt = (e^{2\pi i\lambda} - 1)\Gamma(\lambda+n) \qquad (10$$

where by 144, 8)

$$\Gamma(\lambda+n) = \lambda(\lambda+1)\cdots(\lambda+n-1)\Gamma(\lambda). \qquad (11$$

This in 10) gives

$$U = (-1)^{\lambda} x^{-\lambda}(e^{2\pi i\lambda} - 1) \sum_{n=0}^{s} (-1)^n \Gamma(\lambda+n) c_n x^{-n} \qquad (12$$

$$= x^{-\lambda}\mathfrak{P}$$

where

$$\mathfrak{P} = (-1)^{\lambda}(e^{2\pi i\lambda} - 1)\{c_0\Gamma(\lambda) - c_1\Gamma(\lambda+1)\cdot\frac{1}{x}$$

$$+ c_2\Gamma(\lambda+2)\cdot\frac{1}{x^2} - \cdots\}. \qquad (13$$

251. Relation between $u_{\alpha\beta}$ and u_α, u_β. We have now found three integrals of our differential equation

$$x\frac{d^2u}{dx^2} + (a+bx)\frac{du}{dx} + (c+dx)u = 0, \qquad (1$$

viz.:

$$u_{\alpha\beta} = \int_L e^{xz}(z-\alpha)^{\lambda-1}(z-\beta)^{\mu-1} dz \qquad (2$$

of 249, 17), and

$$u_\alpha = \int_A e^{xz}(z-\alpha)^{\lambda-1}(z-\beta)^{\mu-1}dz, \tag{3}$$

$$u_\beta = \int_B e^{xz}(z-\alpha)^{\lambda-1}(z-\beta)^{\mu-1}dz \tag{4}$$

of 250, 2).

Since 1) is of the second order, a linear relation exists between them. Here the path of integral L in 2) may be taken

$$L = ABA^{-1}B^{-1}.$$

Since $(z-\alpha)^\lambda$ is multiplied by the factor $e^{2\pi i\lambda}$ after describing the loop A, and a similar result holds for B, we have

$$u_{\alpha\beta} = \int_L = \int_A + e^{2\pi i\lambda}\int_B + e^{2\pi i(\lambda+\mu)}\int_{A^{-1}} + e^{2\pi i\mu}\int_{B^{-1}} \cdot \tag{5}$$

Since

$$\int_{AA^{-1}} = 0,$$

we have

$$\int_A + e^{2\pi i\lambda}\int_{A^{-1}} = 0,$$

or

$$\int_{A^{-1}} = - e^{-2\pi i\lambda}\int_A \cdot$$

Similarly

$$\int_{B^{-1}} = - e^{-2\pi i\mu}\int_B \cdot$$

Thus 5) gives

$$u_{\alpha\beta} = (1-e^{2\pi i\mu})\int_A - (1-e^{2\pi i\lambda})\int_B$$

$$= (1-e^{2\pi i\mu})u_\alpha - (1-e^{2\pi i\lambda})u_\beta, \tag{6}$$

and this is the relation sought.

252. Asymptotic Solutions. 1. We show now that the solution u_α admits the asymptotic development

$$u_\alpha e^{-\alpha x}x^\lambda \sim \mathfrak{P} \quad , \quad x \text{ real and } \doteq +\infty. \tag{1}$$

Referring to 250, 8), 12) we have

$$u_\alpha e^{-\alpha x}x^\lambda = \mathfrak{P} + x^\lambda V. \tag{2}$$

Thus 1) holds if
$$\lim_{x=+\infty} x^{s+\lambda} V = 0 \tag{3}$$

where by 250, 8)
$$V = \int_{\mathfrak{A}} e^{xy} y^{\lambda-1} R_s dy. \tag{4}$$

The path of integration $\mathfrak{A}$ we take as follows. About $y = 0$ we describe a circle $\mathfrak{c}$ of radius γ. Let $\mathfrak{a} = (-\infty, -\gamma)$ as in Fig. 1. Then

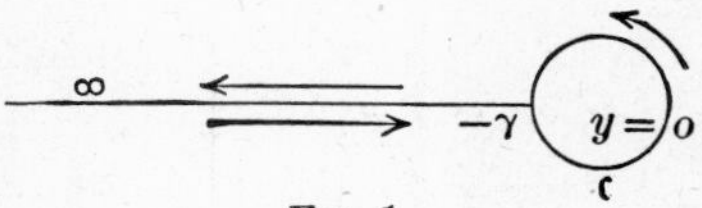

FIG. 1.

$$\mathfrak{A} = \mathfrak{a} \cdot \mathfrak{c} \cdot \mathfrak{a}^{-1}.$$

Hence
$$V = \int_{\mathfrak{a}} + \int_{\mathfrak{c}} + \int_{\mathfrak{a}^{-1}}, \tag{5}$$

and
$$x^{s+\lambda} V = x^{s+\lambda}\int_{\mathfrak{a}} + x^{s+\lambda}\int_{\mathfrak{c}} + x^{s+\lambda}\int_{\mathfrak{a}^{-1}} = A + B + C. \tag{6}$$

We show that A, B, C all $\doteq 0$ as $x \doteq +\infty$.

2. *We consider first A.* From 250, 7) we have
$$R_s = (y+a)^{\mu-1} - (c_0 + c_1 y + \cdots + c_s y^s).$$

Hence
$$A = x^{s+\lambda}\int_{\mathfrak{a}} (y+a)^{\mu-1} e^{xy} y^{\lambda-1} dy - \sum_{k=0}^{s} c_k x^{n+\lambda} \int_{\mathfrak{a}} e^{xy} y^{\lambda+k-1} dy$$
$$= A_0 - \sum_{k=0}^{s} c_k A_k.$$

We show now that $A_0, A_1, \cdots A_s \doteq 0$ as $x \doteq +\infty$, beginning with A_0.

For complex $z = re^{i\theta}$ we have
$$\log z = \log r + i\theta + 2\,m\pi i.$$

Thus for large values of y on the path of integration,
$$|\log y| = \log|y| \quad , \quad \text{nearly}.$$

But from the calculus,
$$\lim_{x=+\infty} \frac{\log x}{x} = 0.$$

Thus for $|y| >$ some Y,
$$|\log y| < |y| \quad , \quad |\log(a+y)| < |y|.$$

Hence for some $\eta > 0$,

$$| \log y^{\lambda-1}(y+a)^{\mu-1} | < \eta | y |.$$

Thus
$$| y^{\lambda-1}(y+a)^{\mu-1} | < e^{-\eta y} \quad , \quad y < \text{some } y_0 < 0.$$

Hence
$$| A_0 | < x^{s+\lambda} \int_{-\infty}^{-\gamma} e^{y(x-\eta)} dy \doteq 0 \quad , \quad \text{as } x \doteq +\infty.$$

We now show that $A_k \doteq 0$. Changing the variable by setting

$$xy = -t,$$

we have
$$A_k = (-1)^{\lambda+k} x^{s-k} \int_{\gamma x}^{+\infty} e^{-t} t^{\lambda+k-1} dt$$
$$\doteq 0 \quad , \quad \text{as } x \doteq +\infty.$$

3. Having shown that $A \doteq 0$, *it is easy to see that* $C \doteq 0$ *also.* For C differs from A only in two respects. The path of integration is reversed and the integrand has another value at $y = -\gamma$, due to the fact that y has described the circle c. After this circuit $y^{\lambda-1}$ is multiplied by the factor $e^{2\pi i\lambda}$, while $(y+a)^{\mu-1}$ is multiplied by $e^{2\pi i\mu}$. Thus the C integral behaves essentially as the A integral, and we see at once that

$$\lim_{x=+\infty} C = 0.$$

4. *We show now that* $B \doteq 0$. We have

$$B = x^{s+\lambda} \int_{\mathfrak{c}} e^{xy} y^{\lambda-1} R_s dy$$

where R_s is the remainder of the series

$$(y+a)^{\mu-1} = c_0 + c_1 y + c_2 y^2 + \cdots$$

beginning with the exponent $s+1$.

If we set $xy = -t$, we get

$$B = (-1)^{\lambda} x^s \int_{\mathfrak{C}} e^{-t} t^{\lambda-1} R_s dt \qquad (7$$

where $\mathfrak{C}$ is the circle corresponding to c in Fig. 1.

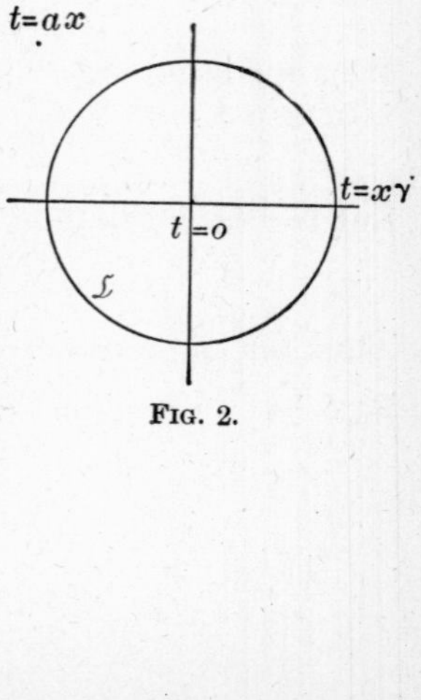

FIG. 2.

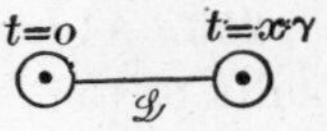

FIG. 3.

As the singular point of R_s is $t = ax$ which lies outside of $\mathfrak{C}$, we can replace $\mathfrak{C}$ by the loop $\mathfrak{L}$ in Fig. 3. This loop is made up of a segment l and two small circles about the points $t = 0$, $t = x\gamma$. Thus B will be the sum of three integrals

$$B = B_0 + B_l + B_{x\gamma} \tag{8}$$

corresponding to these three parts of $\mathfrak{L}$.

Since the integrand in 7) is one-valued about $t = x\gamma$, *the integral* $B_{x\gamma} = 0$.

The integral $B_0 = 0$ *also*. For

$$R_s = c_{s+1}y^{s+1} + c_{s+2}y^{s+2} + \cdots$$

$$= (-1)^{s+1}\frac{t^{s+1}}{x^{s+1}}\left\{c_{s+1} - c_{s+2}\frac{t}{x} + \cdots\right\}. \tag{9}$$

Thus $R_s \doteq 0$ as the radius of the circle about $t = 0$ converges to 0.

On the other hand, the reasoning often employed shows that

$$B_l = (-1)^\lambda \cdot x^s(e^{2\pi i\lambda} - 1)\int_l e^{-t}t^{\lambda-1}R_s dt.$$

To estimate the numerical value of R_s we use 112, 3). Here

$$a = 0, \qquad |t| = \rho \leq |x\gamma| \quad , \quad r = |ax|.$$

Thus G denoting a sufficiently large constant,

$$|R_s| \leq \frac{G}{x^{s+1}}\left|\frac{\gamma}{a}\right|^{s+1}\frac{1}{1 - \dfrac{\gamma}{|\alpha|}} = \frac{H}{x^{s+1}}.$$

Hence

$$|B_l| = \frac{1}{x}|e^{2\pi i\lambda} - 1| \cdot H\int_l e^{-t}t^{\lambda-1}dt, \tag{10}$$

taking the real positive value of the integrand.

Let now $x \doteq +\infty$. Then the integral in 10) converges to $\Gamma(\lambda)$, and hence $B_l \doteq 0$. Thus

$$\lim_{x=+\infty} B = 0.$$

We have now shown that each term of 8) is 0 or $\doteq 0$. Hence $B \doteq 0$ as asserted. Thus the proof of 1) is finished.

253. Asymptotic Development of $J_m(x)$. 1. Let us apply the results of the last articles to the equation 249, 2) which results from Bessel's equation 249, 1) on setting

$$y = x^m u.$$

As in 249, 4

$$\alpha = i \quad , \quad \beta = -i \quad , \quad \lambda = \mu = m + \tfrac{1}{2} \quad , \quad a = \alpha - \beta = 2i.$$

The coefficients c are given by

$$(y+a)^{\mu-1} = c_0 + c_1 y + c_2 y^2 + \cdots$$

$$= (y + 2i)^{m-\frac{1}{2}} = (2i)^p \left\{1 + \frac{y}{2i}\right\}^p \quad , \quad p = m - \frac{1}{2}$$

$$= (2i)^p \left\{1 + \binom{p}{1}\frac{y}{2i} + \binom{p}{2}\frac{y^2}{(2i)^2} + \cdots\right\}.$$

Thus

$$c_r = \frac{(2m-1)(2m-3)\cdots(2m-2r+1)}{1 \cdot 2 \cdots r} 2^{m-2r-\frac{1}{2}} i^{m-r-\frac{1}{2}}.$$

Substituting in 250, 13) and 252, 1), we get

$$u_i e^{-ix} x^{m+\frac{1}{2}} \sim 2^{m-\frac{1}{2}} e^{-\frac{\pi i}{2}\left(m-\frac{1}{2}\right)} (1 + e^{2\pi i m}) \Gamma(m + \tfrac{1}{2}) D, \quad (1$$

where

$$D = 1 + \sum_{s=1}^{\infty} \frac{(-1)^s}{2^s i^s} \cdot \frac{4m^2-1}{4} \cdot \frac{4m^2-9}{4} \cdots \frac{4m^2-(2s-1)^2}{4} \cdot \frac{1}{s^2}. \quad (2$$

In a similar manner we have for the integral $u_\beta = u_{-i}$

$$u_{-i} e^{ix} x^{m+\frac{1}{2}} \sim 2^{m-\frac{1}{2}} e^{\frac{\pi i}{2}\left(m-\frac{1}{2}\right)} (1 + e^{2\pi i m}) \Gamma(m + \tfrac{1}{2}) E, \quad (3$$

where

$$E = 1 + \sum_{s=1}^{\infty} \frac{1}{i^s \cdot s!} \cdot \frac{4m^2-1}{4} \cdot \frac{4m^2-9}{4} \cdots \frac{4m^2-(2s-1)^2}{4} \cdot \frac{1}{x^s}. \quad (4$$

2. Another integral of Bessel's equation is $x^m u_{\alpha\beta}$ as given in 249, 23). Now in 251 we have expressed $u_{\alpha\beta}$ in terms of u_α, u_β. Thus the asymptotic expressions 1), 3) just found enable us to express $J_m(x)$ asymptotically. In fact 251, 6) gives here

$$u_{\alpha\beta} = (1 + e^{2\pi i m})(u_i - u_{-i}).$$

Hence if we take only the first terms in D, E of 2), 4), we have

$$J_m(x) \sim \frac{1}{2^{\frac{1}{2}} x^{\frac{1}{2}} i \Gamma(\frac{1}{2})} \left\{ e^{i\left(x - \frac{\pi}{2}\left(m - \frac{1}{2}\right)\right)} - e^{-i\left(x - \frac{\pi}{2}\left(m - \frac{1}{2}\right)\right)} \right\}$$

or, since $\Gamma \frac{1}{2} = \sqrt{\pi}$ by 144, 15),

$$J_m(x) \sim \sqrt{\frac{2}{\pi x}} \cos \left\{ x - \frac{\pi}{2}\left(m + \frac{1}{2}\right) \right\}. \qquad (5$$

254. An Expansion in a Series of Bessel Functions. Let us show that

$$e^{x \frac{u - u^{-1}}{2}} = \sum_{-\infty}^{\infty} u^n J_n(x) \qquad (1$$

for any x and for $u \neq 0$. For

$$e^{x \frac{u - u^{-1}}{2}} = e^{\frac{1}{2} xu} e^{-\frac{1}{2} \frac{x}{u}}$$

$$= \left\{ 1 + \frac{xu}{2} + \frac{x^2 u^2}{2^2 \cdot 2!} + \cdots \right\} \left\{ 1 - \frac{x}{2u} + \frac{x^2}{2^2 2!\, u^2} - \cdots \right\}.$$

Now for any x, and for any $u \neq 0$, the series in the braces are absolutely convergent. Their product may therefore be written in the form

$$1 - \frac{x^2}{2^2} + \left(\frac{x}{2}\right)^4 \frac{1}{2!\,2!} - \cdots$$

$$+ u \left\{ \frac{x}{2} - \frac{1}{2!}\left(\frac{x}{2}\right)^3 + \frac{1}{3!\,2!}\left(\frac{x}{2}\right)^5 - \cdots \right\}$$

$$- u^{-1} \left\{ \frac{x}{2} - \frac{1}{2!}\left(\frac{x}{2}\right)^3 + \frac{1}{3!\,2!}\left(\frac{x}{2}\right)^5 - \cdots \right\}$$

$$+ \cdot \cdot \cdot \cdot \cdot \cdot \cdot \cdot \cdot \cdot \cdot \cdot$$

$$+ u^n \{ \cdot \cdot \cdot \cdot \cdot \cdot \cdot \cdot \cdot \cdot \}$$

$$+ (-1)^n u^{-n} \{ \cdot \cdot \cdot \cdot \cdot \cdot \cdot \cdot \}$$

$$+ \cdot \cdot \cdot \cdot \cdot \cdot \cdot \cdot \cdot \cdot \cdot \cdot$$

$$= J_0(x) + u J_1(x) + u^2 J_2(x) + \cdots$$

$$- \frac{J_1(x)}{u} + \frac{J_2(x)}{u^2} - \cdots$$

255. $J_n(x)$ expressed as an Integral. 1. Let us show that

$$J_n(x) = \frac{x^n}{2^n\sqrt{\pi}}\frac{1}{\Gamma(n+\frac{1}{2})}\int_0^\pi \cos(x\cos\phi)\sin^{2n}\phi d\phi \qquad (1$$

where n is a positive number.

For

$$\cos u = \sum_0^\infty (-1)^s \frac{u^{2s}}{(2s)!}.$$

Hence

$$\cos(x\cos\phi) = \sum_0^\infty \frac{(-1)^s}{(2s)!}x^{2s}\cos^{2s}\phi.$$

Thus

$$\cos(x\cos\phi)\sin^{2n}\phi = \sum_0^\infty \frac{(-1)^s}{(2s)!}x^{2s}\cos^{2s}\phi\sin^{2n}\phi.$$

As this series converges steadily in the interval $(0, \pi)$ for any value of x, we may integrate termwise, getting

$$\int_0^\pi \cos(x\cos\phi)\sin^{2n}\phi d\phi = \sum_0^\infty \frac{(-1)^s}{(2s)!}x^{2s}\int_0^\pi \cos^{2s}\phi\sin^{2n}\phi d\phi$$

$$= \sum_0^\infty \frac{(-1)^s}{(2s)!}x^{2s}B\left(\frac{2s+1}{2}, \frac{2n+1}{2}\right) \quad , \quad \text{by 141, 7)}$$

$$= \sum_0^\infty \frac{(-1)^s}{(2s)!}x^{2s}\Gamma\frac{\left(\frac{2s+1}{2}\right)\Gamma\left(\frac{2n+1}{2}\right)}{\Gamma(s+n+1)} \quad , \quad \text{by 142, 3)}.$$

But

$$\Gamma\left(\frac{2s+1}{2}\right) = \frac{1\cdot 3\cdot 5 \cdots (2s-1)}{2^s}\sqrt{\pi} \quad , \quad \text{by 144, 16)}.$$

Thus the last series above

$$= \sqrt{\pi}\Gamma\left(\frac{2n+1}{2}\right)\sum_0^\infty \frac{(-1)^s}{(2s)!}\frac{1\cdot 3\cdot 5 \cdots (2s-1)}{2^s\Pi(n+s)}x^{2s}.$$

Thus

$$\frac{x^n}{2^n\sqrt{\pi}\Gamma(n+\frac{1}{2})}\int_0^\pi \cos(x\cos\phi)\sin^{2n}\phi d\phi$$

$$= \sum_{s=0}^\infty \frac{(-1)^s x^{2s+n}}{2^{2s+n}s!\,\Pi(n+s)} = J_n(x).$$

2. Another integral expression is

$$J_m(x) = \frac{1}{\pi}\int_0^{\pi} \cos(m\phi - x \sin \phi) d\phi, \tag{2}$$

where m is a *positive integer*.

For from 254, 1) setting $u = e^{i\phi}$,

$$\begin{aligned} e^{xi\sin\phi} &= \sum_{-\infty}^{\infty} e^{mi\phi} J_m(x) \\ &= J_0(x) + 2\sum_1^{\infty} \cos 2\, m\phi\, J_{2m}(x) \\ &\quad + 2\, i \sum_1^{\infty} \sin(2\, m - 1)\, \phi\, J_{2m-1}(x). \end{aligned}$$

Since
$$e^{ix\sin\phi} = \cos(x \sin \phi) + i \sin(x \sin \phi),$$

we have
$$\cos(x \sin \phi) = J_0(x) + 2\sum_1^{\infty} \cos 2\, m\phi\, J_{2m}(x), \tag{3}$$

$$\sin(x \sin \phi) = 2\sum_1^{\infty} \sin(2\, m - 1)\phi\, J_{2m-1}(x). \tag{4}$$

Let us multiply 3) by $\cos 2\, m\phi$ and integrate, then

$$\int_0^{\pi} \cos 2\, m\phi \cos(x \sin \phi) = \pi J_{2m}(x), \tag{5}$$

since all the other terms $= 0$, by virtue of the relation

$$\begin{aligned} \int_0^{\pi} \cos mx \cos nx dx &= 0 \quad , \quad m \neq n \\ &= \frac{\pi}{2} \quad , \quad m = n. \end{aligned}$$

If we multiply 3) by $\cos(2\, m + 1)\phi$ and integrate, we get

$$\int_0^{\pi} \cos(2\, m + 1)\phi \cos(x \sin \phi) d\phi = 0. \tag{6}$$

Similarly we get

$$\int_0^{\pi} \sin(x \sin \phi) \sin 2\, m\phi d\phi = 0, \tag{7}$$

$$\int_0^{\pi} \sin(x \sin \phi) \sin(2\, m + 1)\phi d\phi = \pi J_{2m+1}(x). \tag{8}$$

Adding 5) and 7), or 6) and 8), we get 2).

256. Bessel's Solution of Kepler's Equation. This equation is

$$\frac{2\,\pi t}{T} = u - e \sin u = \tau, \tag{1}$$

where T is the period of the planet, e the excentricity of its orbit, u the eccentric anomaly, and t the time.

As u is a periodic function of t or of τ, it can thus be developed in Fourier's series,

$$u = \sum_{n=1}^{\infty} a_n \sin n\tau, \tag{2}$$

where

$$a_n = \frac{2}{\pi}\int_0^\pi u \sin n\tau d\tau, \text{ or by partial integration}$$

$$= \frac{2}{\pi}\left\{ \frac{(-1)^{n+1}}{n}\pi + \frac{1}{n}\int_0^\pi \cos n\tau du \right\}.$$

This in 2) gives

$$u = 2\sum_1^\infty (-1)^{n+1}\frac{\sin n\tau}{n} + \frac{2}{\pi}\sum_1^\infty \frac{\sin n\tau}{n}\int_0^\pi \cos n(u - e \sin u)du.$$

But the first series on the right $= \tau$, while the integral in the second series is $\pi J_n(ne)$. Thus 3) gives

$$u = \tau + 2\sum_{n=1}^\infty J_n(ne)\frac{\sin n\tau}{\tau},$$

which is Bessel's solution.

257. Development of $f(x)$ in Terms of J_n. It can be shown that if $f(x)$ is continuous and oscillates but a finite number of times in $\mathfrak{A} = (0, a)$ then $f(x)$ admits a development of the form

$$f(x) = c_1 J_n(\alpha_1 x) + c_2 J_n(\alpha_2 x) + \cdots \tag{1}$$

where

$$\alpha_1 < \alpha_2 < \cdots \tag{2}$$

are the positive roots of $J_n(ax)$.

To determine the coefficients c we make use of the relations

$$\int_0^a x J_n(\alpha_r x) J_n(\alpha_s x) dx = 0 \qquad r \neq s, \tag{3}$$

$$\int_0^a x J_n^2(\alpha_r x) dx = \frac{a^2}{2} J^2{}_{n+1}(\alpha_r a) \tag{4}$$

obtained from 247, 9) and 12).

Let us therefore multiply 1) by $xJ_n(\alpha_m x)$. Granting that the resulting series can be integrated termwise, we have

$$\int_0^a xf(x)J_n(\alpha_m x)dx = c_m\int_0^a xJ_m^2(\alpha_m x)dx \tag{5}$$

since all the terms on the right $= 0$ except the one written down, by 3).

Thus 4), 5) give

$$c_m = \frac{2}{a^2 J_{n+1}^2(\alpha_m a)}\int_0^a xf(x)J_n(\alpha_m x)dx. \tag{6}$$

Hence 1) gives

$$f(x) = \frac{2}{a^2}\sum_{m=1}^{\infty}\frac{J_n(\alpha_m x)}{J_{n+1}^2(\alpha_m a)}\int_0^a xf(x)J_n(\alpha_m x)dx. \tag{7}$$

258. Development of $f(r, \phi)$ in Terms of the J_n. Let $f(r, \phi)$ be a one-valued continuous function in a circle $\mathfrak{A}$ about the origin, of radius a. Then, f admitting the period 2π, we have, for a given r, by Fourier's theorem,

$$f(r, \phi) = a_0 + a_1\cos\phi + a_2\cos 2\phi + \cdots \\ + b_1\sin\phi + b_2\sin 2\phi + \cdots \tag{1}$$

where

$$a_n = \frac{1}{2\pi}\int_0^{2\pi} f(r, \phi)d\phi, \tag{2}$$

$$a_n = \frac{1}{\pi}\int_0^{2\pi} f(r, \phi)\cos n\phi d\phi, \tag{3}$$

$$b_n = \frac{1}{\pi}\int_0^{2\pi} f(r, \phi)\sin n\phi d\phi. \tag{4}$$

But these coefficients a, b are functions of r and may be developed by 257.

Let therefore α_{nk}, $k=1, 2, 3 \cdots$ be the positive roots of

$$J_n(ar) = 0. \tag{5}$$

Then by 257,

$$a_0 = A_{01}J_0(\alpha_{01}r) + A_{02}J_0(\alpha_{02}r) + \cdots \tag{6}$$

$$a_n = A_{n1}J_n(\alpha_{n1}r) + A_{n2}J_n(\alpha_{n2}r) + \cdots \tag{7}$$

$$b_n = B_{n1}J_n(\alpha_{n1}r) + B_{n2}J_n(\alpha_{n2}r) + \cdots \tag{8}$$

where

$$A_{0k} = \frac{1}{a^2\pi J_1^2(\alpha_{0k}a)} \int_0^{2\pi} d\phi \int_0^1 rf(r, \phi) J_0(\alpha_{0k}r) dr, \quad (9$$

$$A_{mk} = \frac{2}{a^2\pi J_{m+1}^2(\alpha_{mk}a)} \int_0^{2\pi} \cos m\phi d\phi \int_0^a rf(r, \phi) J_m(\alpha_{mk}r) dr, \quad (10$$

$$B_{mk} = \frac{2}{a^2\pi J_{m+1}^2(\alpha_{mk}a)} \int_0^{2\pi} \sin m\phi d\phi \int_0 rf(r, \phi) J_m(\alpha_{mk}r) dr. \quad (11$$

259. Solution of $\Delta u = 0$ for the Cylinder. 1. Let us apply the method outlined in 235 to find a solution u of Laplace's equation which takes on assigned values on the surface of a given cylinder C.

Here the triply orthogonal surfaces are a family of cylinders, meridian planes, and planes perpendicular to the axis of C, which we will take to be the z-axis. Our new coördinates are therefore r, ϕ, z, where

$$x = r \cos \phi \quad , \quad y = r \sin \phi.$$

Transforming to the new coördinates, we find that Laplace's equation $\Delta u = 0$ becomes

$$\frac{\partial^2 u}{\partial r^2} + \frac{1}{r}\frac{\partial u}{\partial r} + \frac{1}{r^2}\frac{\partial^2 u}{\partial \phi^2} + \frac{\partial^2 u}{\partial z^2} = 0. \quad (1$$

According to the general scheme, we now set

$$u = R\Phi Z, \quad (2$$

where R is a function of r alone, Φ of ϕ, and Z of z. If we set 2) in 1), we find it gives rise to three equations:

$$\frac{d^2R}{dr^2} + \frac{1}{r}\frac{dR}{dr} + \left(\alpha^2 - \frac{n^2}{r^2}\right)R = 0, \quad (3$$

$$\frac{d^2\Phi}{d\phi^2} + n^2\Phi = 0, \quad (4$$

$$\frac{d^2Z}{dz^2} - \alpha^2 Z = 0. \quad (5$$

The general solution of 4) is

$$\Phi = A \cos n\phi + B \sin n\phi. \tag{6}$$

As Φ must admit the period 2π, we take n a positive integer.

The general solution of 5) is

$$Z = C \cosh \alpha z + D \sinh \alpha z. \tag{7}$$

The equation 3) is a form of Bessel's equation. To reduce it to the standard form we have only to set

$$r = \frac{x}{\alpha}\cdot \tag{8}$$

Thus a special solution of 3) is

$$R = J_n(\alpha r). \tag{9}$$

2. *Problem 1.* It is now time to specify the boundary conditions on the cylinder C, which we will suppose is of length l and radius a.

Let us suppose that on the lower base and on the convex surface of C, u has the value u_0, a constant. On the upper base $z = l$ let

$$u = f(r). \tag{10}$$

The boundary values being symmetrical with respect to the z-axis, Φ is independent of ϕ and is hence a constant. Thus we take $n = 0$. A special solution of 1) is therefore

$$u = RZ = A \sinh(\alpha z) J_0(\alpha r).$$

With special solutions of this form we now construct the series

$$u = \psi(z, r) = u_0 + \sum_{n=1}^{\infty} c_n \frac{\sinh(\alpha_n z)}{\sinh(\alpha_n l)} J_0(\alpha_n r), \tag{11}$$

where $0 > \alpha_1 > \alpha_2 > \cdots$ are roots of $J_0(ar)$.

Since each term of 11) is a solution of $\Delta u = 0$, ϕ is a solution. Let us see if ψ satisfies the boundary conditions.

For

$$z = 0 \quad , \quad \psi = u_0 \qquad \text{since } \sinh(\alpha_n z) = 0.$$

For

$$r = a \quad , \quad \psi = u_0 \qquad \text{since } J_0(\alpha_n a) = 0.$$

Let us now look at the boundary condition 10). If it is satisfied, we must have, setting $z = l$ in 11),

$$u_0 + \sum_{n=1}^{\infty} c_n J_0(\alpha_n r) = f(r); \tag{12}$$

or setting

$$g(r) = f(r) - u_0,$$

we must have

$$g(r) = \sum_{n=1}^{\infty} c_n J_0(\alpha_n r).$$

Using 257, 7), we see 12) is satisfied if we take

$$c_n = \frac{2}{a^2 J_1^2(\alpha_n a)} \int_0^a r g(r) J_0(\alpha_n r) dr. \tag{13}$$

Thus the c_n being taken in this way, the solution of our boundary value problem is 11).

3. *Problem 2.* Let us keep the boundary values as in 2 except for

$$z = l \quad , \quad u = f(r, \phi). \tag{14}$$

In this case u is no longer symmetrical with respect to the axis of C and hence u now depends on ϕ. A special solution of 1) is therefore

$$(A_n \cos n\phi + B_n \sin n\phi) \sinh(\alpha z) J_n(\alpha r).$$

With special solutions of this form we now construct the series

$$\begin{aligned} u &= \psi(z, \phi, r) \\ &= u_0 + \sum_{n=0}^{\infty} \sum_{k=1}^{\infty} (A_{nk} \cos n\phi + B_{nk} \sin n\phi) \frac{\sinh(\alpha_{nk} z)}{\sinh(\alpha_{nk} l)} J_n(\alpha_{nk} r), \end{aligned} \tag{15}$$

where α_{nk}, $k = 1, 2, 3 \cdots$ are the roots of $J_n(ar) = 0$.

Since each term of 15) is a solution of $\Delta u = 0$, we see u is a solution. Let us see if 15) satisfies the boundary conditions. If we set $z = 0$ in 15), we see that

$$u = u_0 \quad , \quad \text{since } \sinh(\alpha_{nk} z) = 0.$$

If we set $r = a$ in 15), we get

$$u = u_0 \quad , \quad \text{since } J_n(\alpha_{nk} a) = 0.$$

Thus two of the boundary conditions are satisfied. If the condition 14) is satisfied, we must have

$$g(r, \phi) = \sum_{n=0}^{\infty} \sum_{k=1}^{\infty} (A_{nk} \cos n\phi + B_{nk} \sin n\phi) J_n(\alpha_{nk} r), \tag{16}$$

where we have set

$$g = f(r, \phi) - u_0. \tag{17}$$

Referring to 258, we see the condition 16) is satisfied if we choose the coefficients A_{nk}, B_{nk} as in 258, 9), 10), 11), where, however, we should replace $f(r, \phi)$ by $g(r, \phi)$ in 17).

Lamé Functions

260. Confocal Quadrics. 1. We wish now to consider very briefly a class of functions introduced by Lamé which play the same role for the ellipsoid as Laplace's functions for the sphere.

Suppose we wish to find a solution of Laplace's equation

$$\frac{\partial^2 u}{\partial x^2} + \frac{\partial^2 u}{\partial y^2} + \frac{\partial^2 u}{\partial z^2} = 0, \tag{1}$$

which takes on assigned values on the surface of an ellipsoid $\mathfrak{E}$ whose equation is

$$\frac{x^2}{a} + \frac{y^2}{b} + \frac{z^2}{c} = 1, \qquad a < b < c. \tag{2}$$

According to the general scheme outlined in 235, our first step is to replace the x, y, z coördinates by a set of coördinates defined by a family of triply orthogonal surfaces, one of which is the given ellipsoid $\mathfrak{E}$. This family is the family of confocal quadrics defined by

$$F = \frac{x^2}{a-\lambda} + \frac{y^2}{b-\lambda} + \frac{z^2}{c-\lambda} - 1 = 0, \tag{3}$$

the parameter λ ranging from $-\infty$ to $+\infty$. We note that for $\lambda = 0$, 3) reduces to 2). We observe that F is

an ellipsoid for $\lambda < a$,
a hyperboloid of one sheet for $a < \lambda < b$,
a hyperboloid of two sheets for $b < \lambda < c$.

Let us give to λ values λ_1, λ_2, λ_3 lying respectively in these three intervals. The corresponding surfaces 3) will cut in 8 points symmetric with respect to the origin, one in each of the 8 octants. Thus, if we state in which octant the point lies, the three numbers $\lambda_1, \lambda_2, \lambda_3$ determine the position of the point in that octant uniquely.

Let us now show that through a *given* point $P = x, y, z$ there passes one and only one of each of these three kinds of surfaces. To this end we have only to show that the cubic equation in λ

$$F(\lambda) = \frac{x^2}{a-\lambda} + \frac{y^2}{b-\lambda} + \frac{z^2}{c-\lambda} - 1 = 0 \qquad (4$$

has a root in each of the above intervals.

Let ϵ be a small positive number. Then

$$F(a-\epsilon) = \frac{x^2}{\epsilon} + \frac{y^2}{b-a+\epsilon} + \frac{z^2}{c-a+\epsilon} - 1 > 0,$$

since the first term $\frac{x^2}{\epsilon} \doteq +\infty$ as $\epsilon \doteq 0$. Let $\lambda = \lambda_0$, a large negative number. Then $F(\lambda_0) < 0$ since $F(\lambda) \doteq -1$ as $\lambda \doteq -\infty$. Thus $F(\lambda)$, having opposite signs at λ_0 and $a - \epsilon$ and being continuous in the interval $(\lambda_0, a-\epsilon)$, must vanish somewhere in this interval. Similarly we see that $F = 0$ for some point within the interval (a, b) and within (b, c). As $F(\lambda) = 0$ is a cubic, it has no other roots.

These considerations show that we may take $\lambda_1, \lambda_2, \lambda_3$ as coördinates of a point. They are called *ellipsoidal coördinates.* When we do not wish to use subscripts, we may denote these coördinates by any three letters as λ, μ, ν.

2. Let us show that the three surfaces λ, μ, ν meeting at a point x, y, z cut orthogonally.

Since the λ and μ surfaces pass through the point xyz, we have

$$\frac{x^2}{a-\lambda} + \frac{y^2}{b-\lambda} + \frac{z^2}{c-\lambda} - 1 = 0 \;, \quad \frac{x^2}{a-\mu} + \frac{y^2}{b-\mu} + \frac{z^2}{c-\mu} - 1 = 0. \qquad (5$$

The direction cosines of the normals to these surfaces at xyz are proportional to

$$\frac{x}{a-\lambda} \;, \quad \frac{y}{b-\lambda} \;, \quad \frac{z}{c-\lambda}$$

and to

$$\frac{x}{a-\mu} \;, \quad \frac{y}{b-\mu} \;, \quad \frac{z}{c-\mu}.$$

These angles are at right angles if

$$\frac{x^2}{(a-\lambda)(a-\mu)}+\frac{y^2}{(b-\lambda)(b-\mu)}+\frac{z^2}{(c-\lambda)(c-\mu)}=0. \qquad (6$$

This is indeed so, for if we subtract the two equations 5) and discard the factor $\lambda-\mu$ we get 6). Thus any two of the three quadrics λ, μ, ν meeting at the point x, y, z cut at right angles.

3. Let us now express x, y, z in terms of λ, μ, ν. To this end let us establish an identity in u which will also be useful later, viz.:

$$\frac{x^2}{a-u}+\frac{y^2}{b-u}+\frac{z^2}{c-u}-1=\frac{(u-\lambda)(u-\mu)(u-\nu)}{(a-u)(b-u)(c-u)}. \qquad (7$$

To prove 7) let us consider

$$G(u)=\left\{\frac{x^2}{a-u}+\frac{y^2}{b-u}+\frac{z^2}{c-u}-1\right\}(a-u)(b-u)(c-u), \qquad (8$$

which is a polynomial of third degree in u. The coefficient of u^3 is 1. Since the λ surface goes through the point xyz, the first factor of G vanishes for $u=\lambda$. Hence $u=\lambda$ is a root of G. Similarly $u=\mu$, $u=\nu$ are roots. Thus

$$G(u)=(u-\lambda)(u-\mu)(u-\nu).$$

Putting this in 8), we get 7).

Having established 7), let us multiply it by $a-u$ and then set $u=a$. We get

$$x^2=\frac{(a-\lambda)(a-\mu)(a-\nu)}{(b-a)(c-a)}.$$

Similarly,

$$y^2=\frac{(b-\lambda)(b-\mu)(b-\nu)}{(c-b)(a-b)},$$

$$z^2=\frac{(c-\lambda)(c-\mu)(c-\nu)}{(a-c)(b-c)}. \qquad (9$$

These determine 8 points $\pm x$, $\pm y$, $\pm z$, one in each octant.

4. For later use, let us find an element of arc, or the value of

$$ds^2=dx^2+dy^2+dz^2 \qquad (10$$

in terms of ellipsoidal coördinates.

Taking the logarithmic derivatives of 9), we get

$$2\frac{dx}{x}=\frac{d\lambda}{\lambda-a}+\frac{d\mu}{\mu-a}+\frac{d\nu}{\nu-a},$$

$$2\frac{dy}{y}=\frac{d\lambda}{\lambda-b}+\frac{d\mu}{\mu-b}+\frac{d\nu}{\nu-b},$$

$$2\frac{dz}{z}=\frac{d\lambda}{\lambda-c}+\frac{d\mu}{\mu-c}+\frac{d\nu}{\nu-c}.$$

Putting these in 10), we get

$$ds^2 = Ad\lambda^2 + Bd\mu^2 + Cd\nu^2, \tag{11}$$

where

$$A=\frac{1}{4}\left\{\frac{x^2}{(a-\lambda)^2}+\frac{y^2}{(b-\lambda)^2}+\frac{z^2}{(c-\lambda)^2}\right\}$$

and similar expressions for B, C. The other terms which result from this substitution vanish by virtue of the relations of the type 6), which express the orthogonality of the λ, μ, ν surfaces.

To eliminate the x, y, z in the coefficients of 11), let us differentiate the identity 7) with respect to u and then set $u = \lambda, \mu, \nu$. This shows that

$$A=\frac{1}{4}\frac{(\lambda-\mu)(\lambda-\nu)}{(a-\lambda)(b-\lambda)(c-\lambda)},$$

$$B=\frac{1}{4}\frac{(\mu-\nu)(\mu-\lambda)}{(a-\mu)(b-\mu)(c-\mu)}, \tag{12}$$

$$C=\frac{1}{4}\frac{(\nu-\lambda)(\nu-\mu)}{(a-\nu)(b-\nu)(c-\nu)}.$$

261. Elliptic Coördinates. 1. The equations 9) show that x, y, z are not determined as one-valued functions of the coördinates λ, μ, ν, or using subscripts λ_1, λ_2, λ_3. We may remove this ambiguity by introducing three other quantities u, v, w or using the subscripts u_1, u_2, u_3 defined by

$$pu_\alpha = \lambda_\alpha \quad , \quad \alpha = 1, 2, 3 \tag{1}$$

as follows.

The ellipsoid $\mathfrak{E}$ on which the boundary values are given is, by 260, 2),

$$\frac{x^2}{a}+\frac{y^2}{b}+\frac{z^2}{c}-1=0.$$

Let us set

$$a=\lambda_0-e_1 \quad , \quad b=\lambda_0-e_2 \quad , \quad c=\lambda_0-e_3, \tag{2}$$

and determine λ_0, e_1, e_2, e_3 so that

$$e_1+e_2+e_3=0 \quad ; \quad e_2<e_3<e_1. \tag{3}$$

Then the equation of $\mathfrak{E}$ is

$$\frac{x_1^2}{\lambda_0-e_1}+\frac{x_2^2}{\lambda_0-e_2}+\frac{x_3^2}{\lambda_0-e_3}-1=0, \tag{4}$$

and the equation of our confocal quadrics is

$$\frac{x_1^2}{\lambda-e_1}+\frac{x_2^2}{\lambda-e_2}+\frac{x_3^2}{\lambda-e_3}-1=0. \tag{5}$$

We see that 5) is

an ellipsoid when $\lambda > e_1$,
a hyperboloid of one sheet when $e_3<\lambda<e_1$,
a hyperboloid of two sheets when $e_2<\lambda<e_3$.

Let us now set

$$4\,p^3-g_2p-g_3=4(p-e_1)(p-e_2)(p-e_3) \tag{6}$$

and suppose the p function introduced in 1) to be constructed on the invariants g_2, g_3, in 6). The periods $2\,\omega_1$, $2\,\omega_2$ of this p function are given by

$$\omega_1=\int_{e_1}^{\infty}\frac{dp}{\sqrt{4\,p^3-g_2p-g_3}} \quad , \quad \omega_2=i\int_{-\infty}^{e_2}\frac{dp}{\sqrt{-(4\,p^3-g_2p-g_3)}}, \tag{7}$$

as we saw in 173, 9), 14). Putting 1) in 260, 9), we get

$$x_\alpha=\sqrt{\frac{(pu_1-e_\alpha)(pu_2-e_\alpha)(pu_3-e_\alpha)}{(e_\alpha-e_\beta)(e_\alpha-e_\gamma)}}, \tag{8}$$

where α, β, γ is a permutation of 1, 2, 3.
Now from 172, 16), 17), we have

$$\sqrt{pu-e_\alpha}=\frac{\sigma_\alpha(u)}{\sigma(u)} \quad , \sqrt{e_\beta-e_\alpha}=\frac{\sigma_\alpha\omega_\beta}{\sigma\omega_\beta}. \tag{9}$$

These in 8) give

$$x_\alpha = \pm \frac{\sigma\omega_\beta\sigma\omega_\gamma}{\sigma_\alpha\omega_\beta\sigma_\alpha\omega_\gamma} \cdot \frac{\sigma_\alpha u_1\sigma_\alpha u_2\sigma_\alpha u_3}{\sigma u_1\sigma u_2\sigma u_3} \qquad \alpha = 1, 2, 3. \tag{10}$$

The quantities u_1, u_2, u_3 are called *elliptic coördinates.* Having once chosen the $\pm$ sign in 10) they determine x, y, z as one-valued functions of u_1, u_2, u_3. Let us agree to take the $+$ sign in 10). From 172 we have

$$\frac{\sigma_\alpha(-u)}{\sigma(-u)} = -\frac{\sigma_\alpha(u)}{\sigma(u)}; \quad \frac{\sigma_\alpha(u \pm 2\,\omega_\alpha)}{\sigma(u \pm 2\,\omega_\alpha)} = \frac{\sigma_\alpha(u)}{\sigma(u)}; \quad \frac{\sigma_\alpha(u \pm 2\,\omega_\beta)}{\sigma(u \pm 2\,\omega_\beta)} = -\frac{\sigma_\alpha(u)}{\sigma(u)}. \tag{11}$$

These relations show that the x's are periodic functions of the u's admitting $4\omega_1$, $4\omega_2$ as periods. They also show that if we restrict

u_1 to range in the interval $(0, \omega_1) = \mathfrak{U}_1$

u_2 to range in $(\omega_2 - \omega_1, \ \omega_2 + \omega_1) = \mathfrak{U}_2$

u_3 to range in $(\omega_1 - 2\,\omega_2, \ \omega_1 + 2\,\omega_2) = \mathfrak{U}_3$

the point x_1, x_2, x_3 passes over every point in space once and only once. Such restricted u's we shall call *normal elliptic coördinates.*

Let u_1^0 be the value of u_1 lying in $\mathfrak{U}_1$ such that

$$pu_1^0 = \lambda_0.$$

Then the point x_1, x_2, x_3 describes the given ellipsoid $\mathfrak{E}$ once and only once when u_2, u_3 range in the normal intervals $\mathfrak{U}_2$, $\mathfrak{U}_3$.

2. The expression for

$$ds^2 = dx^2 + dy^2 + dz^2$$

is extremely simple in elliptical coördinates. We saw in 260, 4 that

$$ds^2 = A_1 d\lambda_1^2 + A_2 d\lambda_2^2 + A_3 d\lambda_3^2, \tag{12}$$

where

$$A_1 = \frac{(\lambda_1 - \lambda_2)(\lambda_1 - \lambda_3)}{4(\lambda_1 - e_1)(\lambda_1 - e_2)(\lambda_1 - e_3)}, \tag{13}$$

and similar expressions for A_2, A_3. Making use of 1) and remembering that

$$du = \frac{dp}{\sqrt{4(p - e_1)(p - e_2)(p - e_3)}},$$

we see that

$$ds^2 = (pu_1 - pu_2)(pu_1 - pu_3)du_1^2 + (pu_2 - pu_3)(pu_2 - pu_1)du_2^2 + (pu_3 - pu_1)(pu_3 - pu_2)du_3^2. \qquad (14$$

262. Transformation of Laplace's Equation. 1. The next step in the solution of Laplace's equation

$$\frac{\partial^2 V}{\partial x^2} + \frac{\partial^2 V}{\partial y^2} + \frac{\partial^2 V}{\partial z^2} = 0 \qquad (1$$

as outlined in 235 is to transform the equation to the new coördinates. This is a lengthy process even in the polar coördinates; for the new coördinates $\lambda_1, \lambda_2, \lambda_3$, or u_1, u_2, u_3 it is far longer. In order to avoid this we will make use of a theorem due to Jacobi: *

Let $\lambda\mu\nu$ be any system of triply orthogonal coördinates in terms of which an element of arc is given by

$$ds^2 = Ad\lambda^2 + Bd\mu^2 + Cd\nu^2. \qquad (2$$

Then Laplace's equation 1) *becomes in the new coördinates*

$$\frac{\partial}{\partial\lambda}\left(\frac{D}{A}\frac{\partial V}{\partial\lambda}\right) + \frac{\partial}{\partial\mu}\left(\frac{D}{B}\frac{\partial V}{\partial\mu}\right) + \frac{\partial}{\partial\nu}\left(\frac{D}{C}\frac{\partial V}{\varrho\nu}\right) = 0, \qquad (3$$

where

$$D = \sqrt{ABC}.$$

2. To illustrate this theorem on a simple case, let us transform 1) to polar coördinates:

$$x = r\cos\theta \quad , \quad y = r\sin\theta\cos\phi \quad , \quad z = r\sin\theta\sin\phi.$$

As

$$ds^2 = dx^2 + dy^2 + dz^2 = dr^2 + r^2d\theta^2 + r^2\sin^2\theta d\phi^2,$$

we have on taking $\lambda = r \quad , \quad \mu = \theta \quad , \quad \nu = \phi,$

$$A = 1 \quad , \quad B = r^2 \quad , \quad C = r^2\sin^2\theta \quad , \quad D = r^2\sin\theta.$$

Thus 3) becomes

$$\frac{\partial}{\partial r}\left(r^2\frac{\partial V}{\partial r}\right) + \frac{1}{\sin\theta}\frac{\partial}{\partial\theta}\left(\sin\theta\frac{\partial V}{\partial\theta}\right) + \frac{1}{\sin^2\theta}\frac{\partial^2 V}{\partial\phi^2} = 0,$$

which agrees with 235, 4).

* For a proof of this theorem the reader may consult: C. Jordan, "Cours d'Analyse," vol. 3, p. 540; H. Weber, "Differential-Gleichungen," vol. 1, p. 94.

3. Let us now transform 1) to ellipsoidal coördinates $\lambda_1, \lambda_2, \lambda_3$. By 261, 12), 13), we have, on setting

$$q_\alpha^2 = 4(\lambda_\alpha - e_1)(\lambda_\alpha - e_2)(\lambda_\alpha - e_3) \quad , \quad \alpha = 1, 2, 3,$$

$$\frac{D}{A} = i(\lambda_3 - \lambda_2)\frac{q_1}{q_2 q_3}.$$

Hence

$$\frac{\partial}{\partial\lambda_1}\left(\frac{D}{A}\frac{\partial V}{\partial\lambda_1}\right) = \frac{i(\lambda_2 - \lambda_3)}{q_2 q_3}\frac{\partial}{\partial\lambda_1}\left(q_1\frac{\partial V}{\partial\lambda_1}\right)$$

Thus Laplace's equation becomes

$$(\lambda_2-\lambda_3)q_1\frac{\partial}{\partial\lambda_1}\left(q_1\frac{\partial V}{\partial\lambda_1}\right)+(\lambda_3-\lambda_1)q_2\frac{\partial}{\partial\lambda_2}\left(q_2\frac{\partial V}{\partial\lambda_2}\right)$$
$$+(\lambda_1-\lambda_2)q_3\frac{\partial}{\partial\lambda_3}\left(q_3\frac{\partial V}{\partial\lambda_3}\right)=0. \quad (4$$

3. Let us pass to elliptic coördinates. We have

$$\frac{\partial}{\partial\lambda_1} = \frac{\partial u_1}{\partial\lambda_1}\cdot\frac{\partial}{\partial u_1} = \frac{1}{q_1}\frac{\partial}{\partial u_1} \text{ etc.}$$

Thus 4) becomes

$$(pu_2 - pu_3)\frac{\partial^2 V}{\partial u_1^2} + (pu_3 - pu_1)\frac{\partial^2 V}{\partial u_2^2} + (pu_1 - pu_2)\frac{\partial^2 V}{\partial u_3^2} = 0, \quad (5$$

whose form is extremely simple.

263. Lamé's Equation. Having reduced Laplace's equations to the new coördinates, the next step in the solution as outlined in 235 is to set

$$V = f(u_1)g(u_2)h(u_3), \quad (1$$

where f, g, h are each functions of one of the variables u_1, u_2, u_3. If we put 1) in the transformed Laplace equation 262, 5), we get

$$\frac{pu_2 - pu_3}{f(u_1)}\frac{d^2f}{du_1^2} + \frac{pu_3 - pu_1}{g(u_2)}\frac{d^2g}{du_2^2} + \frac{pu_1 - pu_2}{h(u_3)}\frac{d^2h}{du_3^2} = 0. \quad (2$$

Suppose f, g, h satisfy the equations,

$$\frac{d^2f}{du_1^2}=(apu_1+b)f(u_1),$$

$$\frac{d^2g}{du_2^2}=(apu_2+b)g(u_2), \tag{3}$$

$$\frac{d^2h}{du_3^2}=(apu_3+b)h(u_3).$$

Putting these in 2), we see that the left side $=0$ identically, however a, b are chosen.

We are thus led to consider differential equations of the type

$$\frac{d^2y}{dx^2}-\{ap(x)+b\}y=0. \tag{4}$$

As in the case of the sphere, we are not looking for the general solution of 4) for arbitrary a and b; rather we seek to determine a and b so as to get an infinite number of particular solutions 1) with which to construct a series which will satisfy the conditions imposed on V on the surface of the given ellipsoid $\mathfrak{E}$.

Let us apply the general method developed in Chapter XIII to the equation 4). Its singular points are those of $p(x)$ or the points $\equiv 0 \bmod 2\,\omega_1,\ 2\,\omega_2$.

Let us consider the *point* $x=0$. Writing 4) in the normal form,

$$x^2y''+0\cdot y'-x^2\{ap(x)+b\}y=0,$$

we have

$$q_0(x)=1\quad,\quad q_1(x)=0\quad,\quad q_2(x)=-ax^2p(x)-bx^2.$$

Hence

$$q_0(0)=1\quad,\quad q_1(0)=0\quad,\quad q_2(0)=-a.$$

The indicial equation for $x=0$ is therefore

$$r^2-r-a=0. \tag{5}$$

This shows that if we take

$$a=n(n+1)\quad,\qquad n \text{ an integer}$$

5) will have

$$-n, \text{ and } n+1$$

as roots. This choice of a gives us especially simple particular solutions, infinite in number. Putting this value in 4) it becomes

$$\frac{d^2y}{dx^2} - \{n(n+1)p(x) + b\}y = 0. \tag{6}$$

These equations are called *Lamé equations*, in honor of Lamé, who first studied them.

264. Lamé Functions. 1. In Lamé's equation, 263, 6), b is still undetermined. Let us see if we cannot choose it so as to get particularly simple solutions of the form

$$\begin{aligned} y &= L(p), \\ y &= L(p)\cdot\frac{\sigma_\alpha(x)}{\sigma(x)}, \\ y &= L(p)\cdot\frac{\sigma_\alpha(x)}{\sigma(x)}\cdot\frac{\sigma_\beta(x)}{\sigma(x)}, \end{aligned} \tag{1}$$

$$y = L(p)\cdot p'(x) \quad , \quad p'(x) = -2\frac{\sigma_1(x)}{\sigma(x)}\cdot\frac{\sigma_2(x)}{\sigma(x)}\cdot\frac{\sigma_3(x)}{\sigma(x)},$$

where L is a polynomial in $p = p(x)$. Since the sigma quotients admit $4\,\omega_1$, $4\,\omega_2$ as periods, as noted in 261, 1, the expression 1) will admit these as periods also.

We set then

$$y = LM \tag{2}$$

where M is the product of $\nu = 0, 1, 2$ or 3 factors

$$\frac{\sigma_1(x)}{\sigma(x)} \quad , \quad \frac{\sigma_2(x)}{\sigma(x)} \quad , \quad \frac{\sigma_3(x)}{\sigma(x)} \tag{3}$$

and

$$L = a_m p^m(x) + a_{m-1}p^{m-1}(x) + \cdots + a_0. \tag{4}$$

If then we set 2) in Lamé's equation

$$\frac{d^2y}{dx^2} - \{n(n+1)p(x) + b\}y = 0, \tag{5}$$

the result should be an identity in x. The coefficients of the different powers of this result developed about $x = 0$ will thus all be 0. These will then give us a system of equations which if consistent will enable us to find the quantities we seek.

To set 2) in 5) we need to calculate y''. Let N be the product of the factors 3) which do not enter M, we call it the **cofactor** of M. Since

$$\frac{\sigma_a(x)}{\sigma(x)} = \sqrt{p(x) - e_a},$$

we observe that

$$\mathfrak{M} = M^2$$

is a polynomial in p. Also let us note that

$$MN = -\tfrac{1}{2}p'(x).$$

We have now

$$y' = LM' + ML'p'(x).$$

But

$$M' = \frac{\mathfrak{M}'p'(x)}{2M} = -\mathfrak{M}'N.$$

Hence

$$y' = -N(2\mathfrak{M}L' + L\mathfrak{M}') = NQ. \qquad (6$$

Thus the first derivative of LM is the product of a polynomial in p and the cofactor of M. Hence at once 6) shows that

$$y'' = MR,$$

where R is a polynomial in p and M is the cofactor of N.

Thus setting 2) in 5), its left side becomes

$$y'' - \{n(n+1)p + b\}LM = \{R - n(n+1)p(x) + bL\}M = \mathfrak{P}M, \qquad (7$$

where $\mathfrak{P}$ is a polynomial in p.

As 7) must $= 0$ identically and as $M \neq 0$ we see $\mathfrak{P}$ must $= 0$ identically.

Now y has a pole of order $2m + \nu$ at $x = 0$, hence the left side of 7) has a pole of order $2m + \nu + 2$. Hence $\mathfrak{P}$ has a pole of order $2(m+1)$. Thus $\mathfrak{P}$ considered as a polynomial in p is of degree $m + 1$, or

$$\mathfrak{P} = \alpha_{m+1}p^{m+1} + \alpha_m p^m + \cdots + \alpha_0. \qquad (8$$

As $\mathfrak{P}$ is to vanish identically, all the α's $= 0$, and conversely if the α's $= 0$, $\mathfrak{P} = 0$ identically.

2. Suppose then we develop 7) about $x = 0$. Equating the first $m + 2$ coefficients of the development to 0 will give us a system of relations between the a's and the α's. These we shall see are linear in these letters. If now we set the α's $= 0$, we have

a set of equations to determine the a's in 4). Let us now carry out this scheme. We have

$$L = \frac{a_m}{x^{2m}} + \frac{a_1'}{x^{2m-2}} + \cdots$$

where a_1', a_2' $\cdots$ are linear and homogeneous in the a's. Also

$$\sigma_k(x) = 1 - \frac{e_k}{2} x^2 + \cdots$$

$$\frac{\sigma_k(x)}{\sigma(x)} = \frac{1}{x} + \epsilon_k x + \cdots$$

$$M = \frac{1}{x^\nu} + \frac{g_1}{x^{\nu-2}} + \cdots$$

Hence

$$y = LM = \frac{a_m}{x^{2m+\nu}} + \frac{a_1''}{x^{2m+\nu-2}} + \cdots$$

where a_1'', a_2'' $\cdots$ are linear and homogeneous in the a's. Hence

$$y'' = \frac{(2m+\nu)(2m+\nu+1)}{x^{2m+\nu+2}} a_m + \frac{A_1}{x^{2m+\nu}} + \cdots$$

where A_1, A_2 $\cdots$ are linear and homogeneous in the a_0, a_1 $\cdots$ Also

$$n(n+1)\, p(x)\, LM = \frac{n(n+1) a_m}{x^{2m+\nu+2}} + \frac{A_1'}{x^{2m+\nu}} + \cdots$$

where the A_1', A_2' $\cdots$ are linear and homogeneous in a_0, a_1 $\cdots$ Finally

$$bLM = \frac{ba_m}{x^{2m+\nu}} + \frac{ba_1''}{x^{2m+\nu-2}} + \cdots$$

These set in the left side of 7) give

$$\begin{aligned} x^{-(2m+\nu+2)} &\{(2m+\nu)(2m+\nu+1)a_m - n(n+1)a_m\} \\ &+ x^{-(2m+\nu)}\{A_1 - A_1' - ba_m\} + x^{-(2m+\nu-2)}\{A_2 - A_2' - ba_1''\} \\ &+ x^{-(2m+\nu-4)}\{A_3 - A_3' - ba_2''\} + \cdots \end{aligned} \tag{9}$$

We turn now to the right side of 7). We have

$$\mathfrak{P} = \frac{\alpha_{m+1}}{x^{2m+2}} + \frac{\alpha_1'}{x^{2m}} + \frac{\alpha_2'}{x^{2m-2}} \cdots \tag{10}$$

where $\alpha_1', \alpha_2' \cdots$ are linear and homogeneous in $\alpha_0, \alpha_1 \cdots$ Hence

$$\mathfrak{P}M = \frac{\alpha_{m+1}}{x^{2m+2+\nu}} + \frac{\alpha_1''}{x^{2m+\nu}} + \frac{\alpha_2''}{x^{2m-2+}} + \cdots \tag{11}$$

where $\alpha_1'', \alpha_2'' \cdots$ are linear and homogeneous in $\alpha_0, \alpha_1 \cdots$

We now equate the coefficients of like powers of x in 9), 11), getting

$$\alpha_{m+1} = \{(2m+\nu)(2m+\nu+1) - n(n+1)\}a_m \tag{12}$$

and the system

$$\begin{aligned} \alpha_1'' &= A_1 - A_1' - ba_m, \\ \alpha_2'' &= A_2 - A_2' - ba_1'', \\ &\cdot \quad \cdot \quad \cdot \quad \cdot \quad \cdot \quad \cdot \quad \cdot \quad \cdot \\ \alpha_{m+1}'' &= A_{m+1} - A_{m+1}' - ba_m''. \end{aligned} \tag{S}$$

As the α's are to be all 0, set $\alpha_{m+1} = 0$, then 12) gives a relation between m, n, and ν, viz.:

$$(2m+\nu)(2m+\nu+1) - n(n+1) = 0,$$

or

$$(2m+\nu)^2 + (2m+\nu) = n(n+1).$$

Hence

$$2m+\nu = n, \quad \text{or} \quad -(n+1).$$

As m and ν are not negative, this gives

$$2m + \nu = n. \tag{13}$$

Consider now the system S). Since $\alpha_1'', \alpha_2'' \cdots$ are linear and homogeneous in $\alpha_0, \alpha_1 \cdots \alpha_{m+1}$, they all vanish when the $\alpha_0, \alpha_1 \cdots$ vanish. Hence S) goes over into the system of $m+1$ equations:

$$\begin{aligned} A_1 - A_1' - ba_m &= 0, \\ A_2 - A_2' - ba_1'' &= 0, \\ &\cdot \quad \cdot \quad \cdot \quad \cdot \quad \cdot \quad \cdot \\ A_{m+1} - A_{m+1}' - ba_m'' &= 0. \end{aligned} \tag{S'}$$

These equations are linear and homogeneous in the unknowns $a_0, a_1 \cdots a_m$. In order that the system S′) has a solution different from $a_0 = 0$, $a_1 = 0 \cdots$ it is necessary that its determinant

$$\Delta(b) = 0. \tag{14}$$

Thus b satisfies an equation of degree $m+1$. Let us put a root of 14) in S′). This system of equations allows us now to determine the ratios

$$a_0 : a_1 : a_2 \cdots : a_m$$

Suppose the a's are determined thus. Then 4) and S) show that

$$\alpha_{m+1}, \alpha_1'', \alpha_2'', \cdots \alpha_{m+1}'' = 0.$$

From this follows that

$$\alpha_0, \alpha_1, \alpha_2, \cdots \alpha_m = 0.$$

For the development 11) shows that α_1'' contains besides α_m at most α_{m+1}; that α_2'' contains besides α_{m-1} at most α_m, α_{m+1}, etc. Thus

$$\alpha_1'' = \phi_1(\alpha_m, \alpha_{m+1}),$$

$$\alpha_2'' = \phi_2(\alpha_{m-1}, \alpha_m, \alpha_{m+1}), \qquad (S''$$

$$\alpha_3''' = \phi_3(\alpha_{m-2}, \alpha_{m-1}, \alpha_m, \alpha_{m+})_1,$$

$$\cdots\cdots\cdots\cdots$$

where the ϕ's are homogeneous functions. Now α_1'' and α_{m+1} being $=0$, the first relation in S″) shows that $\alpha_m = 0$, as ϕ_1 is homogeneous. Putting this in the second equation of S″), we see that $\alpha_{m-1} = 0$, and so on. Thus $\mathfrak{P} = 0$ identically.

3. Let us see in how many ways we can satisfy the relations 12) and S). There are two cases.

Case 1. $n = 2s$. Then 13) gives

$$2m + \nu = 2s \qquad (15$$

and ν is even. Hence

$$\nu = 0, \text{ or } 2.$$

For $\nu = 0$, $m = s$. For each of the $m+1 = s+1$ roots of $\Delta(b) = 0$, the system S′) gives us a set of coefficients for the polynomial L in 2). We thus get $s+1$ polynomials L which satisfy Lamé's equation 5).

For $\nu = 2$ we get, from 15), $m = s-1$. Each of the $m+1 = s$ roots of $\Delta(b)$ gives us a polynomial L of degree $s-1$. As here $\nu = 2$,

$$y = L\frac{\sigma_\alpha(x)}{\sigma(x)}\frac{\sigma_\beta(x)}{\sigma(x)} = LM. \qquad (16$$

Thus we can take the factor M in three ways corresponding to the indices

$$1, 2 \quad ; \quad 1, 3 \quad ; \quad 2, 3.$$

Each of these determinations gives us a new system of equations S) and hence a new equation $\Delta(b) = 0$. Hence ν being $= 2$, there are $3\,s$ values of b, each of which leads to a solution 16).

We thus get in all

$$s + 1 + 3\,s = 4\,s + 1 = 2\,n + 1$$

solutions of the desired type.

Case 2. $n = 2\,s + 1$. Reasoning in exactly the same way, we see that also in this case there are $2\,n + 1$ solutions. As it can be shown that these solutions are distinct we may state the fundamental theorem due to Lamé:

The constant b *in*

$$\frac{d^2y}{dx^2} = \{n(n+1)p(x) + b\}y,$$

may be determined in $2\,n + 1$ *different ways such that this equation admits a solution of the type*

$$L(p) \quad , \quad \sqrt{p - e_\alpha} \cdot L \quad , \quad \sqrt{p - e_\alpha}\sqrt{p - e_\beta} \cdot L \quad ,$$

$$\sqrt{(p - e_1)(p - e_2)(p - e_3)} \cdot L. \qquad (17$$

Moreover the b'*s belonging to different* n'*s are also different.*

The functions 17) are called *Lamé functions* or *polynomials.*

265. Integral Properties. 1. In order to develop an arbitrary function $f(\theta, \phi)$ in terms of Laplace's functions we made use of certain integral relations established in 238. We wish to establish analogous relations for Lamé's functions.

We saw in 264 that for a given n, the constant b can be taken in $2\,n + 1$ ways,

$$b_{n1} \quad , \quad b_{n2}, \cdots b_{n,\,2n+1}, \qquad (1$$

so that

$$y'' = \{n(n + 1)p(u) + b_{n,\,k}\}y \qquad (2$$

admits a Lamé function, denote it by $L_{nk}(u)$, as solution. We saw in 261, 1, that if u_1 has the value u_1^0 lying in $\mathfrak{U}_1 = (0, \omega_1)$ such that

$$pu_1^0 = \lambda_0,$$

and if u_2 ranges in $\mathfrak{U}_2 = (\omega_2 - \omega_1, \omega_2 + \omega_1)$ and u_3 in $\mathfrak{U}_3 = (\omega_1 - 2\omega_2, \omega_1 + 2\omega_2)$, then the point $x_1 x_2 x_3$ corresponding to $u_1^0 u_2 u_3$ describes just once the ellipsoid $\mathfrak{E}$ on which the boundary values are given.

For brevity let us set

$$a = \omega_2 - 2\omega_1 \quad , \quad b = \omega_2 + 2\omega_1 \quad , \quad c = \omega_1 - 2\omega_2 \quad , \quad d = \omega_1 + 2\omega_2.$$

Thus the interval (a, b) is twice as long as $\mathfrak{U}_2$ while the interval (c, d) is the same as $\mathfrak{U}_3$. Obviously if u_2 ranges over (a, b) and u_3 over (c, d), the point $x_1\ x_2\ x_3$ corresponding to u_1^0, u_2, u_3 will now describe the ellipsoid $\mathfrak{E}$ twice.

We wish now to prove :

$$J = \int_a^b du_2 \int_c^d L_{mr}(u_2) L_{mr}(u_3) L_{ns}(u_2) L_{ns}(u_3) (pu_2 - pu_3) du_3 = 0, \quad (3$$

when

$$L_{mr} \neq L_{ns}.$$

For, let us set

$$\begin{aligned} A &= \int_a^b L_{mr}(u_2) L_{ns}(u_2) pu_2\, du_2, \\ B &= \int_c^d L_{mr}(u_3) L_{ns}(u_3) pu_3 du_3, \\ C &= \int_a^b L_{mr}(u_2) L_{ns}(u_2) du_2, \\ D &= \int_c^d L_{mr}(u_3) L_{ns}(u_3) du_3. \end{aligned} \quad (4$$

Then

$$J = AD - BC. \quad (5$$

Now 2) gives, u being either u_2 or u_3,

$$\frac{d^2 L_{mr}(u)}{du^2} = \{m(m+1)pu + b_{mr}\} L_{mr}(u),$$

$$\frac{d^2 L_{ns}(u)}{du^2} = \{n(n+1)pu + b_{ns}\} L_{ns}(u).$$

Let us multiply the first equation by L_{ns} and the second by L_{mr} and subtract. We get on the left side

$$L_{ns} L''_{mr} - L_{mr} L''_{ns} = \frac{d}{du} \{L_{ns} L'_{mr} - L_{mr} L'_{ns}\} = \frac{d}{du} F(u).$$

On the right side we get

$$pu \cdot L_{mr} L_{ns} \{ m(m+1) - n(n+1) \} + L_{mr} L_{ns} (b_{mr} - b_{ns}) = G(u) + H(u).$$

Thus we have

$$\frac{dF(u)}{du} = G(u) + H(u). \tag{6}$$

Set here $u = u_2$ and integrate over (a, b). We get

$$\Big[F(u_2) \Big]_a^b = \{ m(m+1) - n(n+1) \} A + (b_{mr} - b_{ns}) C.$$

As $F(u_2)$ admits the period $4\omega_1$, the left side $= 0$. Thus

$$\{ m(m+1) - n(n+1) \} A + (b_{mr} - b_{ns}) C = 0. \tag{7}$$

Similarly integrating with respect to u_3 over (c, d) gives

$$\{ m(m+1) - n(n+1) \} B + (b_{mr} - b_{ns}) D = 0. \tag{8}$$

Suppose now $m \neq n$. We multiply 7) by D and 8) by C, then subtract. We get

$$J \{ m(m+1) - n(n+1) \} = 0.$$

Hence

$$J = 0.$$

Suppose $r \neq s$. We multiply 2) by B and 3) by A and subtract, getting

$$(b_{mr} - b_{ns}) J = 0.$$

Hence again

$$J = 0.$$

2. We next wish to calculate

$$K = \int_a^b du_2 \int_c^d L^2_{mr}(u_2) L^2_{ns}(u_3) (pu_2 - pu_3) du_3, \tag{9}$$

which is what J becomes for $m = n$. Let us set

$$\begin{aligned} P &= \int_a^b L^2_{mr}(u_2) pu_2 du_2 \\ Q &= \int_c^d L^2_{mr}(u_3) pu_3 du_3, \\ R &= \int_a^b L^2_{mr}(u_2) du_2 \\ S &= \int_c^d L^2_{mr}(u_3) du_3. \end{aligned} \tag{10}$$

Then

$$K = PS - QR. \tag{11}$$

We begin by observing that

$$V = L^2_{mr}(u)p(u) \quad , \quad W = L^2_{mr}(u), \tag{12}$$

admit $2\,\omega_1$, $2\,\omega_2$ as periods. They are even functions and have but a single pole in the parallelogram of periods Ω constructed on $2\,\omega_1$, $2\,\omega_2$. Thus Ω is a primitive parallelogram.

Thus by 168,

$$V(u) = v_0 + v_1 p(u) + v_2 p''(u) + v_3 p^{\text{iv}}(u) + \cdots \tag{13}$$

$$W(u) = w_0 + w_1 p(u) + w_2 p''(u) + w_3 p^{\text{iv}}(u) + \cdots \tag{14}$$

Here we have used the fact that V, W, being even functions of u, cannot contain derivatives of even order of $\zeta(u)$; also that $\zeta'(u) = -p(u)$, $\zeta'''(u) = -p''(u)$, etc.

We have now

$$P = \int_a^b V(u)du = v_0 \int_a^b du + v_1 \int_a^b p(u)du,$$

the other terms dropping out since they admit the period $4\,\omega_1$. Thus

$$P = v_0\{2\,\omega_1 + \omega_2 - (\omega_2 - 2\,\omega_1)\} - v_1\{\zeta(2\,\omega_1 + \omega_2) - \zeta(\omega_2 - 2\,\omega_1)\}.$$

Now

$$\zeta(u + 2\,\omega_1) = \zeta(u) + 2\,\eta_1 \quad , \quad \zeta(u - 2\,\omega_1) = \zeta(u) - 2\,\eta_1.$$

Thus

$$P = 4\,v_0\omega_1 - 4\,v_1\eta_1.$$

Similarly

$$Q = 4\,v_0\omega_2 - 4\,v_1\eta_2.$$

$$R = 4\,w_0\omega_1 - 4\,w_1\eta_1.$$

$$S = 4\,w_0\omega_2 - 4\,w_1\eta_2.$$

Thus

$$K = 16(v_0 w_1 - v_1 w_0)(\omega_2\eta_1 - \omega_1\eta_2)$$

$$= 8\,\pi i(v_0 w_1 - v_1 w_0) \quad , \quad \text{by 171, 8)}.$$

Hence finally

$$\int_a^b du_2 \int_c^d L^2_{mr}(u_2) L^2_{ns}(u_3)(pu_2 - pu_3)du_3 = 8\,\pi i(v_0 w_1 - v_1 w_0), \tag{15}$$

where v_0, w_0, v_1, w_1 are given by the developments 13), 14).

266. Solution of $\Delta V = 0$ for an Ellipsoid. We are now in a position to obtain a solution V of Laplace's equation

$$(pu_2 - pu_3)\frac{\partial^2 V}{\partial u_1^2} + (pu_3 - pu_1)\frac{\partial^2 V}{\partial u_2^2} + (pu_1 - pu_2)\frac{\partial^2 V}{\partial u_3^2} = 0, \qquad (1$$

which will take on assigned values $f(u_2, u_3)$ on the surface of a given ellipsoid $\mathfrak{E}$

$$\frac{x_1^2}{\lambda_0 - e_1} + \frac{x_2^2}{\lambda_0 - e_2} + \frac{x_3^2}{\lambda_0 - e_3} = 1.$$

For let $L_{ns}(u_m)$, $m = 1, 2, 3$ be Lamé polynomials satisfying

$$\frac{d^2 y}{du_m^2} = \{n(n+1)pu_m + b_{ns}\} y.$$

Then by 263, the product $L_{ns}(u_1) L_{ns}(u_2) L_{ns}(u_3)$ is a solution of 1), and hence the series,

$$\phi(u_1, u_2, u_3) = \sum_n \sum_s a_{ns} L_{ns}(u_1) L_{ns}(u_2) L_{ns}(u_3), \qquad (2$$

if convergent, will satisfy 1).

For the boundary values to be satisfied it is necessary for 2) to take on the value $f(u_2, u_3)$ for $u_1 = u_1^0$. If we set

$$a_{ns} L_{ns}(u_1^0) = A_{ns}, \qquad (3$$

the boundary condition is satisfied if

$$f(u_2, u_3) = \sum_{n,s} A_{ns} L_{ns}(u_2) L_{ns}(u_3). \qquad (4$$

To determine the unknown coefficients a_{mr}, or what is the same, A_{mr}, we multiply 4) by $L_{mr}(u_2) L_{mr}(u_3)(pu_2 - pu_3)$ and integrate. Granting that termwise integration is allowed, we get

$$\int_a^b du \int_c^d f(u,v) L_{mr}(u) L_{mr}(v)(pu - pv)\, dv$$
$$= A_{mr} \int_a^b du \int_c^d L_{mr}^2(u) L_{mr}^2(v)(pu - pv)\, dv, \qquad (5$$

since all the other terms $= 0$ by 265, 3).

Let

$$L_{mr}^2(u) p(u) = \alpha_0 + \alpha_1 pu + \alpha_2 p''(u) + \cdots$$
$$L_{mr}(u) = \beta_0 + \beta_1 pu + \beta_2 p''(u) + \cdots$$

Then by 5) and 265, 15)

$$A_{mr} = \frac{1}{8\pi i(\alpha_0 \beta_1 - \alpha_1 \beta_0)} \int_a^b du \int_c^d f(u,v) L_{mr}(u) L_{mr}(v)(pu - pv)\, dv. \qquad (6$$

Thus the coefficients a_{mr} in 2) are given by 3) and 6).

INDEX

(Numbers refer to pages)

LIST OF SYMBOLS

(Numbers refer to pages)

The symbol $\doteq$ is used throughout the book and means *converges to*, or *has as limit.*